OPTIMIZATION THEORY

OPTIMIZATION THEORY
THE FINITE DIMENSIONAL CASE

MAGNUS R. HESTENES

Department of Mathematics
University of California
Los Angeles

A WILEY-INTERSCIENCE PUBLICATION

JOHN WILEY & SONS New York · London · Sydney · Toronto

Library of Congress Cataloging in Publication Data:

Hestenes, Magnus Rudolph, 1906-
  Optimization theory: the finite dimensional case.

  (Pure and applied mathematics)
  "A Wiley-Interscience publication."
  Bibliography: p.
  Includes index.
    1. Mathematical optimization. 2. Calculus of variations. 3. Maxima and minima. I. Title.
  QA402.5.H47   515   75-25670
  ISBN 0-471-37471-7

Printed in the United States of America

10 9 8 7 6 5 4 3 2

To Susan and Carolyn

PREFACE

I have been interested in optimization theory throughout my career. In my research I have been concerned primarily with the infinite dimensional case, commonly known as the calculus of variations. However, I have always been interested also in the finite dimensional situation and consider it to be an integral part of optimization theory. This case is not only of interest in itself, but also affords an excellent introduction to the more complicated situations that arise when the dimension is infinite. Accordingly, in my courses on variational theory, I presented various parts of the material found in this book before I embarked on the study of variational and optimal control problems. Recently I have given courses restricted to the n-dimensional case; the material presented in these courses has been incorporated in this book. The mathematical techniques used are basically the same as those that I have applied for infinite dimensional situations. As a result this book can be viewed as an introduction to variational theory, as well as an exposition of finite dimensional optimization theory.

Optimization theory had its beginnings in the precalculus era. Fermat's principle and the isoperimetric problem, known as the problem of Dido, were formulated before calculus was invented. The development of optimization theory has gone hand in hand with the development of mathematical analysis. The early writers in optimization theory were concerned primarily with infinite dimensional problems. Their researches led to the development of variational theory. From the beginning, constrained as well as unconstrained problems were considered. Euler and Lagrange formulated general constrained minimum problems and derived the appropriate multiplier rules in a formal manner. In two papers in 1913 and 1914 Bolza formulated a very general variational problem with equality and inequality constraints and gave a rigorous derivation of the associated multiplier rule. By 1940 a satisfactory theory for the problem of Bolza had been developed. About 1950 the problem of Bolza was reformulated as an optimal control problem, leading to further advancement of the theory.

Before 1950 very few papers were devoted to the study of n-dimensional optimization problems. Sketchy treatments of a limited class of these problems can be found in books on advanced calculus. A more extensive treatment was given in 1917 by H. Hancock in his book on maxima and minima, where he showed that inequality constraints can be transformed into equality constraints by the introduction of slack variables. Brief discussions of n-dimensional constrained minimum problems can be found in the books on variational theory by G. A. Bliss, C. Caratheodory, J. Hadamard, and others. There is an excellent treatment of the n-dimensional Lagrange multiplier rule in an unpublished master's dissertation written by W. E. Karush in 1939 at The University of Chicago. The use of convex cones in the development of multplier rules for finite and infinite problems was introduced by E. J. McShane in 1939. An elaborate theory of critical points of functions was developed by M. Morse from 1925 on; this is a global as well as a local theory and is a forerunner of a modern theory of global analysis.

With the advent of high-speed computing machines it became apparent that one should be able to obtain numerical solutions for large-scale finite dimensional optimization problems of the type encountered in economics, engineering, and other fields. As a result finite dimensional optimization theory became a discipline in its own right and was no longer subservient to the infinite dimensional case. Linear programming, which was developed by G. Dantzig and others, was followed by the development of nonlinear programming under the leadership of H. Kuhn, A. W. Tucker, P. Wolfe, and others. The validity of the Lagrange multiplier rule (Kuhn-Tucker conditions) was extended to a larger class of problems. One of the most notable contributions made by this group was the development of effective computational procedures for obtaining optimal solutions; such procedures form an integral part of nonlinear programming.

There are many books on nonlinear programming, most of which are concerned primarily with computational methods for obtaining optimal solutions. Although I am greatly interested in computational procedures, I am of the opinion that the mathematical theory of optimization and the computational theory of optimization are two separate although interrelated aspects of optimization theory. It is appropriate therefore to develop them separately. Accordingly, I have limited this book to the development of the mathematical theory with occasional reference to its significance for computational procedures. A third aspect of optimization theory is concerned with its application to other fields. No attempt is made to incorporate this important aspect in this book. Instead I have presented only applications within mathematics itself, in the hope that these applications will be sufficient to motivate the mathematical theory that the book seeks to develop.

The book is divided into six chapters and an appendix. The appendix summarizes the basic topics in analysis and geometry that are used in the text. It is assumed that the reader is already familiar with these topics so that he can begin with Chapter 1. However, experience has shown that a convenient reference is useful. To facilitate the reading of the book, some of the basic material covered in the appendix is reviewed in the text as needed.

The first chapter is concerned with unconstrained and linearly constrained extrema together with mathematical and geometrical applications. Chapter 2 deals with applications to matrices and quadratic forms and is a digression from the main theme of the book; it can be omitted if one so desires. The remaining chapters can be read in any order. In the main they are concerned with various developments of the Lagrange multiplier rule (Kuhn-Tucker theorem), each of which has its counterpart in variational and optimal control theory. Chapters 3 and 4 present the traditional approach to the first- and second-order Lagrange multiplier rules. However, I have chosen to describe the development in geometrical language so that the results become more intuitive. In Chapter 5 a connection is shown between Lagrange multipliers and augmentability. The multiplier rule is re-established in two distinct but related ways. A feature of this approach is that no use is made of implicit function theorems. The results given in this chapter justify the method of penalty functions and the method of multipliers for finding the minimum of a function computationally. Finally, in Chapter 6 the multiplier rule is derived by studying the properties of an associated image set W of the domain X for a constrained minimum problem. It is shown that the Lagrange multipliers depend primarily on the nature of W and only incidentally on the properties of the set X. The dimensionality of X plays no significant role. Accordingly the results obtained are applicable to infinite dimensional as well as to finite dimensional problems. I used this approach initially in my book entitled *Calculus of Variations and Optimal Control Theory*.

I am greatly indebted to the various writers on optimization theory. No attempt has been made to give individual credit to particular researchers, except in very special instances. Since I became familiar with the theory via the infinite dimensional case, I have been significantly influenced by the researchers in this field—in particular, by O. Bolza, G. D. Birkhoff, G. A. Bliss, C. Caratheodory, L. M. Graves, E. J. McShane, M. Morse, W. T. Reid, and L. C. Young. I have also been influenced greatly by the authors on linear and nonlinear programming referred to above and in the bibliography. During the academic year 1973–1974 I had the privilege of being associated with E. Barnes, J. Cullum, P. Wolfe, and their colleagues at the

IBM Thomas J. Watson Research Center at Yorktown Heights, New York. I am grateful for the many suggestions made by this group, especially by Philip Wolfe.

I am indebted to my former students for their assistance. I am especially grateful to R. Dennemeyer, E. Landesman, E. Mookini, R. Rupp, and J. Stein. Rene Dennemeyer, in particular, made very helpful criticisms and suggestions; in addition, I am obliged to him for compiling the bibliography. I also wish to thank my colleague, A. V. Balakrishnan, for his encouragement and for many helpful remarks. Some of the new material appearing in this book was sponsored by the U.S. Army Research Office (Durham), to which I express my appreciation.

MAGNUS R. HESTENES

Los Angeles, California
June 1975

CONTENTS

OPTIMIZATION THEORY

1

UNCONSTRAINED AND LINEARLY CONSTRAINED EXTREMA

1. PRELIMINARY REMARKS

The theory of optimization plays a fundamental role in mathematics and in the application of mathematics to other disciplines. The purpose of this book is to present the theory of optimization for a function f on a set S in an n-dimensional Euclidean space $\mathcal{E}^n$. Our emphasis will be on the mathematical aspects of this theory with occasional references to its applications in other fields. It will be shown that many of the standard theorems in analysis, geometry, and matrix theory can be derived by optimization techniques. The results obtained also form the basis of a large number of computational techniques for finding the extreme points of a function. However, we shall not be concerned with these techniques in this book.

Our optimization problem can be characterized by the type of set S on which f is to be minimized. If S is an open set in $\mathcal{E}^n$, our problem will be said to be unconstrained. If S is the intersection of an open set with a translate of a linear subspace of $\mathcal{E}^n$, our problem will be said to be linearly constrained. Unconstrained and linearly constrained extrema will be studied in this chapter. In later chapters we shall study more general constrained problems.

The principal results in this chapter are found in Sections 2, 3, 5, and 6. The remaining sections are devoted to the applications of these results to matrix theory and to geometry. In Section 7 we develop the geometry associated with the theory of quadratic functions. This theory is the basis for a large class of computational methods for finding the minimum of a general function $f(x)$. In Section 9 we study the eigenvalue theory for symmetric matrix A by optimizing its Rayleigh quotient on suitably chosen subspaces.

Throughout this book we assume that the reader is familiar with the basic results of analysis. A summary of the basic concepts that are needed for our analyses can be found in the appendix, which the reader may wish to scan in order to become more familiar with the concepts and terminology to be used throughout this book. In particular it is recommended that the reader review the material given in Sections 4 and 5. To facilitate the reading of the book, much of the material in the appendix is recalled in the text as it arises.

2. EXISTENCE OF EXTREME POINTS

Let f be a real-valued function on a set S in an n-dimensional Euclidean space $\mathscr{E}^n$ of points $x = (x^1, \ldots, x^n)$. A point x_0 in S is a *minimum point* of f on S if the inequality

$$f(x) \geqslant f(x_0)$$

holds for all points x in S. It is a *maximum point* of f on S if the reverse inequality

$$f(x) \leqslant f(x_0)$$

holds for all x in S. Maximum and minimum points of f on S are called *extreme points* of f on S. A function f on S need not possess extreme points in S. This section is devoted to the study of conditions on f and S which will ensure the existence of maximum and minimum points of f on S. Since a maximum point of f is a minimum point of $-f$, we normally restrict ourselves to the study of minimum points and leave the development of the corresponding results for maximum points as exercises.

In studying the existence of minimum points of a function f, we shall make use of the concept of the *greatest lower bound* or *infimum* of f on S. This number is the largest number m (with $m = -\infty$ admitted) such that the inequality $f(x) \geqslant m$ holds for all x in S. It will be denoted by "$\inf_{x \in S} f(x)$" or by "$\inf f(x)$ on S" or simply by "$\inf f(x)$." Clearly a point x_0 in S minimizes f on S if and only if $f(x_0) = \inf f(x)$ on S. Similarly the *least upper bound* or *supremum* of f on S is the smallest number M (with $M = +\infty$ admitted) such that the inequality $f(x) \leqslant M$ holds on S. It will be denoted by "$\sup_{x \in S} f(x)$" or by "$\sup f(x)$ on S" or simply by "$\sup f(x)$." The relation $f(x_1) = \sup f(x)$ on S at a point x_1 in S signifies that x_1 maximizes f on S.

If S is the real line $-\infty < x < +\infty$ and $f(x) = e^x$, then $\inf e^x = 0$ on S and $\sup e^x = +\infty$. On the other hand, $\inf(e^x + e^{-x}) = 2$ and $\sup e^{-x^2} = 1$. If S is the disk $x^2 + y^2 \leqslant 1$ in the xy-plane and $f(x,y) = e^{x^2+y^2}$, then $\inf f(x,y)$ on $S = 1$ and $\sup f(x,y)$ on $S = e$.

The Bolzano-Weierstrass theorem for sequences plays a significant role in the book, particularly in the study of the existence of extrema of functions on a set S. This theorem states that *a bounded sequence of points in $\mathcal{E}^n$ has a convergent subsequence*. A sequence $\{x_q\}$ is *bounded* if there is a constant K such that $|x_q| \leqslant K$ for every integer q. Here and elsewhere

$$|x| = \left[(x^1)^2 + \cdots + (x^n)^2 \right]^{1/2}.$$

The sequence $\{x_q\}$ *converges to* x_0, written as $x_q \to x_0$ or $x_0 = \lim x_q$, if

$$\lim_{q \to \infty} |x_q - x_0| = 0.$$

A set S of points in $\mathcal{E}^n$ is *closed* if, for every convergent sequence $\{x_q\}$ of points in S, the limit $x_0 = \lim x_q$ is also in S. The set S is bounded if there is a constant K such that $|x| \leqslant K$ for all x in S. From these results it follows that, if a set S in $\mathcal{E}^n$ is bounded and closed, every sequence $\{x_q\}$ in S has a convergent subsequence $\{y_q\}$. Moreover the limit $y_0 = \lim y_q$ is in S. This property of S is sometimes called *sequential compactness* or simply *compactness*. Accordingly we shall call a set S in $\mathcal{E}^n$ *compact* if it is bounded and closed. The term "compactness" in analysis normally signifies the Heine-Borel property of bounded closed sets in $\mathcal{E}^n$. A fuller discussion of these ideas can be found in the appendix.

In the following theorem we shall use the symbol S_c to denote the set of all points x in S for which the inequality $f(x) \leqslant c$ holds. If S is the real line $-\infty < x < \infty$ and $f(x) = e^x$, then S_{10} is the set for which $e^x \leqslant 10$, that is, the interval $-\infty < x \leqslant \log 10$. The set S_0 is the null set. Similarly, if S is the disk, $x^2 + y^2 \leqslant 1$, in the xy-plane and $f(x,y) = e^{x^2+y^2}$, the set S_2 is the disk $x^2 + y^2 \leqslant \log 2$, and the set S_3 coincides with S since $3 > e$. In fact, $S_c = S$ if $c \geqslant e$. On the other hand, S_1 consists of the origin $(x,y) = (0,0)$ and S_c is the null set if $c < 1$.

The following theorem is basic.

THEOREM 2.1

Let f *be a continuous function on a closed set* S. *Suppose that there is a number* b *such that the set* S_b *of all points* x *in* S *having* f(x) $\leqslant$ b *is bounded and nonnull. Then* f *attains its minimum at a point* x_0 *in* S, *that is,* $f(x_0) = \inf f(x)$ *on* S.

Let $m = \inf f(x)$ on S. Then $f(x) \geqslant m$ for all points x in S. We shall show that there is a point x_0 in S such that $f(x_0) = m$. If $b = m$, then $m \leqslant f(x) = b = m$ on S_b. Hence $f(x) = m$ on S_b in this event. Since S_b is nonnull, there exists a point x_0 in S_b. This point minimizes f on S. Suppose next that $b > m$. Select a sequence $\{x_q\}$ in S such that $\lim_{q \to \infty} f(x_q) = m$. Since $b > m$, the inequality $f(x_q) > b$ holds for at most a finite number of q's. Deleting these points, we obtain a sequence in S_b, again denoted by $\{x_q\}$, such that $f(x_q) \to m$. Since S_b is bounded, the sequence $\{x_q\}$ is bounded and accordingly has a convergent subsequence $\{y_q\}$. In view of the closure of S, the limit $x_0 = \lim y_q$ is in S. By virtue of the continuity of f we have

$$f(x_0) = \lim_{q \to \infty} f(y_q) = \lim_{q \to \infty} f(x_q) = m.$$

The point x_0 accordingly minimizes f on S, as was to be proved.

EXAMPLE 2.1

The result given in Theorem 2.1 can be used to establish the following proposition. *Given a point* y *and a closed nonempty set* S, *there is a point* x_0 *in* S *that is nearest to* y. In other words, there is a point x_0 in S such that

$$|y - x_0| \leqslant |y - x|$$

for all points x in S. This follows because the function

$$f(x) = |y - x|$$

is continuous on S. The set S_b of points x in S having $f(x) \leqslant b$ is the set of points x in S whose distance from y is at most b. This set is clearly bounded for every choice of b. It is nonnull if b is large. Theorem 2.1 accordingly assures us of the existence of a nearest point x_0 in S to y. If y is in S, then $x_0 = y$. If y is not in S, the point x_0 need not be unique.

EXAMPLE 2.2

A function f may possess minimum points without satisfying the hypotheses of Theorem 2.1. For example, the function $f(x) = \sin x$ has infinitely many minimum points on the interval $-\infty < x < \infty$ but does not satisfy the hypotheses of our theorem. However, we can apply the theorem if we restrict $f(x)$ to a bounded interval $a \leqslant x \leqslant b$.

We have the following interesting extension of Theorem 2.1, which is applicable to more general situations than those considered elsewhere in this book. It is of the type used in variational theory.

THEOREM 2.2

Let f *be a real-valued function on a nonnull set* S, *and let* m = inf f(x) *in* S. *Suppose that there is a constant* b > m *such that if* c ≤ b *the set* S_c *of all points* x *in* S *having* f(x) ≤ c *is compact. Then* f *attains its minimum at a point* x_0 *in* S.

If $m < c \leqslant b$, the set S_c is nonnull and compact. Moreover, if $c' < c$, then $S_{c'} \subset S_c$. It follows that the intersection S_m of the sets S_c $(m < c \leqslant b)$ is nonnull. There is accordingly a point x_0 in S_m. Since $f(x_0) = m$, the point x_0 minimizes f on S.

This theorem is valid even if f is not continuous on S. For example, in the one-dimensional case it can be applied to function f, defined by the equations $f(x) = -x$ $(x < 0)$, $f(x) = x - 1$ $(x \geqslant 0)$. Even though this function is discontinuous at the origin, it satisfies the hypotheses of our theorem. Its minimum is attained at $x = 0$.

If S is a compact (bounded and closed) set, the hypothesis given in Theorem 2.1 is automatically satisfied. This assures us of the existence of the point x_0, described in

THEOREM 2.3

If f *is continuous on a nonnull compact set* S, *there exist points* x_0 *and* x_1 *in* S *such that*

$$f(x_0) \leqslant f(x) \leqslant f(x_1) \tag{2.1}$$

for every x *in* S. *A continuous function on a compact set attains its maximum and minimum values.*

The existence of the maximum point x_1 follows from the observation that $-f(x)$ has a minimum at a point x_1 in S. Hence $-f(x_1) \leqslant -f(x)$ or $f(x) \leqslant f(x_1)$ for all x in S.

Theorem 2.3 has a useful application in the theory of quadratic forms. By a *quadratic form* $Q(x)$ is meant a function

$$Q(x) = \sum_{i=1}^{n} \sum_{j=1}^{n} a_{ij} x^i x^j$$

in which a_{ij} are constants and $a_{ij} = a_{ji}$. If A is the matrix $A = (a_{ij})$ $(i,j = 1, \ldots, n)$, then $Q(x)$ can be expressed alternatively by the formulas

$$Q(x) = \langle Ax, x \rangle = \langle x, Ax \rangle = x^* A x,$$

where x is a column vector and x^* is its transpose. Here $\langle x, y \rangle$ is the

Euclidean inner product

$$\langle x,y \rangle = \sum_{i=1}^{n} x^i y^i = x^1 y^1 + \cdots + x^n y^n.$$

THEOREM 2.4

Given a quadratic form Q, *there exist unit vectors* y *and* z *such that*

$$Q(y)|x|^2 \leqslant Q(x) \leqslant Q(z)|x|^2 \tag{2.2}$$

for all x *in* $\mathcal{E}^n$.

To prove this result let S be the unit $(n-1)$-sphere $|x|=1$. Clearly S is compact. By Theorem 2.3 there exist vectors y and z in S such that

$$Q(y) \leqslant Q(x) \leqslant Q(z) \qquad \text{whenever } |x|=1.$$

If $x \neq 0$, we have the relation

$$Q\left(\frac{x}{|x|}\right) = \sum_i \sum_j a_{ij} \frac{x^i}{|x|} \frac{x^j}{|x|} = \sum_i \sum_j \frac{a_{ij} x^i x^j}{|x|^2} = \frac{Q(x)}{|x|^2}.$$

Since $x/|x|$ is a unit vector, it is in S and

$$Q(y) \leqslant Q\left(\frac{x}{|x|}\right) = \frac{Q(x)}{|x|^2} \leqslant Q(z).$$

Hence (2.2) holds when $x \neq 0$. It obviously holds when $x = 0$. This proves the theorem.

EXAMPLE 2.3

In the case $n=3$ with Q of the special form

$$Q(x) = 5(x^1)^2 + 3(x^2)^2 - 7(x^3)^2$$

the vectors $y=(0,0,1)$ and $z=(1,0,0)$ have the property described in Theorem 2.4.

A quadratic form $Q(x)$ is said to be *positive, nonnegative, negative, nonpositive* according as $Q(x)>0$, $Q(x)\geqslant 0$, $Q(x)<0$, $Q(x)\leqslant 0$ for all

$x \neq 0$. Taking $m = Q(y)$ and $M = Q(z)$ in Theorem 2.4, we obtain the following

COROLLARY

If a quadratic form $Q(x)$ *is positive, there are positive numbers* m *and* M *such that*

$$m|x|^2 \leqslant Q(x) \leqslant M|x|^2 \qquad (2.3)$$

for all x.

EXAMPLE 2.4

In the three-dimensional case the quadratic form

$$5x^2 + 6y^2 + 2z^2$$

is positive, whereas

$$5x^2 + 6y^2 - 2z^2$$

is not. The quadratic form

$$10x^2 + 2y^2 + 2z^2 + 6xy + 4xz + 2yz$$

is also positive, but this result is more difficult to verify. Methods for determining the positivity of a quadratic form will be given in Section 4.

By the δ-*neighborhood of a set* S is meant the set of points x whose distance from S is less than δ, that is, the set of points x for which there is a point y in S such that $|x - y| < \delta$.

THEOREM 2.5

Suppose that f *is continuous on a neighborhood of a compact set* S. *If the inequality* $f(x) > m$ *holds on* S, *then it holds on a* δ-*neighborhood of* S.

Suppose that the conclusion in the theorem is false. Then for every integer q there is a point x_q in the $(1/q)$-neighborhood of S such that $f(x_q) \leqslant m$. Since S is bounded, so also is the sequence $\{x_q\}$. By virtue of the Bolzano-Weierstrass theorem there is a subsequence $\{y_q\}$ of $\{x_q\}$ which converges to a point y_0. Since $f(y_q) \leqslant m$ and $f(y_q) \rightarrow f(y_0)$, it follows that $f(y_0) \leqslant m$. Because y_q is in the $(1/q)$-neighborhood of S, there is a point z_q in S such that

$$|y_q - z_q| < \frac{1}{q}.$$

From the inequalities

$$|z_q - y_0| \leqslant |z_q - y_q| + |y_q - y_0| \leqslant \frac{1}{q} + |y_q - y_0|$$

and the relation $y_q \to y_0$, it is seen that $z_q \to y_0$. Since $z_q \in S$ and S is closed, the point y_0 is in S. Hence $f(y_0) > m$, contrary to the inequality $f(y_0) \leqslant m$ established above. From this contradiction we infer the truth of the theorem.

EXERCISES

1. Let $f(x,y)$ be the function defined on the xy-plane by the formulas

$$f(0,0) = -1, \qquad f(x,y) = \frac{2xy}{x^2 + y^2}, \qquad (x,y) \neq (0,0).$$

Show that $m = \inf f(x,y) = -1$. Show that $f(x, -x) = -1$ for all x. Show that, if $b \geqslant -1$, the set s_b of points (x,y), such that $f(x,y) \leqslant b$, is closed but not bounded. Is Theorem 2.2 applicable?

2. A function of the form $f(x) = \sum_{i=1}^{n} b_i x^i + c$, where $b_1, \ldots, b_n, c$ are constants, is called a *linear* or *affine function*. The homogeneous part $L(x) = \sum_{i=1}^{n} b_i x^i$ is called a *linear form*. We have $f(x) = L(x) + c$. In terms of inner products we have $L(x) = \langle b, x \rangle$, where b is the vector $(b_1, \ldots, b_n)$. Here we have used subscripts to denote components of b. Show that, if a linear function $f(x) = \langle b, x \rangle + c$ attains a minimum value on a set S at a point x_0, then x_0 is a boundary point of S and the inequality

$$\langle b, x - x_0 \rangle = \sum_{i=1}^{n} b_i(x^i - x_0^i) \geqslant 0$$

holds for all x in S. Derive a corresponding result for a maximum point of a linear function. In the two-dimensional case with x and y as coordinates, find the point (x_0, y_0) at which $f(x,y) = 2x + 3y - 5$ has a minimum on the square $-1 \leqslant x \leqslant 1$, $-1 \leqslant y \leqslant 1$.

3. A function F expressible in the form

$$F(x) = \frac{1}{2} \sum_{i=1}^{n} \sum_{j=1}^{n} a_{ij} x^i x^j + \sum_{i=1}^{n} b_i x^i + c$$

is called a *quadratic function* of x. Here a_{ij}, b_i, c are constants and $a_{ij} = a_{ji}$. If we set

$$Q(x) = \sum_{i=1}^{n} \sum_{j=1}^{n} a_{ij} x^i x^j, \qquad L(x) = \sum_{i=1}^{n} b_i x^i,$$

then

$$F(x) = \tfrac{1}{2}Q(x) + L(x) + c.$$

Show that, if x_0 satisfies the linear equations

$$\sum_{j=1}^{n} a_{ij}x_0^{j} = -b_i \qquad (i = 1, \ldots, n),$$

then

$$F(x) = F(x_0) + \tfrac{1}{2}Q(x - x_0) = F(x_0) + \frac{1}{2}\sum_i \sum_j a_{ij}(x^i - x_0^i)(x^j - x_0^j).$$

Show further that, if Q is nonnegative, x_0 minimizes F. Using x and y coordinates, apply this result to the quadratic function

$$F(x,y) = 5x^2 - 4xy + y^2 + 2x - 2y - 7.$$

4. In matrix notation a quadratic function is expressible in the form

$$F(x) = \tfrac{1}{2}x^*Ax + b^*x + c,$$

where x and b are n-dimensional column vectors, x^* is the transpose of x and hence a row vector, and $A = (a_{ij})$ is a symmetric matrix. A matrix is symmetric if $A = A^*$, where A^* is the transpose of A. Obtain the results described in Exercise 3, using matrix notation.

5. Let S be a closed nonempty set, and let y be a point not in S. Show that there is a nearest point x_0 to y in S, that is, a point x_0 in S such that $|y - x_0| \le |y - x|$ for all x in S. The quantity $d(y) = |y - x_0|$ is the *distance from* y *to* S. Show that a point z in the open sphere

$$|z - y| < d(y)$$

about y is not in S. (See Example 2.1.)

6. Let $d(y)$ be defined as in Exercise 5, and set $d(y) = 0$ if y is in S. Show that

$$|d(y) - d(z)| \le |y - z|$$

for all points y and z.

7. Let x_0 be the point in a closed set S nearest to a point y not in S. Let $\{x_q\}$ be a sequence in S converging to x_0 in such a way that the limit

$$h = \lim_{q \to \infty} \frac{x_q - x_0}{|x_q - x_0|}$$

exists. Show that $\langle y - x_0, h \rangle \le 0$ for every vector h obtained in this manner.

8. In xy-space let S be the points on the circle $x^2+y^2=r^2$. Show that the distance $d(x,y)$ of a point (x,y) to S is given by the formula

    $$d(x,y)=|\sqrt{x^2+y^2}-r|.$$

    Find $d(x,y)$ for the case in which S is the square $0 \leqslant x \leqslant 1, 0 \leqslant y \leqslant 1$.

9. Let S and T be two disjoint closed nonempty sets. Show that there are a point x_0 in S and a point y_0 in T such that $|x-y| \geqslant |x_0-y_0|$ whenever x is in S and y is in T.

10. Let $g(t)$ be a function on $0 \leqslant t \leqslant \infty$ with the property that $\lim_{t \to \infty} g(t)=+\infty$. Let f be a continuous function on a closed nonnull set S with the property that $f(x) \geqslant g(|x|)$ on S. Show that there is a point x_0 in S that minimizes f on S.

11. Show that, if a function f is continuous on the closure $\bar{S}$ of a bounded open set S and vanishes on the boundary of S, then f has an extreme point (maximum or minimum point) x_0 in S.

12. A set S is said to be a *cone* if for each $\alpha \geqslant 0$ the point αx is in S whenever x is in S. If the point $x=0$ is deleted from a cone S, a *deleted cone* S_0 is obtained. It has the property that, if x is in S_0, so also is x for all $\alpha > 0$. A function f will be said to be *positively homogeneous of degree p* if its domain S is a cone or a deleted cone and if $f(\alpha x)=\alpha^p f(x)$ for all x in S and all $\alpha > 0$. Show that $g(x)=|x|^p$ is positively homogeneous of degree p. Show that, if f is positively homogeneous of degree p on S, then

    $$f(x)=|x|^p f\left(\frac{x}{|x|}\right)$$

    for all $x \neq 0$ in S. Show that the values of f on S are determined uniquely by the values of f on the set S_1 of unit vectors in S.

13. For the case $n=2$, using x,y-coordinates, consider the functions $f(x,y)$ defined by the following formulas:

    (a) $(x^2+y^2)^{3/2}$,   (b) $x(x^2+y^2)^{-5/2}$,   (c) $\dfrac{(x^2+y^2)^{1/2}}{x^2-y^2}$,

    (d) $\dfrac{2xy}{x^2+y^2}$,   (e) $\log\dfrac{x+\sqrt{x^2+y^2}}{x}$,   (f) $e^{y/x}$,

    (g) $\dfrac{x^3+y^3}{x^4+y^4}$,   (h) $x\sin\left(\dfrac{y}{x}\right)$.

    In each case the function f is positively homogeneous on the set S in which the formula has meaning. Determine S and the degree of f in each case.

14. Let f be continuous and positively homogeneous of degree p on S and suppose that the set S_1 of unit vectors in S is closed. Show that there exist

points y and z in S_1 such that

$$f(y)|x|^p \leqslant f(x) \leqslant f(z)|x|^p$$

for all x in S. *Hint*: Use Theorem 2.3 on S_1.

15. Let f be positively homogeneous of degree p on a deleted cone S. Assuming the existence of derivatives, show that its first derivatives are positively homogeneous of degree $p-1$, its second derivatives are positively homogeneous of degree $p-2$, and so on. *Hint*: Differentiate the identity $f(\alpha x) = \alpha^p f(x)$ $(\alpha > 0)$ with respect to x^j, then with respect to x^k, and so on.

16. Let f be positively homogeneous of degree p on a deleted cone. Assuming derivatives exist, show that

$$f'(x,x) = pf(x), \qquad f''(x,x) = p(p-1)f(x), \qquad \text{etc.}$$

Hint: Differentiate $f(\alpha x) = \alpha^p f(x)$ with respect to α, and set $\alpha = 1$.

3. UNCONSTRAINED LOCAL MINIMA AND MAXIMA

A point x_0 in S is said to afford a *local minimum* to f on S if there is a neighborhood N of x_0 such that the inequality $f(x) \geqslant f(x_0)$ holds for all points x in $N \cap S$. If local minimum point x_0 of f in S is an interior point of S, we can select N so that $N \subset S$. We then have $f(x) \geqslant f(x_0)$ for all x in N. Accordingly a point x_0 will be said to afford an *unconstrained local minimum* to f on S if it is an interior point of S which affords a local minimum to f on S. Unconstrained local maximum points of f on S are defined in a similar manner. In dealing with unconstrained minima and maxima, we can assume that the set S is open.

In the study of local minimum and maximum points of f on a set S, we shall assume that the function f is continuous and has continuous first and second partial derivatives. Such a function is said to be of class C'' on S. In general, a function f is said to be of class $C^{(k)}$ on S if it is continuous and possesses continuous derivatives of all orders $\leqslant k$. Obviously in a theorem, where only first derivatives occur, we need only to assume that f is of class C'. A discussion of these concepts is found in the appendix.

We shall use the customary notations

$$f_{x^i} = \frac{\partial f}{\partial x^i}, \qquad f_{x^i x^j} = \frac{\partial^2 f}{\partial x^i \partial x^j}$$

for the first and second partial derivatives of f. The linear form

$$f'(x,h) = \sum_{i=1}^{n} f_{x^i}(x) h^i \tag{3.1}$$

in h at x is the *first differential of* f *at* x. It is also the derivative at $t = 0$ of the function $g(t) = f(x + th)$. Accordingly $f'(x, h)$ can be interpreted as the *derivative of* f *at* x *in the direction* h. This interpretation will be emphasized in this book. The vector defined by the first-order partial derivatives of f at x is called the *gradient* of f at x. It is denoted by various symbols, such as

$$\operatorname{grad} f(x) = \nabla f(x) = f'(x) = f_x(x) = (f_{x^i}(x)) = \left(\frac{\partial f(x)}{\partial x^i} \right).$$

Normally, we shall use the notations $\nabla f(x)$ or $f'(x)$ for the gradient. In terms of the Euclidean inner product $\langle x, y \rangle$ we have

$$f'(x, h) = \langle f'(x), h \rangle = \langle \nabla f(x), h \rangle. \tag{3.2}$$

The gradient ∇f is in the direction of *steepest ascent* of f at x. The negative gradient $-\nabla f$ is in the direction of *steepest descent* of f at x.

The quadratic form

$$f''(x, h) = \sum_{i=1}^{n} \sum_{j=1}^{n} f_{x^i x^j}(x) h^i h^j \tag{3.3}$$

in h at x is called the *second differential of* f *at* x. It is also the second derivative at $t = 0$ of the function $g(t) = f(x + th)$. It is accordingly the second-order directional derivative of f at x in the direction h. The matrix of second derivatives of f is denoted by

$$f''(x) = f_{xx}(x) = (f_{x^i x^j}(x)) = \left(\frac{\partial^2 f(x)}{\partial x^i \partial x^j} \right)$$

and is called the *Hessian* of f at x.

A more complete discussion of these ideas can be found in Sections 6 and 7 of the appendix.

A local minimum point x_0 of f on S must satisfy the necessary conditions described in

THEOREM 3.1

Suppose that a point x_0 *affords a local minimum to* f *on an open set* S. *Then*

$$f'(x_0, h) = 0, \qquad f''(x_0, h) \geqslant 0 \tag{3.4}$$

for every vector h *or, equivalently,*

$$\nabla f(x_0) = 0, \qquad f''(x_0, h) \geqslant 0 \qquad \text{for all } h \neq 0, \tag{3.5}$$

where $\nabla f(x)$ *is the gradient of* f *at* x.

To prove this result choose a δ-neighborhood of x_0 such that

$$f(x) \geqslant f(x_0) \qquad \text{whenever } |x - x_0| < \delta.$$

Given a vector $h \neq 0$, choose $\epsilon = \delta/|h|$. Then the points $x = x_0 + th$ ($-\epsilon < t < \epsilon$) satisfy the condition

$$|x - x_0| = |t|\|h\| < \epsilon|h| = \delta.$$

It follows that upon setting $g(t) = f(x_0 + th)$ we have

$$g(t) = f(x_0 + th) \geqslant f(x_0) = g(0) \qquad (-\epsilon < t < \epsilon).$$

Hence (see Theorem 5.6 in the appendix)

$$g'(0) = f'(x_0, h) = 0, \qquad g''(0) = f''(x_0, h) \geqslant 0.$$

Since h is arbitrary, relations (3.4) hold. Because

$$f'(x_0, h) = \sum_{i=1}^{n} f_{x^i}(x_0)h^i = \langle \nabla f(x_0), h \rangle,$$

it follows that

$$f'(x_0, h) = 0 \quad \text{for all } h \neq 0 \quad \text{if and only if } \nabla f(x_0) = 0.$$

This proves Theorem 3.1.

EXAMPLE 3.1

In the two-dimensional case consider the function

$$f(x,y) = 5x^2 + 4xy + y^2 - 6x - 2y + 6.$$

At a minimum point $\nabla f = 0$, that is,

$$f_x(x,y) = 10x + 4y - 6 = 0,$$
$$f_y(x,y) = 4x + 2y - 2 = 0.$$

These equations are satisfied by the point $(x,y) = (1, -1)$, as can readily be verified. The second-order condition

$$f''(x,y; h,k) = 10h^2 + 8hk + 2k^2 > 0$$

holds for all $(h,k) \neq (0,0)$. This can be seen as follows. This inequality holds if $h = 0$ and $k \neq 0$. If $h \neq 0$, its minimum relative to k is found by differentiating with respect to k. The result is

$$8h + 4k = 0 \quad \text{or} \quad k = -2h.$$

If h and k are so related, we have

$$10h^2 + 8hk + 2k^2 = 10h^2 - 16h^2 + 8h^2 = 2h^2 > 0,$$

as was to be proved. According to Theorem 3.2, the point $(1, -1)$ affords a strict local minimum to f. In fact, $(1, -1)$ affords a strict global minimum to f. The minimum of f is $f(1, -1) = 0$. If $c > 0$, the level curves $f(x,y) = c$ are similar ellipses with $(1, -1)$ as their common center.

EXAMPLE 3.2

Of course we cannot apply Theorem 3.1 to a function f which does not have the required differentiability properties. For example, the function $f(x) = |x|$ has a strict minimum at $x_0 = 0$ but fails to have a gradient there. The function $f(x) = |x|^{3/2}$ has the gradient $\nabla f(x_0) = 0$ at $x_0 = 0$ but fails to have a second differential there. The theorem is applicable to a function of the form $f(x) = |x|^2 - 2|x| + 3$ because this function has the assumed differentiability properties in a neighborhood of its minimum points. If a function f is not differentiable at its minimum point x_0, it may have the one-sided directional derivative

$$f'(x_0, h) = \lim_{t \to 0+} \frac{f(x_0 + th) - f(x_0)}{t}.$$

In this event $f'(x_0, h) \geq 0$ for all vectors h. For example, if $f(x) = |x - x_0|$, we have $f'(x_0, h) = |h| \geq 0$. Observe that this directional derivative is not a differential. In this book we shall not pursue the consequences of the lack of differentiability at extreme points. In the main the results given in Chapter 6 are applicable to nondifferentiable functions, although we shall not emphasize this fact.

As a converse to Theorem 3.1 we have

THEOREM 3.2

Suppose that at a point x_0 *in S we have*

$$\nabla f(x_0) = 0, \quad f''(x_0, h) > 0 \quad \text{for all } h \neq 0. \tag{3.6}$$

Then there exist positive numbers δ *and* m *such that*

$$f(x) \geq f(x_0) + m|x - x_0|^2 \quad \text{whenever } |x - x_0| < \delta. \tag{3.7}$$

Consequently x_0 *affords a proper local minimum to* f *on S.*

To establish this result, we use Taylor's formula (6.5) in the appendix to obtain the formula

$$f(x) = f(x_0) + f'(x_0, x - x_0) + \tfrac{1}{2} f''(x_0, x - x_0) + r_2(x_0, x - x_0), \quad (3.8)$$

where

$$\lim_{h \to 0} \frac{r_2(x_0, h)}{|h|^2} = 0. \quad (3.9)$$

In view of (3.6) the quadratic form $f''(x_0, h)$ in h is positive. It follows from the corollary to Theorem 2.4 that there is a number $m > 0$ such that

$$f''(x_0, h) \geqslant 4m|h|^2.$$

By virtue of relation (3.9) there is a constant $\delta > 0$ such that

$$|r_2(x_0, h)| \leqslant m|h|^2 \qquad \text{whenever } |h| < \delta.$$

Consequently

$$\tfrac{1}{2} f''(x_0, h) + r_2(x_0, h) \geqslant 2m|h|^2 - m|h|^2 = m|h|^2. \quad (3.10)$$

Inasmuch as $\nabla f(x_0) = 0$, we have $f'(x_0, x - x_0) = 0$ for all x. Using inequality (3.10) with $h = x - x_0$ in (3.8), we find that

$$f(x) - f(x_0) = \tfrac{1}{2} f''(x_0, x - x_0) + r_2(x_0, x - x_0) \geqslant m|x - x_0|^2$$

$$\text{whenever } |x - x_0| < \delta.$$

This proves Theorem 3.2.

Replacing f by $-f$ in Theorems 3.1 and 3.2, we obtain

THEOREM 3.3

If a point x_0 *in* S *affords a local maximum to* f *on* S, *then*

$$\nabla f(x_0) = 0, \qquad f''(x_0, h) \leqslant 0 \qquad \text{for all } h \neq 0.$$

Conversely, if

$$\nabla f(x_0) = 0, \qquad f''(x_0, h) < 0 \qquad \text{for all } h \neq 0,$$

there exist positive numbers m *and* δ *such that*

$$f(x) \leqslant f(x_0) - m|x - x_0|^2 \qquad \text{whenever } |x - x_0| < \delta.$$

A matrix $A = (a_{ij})$ $(i,j = 1,\ldots,n)$ is said to be *symmetric* if $a_{ij} = a_{ji}$ $(i,j = 1,\ldots,n)$. Associated with each symmetric matrix A is a quadratic form

$$Q(x) = \sum_i \sum_j a_{ij} x^i x^j = \langle Ax, x \rangle = \langle x, Ax \rangle = x^* A x.$$

We say that A is *nonnegative* (written as $A \geqslant 0$) or, equivalently, that Q is *nonnegative* (written as $Q \geqslant 0$) in the case

$$Q(x) \geqslant 0 \qquad \text{for all } x \neq 0.$$

Moreover we say that A is *positive* (written as $A > 0$) or, equivalently, that Q is *positive* (written as $Q > 0$) if

$$Q(x) > 0 \qquad \text{for all } x \neq 0.$$

Similarly we say that A is *nonpositive* ($A \leqslant 0$) or Q is *nonpositive* ($Q \leqslant 0$) if $-Q$ is nonnegative, and that A is *negative* ($A < 0$) or Q is *negative* ($Q < 0$) if $-Q$ is positive. Occasionally we shall use the terminology *positive definite* or *negative definite* in place of "positive" or "negative."

The interpretation of the symbols $A > 0$, $A \geqslant 0$, etc., given above is standard in mathematical analysis. However, they have another interpretation which is standard in the theory of linear inequalities. In this context the symbol $A > 0$ signifies that the elements of A are positive. Similarly $A \geqslant 0$ signifies that the elements of A are nonnegative. Notations of this type will be used in Chapter 4. In the meantime we shall use the interpretations given above.

As an application of Theorem 3.1 we have

THEOREM 3.4

A nonnegative symmetric matrix A *is positive if and only if* A *is nonsingular, that is, if and only if the determinant,* $|\mathrm{A}| = \det \mathrm{A}$, *is different from zero. In fact, if* $\mathrm{A} > 0$, *then* $\det \mathrm{A} > 0$.

From the theory of linear equations it follows that $|A| = 0$ if and only if the system of n linear equations

$$\sum_j a_{ij} x^j = 0 \qquad (i = 1,\ldots,n) \tag{3.11}$$

has a solution $x \neq 0$. If $x \neq 0$ satisfies (3.11), then

$$Q(x) = \sum_i \sum_j x^i a_{ij} x^j = 0$$

and A cannot be positive.

Suppose next that A is nonnegative but is not positive. Then there is a point $x \neq 0$ such that $Q(x) = 0$. Since $Q \geqslant 0$, the point x minimizes Q. Consequently

$$\frac{\partial Q}{\partial x^i} = 2 \sum_j a_{ij} x^j = 0$$

at this point x. It follows that A is singular. This proves the first conclusion in the theorem.

Suppose next that $A > 0$, and let I be the identity matrix. For $0 \leqslant \lambda \leqslant 1$ the quadratic form

$$P(x) = (1-\lambda)|x|^2 + \lambda Q(x) = x^*[(1-\lambda)I + \lambda A]x$$

is positive. The determinant $d(\lambda)$ of the associated matrix $(1-\lambda)I + \lambda A$ is accordingly different from zero. Moreover $d(\lambda)$ is a polynomial in λ and is therefore continuous. Since $d(0) = \det I = 1$, the function $d(\lambda)$, being nonzero, is positive on $0 \leqslant \lambda \leqslant 1$. It follows that $d(1) = \det A > 0$, as was to be proved.

EXAMPLE 3.3

The matrix

$$A = \begin{pmatrix} 3 & 1 & 1 \\ 1 & 2 & 1 \\ 1 & 1 & 2 \end{pmatrix}$$

is associated with the quadratic form

$$Q = 3x^2 + 2y^2 + 2z^2 + 2xy + 2yz + 2zx.$$

Writing Q in the form

$$Q = x^2 + (x+y)^2 + (x+z)^2 + (y+z)^2,$$

we see that $Q > 0$ unless $x = y = z = 0$. Hence A is positive. Its determinant is 7.

A point $x = c$ will be called a *critical point* of f if $\nabla f(c) = 0$. The value $f(c)$ of f at a critical point c will be called a *critical value*. A critical point c will be said to be *nondegenerate* if $f''(c)$ is nonsingular, that is, if the determinant

$$|f_{x^i x^j}(c)|$$

is different from zero.

Inasmuch as $f''(c)$ is the symmetric matrix associated with the quadratic form $f''(c,h)$ in h, it follows from Theorem 3.4 that $f''(c)>0$ if and only if $f''(c)\geqslant 0$ and $|f''(c)|\neq 0$. Combining this result with the preceding theorems, we have

THEOREM 3.5

A nondegenerate critical point c of f affords a strict local minimum to f if and only if the Hessian f"(c) is nonnegative. Similarly a nondegenerate critical point c of f affords a strict local maximum to f if and only if f"(c) is nonpositive.

As is easily seen, the origin is a nondegenerate critical point of the function $f(x,y)=x^2-y^2$ but fails to minimize or maximize f. The origin is a nondegenerate saddle point of f. By a nondegenerate *saddle point* is meant a nondegenerate critical point that is not a local extreme point of f.

EXERCISES

1. Let p and q be real numbers with $0<p<q$. Show that the origin $(x,y)=(0,0)$ minimizes

$$f(x,y)=(y-px^2)(y-qx^2)$$

   locally on each line

$$x=ht, \qquad y=kt$$

   through the origin. Show also that, if $p<m<q$, then $f(x,mx^2)<0$ if $x\neq 0$ and that $f(x,mx^2)\geqslant 0$ if m is not on this interval. The point $(0,0)$ accordingly fails to afford a local minimum to f, even though it affords a local minimum to f on each line through the origin.

2. Show that the curve

$$4x^2-2xy+5y^2-2x+6y-11=0$$

   is an ellipse. Find its center.

3. Find the level curves $f(x,y)=c$ for each of the following functions f through each of the two specified points (x_0,y_0), and determine the sets $f>c$ and $f<c$:
   (a) $f(x,y)=x^2+y^2$ (2,3),   (0,0),
   (b) $f(x,y)=x^2-y^2$ (2,3),   (0,0),.
   (c) $f(x,y)=yx^2$ (2,3),   (0,0).

4. Find the critical points and critical values of the following functions, and determine which critical points determine local extrema:
   (a) $f(x,y)=x^2-x^4-y^4$,
   (b) $f(x,y)=xy^2(3x+6y-2)$,
   (c) $f(x,y)=y^2+x^2y+\frac{1}{2}y^4$,

(d) $f(x,y) = xy + \dfrac{1}{x} + \dfrac{1}{y}$ $(x \neq 0, y \neq 0)$,

(e) $f(x,y) = (x+y)^2 + xy$.

5. Prove the following inequalities for all $x > 0$ and $y > 0$:

(a) $(\dfrac{1}{x} + \dfrac{1}{y})(x+y) \geq 4$,

(b) $\dfrac{1}{x} + x + \dfrac{1}{y} + y \geq 4$,

(c) $\dfrac{x}{y} + \dfrac{y}{x} \geq 2$.

6. Sketch the level curves for the function

$$f(x,y) = 100(y - x^2)^2 + (x-1)^2.$$

Show that the function has a minimum point at $x = y = 1$.

7. Find the critical points of the function

$$f(x,y) = (x^2 - 4)^2 + y^2.$$

Show that f has an absolute minimum at each of the points $(x,y) = (2,0)$ and $(x,y) = (-2,0)$. Show that the point $(0,0)$ is a saddle point. Sketch the level curves $f(x,y) = $ constant for typical values of this constant.

8. Find the maximum and minimum points of $f(x,y) = \sin x + \sin y + \sin(x+y)$ on the square $0 < x < 2\pi$, $0 < y < 2\pi$.

9. Show that the cube is the parallelopiped of given volume which has the least surface area.

10. Find the point in a triangle such that the sum of the squares of its distance from the vertices is a minimum. Show that this point is the intersection of the medians of the triangle.

11. Determine the maximum and minimum values of the ratio $F(x,y)/(x^2+y^2)$ for the following quadratic forms:

(a) $F(x,y) = 5x^2 - 3xy + 4y^2$,

(b) $F(x,y) = 5x^2 - 7xy + 4y^2$,

(c) $F(x,y) = xy - y^2$,

(d) $F(x,y) = -3x^2 + xy - y^2$.

In each case determine whether the curve $F(x,y) = $ constant is an ellipse or an hyperbola.

12. Find the critical points and critical values of the function

$$R(x,y) = \frac{ax^2 + 2bxy + cy^2}{x^2 + y^2}.$$

Show that the critical values λ are solutions of the equation

$$\begin{vmatrix} a - \lambda & b \\ b & c - \lambda \end{vmatrix} = 0.$$

13. Find the critical points and critical values of the functions

$$f(x,y,z) = x^2 + 2y^2 - 3z^2,$$

$$g(x,y,z) = \frac{x^2 + 2y^2 - 3z^2}{x^2 + y^2 + z^2}, \qquad (x,y,z) \neq (0,0,0).$$

14. Establish the following result. Let f be the function

$$f(x,y) = Ax^2 + 2Bxy + Cy^2 + 2Dx + 2Ey + F,$$

where A, B, C, D, E, F are constants such that $AC - B^2 \neq 0$. Then f has a unique critical point (x_0, y_0) defined by the equations

$$Ax_0 + By_0 = -D, \qquad Bx_0 + Cy_0 = -E.$$

The critical value of f is given by the formula

$$f(x_0, y_0) = Dx_0 + Ey_0 + F = \frac{\begin{vmatrix} A & B & D \\ B & C & E \\ D & E & F \end{vmatrix}}{\begin{vmatrix} A & B \\ B & C \end{vmatrix}}.$$

The level curves $F(x,y) = \alpha = $ constant form a one-parameter family of similar conic sections having (x_0, y_0) as their common center. These conic sections are ellipses or hyperbolas according as $AC - B^2 > 0$ or $AC - B^2 < 0$.

15. Let $x_0, x_1, \ldots, x_k$ be $k + 1$ points, and let $\alpha_0, \alpha_1, \ldots, \alpha_k$ be nonnegative so that

$$\alpha_0 + \alpha_1 + \cdots + \alpha_k = 1.$$

Show that the point

$$\bar{x} = \alpha_0 x_0 + \alpha_1 x_1 + \cdots + \alpha_k x_k$$

minimizes the function

$$f(x) = \alpha_0 |x - x_0|^2 + \alpha_1 |x - x_1|^2 + \cdots + \alpha_k |x - x_k|^2.$$

16. Let $A = (a_{ij})$ $(i,j = 1, \ldots, n)$ be a positive symmetric matrix. By the use of Theorem 3.4 show that the matrix $A_p = (a_{\alpha\beta})$ $(\alpha, \beta = 1, \ldots, p)$ is positive for each $p \leqslant n$. *Hint*: Apply Theorem 3.4 to the subspace consisting of all points x having $x^j = 0$ $(j = p+1, \ldots, n)$.

17. Let $\varphi_1(x), \ldots, \varphi_m(x)$ be nonnull continuous functions on an interval $(a \leqslant x \leqslant b)$ with the property that

$$\int_a^b \varphi_\alpha(x)\varphi_\beta(x)\,dx = 0 \qquad (\alpha \neq \beta).$$

Given a piecewise continuous function f on $[a,b]$, show that the values of $c_1, \ldots, c_m$ that minimize the function

$$F(c) = \int_a^b |f - c_1\varphi_1 - c_2\varphi_2 - \cdots - c_m\varphi_m|^2 \, dx$$

are given by the formulas

$$c_\alpha = \frac{\langle \varphi_\alpha, f \rangle}{\langle \varphi_\alpha, \varphi_\alpha \rangle} \qquad (\alpha = 1, \ldots, m)$$

where

$$\langle \varphi, \psi \rangle = \int_a^b \varphi(x)\psi(x) \, dx.$$

18. Least squares solutions of a linear system.
   (a) Let A be an $m \times n$ matrix and b a given $m \times 1$ column vector. The linear system $Ax = b$ may or may not have a solution in the usual sense. Observe that, if we define the *residual* at x to be $r(x) = b - Ax$, then $r(x) = 0$ if and only if x is a solution in the usual sense. Instead of solving the equation, we seek a minimum point of the function

   $$f(x) = \tfrac{1}{2}|r(x)|^2 = \tfrac{1}{2}|Ax - b|^2.$$

   Show that $\nabla f(x) = A^*Ax - A^*b$ and $f''(x,h) = h^*A^*Ah$. In view of Theorem 3.2, what can you say about the existence and uniqueness of solution of this problem? A vector x_0, which minimizes the square $2f(x)$ of the residual, is called a *least squares solution* of $Ax = b$. What is the nature of x_0 if A is nonsingular?
   (b) Compute the least squares solution of the system $x + y = 2$, $x - y = 0$, $x + y = 1$.

   (b)   *Answer:* $(\tfrac{3}{4}, \tfrac{3}{4})$

4. POSITIVE SYMMETRIC MATRICES

Consider for a moment the quadratic form

$$Ax^2 + By^2 + Cz^2 + 2Dxy + 2Exz + 2Fyz$$

in (x,y,z). The associated matrix is

$$\begin{bmatrix} A & D & E \\ D & B & F \\ E & F & C \end{bmatrix}$$

It is known that this quadratic form is positive for all $(x, y, z) \neq (0, 0, 0)$ if and only if the determinants

$$A, \qquad \begin{vmatrix} A & D \\ D & B \end{vmatrix}, \qquad \begin{vmatrix} A & D & E \\ D & B & F \\ E & F & C \end{vmatrix}$$

are all positive. It is the purpose of this section to prove the corresponding result for an $(n \times n)$-dimensional symmetric matrix. The proof is based on the concepts and results developed in Section 3. Before proving this result it is convenient to establish

LEMMA 4.1

Let F *be a quadratic function of the form*

$$F(x) = \sum_i \sum_j a_{ij} x^i x^j + 2 \sum_i b_i x^i + c = x^* A x + 2 b^* x + c \qquad (4.1)$$

where $A = (a_{ij})$ *is a symmetric matrix with constant elements,* $b^* = (b_1, \ldots, b_n)$ *is a constant row vector, and* c *is a constant. Suppose that* A *is nonsingular, that is, that its determinant* $|A| = |a_{ij}|$ *is not zero. The function* F *has a unique critical point*

$$x_0 = -A^{-1} b \qquad (4.2)$$

where A^{-1} *is the inverse of* A. *The corresponding critical value is*

$$F(x_0) = \frac{\begin{vmatrix} A & b \\ b^* & c \end{vmatrix}}{|A|}. \qquad (4.3)$$

Moreover

$$F(x) = F(x_0) + (x - x_0)^* A (x - x_0). \qquad (4.4)$$

If A *is positive,* $F(x_0)$ *is the minimum value of* F. *If* A *is negative,* $F(x_0)$ *is the maximum of* F.

To prove this result, observe that the gradient

$$F'(x) = 2(Ax + b)$$

of F vanishes at a point x_0 if and only if x_0 is a solution of the equation

$$Ax_0 = -b.$$

It follows that F has a unique critical point $x_0 = -A^{-1}b$. Moreover, since

$b^* x_0 = x_0^* b$, we have

$$F(x_0) = x_0^*(Ax_0 + b) + b^* x_0 + c = b^* x_0 + c.$$

In addition, by a well-known property of determinants,

$$\begin{vmatrix} A & b \\ b^* & c \end{vmatrix} = \begin{vmatrix} A & Ax_0 + b \\ b^* & b^* x_0 + c \end{vmatrix} = \begin{vmatrix} A & 0 \\ b^* & F(x_0) \end{vmatrix} = |A| F(x_0).$$

Hence (4.3) holds. Moreover, by the use of Taylor's theorem with $F'(x_0) = 0$ and $F''(x_0) = 2A$, we find that

$$F(x) = F(x_0) + (x - x_0)^* A(x - x_0).$$

Consequently, if $|A| \neq 0$, the point x_0 minimizes F if and only if A if positive. This proves the lemma.

Associated with the function F defined by equation (4.1) is a quadratic form

$$G(x,y) = x^* Ax + 2yb^* x + cy^2 \tag{4.5}$$

in $n+1$ variables $(x^1, \ldots, x^n, y)$. The matrix associated with this quadratic form is

$$B = \begin{pmatrix} A & b \\ b^* & c \end{pmatrix}. \tag{4.6}$$

We have

LEMMA 4.2

The quadratic form (4.5) is positive if and only if A *is a positive matrix and the determinant*

$$\det B = \begin{vmatrix} A & b \\ b^* & c \end{vmatrix}$$

is positive.

Suppose first that the quadratic form (4.5) is positive. Then $\det B > 0$, by Theorem 3.4. Moreover the quadratic form $G(x,0) = x^* Ax$ in n variables is also positive. Consequently A is a positive matrix.

Suppose conversely that A is a positive matrix and $\det B > 0$. Since A is positive, we have $\det A > 0$ and $G(x,0) > 0$ if $x \neq 0$. By Lemma 4.1

$$F(x) = G(x,1) \geq F(x_0) = \frac{\det B}{\det A} > 0.$$

Consequently, if $y \neq 0$, we have

$$G(x,y) = y^2 G\left(\frac{x}{y}, 1\right) \geqslant \frac{\det B}{\det A} y^2 > 0.$$

It follows that $G(x,y) > 0$ unless $(x,y) = (0,0)$, as was to be proved.

We are now in a position to prove

THEOREM 4.1

Let $A = (a_{ij})$ $(i,j = 1, \ldots, n)$ *be a symmetric matrix, and let* A_p *be the principal minor*

$$A_p = (a_{\alpha\beta}) \qquad (\alpha, \beta = 1, \ldots, p).$$

Let d_p *be the determinant of* A_p. *The matrix* A *is positive if and only if the determinants* $d_1, \ldots, d_n$ *are positive.*

The proof will be obtained by induction on the dimension n. It is true when $n = 1$. Suppose that it is true for an n-dimensional matrix A. Let B be the $(n+1)$-dimensional matrix (4.6). Set $d_{n+1} = \det B$. By Lemma 4.2 B is a positive matrix if and only if A is a positive matrix and d_{n+1} is positive. Since A is positive if and only if the determinants $d_1, \ldots, d_n$ are positive, it follows that B is a positive matrix if and only if the determinants $d_1, \ldots, d_{n+1}$ are positive. This proves the theorem.

COROLLARY

If A *is a positive symmetric matrix, the determinants of its principal minors are positive.*

The level surface, $F(x) = $ constant, of a quadratic function

$$F(x) = x^* A x + 2b^* x + c$$

is called a *quadric surface*. If $\det A = 0$, it is said to be *degenerate*. If A is a positive (or negative) matrix, the surface is called an $(n-1)$-dimensional *ellipsoid*. This terminology follows from the fact that the intersection of an ellipsoid with a 2-plane is an ellipse. A nondegenerate quadric surface that is not an ellipsoid will be called an *hyperboloid*. The critical point $x_0 = -A^{-1}b$ of F is called the *center* of the quadric surface $F(x) = \gamma = $ constant.

Suppose that the matrix A is positive. Then the surfaces $F(x) = \gamma$ $[\gamma > F(x_0)]$ form a one-parameter family of ellipsoids, as indicated schematically in Figure 4.1. It should be noted that these ellipsoids are similar. By this is meant that, if x_α and x_β are the points in which a ray emanating from x_0 cuts the level surfaces $F(x) = \alpha$ and $F(x) = \beta$, respectively, the ratio

$$\frac{|x_\beta - x_0|}{|x_\alpha - x_0|} = r$$

of the distances of x_β and x_α from x_0 is independent of the choice of this ray. To see that this is the case, observe that the points x_α and x_β satisfy the relation

$$x_\beta - x_0 = r(x_\alpha - x_0).$$

By the use of (4.5) we see that

$$F(x_\beta) - F(x_0) = (x_\beta - x_0)^* A (x_\beta - x_0) = r^2 (x_\alpha - x_0)^* A (x_\alpha - x_0)$$
$$= r^2 [F(x_\alpha) - F(x_0)].$$

It follows that

$$r^2 = \frac{F(x_\beta) - F(x_0)}{F(x_\alpha) - F(x_0)} = \frac{\beta - F(x_0)}{\alpha - F(x_0)}$$

is a constant, as was to be shown.

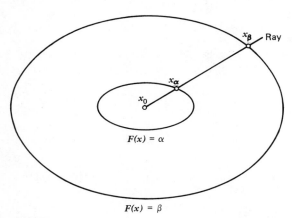

$F(x) = \alpha$

$F(x) = \beta$

Figure 4.1

EXERCISES

1. Let d^i be the cofactor of b_i in the determinant

$$\begin{vmatrix} a_{ij} & b_i \\ b_j & c \end{vmatrix}$$

and let $e = |a_{ij}|$, the cofactor of c. Show that if $A > 0$ the point x having $x^i = -d^i/e$ minimizes the function

$$F(x) = x^* A x + 2 b^* x + c.$$

2. Show that the matrix

$$A = \begin{bmatrix} 1 & \frac{1}{2} & \frac{1}{3} & \frac{1}{4} \\ \frac{1}{2} & \frac{1}{3} & \frac{1}{4} & \frac{1}{5} \\ \frac{1}{3} & \frac{1}{4} & \frac{1}{5} & \frac{1}{6} \\ \frac{1}{4} & \frac{1}{5} & \frac{1}{6} & \frac{1}{7} \end{bmatrix}$$

is positive, by computing the determinants d_1, d_2, d_3, d_4 described in Theorem 4.1. Find the inverse of A.

3. By the use of Theorem 4.1 construct nondiagonal positive matrices of dimensions 3, 4, and 5.

4. Prove the corollary to Theorem 4.1.

5. State the analogue of Theorem 4.1 for negative matrices.

6. Show that, if A is a nonnegative symmetric matrix, then

$$|x^* A y|^2 \leqslant (x^* A x)(y^* A y), \qquad |x^* A y|^2 \leqslant (x^* A^2 x)(y^* y),$$

$$|x^* A^2 y|^2 \leqslant (x^* A^3 x)(y^* A y).$$

7. Let $a_1, \ldots, a_n$, $b_1, \ldots, b_n$ be $2n$ numbers with the property that $a_j + b_k \neq 0$ $(j, k = 1, \ldots, n)$. Show that the determinant D_n of the matrix

$$A_n = \left(\frac{1}{a_j + b_k} \right) \qquad (j, k = 1, \ldots, n)$$

is given by the formula $D_n = \alpha_n / \beta_n$, where

$$\alpha_n = \prod_{\substack{j > k}}^{1-n} (a_j - a_k)(b_j - b_k), \qquad \beta_n = \prod_{\substack{j,k}}^{1-n} (a_j + b_k).$$

Hint: Use induction.

8. Use the result given in Exercise 7, together with Theorem 4.1, to show that the

matrix

$$\left(\frac{1}{a_j + a_k - c}\right) \qquad (j,k=1,\ldots,n)$$

is positive definite if $a_j \neq a_k$ $(j \neq k)$ and $2a_j > c > 0$. In particular, show that the Hilbert matrix

$$\left(\frac{1}{j+k-1}\right) \qquad (j,k=1,\ldots,n)$$

is positive definite.

9. Let A, b, c, and B be interpreted as in (4.6). Suppose that A and B are nonsingular. Let v be the vector $v = -A^{-1}b$, and set $\alpha = \det A / \det B$. Show that B^{-1} is given by the formula

$$B^{-1} = \begin{pmatrix} A^{-1} + \alpha v v^* & \alpha v \\ \alpha v^* & \alpha \end{pmatrix}$$

Hint: Use Lemma 4.1 with $v = x_0$ to show that $b^*v + c = 1/\alpha$.

5. MINIMA OF CONVEX FUNCTIONS

Recall that a set S in $\mathcal{E}^n$ is convex if, given two points x and y in S, the line segment

$$z(t) = (1-t)x + ty \qquad (0 \leqslant t \leqslant 1)$$

is in S. A real-valued function f on a convex set S is said to be *convex* on S if for every pair of points x and y in S the inequality

$$f[(1-t)x + ty] \leqslant (1-t)f(x) + tf(y) \qquad (0 \leqslant t \leqslant 1) \qquad (5.1)$$

holds or, equivalently, if

$$\varphi(t) = (1-t)f(x) + tf(y) - f[(1-t)x + ty] \geqslant 0 \qquad (0 \leqslant t \leqslant 1). \quad (5.2)$$

If $\varphi(t) > 0$ on $0 < t < 1$ for every pair of distinct points x and y in S, then f is said to be *strictly convex* on S. A function f will be said to be *concave* (or *strictly concave*) on S if $-f$ is convex (or strictly convex) on S. Geometrically, a function f is convex on S if the set of $(n+1)$-dimensional points (x,u) with x in S and $u \geqslant f(x)$ is convex. The case $n = 1$ is shown schematically in Figure 5.1 with S as the interval $a \leqslant x \leqslant b$. This figure shows the graph of $u = f(x)$ $(a \leqslant x \leqslant b)$. Let A, B, C be the points on this graph whose abscissas are $x, y, z = (1-t)x + ty$ $(0 < t < 1)$, respectively. The function $\varphi(t)$ is the directed length of the directed vertical line segment CD shown in Figure 5.1. If follows that f is convex if and only if the point C is never above the chord AB for all choices of distinct points x and y. It is strictly convex if C is always below the chord AB.

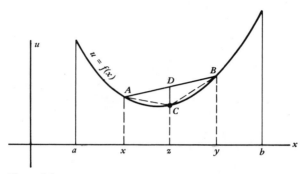

Figure 5.1

Observe that the function $f(x)=|x|$ is convex but not strictly convex.

Since $\varphi(0)=\varphi(1)=0$, we can disregard the values $t=0$ and $t=1$ in considering inequality (5.2). This inequality with $t=0$ and $t=1$ excluded can be put into the form

$$f(y)-f(x) \geqslant \frac{f[x+t(y-x)]-f(x)}{t} \qquad (0<t<1). \qquad (5.3)$$

Consequently f is *convex* on S if and only if inequality (5.3) holds for all points x and y in S. Similarly f is *strictly convex* on S if and only if the inequality

$$f(y)-f(x) > \frac{f[x+t(y-x)]-f(x)}{t} \qquad (0<t<1) \qquad (5.4)$$

holds for every pair of *distinct points* x and y in S.

THEOREM 5.1

Let f be a convex function on a convex set S. If a point x_0 in S affords a local minimum to f on S, then x_0 minimizes f on S. The set of minimum points on S is convex. If f is strictly convex, it has at most one minimum point on S.

Suppose that x_0 affords a local minimum to f on S. Then there is a neighborhood N of x_0 such that $f(x) \geqslant f(x_0)$ for all x in $N \cap S$. Select a point y in S. If t is a sufficiently small number on the interval $0 < t < 1$, the point $x_1 = x_0 + t(y - x_0)$ will be in N. Since S is convex, the point x_1 is also in S and hence in $N \cap S$. Consequently $f(x_1) \geqslant f(x_0)$. Using inequality (5.3) with $x = x_0$, we see that

$$f(y) - f(x_0) \geqslant \frac{f(x_1) - f(x_0)}{t} \geqslant 0.$$

We have accordingly $f(y) \geqslant f(x_0)$, as was to be proved.

Suppose next that f has two minimum points, x_0 and y_0, in S. Then $f(x_0) = f(y_0)$, and, by (5.3),

$$0 \geqslant \frac{f[x_0 + t(y_0 - x_0)] - f(x_0)}{t} \geqslant 0 \qquad (0 < t < 1).$$

Consequently $f[x_0 + t(y_0 - x_0)] = f(x_0)$ for all values of t on the interval $0 \leqslant t \leqslant 1$. It follows that every point on the line segment joining x_0 to y_0 minimizes f on S. If f is strictly convex on S, inequality (5.4) can hold with $x = x_0$ and $y = y_0$ only if $x_0 = y_0$. A strictly convex function therefore can have at most one minimum point.

In the case $n = 1$ the function $f(x) = e^x$ is strictly convex on $-\infty < x < \infty$ but has no minimum point on this set.

In the next theorem we assume that f is of class C' in S and obtain a criterion for convexity involving the directional derivative

$$f'(x, h) = \sum_{i=1}^{n} \frac{\partial f(x)}{\partial x^i} h^i = \lim_{t \to 0} \frac{f(x + th) - f(x)}{t}. \tag{5.5}$$

Setting $h = y - x$, we see that

$$\lim_{t \to 0} \frac{f[x + t(y - x)] - f(x)}{t} = f'(x, y - x). \tag{5.6}$$

Consequently, if x and y belong to a convex set S on which f is convex, it follows from (5.3) that inequality (5.7) in the following theorem holds.

THEOREM 5.2

Suppose that f *is of class* C' *on a convex set* S. *Then* f *is convex on* S *if and only if the inequality*

$$f(y) - f(x) \geqslant f'(x, y - x) \tag{5.7}$$

holds for all points x *and* y *in* S. *Moreover* f *is strictly convex on* S *if the strict inequality*

$$f(y) - f(x) > f'(x, y - x) \qquad (5.8)$$

holds for every pair of distinct points x *and* y *in* S.

We have seen already that (5.7) holds if f is convex on S. Suppose, conversely, that equality (5.7) holds for every pair of distinct points x and y in S. Choose t on the interval $0 < t < 1$, and set $z = (1-t)x + ty$. Then by virtue of our hypotheses

$$f(x) - f(z) \geqslant f'(z, x - z), \qquad (5.9a)$$

$$f(y) - f(z) \geqslant f'(z, y - z). \qquad (5.9b)$$

Moreover by virtue of the linearity of $f'(z, h)$ in h we have

$$(1-t)f'(z, x-z) + tf'(z, y-z) = f'[z, (1-t)x + ty - z] = f'(z, 0) = 0.$$

Using this fact, we find from (5.9) that

$$(1-t)[f(x) - f(z)] + t[f(y) - f(z)] \geqslant 0,$$

and hence that

$$(1-t)f(x) + tf(y) - f[x + t(y - x)] \geqslant 0. \qquad (5.10)$$

Consequently f is convex, as was to be shown.

If the strict inequality (5.8) holds for $x \neq y$ in S, then (5.9) and hence also (5.10) hold with the equality excluded. Criterion (5.8) therefore implies strict convexity for f. Conversely, if f is strictly convex, then by the use of (5.4) and (5.7) we have, with $z = x + t(y - x)$,

$$f(y) - f(x) > \frac{f(z) - f(x)}{t} \geqslant \frac{f'(x, z - x)}{t} = \frac{f'[x, t(y - x)]}{t} = f'(x, y - x)$$

for every pair of distinct points x and y in S. Consequently (5.8) holds, and the theorem is established.

The results given in Theorem 5.2 are frequently expressed in terms of the *E-function*:

$$E(x, y) = f(y) - f(x) - f'(x, y - x). \qquad (5.11)$$

Accordingly to Theorem 5.2, f is convex if and only if $E(x, y) \geqslant 0$ for all points x, y in S. It is strictly convex if and only if $E(x, y) > 0$ for every pair of distinct points x and y in S.

The E-function $E(x_0,x)$ can be interpreted geometrically by considering the graph of the function $u = f(x)$, as indicated schematically in Figure 5.2. The tangent plane to this surface at the point $(x_0, f(x_0))$ is given by the equation

$$u = f(x_0) + f'(x_0, x - x_0).$$

It follows that $E(x_0,x)$ measures the deviation CB of the surface from this tangent plane. The function f is convex if and only if at every point this surface lies above (or on) the tangent plane. If it always lies above the tangent plane, it is strictly convex.

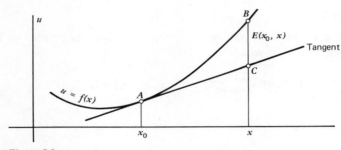

Figure 5.2

A useful test for x_0 to minimize convex function f on S involving the directional derivative $f'(x,h)$ is given in

THEOREM 5.3

Suppose that f *is a convex function of class* C' *on a convex set* S. *A point* x_0 *in* S *minimizes* f *on* S *if and only if the inequality*

$$f'(x_0, x - x_0) \geqslant 0 \tag{5.12}$$

holds for all x *in* S. *If* x_0 *is an interior point of* S, *then* x_0 *minimizes* f *on* S *if and only if* $f'(x_0) = 0$, *where* $f'(x)$ *is the gradient of* f *at* x.

The second conclusion is a simple consequence of the first. To prove the first conclusion, let x_0 minimize f on S. Then, given a point x in S, the function

$$g(t) = f[x_0 + t(x - x_0)] \qquad (0 \leqslant t \leqslant 1)$$

has a minimum at $t = 0$. Hence

$$g'(0) = f'(x_0, x - x_0) \geqslant 0.$$

Inequality (5.12) therefore holds for all x in S.

Conversely, if inequality (5.12) holds for all x in S, then, by (5.7), we have

$$f(x) - f(x_0) \geqslant f'(x_0, x - x_0) \geqslant 0$$

for all x in S. Hence x_0 minimizes f on S. This proves Theorem 5.3.

As a further test for convexity, we have

THEOREM 5.4

Suppose that f *is of class* C″ *on a convex set* S *and, as before, let* f″(x, h) *denote the second differential*

$$f''(x, h) = \sum_i \sum_j f_{x^i x^j}(x) h^i h^j \qquad (i, j = 1, \dots, n)$$

of f. *The function* f *is convex on* S *if and only if at each point* x *in* S *the inequality*

$$f''(x, y - x) \geqslant 0 \qquad\qquad (5.13)$$

holds for all y *in* S. *If (5.13) holds with the equality excluded when* y ≠ x, *then* f *is strictly convex.*

Let x and y be distinct points in S, and set $h = y - x$. Let $E(x, y)$ be the E-function (5.11). By Theorem 5.2 the function

$$g(t) = E(x, x + th) \qquad (0 \leqslant t \leqslant 1)$$

has a minimum at $t = 0$. Moreover $g'(0) = 0$ in view of the formula

$$g'(t) = f'(x + th, h) - f'(x, h).$$

Hence we have

$$g''(0) = f''(x, h) = f''(x, y - x) \geqslant 0.$$

Consequently (5.13) holds for all points x and y in S.

Suppose, conversely, that (5.13) holds for all points x and y in S. Let x and y be distinct points in S. By Taylor's theorem, there is a point

$x_1 = x + t_1(y - x)$ $(0 < t_1 < 1)$ such that

$$f(y) = f(x) + f'(x, y - x) + \tfrac{1}{2} f''(x_1, y - x). \tag{5.14}$$

Since $y - x_1 = (1 - t_1)(y - x)$, we have

$$f''(x_1, y - x) = f''\left(x_1, \frac{y - x_1}{1 - t_1}\right) = \frac{1}{(1 - t_1)^2} f''(x_1, y - x_1).$$

Consequently, by (5.14) and (5.13),

$$f(y) - f(x) - f'(x, y - x) = \frac{1}{2(1 - t_1)^2} f''(x_1, y - x_1) \geqslant 0. \tag{5.15}$$

Criterion (5.7) for convexity therefore holds. Hence the function f is convex whenever inequality (5.13) holds for all points x and y in S. If the equality in (5.13) is excluded when $x \neq y$, inequality (5.15) is a strict inequality and criterion (5.8) for strict convexity holds. This proves Theorem 5.4.

COROLLARY

Let f *be the class* C" *on an open convex set* S. *Then* f *is convex on* S *if and only if at each point* x *in* S *we have*

$$f''(x, h) \geqslant 0$$

for all h $\neq$ 0. *If at each point* x *in* S *we have*

$$f''(x, h) > 0$$

for all h $\neq$ 0, *then* f *is strictly convex on* S.

EXERCISES

1. Find intervals on which each of the following functions is convex:

$$e^x, \qquad e^{-x}, \qquad \frac{x^n}{n}, \qquad \frac{|x|^p}{p} \, (p > 1), \qquad \sqrt{1 + x^2}, \qquad x \ln x, \qquad \cosh x.$$

2. Show that, if n is a positive integer,

$$f(x) = x^n - nb \ln x \qquad (b > 0)$$

is convex on $0 < x < \infty$. Find the minimum point of f.

3. Let f and g be convex functions on a convex set S. Show that $af + bg$ is convex on S for all nonnegative numbers a and b. Show that, if $f(x) \geqslant 0$ on S and $p \geqslant 1$, then f^p is convex on S. Show that, if $f(x) \geqslant 0$ on S and $H(t)$ is a real-valued convex function on $0 \leqslant t < \infty$, then $h(x) = H[f(x)]$ is convex on S. Show that $F(x) = \max[f(x), g(x)]$ is convex on S.

4. Let f be a real-valued function on an interval $a \leqslant x \leqslant b$. Set

$$m(x,y) = \frac{f(y) - f(x)}{y - x} \qquad (y \neq x).$$

    Show that f is convex on $[a,b]$ if and only if $m(x,y)$ is a nondecreasing function of y for each x. Show that f is strictly convex on $[a,b]$ if and only if $m(x,y)$ is an increasing function of y for each x.

5. Suppose that f is convex on $[a,b]$ and that $a < \alpha < \beta < b$. Referring to Exercise 4, show that

$$m(\alpha,a) \leqslant m(x,y) \leqslant m(\beta,b) \qquad (\alpha \leqslant x < y \leqslant \beta).$$

    Setting $M = \max[|m(\alpha,a)|, |m(\beta,b)|]$, show that

$$|f(x) - f(y)| \leqslant M|x - y| \qquad (\alpha \leqslant x < y \leqslant \beta).$$

    Hence show that f is continuous on $\alpha \leqslant x \leqslant \beta$. Show by an example that f may be discontinuous at $x = a$ and at $x = b$.

6. Suppose that f is a convex function on a convex set S. Show that the set S_c of all points x in S having $f(x) \leqslant c$ is a convex set.

7. Suppose that $f(x)$ is differentiable on an interval $a \leqslant x \leqslant b$. Show that f is convex on $[a,b]$ if and only if its derivative $f'(x)$ is nondecreasing on $[a,b]$. Moreover f is strictly convex if and only if $f'(x)$ is increasing on $[a,b]$.

8. Show that, if $f(x)$ is convex and differentiable on $a \leqslant x \leqslant b$. Then $f'(x)$ is continuous on $[a,b]$.

9. Suppose that f is convex on (a,b). Show that at each point x on (a,b) the function f has a finite left-hand derivative $D^-f(x)$ and a finite right-hand derivative $D^+f(x)$. Moreover show that

$$D^-f(x) \leqslant D^+f(x) \leqslant D^-f(y) \leqslant D^+f(y) \qquad \text{if } a < x < y < b.$$

    Show that the set of points on (a,b) at which $D^-f(x) < D^+f(x)$ is at most countable.

10. Show that, if A is a nonnegative symmetric matrix, the quadratic function

$$f(x) = \tfrac{1}{2}x^*Ax - b^*x + c$$

    is convex. *Hint*: Use Theorem 5.4.

11. Let $f(x) = \sqrt{1 + |x|^2}$. Show that its E-function (5.11) can be put into the

form

$$E(x,y) = f(y)(1 - \cos\varphi)$$

where φ is the angle between the $(n+1)$-dimensional vectors $(1, x^1, \ldots, x^n)$ and $(1, y^1, \ldots, y^n)$. Use this result to show that f is strictly convex.

12. Let $f(x) = \sqrt{1 + |x|^2}$. Show that we have

$$f''(x, h) = \frac{|h|^2}{f(x)^3}(1 + \sin^2\theta)$$

where $\theta = 0$ if $x = 0$ or $h = 0$, and θ is the angle between x and h otherwise.

13. Show that $f(x) = [1 - |x|^2]^{-1/2}$ and $g(x) = -[1 - |x|^2]^{1/2}$ are convex in the unit sphere $|x| < 1$.

14. Show that, if f is of class C'' on a convex set S, the function $\varphi(t)$ given by (5.2) has the property that for each t on $0 < t < 1$ there is a point t_1 on $0 < t < 1$ such that

$$\varphi(t) = \tfrac{1}{2}t(1 - t)f''[x + t_1(y - x), y - x].$$

Use this result to prove Theorem 5.4.

15. Show that, if f is of class C' on S, then $E(x,y)$ is the remainder term in the first-order Taylor expansion for f. Hence show that

$$\lim_{y \to x} \frac{E(x,y)}{|y - x|} = 0.$$

16. Suppose that f is convex on a convex set S. Given $k + 1$ points $x_0, x_1, \ldots, x_k$ in S, show that

$$\alpha_0 f(x_0) + \cdots + \alpha_k f(x_k) \geqslant f(\alpha_0 x_0 + \cdots + \alpha_k x_k)$$

whenever $\alpha_j \geqslant 0$ ($j = 0, 1, \ldots, k$) and $\alpha_0 + \cdots + \alpha_k = 1$.

17. Suppose that f is of class C' on a convex set S. Show that f is convex on S if and only if, for every pair of distinct points x and $x + h$ in S, the function $f'(x + th, h)$ is a nondecreasing function of t on $0 \leqslant t \leqslant 1$. Show that f is strictly convex if and only if, for every pair of distinct points x and $x + h$ in S, the function $f'(x + th, h)$ is a strictly increasing function of t on $0 \leqslant t \leqslant 1$. *Hint:* Use the identity

$$E(x + sh, x + th) + E(x + th, x + sh) = (t - s)[f'(x + th, h) - f'(x + sh, h)].$$

18. Suppose that f is class C' on a convex set S. Set

$$H(x,y) = f'(x,y) - f(y).$$

Show that f is convex on S if and only if $H(x,y) \leqslant H(x,x)$ for all x,y in S. Show that f is strictly convex on S if and only if $H(x,y) < H(x,x)$ for all distinct points x and y in S. *Hint*: Observe that $E(x,y) = H(x,x) - H(x,y)$.

19. Let f be a function of class C' on an open set S, and suppose that $E(x,\bar{x}) > 0$ for distinct points x and $\bar{x}$ in S, where E is the E-function (5.5) for f. Show that, if x and $\bar{x}$ are distinct points in S, then

$$E(x,\bar{x}) + E(\bar{x},x) = \langle \nabla f(\bar{x}) - \nabla f(x), \bar{x} - x \rangle > 0.$$

Show that $\nabla f(\bar{x}) \neq \nabla f(x)$ if $\bar{x} \neq x$. Show that the transformation $y = \nabla f(x)$ maps S in a one-to-one manner onto an open set T. This mapping has a continuous inverse $x = \varphi(y)$. The function

$$g(y) = \langle \varphi(y), y \rangle - f[\varphi(y)]$$

is called the *dual* of f. Observe that, if $\bar{x} = \varphi(\bar{y})$ and $x = \varphi(y)$, then

$$E_g(y,\bar{y}) = g(\bar{y}) - g(y) - \langle \varphi(y), \bar{y} - y \rangle = E(\bar{x},x) > 0$$

unless $y = \bar{y}$. Use the relations

$$E_g(y,\bar{y}) > 0, \qquad E_g(\bar{y},y) > 0$$

to show that, if y and $\bar{y}$ are on a compact subset T_0 of T, we have

$$|g(\bar{y}) - g(y)| \leqslant M|\bar{y} - y|,$$

where $M = \max |\varphi(y)|$ on T_0. Use this result to show that

$$\lim_{\bar{y} \to y} \frac{E_g(y,\bar{y})}{|\bar{y} - y|} = 0.$$

Consequently $\varphi(y) = \nabla g(y)$, and $g(y)$ is of class C'. Show that $g(y)$ is convex on every convex subset of T.

20. Let f be convex on an open convex set S. Show that at each point x in S the *one-sided directional derivative*

$$f'(x,h) = \lim_{t \to 0^+} \frac{f(x+th) - f(x)}{t}$$

exists for each vector h. In the expression on the right "$\lim_{t \to 0^+}$" signifies that t is restricted to be positive in the evaluation of this limit. Show that $f'(x,ah) = af'(x,h)$ if $a > 0$. Show that, if $f(x) = |x|$, then $f'(0,h) = |h|$. Hence $f'(x,h)$ need not be linear in h and need not be a differential. Show that Theorem 5.2 is valid when $f'(x,h)$ is defined in this manner. Observe that the same notation is used for a one-sided directional derivative as for a differential.

6. LINEARLY CONSTRAINED LOCAL MINIMA AND MAXIMA

In the chapters that follow, constrained minima and maxima will be studied in great detail. However, there are special classes of constrained local minima and maxima which are important and can be studied with the help of the theory already developed. These are the linearly constrained local minima and maxima. In problems of this type we restrict our points to lie on a k-plane in $\mathcal{E}^n$. A k-plane π_k can be considered to be a k-dimensional Euclidean space embedded in $\mathcal{E}^n$. It need not pass through the origin of $\mathcal{E}^n$. If x_1 is a point in π_k and $u_1,\ldots,u_k$ are k linearly independent vectors in π_k, every point x in π_k is expressible in the form

$$x = x_1 + \alpha_1 u_1 + \cdots + \alpha_k u_k \tag{6.1}$$

with suitably chosen constants $\alpha_1,\ldots,\alpha_k$. A k-plane is therefore uniquely determined by a point x_1 and a set of k linearly independent vectors $u_1,\ldots,u_k$. If $k=1$, we have a line; if $k=2$, we have a two-dimensional plane; and so on.

To relate the ideas here presented to those given for more general constrained minima on arbitrary surfaces, it will be convenient to introduce the concept of the tangent space and the normal space to a k-plane π_k at a point x_1 in π_k. A *tangent vector* h is merely a vector h parallel to π_k. If π_k is represented in form (6.1), a tangent vector h is any vector expressible as a linear combination

$$h = \alpha_1 u_1 + \cdots + \alpha_k u_k \tag{6.2}$$

of the vectors $u_1,\ldots,u_k$. The *tangent space* $\mathcal{H}$ of π_k is the set of all tangent vectors to π_k. It is the k-plane through the origin that is parallel to π_k. Any vector b that is orthogonal to π_k and hence to $\mathcal{H}$ will be called a *normal* to π_k. The set $\mathcal{N}$ of all normals to π_k is the orthogonal complement of the tangent space $\mathcal{H}$. It is of dimension $n-k$. If $b_1,\ldots,b_{n-k}$ form a basis for the normal space $\mathcal{N}$ of π_k at x_1, every normal b is expressible uniquely as a linear combination

$$b = \lambda_1 b_1 + \cdots + \lambda_m b_m \qquad (m = n - k). \tag{6.3}$$

Moreover the k-plane π_k consists of all points x satisfying the conditions

$$g_\alpha(x) = \langle b_\alpha, x - x_1 \rangle = 0 \qquad (\alpha = 1,\ldots,m = n-k). \tag{6.4}$$

These conditions are of the form

$$g_\alpha(x) = \langle b_\alpha, x \rangle + c_\alpha = 0 \qquad (\alpha = 1,\ldots,m = n-k), \tag{6.5}$$

where $c_\alpha = - \langle b_\alpha, x_1 \rangle$. Observe further that h is a tangent vector to π_k if and only if it satisfies the relation

$$g'_\alpha(x_1, h) = \langle b_\alpha, h \rangle = 0 \qquad (\alpha = 1, \ldots, m).$$

This follows because the tangent space is the orthogonal complement of the normal space $\mathfrak{N}$ and the fact that the vectors $b_1, \ldots, b_m$ generate $\mathfrak{N}$.

The set of tangent vectors forming the tangent space to π_k does not change from point to point, and similarly for the normal space. This is not true for the general k-dimensional surfaces considered later in this book.

One other remark is also pertinent. In dealing with points x or tangent vectors h, we use the superscript i to denote the ith components x^i and h^i of x and h. In dealing with a normal b, we usually denote its ith component by b_i because a linear function $g(x)$ is usually written in the form

$$g(x) = \sum_{i=1}^{n} b_i x^i + c$$

The vector $b = (b_1, \ldots, b_n)$ is then the normal to the $(n-1)$-plane $g(x) = 0$. Similarly we usually write equations (6.5) in the form

$$g_\alpha(x) = \sum_{i=1}^{n} b_{\alpha i} x^i + c_\alpha = 0 \qquad (\alpha = 1, \ldots, m). \qquad (6.6)$$

When this notation is used, the vectors $b_\alpha = (b_{\alpha 1}, \ldots, b_{\alpha n})$ $(\alpha = 1, \ldots, m)$ generate the corresponding normal space.

EXAMPLE 6.1

As an illustration consider the problem of finding the shortest distance from a fixed point $\bar{x}$ to a point x on the line

$$\pi_1 : \quad x = x_1 + \alpha h \qquad (h \neq 0).$$

It is analytically simpler to minimize the square of the distance, that is, to minimize the function $f(x) = |x - \bar{x}|^2$. On the line π_1 this function takes the form

$$\varphi(\alpha) = f(x_1 + \alpha h) = |x_1 + \alpha h - \bar{x}|^2 = |x_1 - \bar{x}|^2 + 2\alpha \langle x_1 - \bar{x}, h \rangle + \alpha^2 |h|^2.$$

Consequently

$$\alpha_0 = - \frac{\langle x_1 - \bar{x}, h \rangle}{|h|^2} = \frac{\langle \bar{x} - x_1, h \rangle}{|h|^2}$$

minimizes $\varphi(\alpha)$. At the minimum point

$$x_0 = x_1 + \alpha_0 h$$

of f on π_1 the gradient of f takes the form

$$\nabla f(x_0) = 2(x_0 - \bar{x}) = 2(x_1 - \bar{x} + \alpha_0 h).$$

Forming the inner product of $\nabla f(x_0)$ with h, we see that

$$\langle \nabla f(x_0), h \rangle = 2\langle x_1 - \bar{x} + \alpha_0 h, h \rangle = 2[\langle x_1 - \bar{x}, h \rangle + \alpha_0 |h|^2] = 0.$$

This verifies that the gradient of f at x_0 is orthogonal to h and hence to the line π_1. The second-order condition $f''(x,h) = 2|h|^2 > 0$ holds at every point on the line, particularly at $x = x_0$.

We now turn to the characterization of the minimum point x_0 of a function f on a k-plane π_k. We assume of course that f is of class C''. We begin with the case $k = 1$. In this event π_1 is a line and is representable in the form

$$x = x_1 + \alpha h,$$

where $h \neq 0$ determines the direction of the line π_1. On the line π_1 the function f is a function

$$\varphi(\alpha) = f(x_1 + \alpha h)$$

of a single real variable α. If a point $x_0 = x_1 + \alpha_0 h$ minimizes f locally on π_1, then $\alpha = \alpha_0$ affords a local minimum to $\varphi(\alpha)$. Consequently $\varphi'(\alpha_0) = 0$ and $\varphi''(\alpha_0) \geq 0$. When this result is expressed in terms of f, we find that

$$0 = \varphi'(\alpha_0) = f'(x_0, h) = \langle \nabla f(x_0), h \rangle = \sum_{i=1}^n f_{x^i}(x_0) h^i, \quad (6.7a)$$

$$0 \leq \varphi''(\alpha_0) = f''(x_0, h) = \sum_i \sum_j f_{x^i x^j}(x_0) h^i h^j. \quad (6.7b)$$

Condition (6.7a) states that the gradient $\nabla f(x_0)$ is orthogonal to h and hence is a normal of the line π_1. Conversely, if

$$f'(x_0, h) = 0, \qquad f''(x_0, h) > 0,$$

then $\varphi'(\alpha_0) = 0$, $\varphi''(\alpha_0) > 0$. Consequently α_0 affords a local minimum to $\varphi(\alpha)$, and x_0 affords local minimum to f on π_1.

We are now in a position to establish

THEOREM 6.1

Let f *be a function of class* C″ *in an open set* S, *and let* S_k *be the set of points in* S *lying in a* k-*plane* π_k. *If a point* x_0 *in* S_k *affords a local minimum to* f *on* S_k, *then the gradient* $\nabla f(x_0)$ *of* f *at* x_0 *is normal to* π_k, *that is,*

$$f'(x_0, h) = \langle \nabla f(x_0), h \rangle = \sum_{i=1}^{n} f_{x^i}(x_0) h^i = 0 \qquad (6.8)$$

for every vector h *tangent to* π_k. *Moreover*

$$f''(x_0, h) = \sum_{i,j} f_{x^i x^j}(x_0) h^i h^j \geqslant 0 \qquad (6.9)$$

for every vector h *tangent to* π_k. *Conversely, if a point* x_0 *in* S_k *has the property that*

$$f'(x_0, h) = 0, \qquad f''(x_0, h) > 0 \qquad (6.10)$$

for every vector $h \neq 0$ *tangent to* π_k, *then* x_0 *affords a strict local minimum to* f *on* S_k.

Conditions (6.8) and (6.9) are necessary conditions for a local minimum on S_k. The strengthened conditions (6.10) are sufficient conditions for a local minimum on S_k.

The necessary conditions (6.8) and (6.9) at a minimum point x_0 can be obtained as follows. If $h \neq 0$ is tangent to π_k, then $\alpha = 0$ minimizes

$$\varphi(\alpha) = f(x_0 + \alpha h).$$

Hence, as was seen above,

$$\varphi'(0) = f'(x_0, h) = 0, \qquad \varphi''(0) = f''(x_0, h) \geqslant 0,$$

as was to be proved. This result also follows when Theorem 3.1 is applied to the function

$$\Phi(\gamma) = f(x_0 + \gamma_1 u_1 + \cdots + \gamma_k u_k),$$

obtained by using representation (6.1) of π_k.

Relations (6.10) can be shown to be sufficient conditions for a minimum by applying Theorem 3.5 to the function $\Phi(\gamma)$. However, it is instructive to give an alternative proof by a technique that will be useful in more complicated situations. To this end suppose that x_0 satisfies condition (6.10) but fails to afford a strict local minimum to f on S_k. Then for each integer q there is a point y_q in S_k such that

$$0 < |y_q - x_0| < \frac{1}{q}, \qquad f(y_q) \leqslant f(x_0).$$

Since the vectors

$$\frac{y_q - x_0}{|y_q - x_0|}$$

are unit vectors, we can apply the Weierstrass-Bolzano theorem and obtain a subsequence $\{x_q\}$ of $\{y_q\}$ such that the unit vectors

$$h_q = \frac{x_q - x_0}{|x_q - x_0|}$$

converge to a vector h. The vector h is also a unit vector. It is tangent to π_k since each of the vectors h_q is tangent to π_k. Because $\nabla f(x_0)$ is normal to π_k, we have

$$f'(x_0, h_q) = f'(x_0, h) = 0, \qquad f'(x_0, x_q - x_0) = 0.$$

Making use of the Taylor expansion

$$f(x) = f(x_0) + f'(x_0, x - x_0) + \tfrac{1}{2} f''(x_0, x - x_0) + R_2(x_0, x - x_0),$$

we obtain the relation

$$\frac{f(x_q) - f(x_0)}{|x_q - x_0|^2} = \tfrac{1}{2} f''(x_0, h_q) + \frac{R_2(x_0, x_q - x_0)}{|x_q - x_0|^2}.$$

The limit of the last term is zero. Inasmuch as $f(x_q) \leqslant f(x_0)$, we have

$$\lim_{q \to 0} \frac{f(x_q) - f(x_0)}{|x_q - x_0|^2} = \tfrac{1}{2} f''(x_0, h) \leqslant 0,$$

contrary to our assumption that $f''(x_0, h) > 0$. From this contradiction we infer that conditions (6.10) are sufficient for a strict local minimum at x_0 on S_k. This proves the theorem.

In the case in which π_k is defined by equations of form (6.6), the result given above can be restated as

THEOREM 6.2

Let x_0 be a point satisfying the linear constraints

$$g_\alpha(x) = \sum_i b_{\alpha i}x^i + c_\alpha = \langle b_\alpha, x \rangle + c_\alpha = 0 \quad \cdot(\alpha = 1, \ldots, m). \quad (6.11)$$

If x_0 minimizes f locally subject to these constraints, there exist multipliers $\lambda_1, \ldots, \lambda_m$ such that, if we set

$$F(x) = f(x) + \sum_{\alpha=1}^{m} \lambda_\alpha g_\alpha(x), \quad (6.12)$$

then

$$\nabla F(x_0) = 0, \qquad F''(x_0, h) \geqslant 0 \quad (6.13)$$

for all h satisfying the relations

$$\langle b_\alpha, h \rangle = \sum_i b_{\alpha i}h^i = 0 \quad (\alpha = 1, \ldots, m). \quad (6.14)$$

Conversely, if there exists for x_0 a function F of form (6.12) such that

$$\nabla F(x_0) = 0, \qquad F''(x_0, h) > 0 \quad (6.15)$$

for solutions $h \neq 0$ of (6.14), then x_0 affords a local minimum to f subject to constraints (6.11).

The result here given is known as the *Lagrange multiplier rule*, and the multipliers $\lambda_1, \ldots, \lambda_m$ are called *Lagrange multipliers*. Observe that the condition

$$\nabla F(x_0) = \nabla f(x_0) + \sum_\alpha \lambda_\alpha \nabla g_\alpha(x_0) = \nabla f(x_0) + \sum_\alpha \lambda_\alpha b_\alpha = 0$$

states that $\nabla f(x_0)$ is a linear combination of the normals $b_1, \ldots, b_m$ of the k-plane π_k defined by (6.11). It follows that the condition $\nabla F(x_0) = 0$ is equivalent to the condition that $\nabla f(x_0)$ be normal to π_k. Using this fact, together with the relation

$$F''(x_0, h) = f''(x_0, h),$$

we see that Theorem 6.2 is equivalent to Theorem 6.1.

It should be noted that Theorem 6.2 is valid even though vectors $b_1,\ldots,b_m$ are linearly dependent. However, equations (6.11) must be consistent in order to define a k-plane π_k. In this event $k \geqslant n-m$. If, for example, b_β is a linear combination of remaining b's, we can delete the constraint $g_\beta(x)=0$ without altering the solutions of (6.11). By a repetition of this process we can reduce the system to one of $n-k$ linear constraints which are linearly independent.

EXAMPLE 6.2

As an illustration consider the problem in the xy-plane of minimizing the function

$$f(x,y)=5x^2+4xy+y^2$$

on the line

$$g(x,y)=3x+2y+5=0.$$

We introduce the function

$$F(x,y)=5x^2+4xy+y^2+\lambda(3x+2y+5)=0.$$

At the minimum point we have

$$F_x(x,y)=10x+4y+3\lambda=0,$$
$$F_y(x,y)=4x+2y+2\lambda=0,$$
$$g(x,y)=3x+2y+5=0.$$

These equations are satisfied by the values $x=1$, $y=-4$, and $\lambda=2$. The point $(1,-4)$ minimizes f on the given line. It can be shown that the point $(x,y)=(1,-4)$ affords a global minimum to

$$F=f+2g=5x^2+4xy+y^2+6x+4y+10.$$

EXAMPLE 6.3

An example of a somewhat different nature involves minimizing

$$f(x,y)=x^2-y^2-3y$$

along the x-axis. In this event the origin minimizes f subject to the constraint $y=0$. The Lagrange multiplier is $\lambda=3$. However, the origin fails to minimize

$$F(x,y) = f(x,y) + 3y = x^2 - y^2.$$

EXERCISES

1. By using the Lagrange multiplier rule applied to the function $f(x) = |x - x_1|^2$ subject to the constraint

$$g(x) = \langle b, x \rangle + c = 0 \qquad (b \neq 0),$$

   show that the distance from the point x_1 to the $(n-1)$-plane $g(x) = 0$ is given by the formula

$$d(x_1) = \left| \frac{g(x_1)}{|b|} \right|.$$

2. Let A and C be positive constants, and let F be the function

$$F(x,y) = Ax^2 + Cy^2$$

   in the xy-plane. Given a point $(x_0, y_0) \neq (0,0)$ and a vector $(p,q) \neq (0,0)$, show that the minimum point (x_1, y_1) of F on the line

$$x = x_0 + \alpha p, \qquad y = y_0 + \alpha q$$

   is the midpoint of the chord in which this line intersects the ellipse $F(x,y) = F(x_0, y_0)$. Let $(\bar{x}_0, \bar{y}_0)$ be a point not on this line, and let $(\bar{x}_1, \bar{y}_1)$ minimize $F(x,y)$ on the parallel line

$$x = \bar{x}_0 + \alpha p, \qquad y = \bar{y}_0 + \alpha q.$$

   Show that the line joining (x_1, y_1) to $(\bar{x}_1, \bar{y}_1)$ passes through the origin, the center of the ellipse $F(x,y) = $ constant. Find the equation of this line.

3. By using the result given in Exercise 2, show that the midpoints of parallel chords of an ellipse lie on a line through the center of an ellipse.

4. Given the function

$$F(x,y,z) = \frac{x^2}{a^2} + \frac{y^2}{b^2} + \frac{z^2}{c^2}$$

   in xyz-space, observe that the surface $F(x,y,z) = 1$ is an ellipsoid. Show that the midpoints of the chords of this ellipsoid parallel to a given vector $(p,q,r) \neq (0,0,0)$ lie on the 2-plane

$$\frac{px}{a^2} + \frac{qy}{b^2} + \frac{rz}{c^2} = 0.$$

Hint: Show that the midpoint of the chord in which the line $x = x_0 + \alpha p$, $y = y_0 + \alpha q$, $z = z_0 + \alpha r$ cuts the ellipsoid minimizes F on this line. The gradient of F at this point is orthogonal to (p,q,r).

5. Continuing with Exercise 4, show that the minimum point of F on the 2-plane $Ax + By + Cz + D = 0$ lies on the line

$$x = \alpha A a^2, \qquad y = \alpha B b^2, \qquad z = \alpha C c^2 \qquad (-\infty < \alpha < \infty).$$

Show that parallel planes that cut the ellipsoid $F(x,y,z) = 1$ do so in ellipses whose centers lie on a line through the origin.

6. Let π_k be a k-plane determined by $m = n - k$ linearly independent conditions of the form

$$g_\alpha(x) = \sum_{i=1}^{n} b_{\alpha i} x^i + c_\alpha = 0 \qquad (\alpha = 1, \ldots, m).$$

Then the matrix $B = (b_{\alpha i})$ has rank m; why? A point x_0 on π_k is called a *critical point* of f on π_k if the gradient $\nabla f(x_0)$ is orthogonal to π_k. A critical point x_0 of f on π_k is said to be *nonsingular* if the determinant

$$\begin{vmatrix} f''(x_0) & B^* \\ B & 0 \end{vmatrix}$$

is different from zero, where

$$f''(x) = \left(\frac{\partial^2 f(x)}{\partial x^i \partial x^j} \right)$$

is the Hessian of f. Show that nonsingular critical points of f on π_k are isolated.

7. Continuing with Exercise 6, show that, if x_0 is a nonsingular minimizing point of f on π_k, conditions (6.15) hold with a unique set of multipliers $\lambda_1, \ldots, \lambda_m$.

8. Normally it is difficult to compute the minimum point of a function f, and various methods have been devised for carrying out this computation. One such algorithm is the method of steepest descent. Given an estimate x_1 of the minimum point, choose $\alpha = a_1$ so as to minimize f along the line $x = x_1 - \alpha \nabla f(x_1)$. This yields a second estimate $x_2 = x_1 - a_1 \nabla f(x_1)$ of the minimum point of f. Next minimize f on the line $x = x_2 - \alpha \nabla f(x_2)$ to obtain x_3. Repeating this process yields a sequence of points $x_1, x_2, x_3, \ldots$ that, under favorable circumstances, will converge to a local minimum point of f. In the two-dimensional case apply the method of steepest descent to the function $f(x,y) = bx^2 + y^2$ with $(x_1, y_1) = (1, b)$ as the initial point. Select $b = 0.5$, $b = 0.01$, and $b = 0.001$. How does the rate of convergence vary with b? Experience has shown that the method of steepest descent may converge slowly. Accordingly various algorithms have been devised to obtain more rapid convergence. One such algorithm, called the *method of conjugate gradients*, is based on the results given in the next section.

7. MINIMA OF QUADRATIC FUNCTIONS

The results obtained in Section 6 are particularly significant for the case in which the function to be minimized is a quadratic function

$$F(x) = \tfrac{1}{2}x^*Ax - b^*x + c = \frac{1}{2}\sum_{i,j} a_{ij}x^i x^j - \sum_i b_i x^i + c,$$

where $A = (a_{ij})$ $(i,j = 1,\ldots,n)$ is a positive symmetric matrix, $b = (b_i)$ is a fixed vector, and c is a constant. With the help of these results we can establish geometrical properties of ellipsoids which are not only of theoretical interest but are also useful in devising computational methods for finding the minimum point of a function. This is the basis of the conjugate direction methods[†] for finding a minimum point of a function.

It should be noted that we have made a minor change in the representation of the quadratic function from that given in Section 4. We have multiplied the function by $\tfrac{1}{2}$ in order to eliminate a factor 2. We have also reversed the direction of the vector b. In terms of the present notations we have

$$\nabla F(x) = F'(x) = Ax - b, \qquad F''(x) = A.$$

As was seen in Section 4, the point

$$x_0 = A^{-1}b \tag{7.1}$$

minimizes F. The quantity

$$m = F(x_0) = c - \tfrac{1}{2}b^*A^{-1}b$$

is the minimum value of F. It is clear that the problem of minimizing F is equivalent to solving the linear equation

$$Ax = b. \tag{7.2}$$

As was seen in Section 4, the level surfaces

$$F(x) = \gamma \qquad (\gamma > m)$$

form a family of similar $(n-1)$-dimensional ellipsoids having x_0 as their

[†]See, for example, M. R. Hestenes and E. Stiefel, "Methods of Conjugate Gradients for Solving Linear Systems," *Journal of Research of the National Bureau of Standards*, Vol. 49 (1952), No. 6.

common center. The problem of minimizing F is accordingly equivalent to that of finding the center of an ellipsoid.

THEOREM 7.1

The minimum point of F *on a line* L *parallel to a fixed nonnull vector* p *lies on the* $(n-1)$-*plane*

$$p^*(Ax - b) = 0, \tag{7.3}$$

whose normal is Ap. *This* $(n-1)$-*plane contains the minimum point* $x_0 = A^{-1}b$ *of* F *on* $\mathcal{E}^n$ *and is said to be conjugate to the vector* p.

As was seen in Section 6, the gradient $Ax - b$ of F at its minimum point on the line L is orthogonal to L and hence is orthogonal to the vector p. This fact is expressed by equation (7.3). Since $Ax_0 = b$, the minimum point x_0 of F lies on the $(n-1)$-plane (7.3).

The result given in Theorem 7.1 is illustrated in Figure 7.1 for the case $n = 3$. Here L is the given line with direction p. The point x_2 minimizes F on L. The gradient ∇F_2 of F at x_2 is perpendicular to L and is normal to the ellipsoid E_2, whose equation is $F(x) = F(x_2)$. The line L is tangent to E_2 at x_2. The plane π_2 through x_2, whose normal is Ap, is conjugate to p and contains the minimum point x_0 of F in $\mathcal{E}^3$. The point x_0 is the center of the ellipsoid E_2. It is also the center of the ellipse in which π_2 cuts E_2.

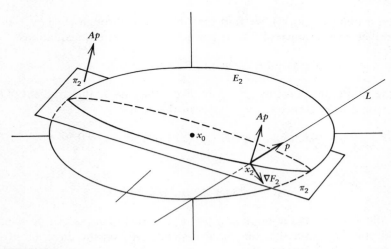

Figure 7.1

EXAMPLE 7.1

Consider the three-dimensional case in which

$$A = \begin{pmatrix} 3 & 1 & 1 \\ 1 & 2 & 1 \\ 1 & 1 & 2 \end{pmatrix}, \qquad b = \begin{pmatrix} 3 \\ 0 \\ 2 \end{pmatrix}, \qquad p = \begin{pmatrix} 4 \\ 5 \\ 6 \end{pmatrix}.$$

Observe that the matrix A is positive definite. This follows because the determinants

$$\det(3) = 3, \qquad \det\begin{pmatrix} 3 & 1 \\ 1 & 2 \end{pmatrix} = 5, \qquad \det A = 7$$

are all positive. Using the standard xyz-coordinates, we find that the function F takes the form

$$F(x,y,z) = \tfrac{1}{2}(3x^2 + 2y^2 + 2z^2 + 2xy + 2yz + 2zx) - 3x - 2z.$$

The minimum point of F is the solution $(x,y,z) = (1, -1, 1)$ of the linear equations

$$F_x = 3x + y + z - 3 = 0,$$

$$F_y = x + 2y + z = 0,$$

$$F_z = x + y + 2z - 2 = 0.$$

Given a point (x_1, y_1, z_1), we find that the line L through (x_1, y_1, z_1) in the prescribed direction $p = (4, 5, 6)$ is given by the parametric equations

$$x = x_1 + 4\alpha, \qquad y = y_1 + 5\alpha, \qquad z = z_1 + 6\alpha.$$

At the minimum point (x_2, y_2, z_2) of F on the line L the gradient ∇F is orthogonal to p. Hence (x_2, y_2, z_2) lies in the plane

$$4F_x(x,y,z) + 5F_y(x,y,z) + 6F_z(x,y,z) = 0$$

or

$$\pi_2: \qquad 23x + 20y + 21z - 24 = 0.$$

This plane contains the minimum point $(1, -1, 1)$ of F, as can be seen by substitution. Observe that this plane depends only on the direction p of L and not on the point (x_1, y_1, z_1) determining the position of L. This plane contains the minimum point of F on every line with direction p. If we take

$(x_1, y_1, z_1) = (0, 0, 0)$, the value of F along the line L_1, so determined, is

$$F(4\alpha, 5\alpha, 6\alpha) = \frac{\alpha^2}{2}(318) - 24\alpha.$$

This function has a minimum when

$$318\alpha - 24 = 0 \quad \text{or} \quad \alpha = \frac{12}{159}.$$

The minimum point of F on L_1 is therefore the point

$$(x_2, y_2, z_2) = (4\alpha, 5\alpha, 6\alpha) = \left(\frac{48}{159}, \frac{60}{159}, \frac{72}{159}\right).$$

It is readily verified that this point is on the plane π_2. Similarly, if we take $(x_1, y_1, z_1) = (1, 1, 1)$, a second line L_2 is obtained. Along this line we have

$$F(1 + 4\alpha, 1 + 5\alpha, 1 + 6\alpha) = \tfrac{3}{2} + 40\alpha + 159\alpha^2.$$

At the minimum point $\alpha = -20/159$. The corresponding minimum point $(\bar{x}_2, \bar{y}_2, \bar{z}_2)$ for F along this second line L_2 is

$$(\bar{x}_2, \bar{y}_2, \bar{z}_2) = \left(1 - 4\left(\frac{20}{159}\right), 1 - 5\left(\frac{20}{159}\right), 1 - 6\left(\frac{20}{159}\right)\right) = \left(\frac{79}{159}, \frac{59}{159}, \frac{39}{159}\right).$$

Again the point lies in the plane π_2. The vector q joining (x_2, y_2, z_2) to $(\bar{x}_2, \bar{y}_2, \bar{z}_2)$ is

$$q = (\bar{x}_2 - x_2, \bar{y}_2 - y_2, \bar{z}_2 - z_2) = \left(\frac{31}{159}, -\frac{1}{159}, -\frac{33}{159}\right).$$

It is readily verified that

$$q^*Ap = \left(\frac{31}{159}, \frac{-1}{159}, \frac{-33}{159}\right)\begin{bmatrix} 3 & 1 & 1 \\ 1 & 2 & 1 \\ 1 & 1 & 2 \end{bmatrix}\begin{bmatrix} 4 \\ 5 \\ 6 \end{bmatrix} = 0.$$

Consequently, q is orthogonal to Ap and p is orthogonal to Aq. In general, we shall say that a vector q is *conjugate* to a vector p if it is orthogonal to Ap, that is, if

$$q^*Ap = 0.$$

The concept of conjugate directions plays a very important role in minimization algorithms. Observe that, if A is the identity matrix, conjugacy becomes perpendicularity.

THEOREM 7.2

Let x_1 *and* x_2 *minimize* F *on two distinct parallel lines* L_1 *and* L_2 *parallel to a nonnull vector* p. *The vector* $q = x_2 - x_1$ *is nonnull and is conjugate to* p *in the sense that*

$$p^*Aq = q^*Ap = 0. \tag{7.4}$$

Since x_1 and x_2 minimize F on two lines parallel to p, we have, by Theorem 7.1,

$$p^*(Ax_1 - b) = 0, \qquad p^*(Ax_2 - b) = 0.$$

Subtracting the first of these equations from the second, we find that

$$p^*A(x_2 - x_1) = 0,$$

as was to be proved.

This result is illustrated in Figure 7.2 for the case $n = 3$. The point $x_1 = \bar{z}$ is the minimum point of F on L_1. The point $x_2 = \bar{w}$ is the minimum point of F on the line L_2 parallel to L_1. The vector $q = x_2 - x_1 = \bar{w} - \bar{z}$ lies in the plane π_2 conjugate to L_1 and L_2.

The result given in Theorem 7.1 can be stated geometrically as

THEOREM 7.3

The midpoint of parallel chords of an $(n-1)$-*dimensional ellipsoid* E_{n-1} *lies on an* $(n-1)$-*plane* π_{n-1} *through its center. The* $(n-1)$-*plane* π_{n-1} *is said to be conjugate to these chords.*

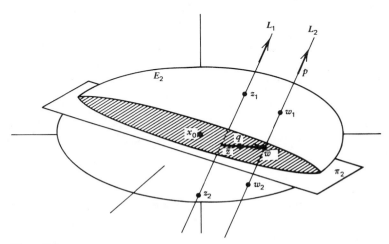

Figure 7.2

This phenomenon is illustrated in Figure 7.2.

Let w_1 and w_2 be the end points of a chord of the ellipsoid

$$F(x) = \gamma$$

parallel to a fixed vector p. Then there is a constant $\beta \neq 0$ such that

$$w_2 - w_1 = 2\beta p.$$

The midpoint $\overline{w}$ of the chord is given by the formulas

$$\overline{w} = \tfrac{1}{2}(w_1 + w_2) = w_1 + \beta p = w_2 - \beta p.$$

By a simple computation we find that

$$\gamma = F(w_1) = F(\overline{w} - \beta p) = F(\overline{w}) - \beta p^*(A\overline{w} - b) + \frac{\beta^2}{2} p^* A p,$$

$$\gamma = F(w_2) = F(\overline{w} + \beta p) = F(\overline{w}) + \beta p^*(A\overline{w} - b) + \frac{\beta^2}{2} p^* A p.$$

Since $\beta \neq 0$, this is possible if and only if

$$p^*(A\overline{w} - b) = 0.$$

The midpoint of a chord of E_{n-1} in the direction p therefore lies on the hyperplane

$$p^*(Ax - b) = 0.$$

The center $x_0 = A^{-1}b$ of E_{n-1} obviously lies in this plane also, and the theorem is established.

Incidentally, we have shown that the midpoint of the chord of E_{n-1} minimizes F along the line determined by this chord.

THEOREM 7.4

A line

$$x = x_0 + \alpha p \qquad (p \neq 0)$$

through the common center x_0 of the ellipsoids

$$F(x) = \gamma \qquad [\gamma > F(x_0)]$$

cuts these ellipsoids in equal angles. This angle is the complement of the angle between p and Ap.

This follows because the gradient of F at the point $x = x_0 + \alpha p$ is

$$\nabla F(x) = Ax - b = Ax_0 - b + \alpha Ap = \alpha Ap.$$

Consequently, if $\alpha > 0$, the gradient of F has the same direction as Ap and hence makes a fixed angle θ with p. Similarly, if $\alpha < 0$, the gradient of F is in the direction $-Ap$ and makes the angle θ with $-p$. The complement of θ is the angle between the line and the ellipsoid.

Interchanging the roles of $(n-1)$-planes and lines in Theorem 7.1, we obtain

THEOREM 7.5

The minimum points of F *on parallel* $(n-1)$*-planes lie on a line* L *through the minimum point* x_0 *of* F. *The minimum point of* F *on the* $(n-1)$*-plane* π_{n-1} *defined by the equation*

$$q^*x = \rho = constant \qquad (7.5)$$

lies on the line

$$x = x_0 + \alpha A^{-1}q \qquad (-\infty < \alpha < \infty) \qquad (7.6)$$

through the minimum point x_0 *of* F. *The line* (7.6) *is conjugate to the plane* π_{n-1}.

Let x_1 be the minimum point of F on the $(n-1)$-plane π_{n-1}. At the point x_1 the gradient $\nabla F(x_1) = Ax_1 - b$ is orthogonal to π_{n-1} and hence must be a multiple of the normal q of π_{n-1}. Therefore

$$Ax_1 - b = \alpha_1 q \qquad \text{or} \qquad x_1 = A^{-1}b + \alpha_1 A^{-1}q.$$

Since $x_0 = A^{-1}b$, we have

$$x_1 = x_0 + \alpha_1 A^{-1}q.$$

The point x_1 therefore lies on the line (7.6), as was to be proved.

The situation described in Theorem 7.5 is illustrated in Figure 7.3 for the case $n = 3$. The point x_1 is the minimum point of F on a plane π_2. The point $\bar{x}_1$ minimizes F on a plane $\bar{\pi}_2$ parallel to π_2. The minimum point x_0 of F on $\mathcal{E}^3$ lies on the line passing through the points x_1 and $\bar{x}_1$. The planes π_2 and $\bar{\pi}_2$ cut an ellipsoid E_2, whose equation is $F(x) = \gamma$, in ellipses E_1 and $\bar{E}_1$, respectively. According to the theorems that follow, the centers of E_1 and $\bar{E}_1$ lie on a line through the center x_0 of E_2. The centers of E_1 and $\bar{E}_1$ are, of course, the points x_1 and $\bar{x}_1$ described above.

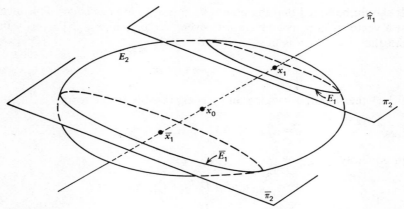

Figure 7.3

As an immediate extension of Theorem 7.5 we have

THEOREM 7.6

The minimum points of F *on parallel* k*-planes lie on a* $(n-k)$*-plane* $\hat{\pi}_{n-k}$ *through the minimum point* x_0 *of* F. *The minimum of* F *on the* k*-plane* π_k *defined by the equations*

$$q_j^* x = \rho_j \qquad (j = 1, \ldots, n-k) \qquad (7.7)$$

lies on the $(n-k)$*-plane* $\hat{\pi}_{n-k}$ *through the minimum point* x_0 *of* F *defined by the parametric equations*

$$x = x_0 + \alpha_1 A^{-1} q_1 + \cdots + \alpha_{n-k} A^{-1} q_{n-k} \qquad (-\infty < \alpha_j < \infty). \qquad (7.8)$$

It is understood that the vectors $q_1, \ldots, q_{n-k}$ are linearly independent. Otherwise equations (7.7) could not define a k-plane π_k. The vectors $q_1, \ldots, q_{n-k}$ form a basis for the normals to the k-plane π_k. At the minimum point x_1 of F on π_k the gradient $\nabla F'(x) = Ax_1 - b$ is orthogonal to π_k and hence is a normal of π_k. It is therefore a linear combination

$$Ax_1 - b = \alpha_1 q_1 + \cdots + \alpha_{n-k} q_{n-k}$$

of the normals $q_1, \ldots, q_{n-k}$ of π_k. Since $x_0 = A^{-1} b$, it follows that

$$x_1 = x_0 + \alpha_1 A^{-1} q_1 + \cdots + \alpha_{n-k} A^{-1} q_{n-k}.$$

The point x_1 therefore lies on the $(n-k)$-plane defined by the parametric equations (7.8).

It should be noted that the planes π_k and $\hat{\pi}_{n-k}$ are *conjugate*. This means that a vector u in π_k is conjugate to every vector v in $\hat{\pi}_{n-k}$. To verify this, recall that a vector u is in π_{n-k} if and only if

$$q_j^* u = 0 \qquad (j=1,\dots,n-k).$$

On the other hand, a vector v in π_k is expressible in the form

$$v = \alpha_1 A^{-1} q_1 + \cdots + \alpha_{n-k} A^{-1} q_{n-k}.$$

Consequently

$$u^* A v = \sum_{j=1}^{n-k} \alpha_j u^* A A^{-1} q_j = \sum_{j=1}^{n-k} \alpha_j u^* q_j = 0.$$

THEOREM 7.7

A k-*plane* π_k *cutting an* (n$-$1)-*dimensional ellipsoid*

$$E_{n-1}: \qquad F(x) = \gamma$$

cuts E_{n-1} *in a* (k$-$1)-*dimensional ellipsoid* E_{k-1} *whose center affords a minimum to* F *on* π_k.

Let x_1 be the minimum point of F on π_k. Select k linearly independent vectors $v_1,\dots,v_k$ in π_k. Then every point x in π_k is expressible uniquely in the form

$$x = x_1 + \alpha_1 v_1 + \cdots + \alpha_k v_k.$$

Since F has a minimum at x_1 on π_k, the gradient

$$\nabla F(x_1) = F'(x_1) = A x_1 - b$$

is orthogonal to each of the vectors $v_1,\dots,v_k$, that is,

$$v_j^* (A x_1 - b) = 0 \qquad (j=1,\dots,k).$$

When this fact is used, it follows from the formula

$$F(x_1 + p) = F(x_1) + p^*(A x_1 - b) + \tfrac{1}{2} p^* A p,$$

with $x = x_1$ and $p = \alpha_1 v_1 + \cdots + \alpha_k v_k$, that

$$F(x_1 + \alpha_1 v_1 + \cdots + \alpha_k v_k) = F(x_1) + \frac{1}{2} \sum_{i,j=1}^{k} v_i^* A v_j \alpha_i \alpha_j$$

is a quadratic function of $\alpha = (\alpha_1, \ldots, \alpha_k)$. The $(k \times k)$-dimensional matrix $(v_i^* A v_j)$ is positive definite since A is positive definite. The manifold of points $x = x_1 + \alpha_1 v_1 + \cdots + \alpha_k v_k$ such that

$$F(x_1 + \alpha_1 v_1 + \cdots + \alpha_k v_k) = \gamma$$

is therefore a k-dimensional ellipsoid E_{k-1} in π_k. Its center is given by the parameter values $\alpha_1 = \alpha_2 = \cdots = \alpha_k = 0$ of the point $x = x_1$. The minimum point x_1 of F on π_k is therefore the center of E_{k-1}, as was to be proved.

With the help of this result Theorems 7.5 and 7.6 can be restated geometrically as

THEOREM 7.8

Parallel k-planes cutting an ellipsoid E_{n-1} *cut this* $(n-1)$-*dimensional ellipsoid in* $(k-1)$-*dimensional ellipsoids whose centers lie on an* $(n-k)$-*plane containing the center of* E_{n-1}.

EXERCISES

1. Complete the proof of Theorem 7.8.
2. Given the function $F(x,y) = 4x^2 + 9y^2$, find the line π_1 determined by the minimum points of F along the parallel lines $4x + y = $ constant. Then find the minimizing point of F on π_1.
3. Given the function

$$F(x,y,z) = \frac{x^2}{25} + \frac{y^2}{16} + \frac{z^2}{9},$$

find the line determined by the minimum points of F on the parallel planes $3x + 2y + z = $ constant. Show that the gradients of F along this line are parallel.
4. Show that the $(n-1)$-plane

$$\tfrac{1}{2} x_1^* A x - b^* \left(\frac{x + x_1}{2} \right) + c = \gamma$$

determined by a point x_1 is tangent to the ellipsoid

$$F(x) = \tfrac{1}{2} x^* A x - b^* x + c = \gamma$$

at $x = x_1$ if $\gamma = F(x_1)$. Show that, if $\gamma \neq F(x_1)$, the minimum point x_2 of F on this plane lies on the line through x_1 and the minimum point x_0 of F. This $(n-1)$-plane is called the polar $(n-1)$-plane of x_1 relative to the ellipsoid $F(x) = \gamma$. Show that x_1 is on the polar $(n-1)$-plane of the point x_2 relative to $F(x) = \gamma$.

5. Given a point x_1 and a vector $p_1 \neq 0$, show that the minimum point of F on the line $x = x_1 + \alpha p_1$ is the point $x_2 = x_1 + a_1 p_1$, where $a_1 = c_1/d_1$, $d_1 = p_1^* A p_1$, $c_1 = p_1^*(b - Ax_1) = -p_1^* \nabla F(x_1)$.

6. Continuing with Exercise 5, choose a vector $p_2 \neq 0$ conjugate to p_1 $(p_1^* A p_2 = 0)$. Show that the minimum point $x_3 = x_2 + a_2 p_2$ of F on the line $x = x_2 + \alpha p_2$ minimizes F on the 2-plane $x = x_1 + \alpha_1 p_1 + \alpha_2 p_2$.

7. Let $p_1, p_2, \ldots, p_n$ be (mutually conjugate) vectors so that $p_i^* A p_j = 0$ $(i \neq j)$, $p_i^* A p_i \neq 0$. Starting with a point x_1, show that the minimum point x_0 of F can be obtained by minimizing F successively in the directions $p_1, \ldots, p_n$. Denote the minimum point of F on the line $x = x_k + \alpha p_k$ by $x_{k+1} = x_k + a_k p_k$. Obtain formulas for the numbers $a_1, \ldots, a_n$. This procedure is called the *method of conjugate directions* for minimizing a quadratic function F.

8. Let $F(x) = \frac{1}{2} x^* A x - b^* x$, and let p_1, p_2, p_3, p_4 be the column vectors of p, where

$$A = \begin{bmatrix} 1 & 2 & -1 & 1 \\ 2 & 5 & 0 & 2 \\ -1 & 0 & 6 & 0 \\ 1 & 2 & 0 & 3 \end{bmatrix}, \quad P = \begin{bmatrix} 1 & -6 & -30 & -20 \\ 0 & 2 & 12 & 10 \\ 0 & -1 & -6 & 0 \\ 0 & 1 & 0 & 0 \end{bmatrix},$$

$$b = \begin{bmatrix} 0 \\ 2 \\ -1 \\ 1 \end{bmatrix}, \quad x_1 = \begin{bmatrix} 1 \\ 0 \\ 0 \\ 0 \end{bmatrix}.$$

Show that p_1, p_2, p_3, p_4 are mutually conjugate relative to A. Verify the results given in Exercises 5, 6, and 7 for this problem. Verify that, starting with x_1, the successive minimum points x_2, x_3, x_4, x_5 of F in the directions p_1, p_2, p_3, p_4 are $(0,0,0,0)$, $(-36, 12, -6, 6)$, $(-61, 22, -11, 6)$, and $(-65, 24, -11, 6)$ when expressed as row vectors. Show that x_5 is the minimum point of F.

9. Let $x_1, x_{11}, \ldots, x_{1n}$ be $(n+1)$-points which do not lie on an $(n-1)$-plane. Set $p_1 = x_{11} - x_1$. For $j = 1, \ldots, n$ let x_{2j} be the minimum point of F on the line $x = x_{1j} + \alpha p_1$. Show that the points $x_2 = x_{21}, x_{22}, \ldots, x_{2n}$ determine an $(n-1)$-plane π_{n-1} conjugate to p_1. Show that the minimum point x_0 of F is in π_{n-1}. Set $p_2 = x_{22} - x_2$. For $j = 2, \ldots, n$ let x_{3j} be the minimum point of F on the line $x = x_{2j} + \alpha p_2$. Show that the points $x_3 = x_{32}, x_{33}, \ldots, x_{3n}$ define an $(n-2)$-plane π_{n-2} in π_{n-1} conjugate to p_1 and p_2. Show that π_{n-2} contains the minimum point x_0 of F. Continue this process in the same manner with $p_3 = x_{33} - x_3$ to obtain points $x_4 = x_{43}, x_{44}, \ldots, x_{4n}$ by minimizing F on the line $x = x_{3j} + \alpha p_3$. Show that the point x_{n+1} obtained after n steps of this process is the minimum point of F. We call this method for minimizing F a *method of parallel displacement*. It can be applied to a nonquadratic function by restarting after each cycle of n steps with x_{n+1} as the new x_1.

10. Apply the method of parallel displacement given in Exercise 9 to the function F given in Exercise 8. Choose $x_1, x_{11}, x_{12}, x_{13}, x_{14}$ to be the transposes of the vectors $(0,0,0,0)$, $(1,0,0,0)$, $(0,1,0,0)$, $(0,0,1,0)$, $(0,0,0,1)$. Observe that this method solves $Ax = b$ by a Gaussian elimination procedure.

11. Let F be a function of class C''' with a positive definite Hessian $f''(x)$. Given a point x_1, show that $x_2 = x_1 - f''(x_1)^{-1}\nabla f(x_1)$ is the minimum point of the quadratic function $F(x) = f(x_1) + f'(x_1, x - x_1) + \frac{1}{2}f''(x_1, x - x_1)$. The algorithm $\bar{x} = x - f''(x)^{-1}\nabla f(x)$ is *Newton's algorithm* for minimizing a function f.

12. Let $F(x) = \frac{1}{2}x^*Ax - bx + c$ with $A = A^* > 0$. Set $G(x) = \frac{1}{2}|\nabla F(x)|^2 = \frac{1}{2}|Ax - b|^2$. Given a point x_1, set $y_1 = x_1$ and $p_1 = -\nabla F(y_1)$. Let x_2, y_2 be, respectively, the minimum points of F, G on the line $x = x_1 + \alpha p_1$. Having obtained x_k, y_k, set $p_k = -\nabla F(y_k)$. Let x_{k+1} be the minimum point of F on the line $x = x_k + \alpha p_k$, and let y_{k+1} be the minimum point of G on the line through y_k and x_{k+1}. It can be shown that the vectors $p_1, p_2, p_3, \ldots$ are mutually conjugate and that, after $m \leqslant n$ steps, we have $y_{m+1} = x_{m+1}$. The point x_{m+1} so obtained minimizes F and also G. Verify this result numerically for the problem given in Exercise 8.

13. With F and x_1 as in Exercise 12, set $r_1 = -\nabla F(x_1)$. Determine the minimum point x_2 of F on the line $x = x_1 + \alpha r_1$. Having found the points $x_1, \ldots, x_k$, set $r_k = -\nabla F(x_k)$ and obtain the minimum point y_k of F on the line $x = x_k + \alpha r_k$. Then find the minimum point x_{k+1} of F on the line through x_{k-1} and y_k. It can be shown that the vectors $r_1, r_2, r_3, \ldots$ are mutually orthogonal and that the points $x_1, x_2, x_3, \ldots$ coincide with those given by the algorithm described in Exercise 12. The terminal point x_{m+1} minimizes F. Verify this result numerically for the problem given in Exercise 8.

The algorithms presented above were given implicitly in the paper by Hestenes and Stiefel, *loc. cit.*, and in a paper written in 1951 by Hestenes and published in 1973 in the *Journal of Optimization and Applications*, Vol. 11, as an Historical Paper under the title "Iterative Methods for Solving Linear Equations."

8. INNER PRODUCT SPACES AND THE GRAM-SCHMIDT PROCESS

The theory developed in the preceding pages has an interesting application to inner product spaces. Let $\mathcal{E}$ be a real linear space possessing an inner product $\langle x, y \rangle$. The dimension of $\mathcal{E}$ may be infinite. An *inner product* $\langle x, y \rangle$ on $\mathcal{E}$ is characterized by the following three properties:

(1) $\langle x, x \rangle \geqslant 0$ on $\mathcal{E}$ with $\langle x, x \rangle = 0$ if and only if $x = 0$,
(2) $\langle x, y \rangle = \langle y, x \rangle$,
(3) $\langle x, \alpha y + \beta z \rangle = \alpha \langle x, y \rangle + \beta \langle x, z \rangle$,

for all x, y, z in $\mathcal{E}$ and all real numbers α and β. As is seen in Section 2 of the appendix, we have

(4) $|\langle x, y \rangle| \leqslant |x||y|$,

where

$$|x| = \langle x, x \rangle^{1/2} \tag{8.1}$$

is the *norm* of x. In view of these relations we have the identity

$$|\alpha x + \beta y|^2 = \alpha^2 |x|^2 + 2\alpha\beta\langle x,y\rangle + \beta^2 |y|^2. \tag{8.2}$$

The following lemma will be useful.

LEMMA 8.1

A set of vectors $y_1, \ldots, y_m$ *in* $\mathscr{E}$ *are linearly independent if and only if the determinant*

$$|\langle y_i, y_j\rangle| \qquad (i,j = 1, \ldots, m) \tag{8.3}$$

is different from zero. This determinant is different from zero if and only if the matrix

$$(\langle y_i, y_j\rangle)$$

is a positive symmetric matrix.

To prove this result, fix the vectors $y_1, \ldots, y_m$, and consider the function

$$F(\alpha) = |\alpha_1 y_1 + \cdots + \alpha_m y_m|^2 = \sum_{i=1}^{m} \sum_{j=1}^{m} \alpha_i \langle y_i, y_j\rangle \alpha_j.$$

This function is nonnegative. Its minimum value $F(\alpha) = 0$ is attained for $\alpha = (\alpha_1, \ldots, \alpha_m) \neq (0, \ldots, 0)$ if and only if $\alpha_1 y_1 + \cdots + \alpha_m y_m = 0$, that is, if and only if $y_1, \ldots, y_m$ are linearly dependent. Moreover $F(\alpha) = 0$ for $\alpha \neq 0$ if and only if α is a solution of the equations

$$\frac{1}{2} \frac{\partial F}{\partial \alpha_k} = \sum_{j=1}^{m} \langle y_k, y_j\rangle \alpha_j = 0 \qquad (k = 1, \ldots, m).$$

This equation has a nonnull solution α if and only if $|\langle y_i, y_j\rangle| = 0$. Consequently $y_1, \ldots, y_m$ are linearly dependent if and only if $|\langle y_i, y_j\rangle| = 0$. This proves the lemma.

The determinant $|\langle y_i, y_j\rangle|$ is called the *Grammian* of $y_1, \ldots, y_m$. Similarly the matrix $(\langle y_i, y_j\rangle)$ is called the *Grammian matrix* of $y_1, \ldots, y_m$.

A linear subspace $\mathscr{B}$ of $\mathscr{E}$ is of finite dimension m if it is *generated by* a set m of linearly independent vectors $y_1, \ldots, y_m$. The vectors y in $\mathscr{B}$ are then expressible uniquely in the form

$$y = \alpha_1 y_1 + \cdots + \alpha_m y_m,$$

where $\alpha_1, \ldots, \alpha_m$ are real numbers. Such a set of vectors $y_1, \ldots, y_m$ is called a *basis* for $\mathscr{B}$.

One of the basic elementary theorems for inner product spaces is the following one. In this theorem and elsewhere the quantity $|x - y|$ is the distance from x to y.

THEOREM 8.1

Let $\mathcal{B}$ be a finite dimensional linear subspace of $\mathcal{E}$. Given a vector $\bar{x}$ in $\mathcal{E}$, there is a unique vector $\bar{y}$ in $\mathcal{B}$ that is nearest to $\bar{x}$. The vector $\bar{y}$ accordingly minimizes the function

$$f(y) = |\bar{x} - y|^2 = |\bar{x}|^2 - 2\langle \bar{x}, y \rangle + |y|^2 \tag{8.4}$$

on $\mathcal{B}$. The vector $\bar{z} = \bar{x} - \bar{y}$ is orthogonal to $\mathcal{B}$ and

$$|\bar{x}|^2 = |\bar{y}|^2 + |\bar{z}|^2. \tag{8.5}$$

The vector $\bar{y}$ is called the orthogonal projection of $\bar{x}$ on $\mathcal{B}$.

The existence of a point $\bar{y}$ in $\mathcal{B}$ that is nearest $\bar{x}$ is a simple consequence of Theorem 2.1 applied to the function $f(y) = |\bar{x} - y|^2$ (see Example 2.1). Set $\bar{z} = \bar{x} - \bar{y}$, and select a vector y in $\mathcal{B}$. Then $\bar{y} + \epsilon y$ is in $\mathcal{B}$, and

$$f(\bar{y} + \epsilon y) = |\bar{z} - \epsilon y|^2 = |\bar{z}|^2 - 2\epsilon\langle \bar{z}, y \rangle + \epsilon^2 |y|^2 \geqslant f(\bar{y})$$

for all values of ϵ. The function $\varphi(\epsilon) = f(\bar{y} + \epsilon y)$ has the minimum value $\varphi(0) = f(\bar{y})$ at $\epsilon = 0$. Hence

$$\varphi'(0) = -2\langle \bar{z}, y \rangle = 0.$$

Since y is any vector in $\mathcal{B}$, it follows that the vector $\bar{z} = \bar{x} - \bar{y}$ is orthogonal to every vector in $\mathcal{B}$. In particular, $\langle \bar{z}, \bar{y} \rangle = 0$. Consequently

$$|\bar{x}|^2 = |\bar{y} + \bar{z}|^2 = |\bar{y}|^2 + 2\langle \bar{y}, \bar{z} \rangle + |\bar{z}|^2 = |\bar{y}|^2 + |\bar{z}|^2$$

as stated in equation (8.5). This proves the theorem.

EXAMPLE 8.1

The set of points y of the form

$$y^1 = \alpha + 2\beta, \qquad y^2 = \alpha + 2\beta, \qquad y^3 = \alpha, \qquad y^4 = \alpha,$$

with α and β as parameters, form a two-dimensional linear manifold $\mathcal{B}$ in $\mathcal{E}^4$. The square of the distance from a point y in $\mathcal{B}$ to the point

$\bar{x} = (3, 1, 1, -1)$ is given by the formula

$$F(\alpha, \beta) = |\bar{x} - y|^2 = (3 - \alpha - 2\beta)^2 + (1 - \alpha - 2\beta)^2 + (1 - \alpha)^2 + (-1 - \alpha)^2.$$

This function has a minimum when

$$\frac{1}{2} \frac{\partial F}{\partial \alpha} = (\alpha + 2\beta - 3) + (\alpha + 2\beta - 1) + (\alpha - 1) + (1 + \alpha) = 0,$$

$$\frac{1}{2} \frac{\partial F}{\partial \beta} = 2(\alpha + 2\beta - 3) + 2(\alpha + 2\beta - 1) = 0,$$

that is, when

$$4\alpha + 4\beta - 4 = 0, \qquad 2\alpha + 4\beta - 4 = 0.$$

Consequently $\alpha = 0$ and $\beta = 1$. The vector $\bar{y} = (2, 2, 0, 0)$ is therefore the nearest point in $\mathscr{B}$ to $\bar{x}$. Hence the vector $\bar{z} = \bar{x} - \bar{y} = (1, -1, 1, -1)$ is orthogonal to $\mathscr{B}$.

The vectors in the set $p_1, p_2, p_3, \ldots$ in $\mathscr{E}$ are said to be *mutually orthogonal* if

$$\langle p_i, p_j \rangle = 0 \qquad (i \neq j), \qquad d_i = |p_i|^2 = \langle p_i, p_i \rangle \neq 0.$$

Observe that we exclude the vector $p_i = 0$. These vectors are said to be orthonormal if in addition $d_i = 1$. An *orthonormal set* of vectors $q_1, q_2, q_3, \ldots$ is therefore characterized by the relations

$$\langle q_i, q_j \rangle = \delta_{ij},$$

where $\delta_{ii} = 1$ and $\delta_{ij} = 0$ $(i \neq j)$. A set of mutually orthogonal vectors $p_1, p_2, p_3, \ldots$ can be transformed into an orthonormal set $q_1, q_2, q_3, \ldots$ by setting

$$q_i = \frac{p_i}{|p_i|} \qquad (i = 1, 2, 3, \ldots).$$

THEOREM 8.2

Let $\mathscr{B}$ be a linear subspace of $\mathscr{E}$ generated by a set of mutually orthogonal vectors $p_1, \ldots, p_m$. For a given point $\bar{x}$ in $\mathscr{E}$, the vector $\bar{y}$ nearest to $\bar{x}$ in $\mathscr{B}$ is expressed by the formula

$$\bar{y} = a_1 p_1 + \cdots + a_m p_m, \tag{8.6}$$

where

$$a_j = \frac{c_j}{d_j}, \qquad c_j = \langle \bar{x}, p_j \rangle = \langle p_j, \bar{x} \rangle, \qquad d_j = |p_j|^2. \tag{8.7}$$

Moreover

$$|\bar{y}|^2 = \sum_{j=1}^m a_j^2 d_j. \tag{8.8}$$

Finally the vector

$$p = \bar{x} - \bar{y} = \bar{x} - \sum_{j=1}^m a_j p_j$$

is orthogonal to $\mathcal{B}$.

This is an immediate consequence of the fact that the function

$$F(\alpha) = |\bar{x} - (\alpha_1 p_1 + \cdots + \alpha_m p_m)|^2$$

is expressible in the form

$$F(\alpha) = |\bar{x}|^2 - 2\sum_{j=1}^m c_j \alpha_j + \sum_{j=1}^m \alpha_j^2 d_j$$

and hence in the form

$$F(\alpha) = |\bar{x}|^2 - \sum_{j=1}^m a_j^2 d_j + \sum_{j=1}^m (\alpha_j - a_j)^2 d_j,$$

where a_j, c_j, and d_j are given by (8.7). Clearly $F(\alpha)$ has a minimum when $\alpha_j = a_j$ $(j=1,\ldots,m)$. The vector $\bar{y}$ is therefore of form (8.6). The last statement follows from the last statement in Theorem 8.1.

EXAMPLE 8.2

Let $\mathcal{E}$ be the class of continuous real-valued functions

$$x: \qquad x(t) \qquad (0 \le t \le \pi)$$

with

$$\langle x, y \rangle = \int_0^\pi x(t) y(t)\, dt$$

as its inner product. The functions

$$p_k(t) = \sin kt \qquad (k = 1, 2, 3, \ldots)$$

form an orthogonal set. These functions are mutually orthogonal in view of the relations

$$\langle p_j, p_k \rangle = \int_0^{\pi} \sin jt \sin kt \, dt$$

$$= \frac{1}{2} \int_0^{\pi} [\cos(j-k)t - \cos(j+k)t] \, dt = 0$$

when $j \neq k$. If $j = k$, we have

$$d_k = |p_k|^2 = \int_0^{\pi} \sin^2 kt \, dt = \frac{\pi}{2} \, .$$

It follows that for a given vector x we have

$$a_j = \frac{\langle x, p_j \rangle}{d_j} = \frac{2}{\pi} \int_0^{\pi} x(t) \sin jt \, dt.$$

According to Theorem 8.2, the numbers $\alpha_j = a_j$ $(j = 1, \ldots, m)$ minimize the function

$$F(\alpha) = \int_0^{\pi} [x(t) - (\alpha_1 \sin t + \alpha_2 \sin 2t + \cdots + \alpha_m \sin mt)]^2 \, dt.$$

This result can also be verified by showing that the solution of the equations

$$\frac{1}{2} \frac{\partial F}{\partial \alpha_j} = \int_0^{\pi} x(t) \sin jt \, dt - \alpha_j \frac{\pi}{2} = 0 \qquad (j = 1, \ldots, m)$$

minimizes $F(\alpha)$.

The results given in Theorems 8.1 and 8.2 can be used to transform a set of vectors $y_1, y_2, y_3, \ldots$ into a set of mutually orthogonal vectors $p_1, p_2, p_3, \ldots$ by what is known as a Gram-Schmidt process. We illustrate this process in $\mathcal{E}^3$ in Figure 8.1. A set of linearly independent vectors y_1, y_2, y_3 is given. Let $\mathcal{B}_1$ be the line generated by y_1. As indicated in Figure 8.1(a), we set $p_1 = y_1$ and project y_2 on the line $\mathcal{B}_1$ to obtain the orthogonal projection $\bar{y}_1$. Set $p_2 = y_2 - \bar{y}_1$. As indicated in Figure 8.1(b), the plane $\mathcal{B}_2$ generated by y_1

and y_2 is also generated by p_1 and p_2. Project y_3 onto $\mathcal{B}_2$ to obtain the orthogonal projection $\bar{y}_2$. Set $p_3 = y_3 - \bar{y}_2$. The vectors p_1, p_2, p_3 are mutually orthogonal vectors in $\mathcal{E}^3$.

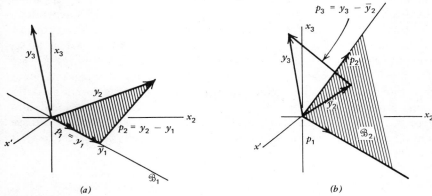

Figure 8.1

The general situation is described in

THEOREM 8.3

Let $y_1, y_2, y_3, \ldots$ be a sequence of linearly independent vectors in $\mathcal{E}$. Let $\mathcal{B}_k$ be the linear subspace of $\mathcal{E}$ generated by $y_1, \ldots, y_k$. Choose $p_1 = y_1$. For $k > 1$ choose $p_k = y_k - \bar{y}_{k-1}$, where $\bar{y}_{k-1}$ is the vector in $\mathcal{B}_{k-1}$ nearest to y_k. The vectors $p_1, p_2, p_3, \ldots$ obtained in this manner are mutually orthogonal. The vectors $p_1, \ldots, p_k$ generate $\mathcal{B}_k$. Finally the vectors $p_1, p_2, \ldots$ are generated by the algorithm

$$p_1 = y_1, \qquad p_k = y_k - \sum_{j=1}^{k-1} a_{kj} p_j \qquad (k > 1), \qquad (8.9a)$$

where

$$a_{kj} = \frac{c_{kj}}{d_j}, \qquad c_{kj} = \langle y_k, p_j \rangle, \qquad d_j = |p_j|^2 \qquad (j = 1, \ldots, k-1). \quad (8.9b)$$

Algorithm (8.9) is called a *Gram-Schmidt process*. If we wish to normalize the vectors p_k, we can do so by replacing (8.9a) by

$$p_1 = \rho_1 y_1, \qquad p_k = \rho_k \bar{p}_k, \qquad \bar{p}_k = y_k - \sum_{j=1}^{k-1} a_{kj} p_j \qquad (k > 1),$$

where ρ_k is a nonzero scale factor. In view of this theorem the Gram-Schmidt process (8.9) can be interpreted in terms of an optimization procedure.

If $\mathcal{E}$ is infinite dimensional, the sequence $y_1, y_2, y_3, \ldots$ may be infinite. The statement that the vectors in this sequence are linearly independent means that for each integer k the vectors $y_1, \ldots, y_k$ are linearly independent.

The proof of the theorem is an immediate consequence of Theorems 8.1 and 8.2. By Theorem 8.1 there is a vector $\bar{y}_{k-1}$ in $\mathcal{B}_{k-1}$ nearest to y_k. Moreover $p_k = y_k - \bar{y}_{k-1}$ is orthogonal to $\mathcal{B}_{k-1}$. Since y_k is not in $\mathcal{B}_{k-1}$, we have $p_k \neq 0$. By construction the vectors $p_1, \ldots, p_{k-1}$ are in $\mathcal{B}_{k-1}$ and hence are orthogonal to p_k. The sequence $p_1, p_2, p_3, \ldots$ therefore forms an orthogonal sequence. Inasmuch as $p_1, \ldots, p_k$ belong to the k-dimensional subspace $\mathcal{B}_k$, they form an orthogonal basis for $\mathcal{B}_k$. Using this fact, we see from Theorem 8.2 that for $k > 1$ the vector $\bar{y}_{k-1}$ in $\mathcal{B}_{k-1}$ nearest to y_k is given by the formula

$$\bar{y}_{k-1} = \sum_{j=1}^{k-1} a_{kj} p_j,$$

where a_{kj} is given by (8.9b). Therefore the formula in (8.9a) for $p_k = y_k - \bar{y}_{k-1}$ holds, and the theorem is established.

EXAMPLE 8.3

Consider the four-dimensional case in which

$$y_1 = (1,1,1,1), \qquad y_2 = (3,3,1,1), \qquad y_3 = (3,1,5,3), \qquad y_4 = (4,0,0,0).$$

Using the Gram-Schmidt process, we set $p_1 = y_1$. Then $d_1 = |p_1|^2 = 4$, $c_{21} = \langle y_2, p_1 \rangle = 8$, $a_{21} = c_{21}/d_1 = 2$, and

$$p_2 = y_2 - 2p_1 = (1,1,-1,-1), \qquad d_2 = |p_2|^2 = 4.$$

Since $c_{31} = \langle y_3, p_1 \rangle = 12$, $c_{32} = \langle y_3, p_2 \rangle = -4$, $a_{31} = 12/4 = 3$, $a_{32} = -4/4 = -1$, we find that

$$p_3 = y_3 - 3p_1 + p_2 = (1,-1,1,-1), \qquad d_3 = |p_3|^2 = 4.$$

From the relations $c_{4j} = \langle y_4, p_j \rangle = 4$, $a_{4j} = c_{4j}/d_j = 1$ $(j=1,2,3)$, we obtain

$$y_4 = y_4 - p_1 - p_2 - p_3 = (1,-1,-1,1), \qquad d_4 = |p_4|^2 = 4.$$

The vectors

$$p_1 = (1, 1, 1, 1), \qquad p_2 = (1, 1, -1, -1),$$
$$p_3 = (1, -1, 1, -1), \quad p_4 = (1, -1, -1, 1)$$

are mutually orthogonal. Every vector x in $\mathcal{E}^4$ is expressible in the form

$$x = a_1 p_1 + a_2 p_2 + a_3 p_3 + a_4 p_4,$$

where

$$a_j = \frac{\langle p_j, x \rangle}{d_j} = \tfrac{1}{4} \langle p_j, x \rangle.$$

In addition, $|x|^2 = 4(a_1^2 + a_2^2 + a_3^2 + a_4^2)$.

EXAMPLE 8.4

Let $\mathcal{E} = \mathcal{E}^n$ be an n-dimensional Euclidean space, and $A = (A_{ij})$ $(i, j = 1, \ldots, n)$ be a positive symmetric matrix. We replace the usual inner product by the bilinear form

$$\langle x, y \rangle = \sum_{i}^{n} \sum_{j=1}^{n} A_{ij} x^i y^j = x^* A y.$$

Here x and y denote column vectors, and x^* is the transpose of x. Clearly x^* is a row vector. If two vectors x, y satisfy the relation

$$\langle x, y \rangle = x^* A y = 0,$$

they are said to be A-orthogonal or to be conjugate (relative to A). A set of n vectors accordingly is said to be mutually conjugate in the case

$$p_i^* A p_j = 0 \quad (i \neq j), \qquad d_j = p_j^* A p_j \neq 0.$$

Given a set of linearly independent vectors $y_1, \ldots, y_n$, we find that Gram-Schmidt process (8.9a) takes the form

$$p_1 = y_1, \qquad p_k = y_k - \sum_{j=1}^{k-1} a_{kj} p_j. \qquad (8.10a)$$

$$a_{kj} = \frac{c_{kj}}{d_j}, \qquad c_{kj} = y_k^* A p_j, \qquad d_j = p_j^* A p_j \qquad (j = 1, \ldots, k-1). \quad (8.10b)$$

These concepts form the basis of the conjugate direction method for minimizing a function of n-variables.

As a numerical illustration consider the case in which

$$A = \begin{bmatrix} 6 & -2 & -2 \\ -2 & 5 & 0 \\ -2 & 0 & 7 \end{bmatrix} \tag{8.11}$$

and $y_1^* = (1,0,0)$, $y_2^* = (0,1,0)$, $y_3^* = (0,0,1)$. We have $p_1^* = (1,0,0)$, $d_1 = p_1^* A p_1$ $= 6$, $c_{21} = y_2^* A p_1 = -2$, $a_{21} = c_{21}/d_1 = -\frac{1}{3}$, and

$$p_2^* = y_2^* + \tfrac{1}{3} y_1^* = (\tfrac{1}{3}, 1, 0), \qquad d_2 = p_2^* A p_2 = \tfrac{13}{3}.$$

It follows that, with $a_{kj} = c_{kj}/d_j$,

$$c_{31} = y_3^* A p_1 = -2, \qquad c_{32} = y_3^* A p_2 = -\tfrac{2}{3}, \qquad a_{31} = -\tfrac{1}{3}, \qquad a_{32} = -\tfrac{2}{13},$$

$$p_3^* = y_3^* + \tfrac{1}{3} p_1^* + \tfrac{2}{13} p_2^* = (\tfrac{5}{13}, \tfrac{2}{13}, 1), \qquad d_3 = p_3^* A p_3 = \tfrac{71}{13}.$$

The vectors

$$p_1 = \begin{bmatrix} 1 \\ 0 \\ 0 \end{bmatrix}, \qquad p_2 = \begin{bmatrix} \tfrac{1}{3} \\ 1 \\ 0 \end{bmatrix}, \qquad p_3 = \begin{bmatrix} \tfrac{5}{13} \\ \tfrac{2}{13} \\ 1 \end{bmatrix} \tag{8.12}$$

therefore are mutually conjugate.

EXAMPLE 8.5

Let $\mathcal{E}$ be the class of all continuous functions

$$x: \qquad x(t) \qquad (-1 \leqslant t \leqslant 1)$$

with

$$\langle x, y \rangle = \int_{-1}^{1} x(t) y(t) \, dt$$

as its inner product. Let

$$y_0(t) = 1, \qquad y_1(t) = t, \qquad y_2(t) = t^2, \ldots, y_k(t) = t^k, \ldots.$$

By the Gram-Schmidt process, we can obtain the sequence of mutually orthogonal polynomials $p_0(t), p_1(t), \ldots, p_k(t), \ldots$ with the additional property that

$$p_k(1) = 1 \qquad (k = 0, 1, 2, \ldots).$$

We see at once that $p_0(t) = 1$ and $p_1(t) = t$. To find $p_2(t)$, we observe that

$$d_0 = |p_0|^2 = 2, \quad d_1 = |p_1|^2 = \int_{-1}^1 t^2 \, dt = \frac{2}{3} = \langle y_2, p_0 \rangle, \quad \langle y_2, p_1 \rangle = \int_{-1}^1 t^3 \, dt = 0.$$

Hence, with ρ_2 as a scale factor, we have

$$p_2(t) = \rho_2 \left[y_2 - \tfrac{1}{3} p_0 - (0) p_1 \right] = \rho_2 \left(t^2 - \tfrac{1}{3} \right).$$

Choosing ρ_2 such that $p_2(1) = 1$, we find that $\rho_2 = \tfrac{3}{2}$. It follows that

$$p_2(t) = \frac{3t^2 - 1}{2}, \qquad d_2 = |p_2|^2 = \int_{-1}^1 \frac{(3t^2 - 1)^2}{4} \, dt = \tfrac{2}{5}.$$

To find $p_3(t)$, observe that

$$\langle y_3, p_0 \rangle = \int_{-1}^1 t^3 \, dt = 0, \qquad \langle y_3, p_2 \rangle = \int_{-1}^1 \frac{3t^2 - 1}{2} t^3 \, dt = 0$$

since the integrands are odd functions of t. Moreover

$$\langle y_3, p_1 \rangle = \int_{-1}^1 t^4 \, dt = \tfrac{2}{5}.$$

Consequently

$$a_{31} = \frac{\langle y_3, p_0 \rangle}{d_1} = \frac{1}{5}, \qquad a_{30} = a_{32} = 0.$$

The polynomial p_3 therefore takes the form

$$p_3(t) = \rho_3 \left[y_3(t) - a_{31} p_1(t) \right] = \rho_3 \left(t^3 - \frac{t}{5} \right) = \frac{5t^3 - t}{4},$$

where ρ_3 has been chosen so that $p_3(1) = 1$.

Proceeding in this manner, we obtain a sequence $p_0, p_1, p_2, \ldots$ of orthogonal polynomials on $-1 \leqslant t \leqslant 1$. These polynomials, called *Legendre* polynomials, can be generated by the recursion formula

$$p_{k+1} = \frac{2k+1}{k+1} tp_k - \frac{k}{k+1} p_{k-1} \qquad (k=1,2,3,\dots)$$

with $p_0 = 1$ and $p_1 = t$. However, we shall not pause to prove this result. The polynomial $p_k(t)$ satisfies the differential equation

$$\frac{d}{dt}\left[(1-t^2)p_k'(t)\right] + k(k+1)p_k(t) = 0.$$

EXERCISES

1. Find an orthonormal basis for the subspace $\mathcal{B}$ in $\mathcal{E}^4$ described in Example 8.1. Find the point $\bar{y}$ in $\mathcal{B}$ nearest to the point $\bar{x} = (0,0,0,1)$. How far is $\bar{x}$ from $\mathcal{B}$?

2. Given n-dimensional column vectors p and q, show that the matrix pq^* has rank 1. For the case at $n=3$ and $p^* = (1,-2,3)$, $q^* = (3,4,-1)$, verify that

$$\frac{pq^*}{5} = \begin{bmatrix} \frac{3}{5} & \frac{4}{5} & -\frac{1}{5} \\ -\frac{6}{5} & -\frac{8}{5} & \frac{2}{5} \\ \frac{9}{5} & \frac{12}{5} & -\frac{3}{5} \end{bmatrix}.$$

3. For the case $n=3$ let A be matrix (8.11), and let p_1,p_2,p_3 be mutually conjugate vectors (8.12). Then $d_1 = 6$, $d_2 = \frac{13}{3}$, $d_3 = \frac{71}{13}$, where $d_i = p_i^* A p_i$. Verify that the inverse of A is given by

$$A^{-1} = \frac{p_1 p_1^*}{d_1} + \frac{p_2 p_2^*}{d_2} + \frac{p_3 p_3^*}{d_3}.$$

4. Let A be a nonsingular symmetric matrix, and let $p_1,\dots,p_n$ be vectors such that

$$p_i^* A p_j = 0 \quad (i \neq j), \qquad p_j^* A p_j = d_j \neq 0.$$

Show that the matrix

$$B = \sum_{j=1}^{n} \frac{p_j p_j^*}{d_j}$$

is the inverse of A. Hint: Show that $BAp_k = p_k$ $(k=1,\dots,n)$ and hence that $BA = I$.

5. Continuing with Exercise 4, set $s_j = Ap_j$ $(j = 1, \ldots, n)$. Show that

$$\sum_{j=1}^{n} \frac{p_j s_j^*}{d_j} = I, \qquad \sum_{j=1}^{n} \frac{s_j s_j^*}{d_j} = A.$$

Verify this result for the numerical case considered in Exercise 3.

6. For the case $n = 3$ let A be matrix (8.11). Let $y_1^* = (1, 0, 0)$, $y_2^* = (1, 1, 0)$, and $y_3^* = (1, 1, 1)$. Use the Gram-Schmidt method illustrated in Example 8.4 to obtain mutually conjugate vectors p_1, p_2, p_3. How are these related to vectors (8.12)?

7. Given a symmetric matrix A, show that, if $p_1, \ldots, p_n$ are mutually orthogonal and mutually conjugate (A-orthogonal) nonnull vectors, $p_1, \ldots, p_n$ are eigenvectors of A. *Hint*: Observe that the vectors Ap_k and p_k are orthogonal to $p_1, \ldots, p_{k-1}, p_{k+1}, \ldots, p_n$ and hence are collinear.

8. Given a positive symmetric matrix A and a vector $p_1 \neq 0$, select $a_1 \neq 0$ and determine b_1 so that the vector

$$p_2 = (1 + b_1) p_1 - a_1 A p_1$$

is conjugate to p_1 (i.e., $p_2^* A p_1 = 0$). Choose a_2 and b_2 so that

$$p_3 = (1 + b_2) p_2 - a_2 A p_2 - b_1 p_1$$

will be conjugate to p_2 and p_1. In general, for $k = 2, 3, \ldots$, choose a_k and b_k so that

$$p_{k+1} = (1 + b_k) p_k - a_k A p_k - b_{k-1} p_{k-1}$$

is conjugate to p_k and p_{k-1}. Show that the vectors $p_1, p_2, p_3, \ldots$ so obtained are mutually conjugate. Obtain formulas for a_k and b_k. Show that the algorithm will terminate for an index $k \leqslant n$ such that $p_{k+1} = 0$.

9. Given a positive symmetric matrix A and a nonnull vector $r_1 \neq 0$, construct vectors $r_1, r_2, \ldots$ and $p_1, p_2, \ldots$ by the algorithm

$$p_1 = r_1, \qquad r_{k+1} = r_k - a_k A p_k, \qquad p_{k+1} = r_{k+1} + b_k p_k,$$

subject to the constraints

$$p_k^* r_{k+1} = 0, \qquad p_k^* A p_{k+1} = 0.$$

Show that $r_1, r_2, \ldots$ are mutually orthogonal and that $p_1, p_2, \ldots$ are mutually conjugate. When will the algorithm terminate? Setting

$$c_k = |r_k|^2, \qquad d_k = p_k^* A p_k, \qquad e_k = -p_k^* A r_{k+1},$$

show that

$$c_k = p_k^* r_k, \qquad a_k = \frac{c_k}{d_k}, \qquad b_k = \frac{c_{k+1}}{c_k} = \frac{e_k}{d_k}.$$

10. Apply the algorithms given in Exercises 8 and 9 to the case in which $n=4$,

$$A = \begin{bmatrix} 1 & 2 & -1 & 1 \\ 2 & 5 & 0 & 2 \\ -1 & 0 & 6 & 0 \\ 1 & 2 & 0 & 3 \end{bmatrix}, \qquad p_1 = r_1 = \begin{bmatrix} -1 \\ 0 \\ 0 \\ 0 \end{bmatrix}.$$

9. EIGENVALUES AND EIGENVECTORS OF A REAL SYMMETRIC MATRIX

Consider an n-square symmetric matrix A, that is, a matrix $A = (a_{ij})$ such that $a_{ij} = a_{ji}$ $(i,j = 1,\ldots,n)$. Let $I = (\delta_{ij})$ be the identity matrix. Then $\delta_{ii} = 1$, $\delta_{ij} = 0$ $(i \neq j)$. The determinant

$$\Delta(\lambda) = |A - \lambda I| = \det(A - \lambda I) \tag{9.1}$$

is a polynomial of degree n in λ and is called the *characteristic polynomial* of A. Its zeros are called *eigenvalues* or *characteristic values* of A. They are also called *proper values* or *latent roots*. We shall use the term *eigenvalue*. We shall show presently that the eigenvalues of A are real.

A number λ satisfies the equation

$$\Delta(\lambda) = |A - \lambda I| = 0$$

if and only if there is a vector $x \neq 0$ such that

$$(A - \lambda I)x = 0 \qquad \text{or} \qquad Ax = \lambda x.$$

Such a vector x is called an *eigenvector* or a *characteristic vector* of A corresponding to the eigenvalue λ. A vector x is accordingly an eigenvector of A if and only if $x \neq 0$ and there is a number λ such that

$$Ax = \lambda x. \tag{9.2}$$

The number λ is the eigenvalue of A corresponding to the eigenvector x.

EXAMPLE 9.1.

To illustrate these ideas, consider the matrix

$$A = \begin{bmatrix} 6 & -2 & -2 \\ -2 & 5 & 0 \\ -2 & 0 & 7 \end{bmatrix}. \tag{9.3}$$

Its characteristic polynomial is

$$\Delta(\lambda) = \begin{vmatrix} 6-\lambda & -2 & -2 \\ -2 & 5-\lambda & 0 \\ -2 & 0 & 7-\lambda \end{vmatrix} = 162 - 99\lambda + 18\lambda^2 - \lambda^3 = (3-\lambda)(6-\lambda)(9-\lambda).$$

Its eigenvalues are accordingly $\lambda_1 = 3$, $\lambda_2 = 6$, and $\lambda_3 = 9$. From the computations

$$\begin{bmatrix} 6 & -2 & -2 \\ -2 & 5 & 0 \\ -2 & 0 & 7 \end{bmatrix} \begin{pmatrix} 2a \\ 2a \\ a \end{pmatrix} = \begin{bmatrix} 6a \\ 6a \\ 3a \end{bmatrix} = 3 \begin{pmatrix} 2a \\ 2a \\ a \end{pmatrix}$$

it is seen that the vector x_1 in the set

$$x_1 = \begin{pmatrix} 2a \\ 2a \\ a \end{pmatrix}, \qquad x_2 = \begin{bmatrix} b \\ -2b \\ 2b \end{bmatrix}, \qquad x_3 = \begin{pmatrix} -2c \\ c \\ 2c \end{pmatrix}$$

is an eigenvector corresponding to $\lambda_1 = 3$ for all $a \neq 0$. If $a = \pm \frac{1}{3}$, the vector is a unit vector. Similarly, if $b \neq 0$, it can be seen that x_2 is an eigenvalue of A corresponding to $\lambda_2 = 6$ and is a unit vector if $b = \pm \frac{1}{3}$. Likewise x_3 is an eigenvector of A corresponding to $\lambda_3 = 9$ whenever $c \neq 0$ and is a unit vector if $c = \pm \frac{1}{3}$. Observe that

$$x_1^* x_2 = 2ab - 4ab + 2ab = 0.$$

Consequently x_1 is orthogonal to x_2. Similarly x_1 is orthogonal to x_3, and x_2 is orthogonal to x_3.

These orthogonality relations hold in general as stated in

THEOREM 9.1

Let x *and* y *be linearly independent eigenvectors of a symmetric matrix* A, *and let* λ *and* μ *be the corresponding eigenvalues of* A. *If* $\lambda \neq \mu$, *then* x *and* y *are orthogonal. If* $\lambda = \mu$, *then every nonnull linear combination* z = ax + by *of* x *and* y *is an eigenvector of* A *corresponding to* λ. *This linear combination can be chosen so that* z *is orthogonal to* x.

By using the relations

$$Ax = \lambda x, \qquad Ay = \mu y \tag{9.4}$$

and the symmetry of A, it is seen that

$$\lambda y^* x = y^* A x = x^* A y = \mu x^* y = \mu y^* x.$$

Hence $(\lambda - \mu)y^*x = 0$. If $\lambda \neq \mu$, this is possible only if $y^*x = 0$, that is, only if x and y are orthogonal. This proves the first conclusion in the theorem.

Suppose next that $\mu = \lambda$. Then by (9.4) with $\mu = \lambda$ we have

$$a(Ax) + b(Ay) = A(ax + by) = a(\lambda x) + b(\lambda y) = \lambda(ax + by).$$

Consequently $z = ax + by$ is an eigenvector of A unless $z = 0$. Since x and y are linearly independent, $z = 0$ only if $a = b = 0$. By choosing $a = x^*y$ and $b = -x^*x$, we see that

$$x^*z = ax^*x + bx^*y = 0$$

and hence that z is orthogonal to x. This proves the theorem.

Heretofore we have tacitly assumed that the eigenvalues of a real symmetric matrix are real. Although this result will follow from the results given in Theorem 9.5, it is instructive to present an independent proof. This is given in

THEOREM 9.2

The eigenvalues of a real symmetric matrix A *are real.*

Suppose that there exists a complex eigenvalue $\lambda = \alpha + i\beta$ with α, β real and $\beta \neq 0$. Then the equations

$$(A - \lambda I)x = 0 \qquad \text{or} \qquad Ax = \lambda x$$

will have a nonnull complex solution $x = y + iz$, where y and z are real. Since A is real, we find, by taking conjugates, that

$$A\bar{x} = \bar{\lambda}\bar{x},$$

where $\bar{\lambda} = \alpha - i\beta$ and $\bar{x} = y - iz$. From this result we see that, if $x^* = y^* + iz^*$ and $\bar{x}^* = y^* - iz^*$, we have, by the symmetry of A,

$$\lambda\bar{x}^*x = \bar{x}^*(\lambda x) = \bar{x}^*Ax = x^*A\bar{x} = x^*(\bar{\lambda}\bar{x}) = \bar{\lambda}x^*\bar{x} = \bar{\lambda}\bar{x}^*x.$$

Hence

$$(\lambda - \bar{\lambda})\bar{x}^*x = 2i\beta(y^2 + z^2) = 0,$$

which is impossible. It follows that the matrix A cannot have a complex eigenvalue, as was to be proved.

We proceed to develop the eigenvalue theory for a symmetric matrix A by optimization techniques. To this end we begin with the equation

$$Ax = \lambda x,$$

which states that x is an eigenvector A provided that $x \neq 0$, as we shall suppose. Multiplying both members of this equation by x^*, we find that the corresponding eigenvalue λ is given by the formula

$$\lambda = \frac{x^* A x}{x^* x}. \tag{9.5}$$

This suggests that the eigenvalues and eigenvectors of A may be determined by the function

$$R(x) = \frac{x^* A x}{x^* x} = \frac{x^* A x}{|x|^2}, \qquad (x \neq 0), \tag{9.6}$$

called the *Rayleigh quotient of A*. This is indeed the case. We shall show that *a vector* x *is an eigenvector of* A *if and only if it is a critical point of* R, *that is, if and only if the gradient* R'(x) *of* R *at* x *vanishes.* Observing that

$$\frac{\partial}{\partial x^k} x^* A x = \frac{\partial}{\partial x^k} \sum_i \sum_j a_{ij} x^i x^j = \sum_j a_{kj} x^j + \sum_i a_{ik} x^i = 2 \sum_j a_{kj} x^j$$

$$\frac{\partial}{\partial x^k} x^* x = \frac{\partial}{\partial x^k} \left[(x^1)^2 + \cdots + (x^n)^2 \right] = 2x^k,$$

we see that

$$\frac{\partial R}{\partial x^k} = \frac{1}{x^* x} \frac{\partial}{\partial x^k} (x^* A x) - \frac{x^* A x}{(x^* x)^2} \frac{\partial (x^* x)}{\partial x^k} = \frac{2}{x^* x} \left[\sum_j a_{kj} x^j - R(x) x^k \right].$$

The gradient R' of R is accordingly given by the formula

$$R'(x) = \frac{2}{|x|^2} [A x - R(x) x]. \tag{9.7}$$

From (9.7) it is seen that if $x \neq 0$ then $R'(x) = 0$ if and only if $A x = R(x) x$, that is, if and only if x is an eigenvector of A with $\lambda = R(x)$ as the corresponding eigenvalue. This result can be summarized as follows.

The eigenvectors of a symmetric matrix A *are given by the critical points of the Rayleigh quotient* R *of* A. *The eigenvalues of* A *are the critical values of* R.

EXAMPLE 9.2

The Rayleigh quotient for the matrix A given by (9.3) is

$$R(x) = \frac{6(x^1)^2 + 5(x^2)^2 + 7(x^3)^2 - 4x^1 x^2 - 4x^1 x^3}{(x^1)^2 + (x^2)^2 + (x^3)^2}.$$

If we use the more customary notation (x,y,z) in place of (x^1, x^2, x^3), this becomes

$$R(x,y,z) = \frac{6x^2 + 5y^2 + 7z^2 - 4xy - 4xz}{x^2 + y^2 + z^2}.$$

Setting $r^2 = x^2 + y^2 + z^2$, we readily see that its partial derivatives R_x, R_y, and R_z are given by the formulas

$$R_x = \frac{2}{r^2}(6x - 2y - 2z - Rx),$$

$$R_y = \frac{2}{r^2}(-2x + 5y - Ry),$$

$$R_z = \frac{2}{r^2}(-2x + 7z - Rz).$$

If $x = 2$, $y = 2$, and $z = 1$, then $r^2 = 9$, $R = 3$, and $R_x = R_y = R_z = 0$, as can readily be verified. Similarly $R_x = R_y = R_z = 0$ when $x = 1$, $y = -2$, $z = 2$, and when $x = -2$, $y = 1$, $z = 2$. This verifies that the gradient of R vanishes for the eigenvectors of matrix (9.3).

It should be noted that the Rayleigh quotient $R(x)$ of A *is a homogeneous function of degree* zero, that is, for every vector $x \neq 0$

$$R(ax) = R(x) \qquad \text{for all } a \neq 0.$$

This follows because

$$R(ax) = \frac{(ax)^* A(ax)}{|ax|^2} = \frac{a^2 x^* A x}{a^2 |x|^2} = \frac{x^* A x}{|x|^2} = R(x).$$

Upon selecting $a = 1/|x|$, we have the useful identity

$$R\left(\frac{x}{|x|}\right) = R(x). \tag{9.8}$$

Since $x/|x|$ is a unit vector, it follows that *the range of* R(x) *on any linear subspace* $\mathcal{B}$ *(with* x = 0 *excluded) is determined by the unit vectors in* $\mathcal{B}$.
With the help of this result we can establish

LEMMA 9.1

Let $\mathcal{B}$ *be a linear subspace of our Euclidean space* $\mathcal{E}^n$. *There exist unit vectors* y *and* z *in* $\mathcal{B}$ *such that*

$$R(y) \leqslant R(x) \leqslant R(z) \qquad \textit{for all } x \neq 0 \textit{ in } \mathcal{B}.$$

The values $\mu = R(y)$ *and* $\nu = R(z)$ *are the minimum and maximum values of* R *on* $\mathscr{B}$ *(with* $x \neq 0$ *excluded). The gradients*

$$R'(y) = 2(Ay - \mu y), \qquad R'(z) = 2(Az - \nu z) \qquad (9.9)$$

of R *at* y *and* z *are orthogonal to* $\mathscr{B}$. *If* $\mu < \nu$, *then* y *is orthogonal to* z. *If* $\mu = \nu$ *and* dim $\mathscr{B} > 1$, *then* y *and* z *can be chosen to be orthogonal.*

The set S of all unit vectors in $\mathscr{B}$ is a compact set. Since $R(x)$ is continuous on S, it follows from Theorem 2.3 that $R(x)$ attains its minimum value μ on S at a point y in S and its maximum value ν at a point z in S. We have accordingly

$$\mu = R(y) \leqslant R(x) \leqslant R(z) = \nu$$

for all x in S and hence, by (9.8), for all $x \neq 0$ in $\mathscr{B}$. This proves the first conclusion in the lemma.

Observe that $\mathscr{B}$ is an m-plane through the origin, where m is the dimension of $\mathscr{B}$. By virtue of Theorem 6.1, the gradient $R'(y)$ of the minimum point y of R on $\mathscr{B}$ is orthogonal to $\mathscr{B}$. Similarly $R'(z)$ is orthogonal to $\mathscr{B}$. Since $|y| = |z| = 1$, the gradients $R'(y)$ and $R'(z)$ are given by formulas (9.9). Using the fact that z is orthogonal to $R'(y)$ and y is orthogonal to $R'(z)$, we obtain the relations

$$z^* R'(y) = 2(z^* A y - \mu z^* y) = 0, \qquad y^* R'(z) = 2(y^* A z - \nu y^* z) = 0.$$

By the symmetries $z^* A y = y^* A z$ and $z^* y = y^* z$, we conclude that

$$\mu z^* y = \nu z^* y.$$

If $\mu < \nu$, this is possible only if $z^* y = 0$, that is, if and only if y and z are orthogonal. If $\mu = \nu$, then $R(x) = \mu = \nu$ for all $x \neq 0$ in $\mathscr{B}$. Consequently every vector $x \neq 0$ in $\mathscr{B}$ maximizes and minimizes R on $\mathscr{B}$. If $m = \dim \mathscr{B} > 1$, there is accordingly a unit vector z in $\mathscr{B}$ orthogonal to y. Moreover z maximizes R on $\mathscr{B}$. This completes the proof of Lemma 2.1.

If $\mathscr{B} = \mathscr{E}^n$, then $R'(y)$ and $R'(z)$ are orthogonal to every vector x and hence are zero. It follows that y and z are eigenvectors of A. This yields

THEOREM 9.3

A minimum point y *of* R *on* $\mathscr{E}^n$ *(with* $x = 0$ *excluded) is an eigenvector of* A, *and* $\mu = R(y)$ *is the least eigenvalue of* A. *Similarly a maximum point* z *of* R *on* $\mathscr{E}^n$ *(with* $x = 0$ *excluded) is an eigenvector of* A, *and* $\nu = R(z)$ *is the greatest eigenvalue of* A.

EXAMPLE 9.3

As was seen earlier, the eigenvalues of the matrix

$$A = \begin{bmatrix} 6 & -2 & -2 \\ -2 & 5 & 0 \\ -2 & 0 & 7 \end{bmatrix}$$

are 3, 6, and 9. It follows that 3 is the minimum of $R(x)$ and that 9 is the maximum of $R(x)$ on $\mathcal{E}^3$. If we restrict x to lie on the subspace $\mathcal{B}$ of points x having $x^3 = 0$, the Rayleigh quotient of A takes the simpler form

$$R(x) = \frac{6(x^1)^2 - 4x^1x^2 + 5(x^2)^2}{(x^1)^2 + (x^2)^2}.$$

This is the Rayleigh quotient for the (2×2)-dimensional matrix

$$B = \begin{pmatrix} 6 & -2 \\ -2 & 5 \end{pmatrix}.$$

Its eigenvalues are $(11 \pm \sqrt{17})/2$. Hence $\lambda = (11 - \sqrt{17})/2 \leqslant R(x) \leqslant \mu = (11 + \sqrt{17})/2$ for all $x \neq 0$ on $\mathcal{B}$. The extreme values λ and μ of R on $\mathcal{B}$ are attained at the points

$$y = a\begin{bmatrix} 2 \\ 6-\lambda \\ 0 \end{bmatrix}, \qquad z = b\begin{bmatrix} 2 \\ 6-\mu \\ 0 \end{bmatrix} \qquad (a \neq 0, b \neq 0).$$

The gradients $R'(y)$ and $R'(z)$ are given by the formula

$$R'(y) = \frac{2a}{4 + (6-\lambda)^2}\begin{bmatrix} 0 \\ 0 \\ -4 \end{bmatrix}, \qquad R'(z) = \frac{2b}{4 + (6-\mu)^2}\begin{bmatrix} 0 \\ 0 \\ -4 \end{bmatrix}.$$

Clearly, $R'(y)$ and $R'(z)$ are orthogonal to $\mathcal{B}$, as implied by Lemma 2.1. It is easily verified that y and z are orthogonal.

The following lemma will be useful in the proof of the next theorem.

LEMMA 9.2

If a vector $y \neq 0$ *is orthogonal to an eigenvector* x, *then* Ay *and* R'(y) *are orthogonal to* x.

From the relations $Ax = \lambda x, y^*x = 0$ and the symmetry of A, it follows that

$$x^*Ay = y^*Ax = y^*(\lambda x) = \lambda y^*x = 0, \qquad x^*y = 0.$$

Hence y is orthogonal to Ax, and x is orthogonal to Ay. Moreover

$$x^*R'(y) = \frac{2}{y^*y}[x^*Ay - R(y)x^*y] = 0,$$

as was to be proved.

Recall that a set of vectors $x_1, \ldots, x_r$ is *orthonormal* if

$$x_\alpha^* x_\beta = \delta_{\alpha\beta} \qquad (\alpha, \beta = 1, \ldots, r),$$

where, as before, $\delta_{\alpha\alpha} = 1$ and $\delta_{\alpha\beta} = 0$ $(\alpha \neq \beta)$. With this concept in mind we can establish the following result.

THEOREM 9.4

Let $x_1, \ldots, x_{k-1} (k \leqslant n)$ *be an orthonormal set of eigenvectors, and let* $\mathcal{B}_k$ *be the class of all vectors orthogonal to these eigenvectors. There exists a unit vector* x_k *in* $\mathcal{B}_k$ *which minimizes* $R(x)$ *on* $\mathcal{B}_k$ *(with* $x = 0$ *excluded). The vector* x_k *is an eigenvector of* A *and the vectors* $x_1, \ldots, x_k$ *are orthonormal. Moreover*

$$x_\alpha^* A x_\beta = \lambda_\beta \delta_{\alpha\beta} \qquad (\alpha, \beta = 1, \ldots, k), \tag{9.10}$$

where $\lambda_\beta = R(x_\beta)$ *is the eigenvalue of* A *corresponding to* x_β.

It is easily verified that $\mathcal{B}_k$ is a linear subspace of $\mathcal{E}^n$. Since $x_1, \ldots, x_{k-1}$ are eigenvectors of A, it follows from Lemma 9.2 that the gradient $R'(x)$ of R is orthogonal to these vectors whenever x is. Consequently $R'(x)$ is in $\mathcal{B}_k$ for every vector x in $\mathcal{B}_k$. By Lemma 9.1 there is a unit vector x_k in $\mathcal{B}_k$ which minimizes R on $\mathcal{B}_k$. The gradient $R'(x_k)$ of R at x_k is accordingly orthogonal to $\mathcal{B}_k$. Since $R'(x_k)$ is in $\mathcal{B}_k$, it is orthogonal to itself. This is possible, however, only if $R'(x_k) = 0$. The vector x_k is therefore an eigenvector of A. Because of the orthogonality of x_k to the vectors $x_1, \ldots, x_{k-1}$, the vectors $x_1, \ldots, x_k$ are orthonormal. Since $\lambda_\beta = R(x_\beta)$ is the eigenvalue of A corresponding to x_β, we have

$$Ax_\beta = \lambda_\beta x_\beta \qquad (\beta = 1, \ldots, k).$$

Inasmuch as $x_\alpha^* x_\beta = \delta_{\alpha\beta}$, it follows from this relation that

$$x_\alpha^* A x_\beta = \lambda_\beta x_\alpha^* x_\beta = \lambda_\beta \delta_{\alpha\beta} \qquad (\alpha, \beta = 1, \ldots, k),$$

as was to be proved.

THEOREM 9.5

There exists an orthonormal set of eigenvectors $x_1, \ldots, x_n$ *of A. These eigenvectors can be chosen so that*

$$\lambda_1 \leqslant \lambda_2 \leqslant \cdots \leqslant \lambda_n, \tag{9.11}$$

where $\lambda_\beta = R(x_\beta)$ *is the eigenvalue of A corresponding to the eigenvector* x_β. *The vector* x_1 *minimizes the Rayleigh quotient R(x) of A, and the vector* x_n *maximizes R(x). The vector* x_k $(1 < k < n)$ *minimizes R(x) on the class* $\mathcal{B}_k$ *of all vectors orthogonal to* $x_1, \ldots, x_{k-1}$ *or equivalently, on the class generated by* $x_k, \ldots, x_n$. *Similarly the vector* x_k $(1 < k < n)$ *maximizes R(x) on the class* $\mathcal{C}_k$ *of vectors orthogonal to* $x_{k+1}, \ldots, x_n$ *or, equivalently, on the class generated by* $x_1, \ldots, x_k$.

Let x_1 be a unit vector which minimizes $R(x)$ on $\mathcal{E}^n$. By Theorem 9.3 the vector x_1 is an eigenvector of A corresponding to the eigenvalue $\lambda_1 = R(x_1)$. The vectors $x_2, \ldots, x_n$ are obtained succesively by choosing $x_k (k > 1)$ to be a unit vector minimizing $R(x)$ on the class of vectors $\mathcal{B}_k$ orthogonal to the vectors $x_1, \ldots, x_{k-1}$ previously chosen. By virtue of Theorem 9.4 the vectors $x_1, \ldots, x_n$ so obtained form an orthonormal set of eigenvectors of A. Moreover $\lambda_j = R(x_j) \leqslant \lambda_k = R(x_k)$ $(j < k)$, since $\mathcal{B}_k$ is a subspace of $\mathcal{B}_j$ and λ_j is the minimum of R on $\mathcal{B}_j$. Because the vectors $x_k, \ldots, x_n$ are orthogonal to $x_1, \ldots, x_{k-1}$, they generate $\mathcal{B}_k$.

Observe that since $x_1, \ldots, x_n$ are orthonormal they generate $\mathcal{E}^n$. If x is in $\mathcal{E}^n$, we have

$$x = x_1 c_1 + \cdots + x_n c_n, \qquad c_k = \langle x_k, x \rangle$$

and hence also

$$Ax = \lambda_1 x_1 c_1 + \cdots + \lambda_n x_n c_n.$$

Moreover

$$x^* A x = \lambda_1 c_1^2 + \cdots + \lambda_n c_n^2, \qquad x^* x = c_1^2 + \cdots + c_n^2.$$

Consequently

$$R(x) = \frac{\lambda_1 c_1^2 + \cdots + \lambda_n c_n^2}{c_1^2 + \cdots + c_n^2}.$$

From these formulas it is seen that, if $x \neq 0$ is orthogonal to $x_{k+1}, \ldots, x_n$, then $c_j = \langle x_j, x \rangle = 0$ $(j = k+1, \ldots, n)$ and

$$R(x) = \frac{\lambda_1 c_1^2 + \cdots + \lambda_k c_k^2}{c_1^2 + \cdots + c_k^2} \leq \lambda_k,$$

the equality holding if x is a multiple $c_k x_k$ of x_k. This proves the last conclusion in the theorem.

We are now in a position to prove the following *min-max and max-min principle for the eigenvalues of* A.

THEOREM 9.6

Let $\lambda_1 \leq \lambda_2 \leq \cdots \leq \lambda_n$ *be the* n *eigenvalues of* A, *and let* R(x) *be the Rayleigh quotient of* A. *Then for each integer* k

$$\lambda_k = \min_{\mathscr{C}^k} \left[\max_{\substack{x \in \mathscr{C}^k \\ x \neq 0}} R(x) \right] = \max_{\mathscr{C}^{n-k+1}} \left[\min_{\substack{x \in \mathscr{C}^{n-k+1} \\ x \neq 0}} R(x) \right], \qquad (9.12)$$

where $\mathscr{C}^k$ *denotes a linear subspace of* $\mathscr{E}^n$ *of dimension* k.

Let $x_1, \ldots, x_n$ be an orthonormal set of eigenvectors related to $\lambda_1, \ldots, \lambda_n$ as described in Theorem 9.5. We have already seen that λ_k is the maximum of $R(x)$ on the k-dimensional space $\mathscr{C}^k$ generated by $x_1, \ldots, x_k$. In this event we have $\lambda_k = R(x_k) = \max R(x)$ on $\mathscr{C}^k$.. Consider next an arbitrary k-dimensional subspace $\mathscr{C}^k$. Since $\mathscr{C}^k$ is of dimension k, there is a vector $y \neq 0$ in $\mathscr{C}^k$ orthogonal to the $k-1$ eigenvectors $x_1, \ldots, x_{k-1}$. By virtue of Theorem 9.5 it follows that $R(y) \geq R(x_k) = \lambda_k$. This establishes the first equality in (9.12). The second equality can be established by a similar argument. It also follows from the first by observing that $-\lambda_n \leq -\lambda_{n-1}, \ldots, \leq -\lambda_1$ are the eigenvalues of $-A$.

Let X be the matrix whose column vectors $x_1, \ldots, x_n$ form the orthonormal set of eigenvectors of A described in Theorem 9.5. The relations

$$Ax_\beta = \lambda_\beta x_\beta, \qquad x_\alpha^* x_\beta = \delta_{\alpha\beta}$$

are equivalent to the relations

$$AX = X\Lambda, \qquad X^*X = I, \tag{9.13}$$

where I is the identity matrix and Λ is a diagonal matrix whose diagonal elements are the eigenvalues $\lambda_1, \ldots, \lambda_n$ corresponding to the eigenvectors $x_1, \ldots, x_n$. Since $X^*X = I$, it follows that $X^* = X^{-1}$ and hence that X is an orthogonal matrix. Using relations (9.13), we see that

$$X^*AX = \Lambda, \qquad A = X\Lambda X^* \tag{9.14}$$

Consequently A is diagonalized by the orthogonal matrix X. Conversely, if an orthogonal matrix X and a diagonal matrix Λ are such that $X^*AX = \Lambda$, (9.13) and (9.14) hold. Moreover the column vectors $x_1, \ldots, x_n$ of X are orthonormal eigenvectors of A whose corresponding eigenvalues are the diagonal elements $\lambda_1, \ldots, \lambda_n$ of Λ.

As a consequence of equations (9.14) we see that

$$A^2 = X\Lambda X^* X\Lambda X^* = X\Lambda^2 X^*,$$

and in general

$$A^k = X\Lambda^k X^*.$$

The matrix Λ^k is a diagonal matrix whose diagonal elements are the kth powers $\lambda_1^k, \ldots, \lambda_n^k$ of the eigenvalues $\lambda_1, \ldots, \lambda_n$ of A. If A is nonnegative, $\lambda_1, \ldots, \lambda_n$ are also nonnegative. In this event we denote by $\Lambda^{1/k}$ the matrix whose diagonal elements are the nonnegative kth roots $\lambda_1^{1/k}, \ldots, \lambda_n^{1/k}$ of $\lambda_1, \ldots, \lambda_n$. The matrix

$$A^{1/k} = X\Lambda^{1/k}X^*$$

is a nonnegative symmetric matrix whose kth power is A. It is called the *kth root of* A. If A is nonsingular, $\lambda_1, \ldots, \lambda_n$ are different from zero, and the diagonal matrix Λ^{-1} whose elements are the reciprocals $1/\lambda_1, \ldots, 1/\lambda_n$ is the inverse of Λ. Moreover,

$$A^{-1} = X\Lambda^{-1}X^*$$

is the inverse of A. The eigenvalues of A^{-1} are the reciprocals of the eigenvalues of A. Similarly $A^{-k} = (A^{-1})^k$ is the inverse of A^k. If $p(\lambda)$ is the polynomial

$$p(\lambda) = c_0 + c_1\lambda + c_2\lambda^2 + \cdots + c_k\lambda^k,$$

the matrix

$$p(A)=c_0I+c_1A+c_2A^2+\cdots+c_kA^k$$

has

$$\mu_j=p(\lambda_j)=c_0+c_1\lambda_j+c_2\lambda_j^2+\cdots+c_k\lambda_j^k \qquad (j=1,\ldots,n)$$

as its eigenvalues. If $p(\lambda)=\Delta(\lambda)$, the characteristic polynomial of A, then $\Delta(A)=0$. The eigenvectors of A are also eigenvectors of all matrices of this type.

EXERCISES

1. Find the eigenvalues and eigenvectors of the matrices

$$A=\begin{pmatrix} 0 & -2 & -2 \\ -2 & -1 & 0 \\ -2 & 0 & 1 \end{pmatrix}, \quad B=\begin{pmatrix} 1 & -1 & 3 \\ -1 & 5 & -1 \\ 3 & -1 & 1 \end{pmatrix}$$

Answer: $-3,0,3$ are eigenvalues of A, and $3,6,-2$ are eigenvalues of B.

2. Given the matrices

$$A=\begin{bmatrix} 5 & -1 & -2 & 0 \\ -1 & 5 & 0 & -2 \\ -2 & 0 & 5 & -1 \\ 0 & -2 & -1 & 5 \end{bmatrix}, \quad X=\begin{bmatrix} 0.5 & -0.5 & -0.5 & 0.5 \\ 0.5 & 0.5 & -0.5 & -0.5 \\ 0.5 & -0.5 & 0.5 & -0.5 \\ 0.5 & 0.5 & 0.5 & 0.5 \end{bmatrix}$$

show that X is an orthogonal matrix that diagonalizes A. Find the eigenvalues and eigenvectors of A and the characteristic polynomial of A.

3. Show that a (2×2)-dimensional orthogonal matrix X is expressible in the form

$$X=\begin{pmatrix} \cos\theta & \sin\theta \\ -\sin\theta & \cos\theta \end{pmatrix}$$

for a suitable choice of θ.

4. Show that the product of two orthogonal matrices is an orthogonal matrix. Use this result to prove that the product

$$\begin{pmatrix} \cos\theta & \sin\theta & 0 \\ -\sin\theta & \cos\theta & 0 \\ 0 & 0 & 1 \end{pmatrix}\begin{pmatrix} \cos\varphi & 0 & \sin\varphi \\ 0 & 1 & 0 \\ -\sin\varphi & 0 & \cos\varphi \end{pmatrix}$$

is an orthogonal matrix.

5. Show that, if Y is an $(n \times n)$-dimensional orthogonal matrix, then

$$X = \frac{1}{\sqrt{2}} \begin{pmatrix} Y & Y \\ -Y & Y \end{pmatrix}$$

is a $(2n \times 2n)$-dimensional orthogonal matrix. With the help of this result construct $(2n \times 2n)$-dimensional orthogonal matrices for $n = 1, 2, 3, 4$.

6. Construct a (3×3)-dimensional matrix with $\lambda_1 = -2$, $\lambda_2 = 1$, $\lambda_3 = 3$ as eigenvalues and

$$x_1 = \begin{pmatrix} 1 \\ 2 \\ 2 \end{pmatrix}, \qquad x_2 = \begin{pmatrix} 2 \\ -2 \\ 1 \end{pmatrix}, \qquad x_3 = \begin{pmatrix} -2 \\ -1 \\ 2 \end{pmatrix}$$

as eigenvectors. *Hint*: Use formula (9.14).

7. Apply the results given above to construct a matrix A with prescribed eigenvalues and eigenvectors. Construct a $(n \times n)$-dimensional nondiagonal matrix with prescribed eigenvalues for $n = 4, 6, 8$.

8. Show that for every vector $x \neq 0$ the gradient $R'(x)$ of R at x is orthogonal to x.

9. Show that the gradient R' of R is homogeneous of degree -1, that is, $R'(ax) = a^{-1}R'(x)$ for all $x \neq 0$ and all $a \neq 0$.

10. Let x and y be mutually orthogonal unit eigenvectors of A. Let $\lambda = R(x)$ and $\mu = R(y)$ be the corresponding eigenvalues. Show that $R(x+y) = \frac{1}{2}(\lambda + \mu)$. Show that $R'(x+y) = 0$ if and only if $\lambda = \mu$.

11. In the two-dimensional case let $F(x,y) = 5x^2 - 4xy + 5y^2$, $G(x,y) = x^2 + y^2$. Find the maximum and minimum values of $R = F/G$. Find the maximum and minimum values of $F(x,y)$ on the unit circle $G(x,y) = 1$. Find the maximum and minimum values of $1/G(x,y)$ on the ellipse $F(x,y) = 1$.

12. A vector $x \neq 0$ in a linear subspace $\mathscr{B}$ of $\mathscr{E}^n$ will be said to be an *eigenvector* of a symmetric matrix A on $\mathscr{B}$ if there is a number λ such that the vector $Ax - \lambda x$ is orthogonal to $\mathscr{B}$. The number λ is the corresponding *eigenvalue* of A on $\mathscr{B}$. Show that a vector $x \neq 0$ in $\mathscr{B}$ is an eigenvector of A on $\mathscr{B}$ if and only if the gradient $R'(x)$ of the Rayleigh quotient R of A is orthogonal to $\mathscr{B}$. Show that $\lambda = R(x)$ is the eigenvalue of A on $\mathscr{B}$ corresponding to an eigenvector x on $\mathscr{B}$. Show that a vector $y \neq 0$ in $\mathscr{B}$ that maximizes or minimizes R on $\mathscr{B}$ is an eigenvector of A on $\mathscr{B}$ (see Section 3, Chapter 2).

13. Let D be an $(n \times r)$-dimensional matrix of rank $r < n$. Let $\mathscr{B}$ be the $(n-r)$-dimensional subspace of all x in $\mathscr{E}^n$ such that $D^*x = 0$. Set $k = n - r$. Show that λ is an eigenvalue of a symmetric matrix A on $\mathscr{B}$ if and only if it is a zero of the determinant

$$\Delta_k(\lambda) = \begin{vmatrix} A - \lambda I & D \\ D^* & 0 \end{vmatrix}.$$

Show that $\Delta_k(\lambda)$ is a polynomial in λ of degree k. Show that A possesses a set of k orthonormal eigenvectors $x_1,\ldots,x_k$ on $\mathcal{B}$ corresponding to the k eigenvalues $\lambda_1 \leqslant \lambda_2 \leqslant \cdots \leqslant \lambda_k$ of A on $\mathcal{B}$.

14. Let Y be an $(n \times k)$-dimensional matrix whose column vectors $y_1,\ldots,y_k$ form an orthonormal basis for a k-dimensional subspace $\mathcal{B}$ of $\mathcal{E}^n$. Show that λ is an eigenvalue of A on $\mathcal{B}$ if and only if it is an eigenvalue of the $(k \times k)$-dimensional matrix $A_k = Y^*AY$ in the usual sense.

15. Let A and Y be the first two of the matrices

$$A = \begin{pmatrix} 1 & 0 & 0 \\ 0 & 2 & 0 \\ 0 & 0 & 3 \end{pmatrix}, \quad Y = \begin{bmatrix} \dfrac{1}{\sqrt{2}} & \dfrac{1}{\sqrt{6}} \\ -\dfrac{1}{\sqrt{2}} & \dfrac{1}{\sqrt{6}} \\ 0 & -\dfrac{2}{\sqrt{6}} \end{bmatrix}, \quad Y^*AY = \begin{bmatrix} \dfrac{3}{2} & -\dfrac{1}{2\sqrt{3}} \\ -\dfrac{1}{2\sqrt{3}} & \dfrac{5}{2} \end{bmatrix},$$

and verify the computation of Y^*AY. Show that the column vectors of Y generate the 2-space $\mathcal{B}$ of all vectors

$$x = \begin{pmatrix} u \\ v \\ w \end{pmatrix}$$

having $u+v+w=0$. Obtain the eigenvalues $\mu_1 = 2 - 1/\sqrt{3}$, $\mu_2 = 2 + 1/\sqrt{3}$ of A on $\mathcal{B}$. Show that μ_1 and μ_2 are the eigenvalues of Y^*AY. Verify that μ_1 and μ_2 are the zeros of the polynomial

$$\begin{vmatrix} 1-\lambda & 0 & 0 & 1 \\ 0 & 2-\lambda & 0 & 1 \\ 0 & 0 & 3-\lambda & 1 \\ 1 & 1 & 1 & 0 \end{vmatrix}.$$

Show that the vector x_1 having $x_1^* = (\sqrt{2} + 2\sqrt{\frac{2}{3}}, -2 - \sqrt{\frac{2}{3}}, -\sqrt{\frac{2}{3}})$ is the eigenvector of A on $\mathcal{B}$ corresponding to μ_1. Verify directly that the gradient $R'(x_1)$ of the Rayleigh quotient R of A at x_1 is orthogonal to $\mathcal{B}$ and that $R(x_1) = \mu_1$. Find an eigenvector x_2 of A on $\mathcal{B}$ corresponding to μ_2.

16. Let $\mathcal{B}^k$ and $\mathcal{B}^{k+1}$ be linear subspaces of $\mathcal{E}^n$ of dimensions k and $k+1$ such that $\mathcal{B}^k \subset \mathcal{B}^{k+1}$. Let $\lambda_1 \leqslant \lambda_2 \leqslant \cdots \leqslant \lambda_k$ be the eigenvalues of A on $\mathcal{B}^k$, and let $\mu_1 \leqslant \mu_2 \leqslant \cdots \leqslant \mu_{k+1}$ be the eigenvalues of A on $\mathcal{B}^{k+1}$. Establish the relations $\mu_j \leqslant \lambda_j \leqslant \mu_{j+1}$ $(j=1,\ldots,k)$.

17. Given a symmetric matrix $A = (a_{ij})$ $(i,j=1,\ldots,n)$, let A_k be the matrix $A_k = (a_{\alpha\beta})$ $(\alpha,\beta=1,\ldots,k \leqslant n)$. Show that the eigenvalues $\lambda_1,\ldots,\lambda_k$ of A_k separate the eigenvalues $\mu_1,\ldots,\mu_{k+1}$ of A_{k+1} in the sense that they can be ordered so that $\mu_j \leqslant \lambda_j \leqslant \mu_{j+1}$ $(j=1,\ldots,k)$.

18. Verify the result described in Exercise 17 for the matrix A given in Exercise 2.

19. Show that $\det A = 0$ if and only if $\lambda = 0$ is an eigenvalue of A. Show that the product $\lambda_1 \lambda_2 \cdots \lambda_n$ of the eigenvalues of A is equal to the determinant of A. Show that the sum $\lambda_1 + \cdots + \lambda_n$ of its eigenvalues is equal to the sum $T = a_{11} + a_{22} + \cdots + a_{nn}$ of the diagonal elements of A. The sum T is called the *trace* of A.

20. Show that the number of negative eigenvalues of A on $\mathcal{E}^n$ is equal to the dimension of a maximal linear subspace $\mathcal{B}$ on $\mathcal{E}^n$ on which the quadratic form $J(x) = x^* A x$ is negative. Here an eigenvalue is counted a number of times equal to its multiplicity as a root of $\Delta(\lambda) = |A - \lambda I| = 0$. For example, if $\Delta(\lambda) = 0$ has $-2, -1, -1, 0, 5$ as its roots, it has three negative roots.

21. Let z_0 be a vector that is not orthogonal to the eigenvectors corresponding to the largest eigenvalue ν of A. Let $\{z_q\}$ be the sequence defined by the algorithm

$$z_q = \rho_q A z_{q-1} \qquad (q = 1, 2, 3, \ldots),$$

where ρ_q is a positive scale factor. Show that

$$\lim_{q \to \infty} R(z_q) = \nu.$$

Show that, if ρ_q is chosen so that the z_q is a unit vector, then $z_q \to z$, where z is an eigenvector corresponding to ν. What happens if z_0 is orthogonal to the eigenvectors corresponding to ν? This procedure is called the *power method* for finding the eigenvalues of A. This is so because z_q is of the form $z_q = \sigma_q A^k z_0$, where $\sigma_q = \rho_1 \rho_2 \cdots \rho_q$.

22. Let A be matrix (9.3). The surface

$$6x^2 + 5y^2 + 7z^2 - 4xy - 4xz = 16$$

is an ellipsoid. Show that the eigenvectors of A determine the principal axes of this ellipsoid. Show that the lengths of the semiaxes are $4/\sqrt{\lambda}$, where λ ranges over the eigenvalues of A. The plane $\mathcal{B}$ defined by the equation $x - y + z = 0$ cuts the ellipsoid in an ellipse. Show that the eigenvectors of A relative to $\mathcal{B}$ determine the principal axes of this ellipse and that the lengths of its semiaxes are determined by the eigenvalues of A relative to $\mathcal{B}$.

23. Generalize the result given in Exercise 22 to the n-dimensional case.

2

APPLICATIONS TO MATRICES AND QUADRATIC FORMS

1. INTRODUCTION

The present chapter is a digression from the main theme of this book. Accordingly the reader may proceed directly to Chapter 3 without loss of continuity in the theory of optimization. However, a reader concerned with further applications of unconstrained and linearly constrained optimization may wish to pursue the ideas presented here before considering the general problem of minimizing a function subject to nonlinear equality or inequality constraints.

In this chapter we pursue the theory of eigenvalues of a symmetric matrix relative to another such matrix. We consider also the eigenvalues of symmetric matrices and quadratic forms on subspaces. These results are extended to the study of a special quadratic form of arcs, thereby illustrating eigenvalue theory of quadratic forms on an infinite dimensional space.

In addition we discuss briefly the principal value theory for an arbitrary matrix. This leads us to a consideration of the pseudoinverse of a matrix. It is shown that these concepts can be studied by the use of optimization procedures. Because, as mentioned above, this chapter is a digression, some of the material is presented in condensed form.

2. RELATIVE EIGENVALUES AND EIGENVECTORS

The results obtained in Section 9 of Chapter 1 have a useful extension in which a positive symmetric matrix B plays the role of the identity I. Recall that B is positive if $x^*Bx>0$ for all $x\neq0$. Let A be a second symmetric matrix; the matrix A need not be positive. A vector $x\neq0$ will be said to be an *eigenvector of* A *relative to* B if there is a number λ such that

$$Ax=\lambda Bx. \tag{2.1}$$

The number λ is called the *eigenvalue of* A *relative to* B corresponding to x. Conversely λ is an eigenvalue of A relative to B if there is a vector $x\neq0$ such that (2.1) holds. The vector x is called the *eigenvector corresponding to* λ. If relation (2.1) holds for a number λ and a vector $x\neq0$, then λ must be a zero of the determinant

$$\Delta(\lambda)=|A-\lambda B|.$$

By the argument given in Chapter 1, Section 9, it is seen that the polynomial $\Delta(\lambda)$ has no complex roots. Consequently, if $\Delta(\lambda)=0$, then λ is real and equation (2.1) has a solution $x\neq0$.

The ratio

$$R(x)=\frac{x^*Ax}{x^*Bx} \tag{2.2}$$

is called the *Rayleigh quotient* of A *relative* to B. In dealing with Rayleigh quotients it is understood that $x\neq0$. If x is an eigenvector of A relative to B, then, by (2.1),

$$R(x)=\frac{x^*Ax}{x^*Bx}=\frac{\lambda x^*Bx}{x^*Bx}=\lambda$$

is the corresponding eigenvalue. A simple computation yields the formula

$$R'(x)=\frac{2}{x^*Bx}[Ax-R(x)Bx] \tag{2.3}$$

for the gradient R' of R. From this formula it follows that $R'(x)=0$ if and only if $Ax=R(x)Bx$, that is, if and only if x is an eigenvector of A relative to B. *The eigenvectors of* A *relative to* B *are therefore the critical points of the Rayleigh quotient* R, *and the eigenvalues of* A *relative to* B *are the critical values of* R.

As an example, consider the case in which

$$A=\begin{bmatrix}6&2&4\\2&6&0\\4&0&6\end{bmatrix}, \quad B=\begin{bmatrix}3&1&1\\1&3&-1\\1&-1&3\end{bmatrix}.$$

In this event $\Delta(\lambda)$ is the polynomial

$$\Delta(\lambda) = \begin{vmatrix} 6-3\lambda & 2-\lambda & 4-\lambda \\ 2-\lambda & 6-3\lambda & \lambda \\ 4-\lambda & \lambda & 6-3\lambda \end{vmatrix},$$

that is,

$$\Delta(\lambda) = 16(1-\lambda)(2-\lambda)(3-\lambda).$$

Consequently $\lambda_1 = 1$, $\lambda_2 = 2$, $\lambda_3 = 3$ are the eigenvalues of A relative to B. From the relations

$$\begin{bmatrix} 6 & 2 & 4 \\ 2 & 6 & 0 \\ 4 & 0 & 6 \end{bmatrix} \begin{bmatrix} 0 \\ 0.5 \\ 0.5 \end{bmatrix} = \begin{bmatrix} 3 \\ 3 \\ 3 \end{bmatrix}, \qquad \begin{bmatrix} 3 & 1 & 1 \\ -1 & 3 & -1 \\ 1 & -1 & 3 \end{bmatrix} \begin{bmatrix} 0 \\ 0.5 \\ 0.5 \end{bmatrix} = \begin{bmatrix} 1 \\ 1 \\ 1 \end{bmatrix},$$

it is seen that the vector x_3 in the set

$$x_1 = \begin{bmatrix} 0.5 \\ 0 \\ -0.5 \end{bmatrix}, \qquad x_2 = \begin{bmatrix} 0.5 \\ -0.5 \\ 0 \end{bmatrix}, \qquad x_3 = \begin{bmatrix} 0 \\ 0.5 \\ 0.5 \end{bmatrix}$$

is an eigenvector of A relative to B corresponding to the eigenvalue $\lambda_3 = 3$. In a similar manner it is seen that x_1 and x_2 are eigenvectors corresponding to λ_1 and λ_2, respectively. Moreover

$$x_i^* B x_i = 1, \qquad R(x_i) = x_i^* A x_i = \lambda_i \qquad (i = 1, 2, 3).$$

Returning to the general case, it should be observed that the Rayleigh quotient $R(x)$ of A relative to B is homogeneous of order zero, that is,

$$R(ax) = R(x)$$

for all $a \neq 0$. This is an immediate consequence of formula (2.2) for R. It follows that the values of the function $R(x)$ are completely determined by the points x on the ellipsoid

$$x^* B x = 1.$$

With this result in mind we can establish

THEOREM 2.1

There exist points y *and* z *at which* R *attains its minimum and maximum values. We have*

$$R(y) \leqslant R(x) \leqslant R(z) \tag{2.4}$$

for all $x \neq 0$. *The vectors* y *and* z *are critical points of* R. *The value* $\mu = R(y)$ *is the least eigenvalue, and* $\nu = R(z)$ *is the largest eigenvalue of* A *relative to* B. *The vectors* y *and* z *satisfy the relations*

$$Ay = \mu By, \qquad Az = \nu Bz. \tag{2.5}$$

If $\mu < \nu$, *then*

$$y^*Az = 0, \qquad y^*Bz = 0. \tag{2.6}$$

If $\mu = \nu$ *and* $n > 1$, *then* y *and* z *can be chosen so that relations* (2.6) *hold. Furthermore, the vectors* y *and* z *can be chosen so that*

$$y^*By = 1, \qquad z^*Bz = 1. \tag{2.7}$$

As was seen above, the values of R are determined by the points x on the ellipsoid $x^*Bx = 1$. Since this ellipsoid is compact (bounded and closed), it follows from Theorem 2.3 in Chapter 1 that there exist points y and z on this ellipsoid that minimize and maximize R. Hence (2.4) holds when $x^*Bx = 1$. Since R is homogeneous of order zero, relations (2.4) hold for all $x \neq 0$. By Theorems 3.1 and 3.3 in Chapter 1 we have $R'(y) = R'(z) = 0$. The vectors y and z are accordingly eigenvectors of A relative to B. Moreover $\mu = R(y)$ and $\nu = R(z)$ are the corresponding eigenvalues. If x is any eigenvector, the corresponding eigenvalue is $\lambda = R(x)$. We have, by (2.4), $\mu \leqslant \lambda \leqslant \nu$. Consequently μ is the least eigenvalue and ν is the greatest eigenvalue of A relative to B. By the use of relations (2.5) and the symmetry of A and B we see that

$$\mu z^* By = z^* Ay = y^* Az = \nu y^* Bz = \nu z^* By.$$

If $\nu > \mu$, this is possible only if (2.6) holds. If $\nu = \mu$, then every nonzero vector minimizes and maximizes R. If $n > 1$, we can select y and z so that relations (2.6) and (2.7) hold, as can readily be verified.

In the proof of the next theorem we shall make use of the directional derivative

$$R'(x,y) = \frac{d}{d\epsilon} R(x + \epsilon y) \Big|_{\epsilon = 0}$$

of R at x in the direction y. As was seen in Section 3 of Chapter 1 with $h = y$, we have

$$R'(x,y) = \langle R'(x), y \rangle = R'(x)^* y = y^* R'(x).$$

Using (2.2) and (2.3), we find that

$$R'(x,y) = \frac{2}{x^*Bx}[Ax - R(x)Bx]^*y. \tag{2.8}$$

Observe that $R'(x,y) = 0$ for all y if and only if $R'(x) = 0$, that is, if and only if x is an eigenvector of A relative to B.

THEOREM 2.2

Let $x_1, \ldots, x_{k-1}$ *be eigenvectors of* A *relative to* B *such that*

$$x_\alpha^* Bx_\beta = \delta_{\alpha\beta} \qquad (\alpha, \beta = 1, \ldots, k-1), \tag{2.9}$$

where $\delta_{\alpha\alpha} = 1$, $\delta_{\alpha\beta} = 0$ $(\alpha \neq \beta)$. *Let* $\mathcal{B}_k$ *be the class of all* y *having*

$$x_\alpha^* By = 0 \qquad (\alpha = 1, \ldots, k-1). \tag{2.10}$$

There exists a vector x_k *in* $\mathcal{B}_k$ *such that* $x_k^* Bx_k = 1$ *and such that* $R(x_k)$ $\leqslant R(y)$ *for all* $y \neq 0$ *in* $\mathcal{B}_k$. *The vector* x_k *is an eigenvector of* A *relative to* B, *and relations* (2.9) *hold with* α *and* β *in the range* $1, \ldots, k$.

Again the set of all vectors y in $\mathcal{B}_k$ having $y^*By = 1$ is compact. There is accordingly a point x_k in $\mathcal{B}_k$ having $x_k^* Bx_k = 1$ which minimizes R on $\mathcal{B}_k$ with $y = 0$ excluded. By Theorem 6.2 in Chapter 1 there exist multipliers $a_1, \ldots, a_{k-1}$ such that the gradient of

$$F(x) = R(x) - \sum_{\alpha=1}^{k-1} a_\alpha x_\alpha^* Bx$$

is zero at x_k or, equivalently, such that

$$F'(x_k,y) = R'(x_k,y) - \sum_\alpha a_\alpha x_\alpha^* By = 0 \qquad (\alpha = 1, \ldots, k-1) \tag{2.11}$$

for all vectors y. Choosing $y = x_\beta$ and using (2.9) with (2.8), we find that

$$a_\beta = R'(x_k, x_\beta) = 2[x_k^* Ax_\beta - R(x_k)x_k^* Bx_\beta].$$

Since x_β is an eigenvector, we have

$$x_k^* Ax_\beta = R(x_\beta)x_k^* Bx_\beta.$$

But x_k is in $\mathcal{B}_k$, so that, $x_k^* Bx_\beta = x_\beta^* Bx_k = 0$. It follows that

$$a_\beta = R'(x_k, x_\beta) = 0 \qquad (\beta = 1, \ldots, k-1).$$

Relation (2.11) therefore tells us that $R'(x_k, y) = 0$ for all y and hence that $R'(x_k) = 0$. The vector x_k is accordingly an eigenvector of A relative to B and has the properties described in the theorem.

THEOREM 2.3

There exist n *eigenvectors* $x_1, \ldots, x_n$ *of* A *relative to* B *such that*

$$x_\alpha^* B x_\beta = \delta_{\alpha\beta} \qquad (\alpha, \beta = 1, \ldots, n) \tag{2.12}$$

and such that

$$\lambda_1 \leqslant \lambda_2 \leqslant \cdots \leqslant \lambda_n, \tag{2.13}$$

where $\lambda_\beta = R(x_\beta)$ *is the eigenvalue corresponding to* x_β. *We have*

$$A x_\beta = \lambda_\beta B x_\beta \qquad (\beta = 1, \ldots, n) \tag{2.14}$$

and

$$x_\alpha^* A x_\beta = \lambda_\beta \delta_{\alpha\beta} \qquad (\alpha, \beta = 1, \ldots, n). \tag{2.15}$$

Let $\mathcal{B}_1 = \mathcal{E}^n$, *and let* $\mathcal{B}_k$ ($k > 1$) *be all* y *having*

$$x_\alpha^* B y = 0 \qquad (\alpha = 1, \ldots, k - 1). \tag{2.16}$$

The vector x_k *minimizes* R *on* $\mathcal{B}_k$ *with* y = 0 *deleted.*

This result is an immediate consequence of Theorems 2.1 and 2.2 by selecting $\mathcal{B}_1 = \mathcal{E}^n$, $\mathcal{B}_2, \ldots, \mathcal{B}_{n-1}$ as described in Theorem 2.3 and selecting x_k on $x_k^* B x_k = 1$ at each step so as to minimize $R(x)$ on $\mathcal{B}_k$ with $x = 0$ excluded.

The value λ_k in (2.13) will be called the kth *eigenvalue* of A *relative to* B. An alternative characterization of λ_k is given in

THEOREM 2.4

Let $\mathcal{C}^k$ *denote a* k-*dimensional linear subspace of* $\mathcal{E}$. *Then the* k*th eigenvalue* λ_k *and* (n − k + 1)th *eigenvalue* λ_{n-k+1} *of* A *relative to* B *is given by the formulas*

$$\lambda_k = \min_{\mathcal{C}^k} \left[\max_{x \in \mathcal{C}^k} R(x) \right],$$

$$\lambda_{n-k+1} = \max_{\mathcal{C}^k} \left[\min_{x \in \mathcal{C}^k} R(x) \right], \tag{2.17}$$

where R(x) *is the Rayleigh quotient* (2.2).

It is understood that $x = 0$ is excluded in formula (2.17). As a first step let $x_1, \ldots, x_k$ be the eigenvectors corresponding to $\lambda_1, \ldots, \lambda_k$ as described in Theorem 2.3. Let $\mathcal{C}^k$ be the k-dimensional subspace of $\mathcal{E}^n$ generated by $x_1, \ldots, x_k$. A vector x in $\mathcal{C}_k$ is accordingly of the form

$$x = a_1 x_1 + \cdots + a_k x_k.$$

By virtue of (2.17) and (2.14) we have

$$R(x) = \frac{\lambda_1 a_1^2 + \cdots + \lambda_k a_k^2}{a_1^2 + \cdots + a_k^2} \leqslant \lambda_k,$$

the equality holding when $a_i = 0$ $(i < k)$, $a_k = 1$. Hence λ_k is the maximum of $R(x)$ on the manifold $\mathcal{C}^k$ chosen in this manner.

Consider next an arbitrary k-dimensional manifold $\mathcal{C}^k$. Let $y_1, \ldots, y_k$ be a set of generators of $\mathcal{C}^k$. Select numbers $a_1, \ldots, a_k$, not all zero, such that

$$\sum_\beta x_\alpha^* B y_\beta a_\beta = 0 \qquad (\alpha = 1, \ldots, k-1; \beta = 1, \ldots, k).$$

The vector $y = \sum y_\beta a_\beta$ is a nonnull vector satisfying the relations

$$x_\alpha^* B y = 0 \qquad (\alpha = 1, \ldots, k-1).$$

Hence y is in the class $\mathcal{B}_k$ described in Theorem 2.3. We have accordingly

$$R(y) \geqslant R(x_k) = \lambda_k.$$

We conclude that

$$\lambda_k \leqslant \max_{y \in \mathcal{C}^k} R(y)$$

for every manifold $\mathcal{C}^k$ of dimension k. Similarly

$$\lambda_{n-k+1} \geqslant \min_{y \in \mathcal{C}^k} R(y),$$

the equality holding if $\mathcal{C}^k$ is generated by $x_{n-k+1}, x_{n-k+2}, \ldots, x_n$. This can be verified by an argument like that given above or by interchanging the roles of maxima and minima.

When $B = I$, the identity, the above results take the form given in Section 9 of Chapter 1. These results can also be put into a form which has an immediate generalization in the infinite dimensional case. This is done by expressing the results in terms of two quadratic forms:

$$J(x) = x^*Ax, \qquad K(x) = x^*Bx.$$

Denoting the corresponding bilinear forms by

$$J(x,y) = x^*Ay, \qquad K(x,y) = x^*By,$$

we have

$$J(x,y) = J(y,x), \qquad J(x) = J(x,x),$$
$$K(x,y) = K(y,x), \qquad K(x) = K(x,x).$$

The equation

$$Ax = \lambda Bx$$

is equivalent to the condition that

$$J(x,y) = \lambda K(x,y)$$

for all vectors y. We say that a vector $x \neq 0$ *is an eigenvector of J relative to K* if there is a number λ such that this equation holds for all y. The number λ is called the *eigenvalue of J relative to K* corresponding to x.

The ratio

$$R(x) = \frac{J(x)}{K(x)}$$

is the *Rayleigh quotient of J* relative to K. From the identity

$$R(x + \epsilon y) = \frac{J(x + \epsilon y)}{K(x + \epsilon y)} = \frac{J(x) + 2\epsilon J(x,y) + \epsilon^2 J(y)}{K(x) + 2\epsilon K(x,y) + \epsilon^2 K(y)}$$

it is seen that the directional derivative

$$R'(x,y) = \frac{d}{d\epsilon} R(x + \epsilon y) \Big|^{\epsilon = 0}$$

is given by the formula

$$R'(x,y) = \frac{2}{K(x)} [J(x,y) - R(x)K(x,y)].$$

It follows that $R'(x,y)=0$ for all y if and only if $J(x,y)=R(x)K(x,y)$ for all y, and hence if and only if x is an eigenvector of J relative to K. The number $\lambda=R(x)$ is the corresponding eigenvalue.

Thus we see that our results can be expressed in terms of quadratic forms without reference to the corresponding matrices. In Section 5 we shall generalize this approach to the study of quadratic forms of arcs and obtain thereby the corresponding eigenvalue theory for a set of differential equations.

EXERCISES

1. Restate the results given in this section for the case $B=I$, and identify them with the corresponding results given in Section 9 of Chapter 1.

2. Let $x_1,\ldots,x_n$ be eigenvectors of A relative to B as described in Theorem 2.3. Let X be the matrix whose column vectors are $x_1,\ldots,x_n$. Show that

$$X^*AX=\Lambda, \qquad X^*BX=I,$$

where Λ is a diagonal matrix with $\lambda_1,\ldots,\lambda_n$ as diagonal elements. Show that $B^{-1}=XX^*$. Setting $Y=X^{*-1}$, show that

$$A=Y\Lambda Y^*, \qquad B=YY^*.$$

3. By choosing Y to be a nonsingular matrix and Λ to be a diagonal matrix, say

$$Y=\begin{pmatrix} 1 & 1 & 1 \\ 0 & 1 & 1 \\ 0 & 0 & 1 \end{pmatrix}, \quad \Lambda=\begin{pmatrix} 2 & 0 & 0 \\ 0 & -2 & 0 \\ 0 & 0 & 3 \end{pmatrix},$$

construct matrices

$$A=Y\Lambda Y^*, \qquad B=YY^*$$

illustrating the theory developed in this section. Determine the eigenvalues and eigenvectors of A relative to B.

4. Extend the results given in this section to the complex case, the matrices A and B being Hermitian. In the complex case A^* denotes the conjugate transpose of A.

5. For the case $n=2$ express A and B in the form

$$A=\begin{pmatrix} a & b \\ b & c \end{pmatrix}, \qquad B=\begin{pmatrix} \alpha & \beta \\ \beta & \gamma \end{pmatrix},$$

where $\alpha>0$, $\alpha\gamma>\beta^2$. Obtain formulas for the eigenvalues λ_1, λ_2 and eigenvectors x_1, x_2 of A relative to B such that

$$x_i^*Bx_j=\delta_{ij} \qquad (i=1,2).$$

6. Let $\mathcal{C}^k$ be a linear subspace of dimension k. A vector $x \neq 0$ in $\mathcal{C}^k$ will be called an eigenvector of A relative to B on $\mathcal{C}^k$ if the gradient $R'(x)$ of the Rayleigh quotient R is orthogonal to $\mathcal{C}^k$, and $\lambda = R(x)$ will be called the corresponding eigenvalue. Extend the results given in Theorems 3.1 to 3.4 to this case (see Section 3).

7. Let D be an $(n \times r)$-dimensional matrix of rank r, and set $k = n - r$. Let $\mathcal{C}^k$ be the set of all vectors x such that $Dx = 0$. Show that λ is an eigenvalue of A relative to B on $\mathcal{C}^k$ if and only if (see Section 3)

$$\begin{vmatrix} A - \lambda B & D \\ D^* & 0 \end{vmatrix}.$$

8. Let $y_1, \ldots, y_k$ be a basis for a linear space $\mathcal{C}^k$, and let Y be the matrix having $y_1, \ldots, y_k$ as its column vectors. Show that λ is an eigenvalue of A relative to B on $\mathcal{C}^k$ if and only if λ is an eigenvalue of Y^*AY relative to Y^*BY.

9. Express the result given in Exercise 6 in terms of quadratic forms.

3. EIGENVALUES ON SUBSPACES

Let $\mathcal{C}^k$ be a k-dimensional subspace of n-dimensional Euclidean space $\mathcal{E}$. Let A and B be two symmetric matrices, and suppose that B is positive. A value λ will be called an *eigenvalue of A relative to B on $\mathcal{C}^k$* if there is a nonzero vector z in $\mathcal{C}^k$ such that the vector

$$y = Az - \lambda Bz \qquad (3.1)$$

is orthogonal to $\mathcal{C}^k$. The vector z is called a corresponding *eigenvector of A relative to B on $\mathcal{C}^k$*. Alternatively, a vector $z \neq 0$ in $\mathcal{C}^k$ is an eigenvector of A relative to B on $\mathcal{C}^k$ if there is a number λ such that the vector y defined by (3.1) is orthogonal to $\mathcal{C}^k$ and λ is the corresponding eigenvalue of A relative to B on $\mathcal{C}^k$. Since y is orthogonal to $\mathcal{C}^k$, it is orthogonal to z, and by (3.1)

$$0 = z^*y = z^*Az - \lambda z^*Bz.$$

Hence λ is given by the Rayleigh quotient,

$$\lambda = \frac{z^*Az}{z^*Bz} = R(z).$$

Recall that the gradient of R is given by the formula

$$R'(z) = \frac{2}{z^*Bz} \left[Az - R(z)Bz \right].$$

Consequently an eigenvector z of A relative to B on $\mathcal{C}^k$ is one at which the gradient $R'(z)$ of R is orthogonal to $\mathcal{C}^k$.

If $B = I$, the identity, the phrase "relative to B" in these definitions is dropped. It is clear that if $k = n$, so that $\mathcal{C}^k = \mathcal{E}$, these definitions reduce to the ones given in Section 2.

Let C be an $(n \times k)$-dimensional matrix whose column vectors generate $\mathcal{C}^k$. A vector z is in $\mathcal{C}^k$ if and only if it is expressible in the form

$$z = Cv, \tag{3.2}$$

where v is a k-dimensional vector. Since C has rank k, we have $z = 0$ in (3.2) if and only if $v = 0$. Let A_k and B_k be the $(k \times k)$-dimensional matrices

$$A_k = C^* A C, \qquad B_k = C^* B C. \tag{3.3}$$

We shall show that λ is an eigenvalue of A relative to B on $\mathcal{C}^k$ if and only if

$$\Delta_k(\lambda) = \det(A_k - \lambda B_k) = 0. \tag{3.4}$$

Suppose that λ is an eigenvalue of A relative to B on $\mathcal{C}^k$ and z is a corresponding eigenvector. Choose v so that (3.2) holds. Since $z \neq 0$, we have $v \neq 0$. Vector (3.1) takes the form

$$y = ACv - \lambda BCv.$$

Since y is orthogonal to $\mathcal{C}^k$, we have

$$0 = C^* y = C^* ACv - \lambda C^* BCv = (A_k - \lambda B_k)v = 0.$$

Hence $\Delta_k(\lambda) = 0$. Conversely, if $\Delta_k(\lambda) = 0$, we can select $v \neq 0$ so that

$$0 = (A_k - \lambda B_k)v = C^*(ACv - \lambda BCv) = C^*(Az - \lambda Bz),$$

where $z = Cv \neq 0$. This equation tells us that $y = Az - \lambda Bz$ is orthogonal to the column vectors of C and hence to the subspace $\mathcal{C}^k$ generated by these column vectors. Consequently, λ is an eigenvalue of A relative to B on $\mathcal{C}^k$ if and only if $\Delta_k(\lambda) = 0$.

There is a second determinant $d_k(\lambda)$ that will yield the eigenvalues of A relative to B on $\mathcal{C}^k$. This determinant is of the form

$$d_k(\lambda) = \det\begin{pmatrix} A - \lambda B & D \\ D^* & 0 \end{pmatrix}, \tag{3.5}$$

where D is an $[n \times (n-k)]$-dimensional matrix of rank $n - k$ whose column vectors are orthogonal to $\mathbb{C}^k$. The column vectors of D generate the orthogonal complement $\mathbb{C}^{k\perp}$ of $\mathbb{C}^k$. A vector y is orthogonal to $\mathbb{C}^k$ if and only if it is of the form

$$y = Dw, \tag{3.6}$$

where w is an $(n-k)$-dimensional vector. Clearly $y = 0$ in (3.6) if and only if $w = 0$. A vector z is in $\mathbb{C}^k$ if and only if

$$D^*z = 0. \tag{3.7}$$

If λ is an eigenvalue of A relative to B on $\mathbb{C}^k$, we can select a vector $z \neq 0$ in $\mathbb{C}^k$ so that $y = Az - \lambda Bz$ is orthogonal to $\mathbb{C}^k$ and hence is of form (3.6). We have accordingly

$$(A - \lambda B)z - Dw = 0, \tag{3.8a}$$

$$D^*z \quad\quad = 0, \tag{3.8b}$$

from which we conclude that $d_k(\lambda) = 0$. Conversely, if $d_k(\lambda) = 0$, we can select vectors z and w, not both zero, so that (3.8) holds. If $z = 0$, then $Dw = 0$ and $w = 0$. Hence $z \neq 0$, and the vector $y = (A - \lambda B)z = Dw$ is orthogonal to $\mathbb{C}^k$. Consequently λ is an eigenvalue of A relative to B on $\mathbb{C}^k$, as was to be proved.

We have the following extension of Theorem 2.3. In this theorem

$$J(x,y) = x^*Ay, \quad\quad K(x,y) = x^*By.$$

THEOREM 3.1

There exist k *eigenvectors* $z_1, \ldots, z_k$ *of* A *relative to* B *on* $\mathbb{C}^k$ *such that*

$$K(z_\alpha, z_\beta) = z_\alpha^* B z_\beta = \delta_{\alpha\beta} \quad\quad (\alpha, \beta = 1, \ldots, k)$$

and such that

$$\lambda_1 \leqslant \lambda_2 \leqslant \cdots \leqslant \lambda_k,$$

where $\lambda_\beta = R(z_\beta)$ *is the eigenvalue corresponding to* z_β. *The vector*

$$y_\beta = Az_\beta - \lambda Bz_\beta \quad\quad (\beta = 1, \ldots, k)$$

is orthogonal to z_k *and*

$$J(z_\alpha, z_\beta) = z_\alpha^* A z_\beta = \lambda_\beta \delta_{\alpha\beta} \quad\quad (\alpha, \beta = 1, \ldots, k).$$

Setting $\mathcal{B}_1 = \mathcal{E}^n$, *let* $\mathcal{B}_j$ ($j > 1$) *be all z in* $\mathcal{C}^k$ *having*

$$K(z_\alpha, z) = z_\alpha^* B z = 0 \qquad (\alpha = 1, \ldots, j - 1).$$

The vector z_j *minimizes the Rayleigh quotient* R *on* $\mathcal{B}_j$ *with* $z = 0$ *deleted.*

This result is obtained from Theorem 2.3 applied to the matrices A_k and B_k given by (3.3). If we denote the eigenvectors of A_k relative to B_k by $v_1, \ldots, v_k$, then $z_1 = Cv_1, \ldots, z_k = Cv_k$ have the properties described in Theorem 3.1.

THEOREM 3.2

Let $\mathcal{C}^k$ *and* $\mathcal{C}^{k+1}$ *be linear subspaces of* $\mathcal{E}$ *of dimensions* k *and* k + 1, *respectively. Suppose that* $\mathcal{C}^k$ *is a subspace of* $\mathcal{C}^{k+1}$. *Let* $\lambda_1, \ldots, \lambda_k$ *be the eigenvalues of* A *relative to* B *on* $\mathcal{C}^k$, *ordered as described in Theorem 3.1. Similarly let* $\mu_1, \ldots, \mu_{k+1}$ *be the eigenvalues of* A *relative to* B *on* $\mathcal{C}^{k+1}$ *ordered in the same manner; then*

$$\mu_j \leqslant \lambda_j \leqslant \mu_{j+1} \qquad (j = 1, \ldots, k).$$

In the proof it can be assumed that $\mathcal{C}^{k+1} = \mathcal{E}$. The proof can then be obtained with the help of Theorem 2.4 and is left to the reader.

EXERCISES

1. Let $A = (a_{ij})$ be a symmetric matrix, and let A_k be the submatrices

$$A_k = (a_{ij}) \qquad (i, j = 1, \ldots, k).$$

Let $\lambda_j^{(k)}$ be the *j*th eigenvalue of A_k. Establish the inequalities

$$\lambda_j^{(k+1)} \leqslant \lambda_j^{(k)} \leqslant \lambda_{j+1}^{(k+1)} \qquad (j = 1, \ldots, k).$$

Hint: Let $\mathcal{C}^k$ be the subspace of points $x = (x^1, \ldots, x^n)$ having $x^i = 0$ ($i > k$), and apply Theorem 3.2.

2. Extend the results given here to the complex case in which A and B are Hermitian matrices.

3. Restate the results given in this section for the case $B = I$.

4. Show that the polynomial $d_k(\lambda)$ given by (3.5) is of degree k.

4. A FUNDAMENTAL LEMMA

In the next section we shall extend the results given above to an infinite dimensional case. In doing so, we shall make use of a lemma, commonly called the fundamental lemma in the calculus of variations. The lemma is established in this section.

Let $\mathcal{E}$ be the class of arcs (or functions)

$$x: \quad x(t) \quad (a \leqslant t \leqslant b)$$

in tx-space of the type indicated in Figure 4.1. Of course, the arc could cross the t-axis. Observe that we allow the arc to have corners. It is understood that $[a,b]$ is a fixed interval on the t-axis. The function $x(t)$ is a real-valued continuous function of t having a piecewise continuous derivative $\dot{x}(t)$. By this we mean that $\dot{x}(t)$ is continuous except possibly at a finite number of points, defining corner points of the arc x. At a value $t = c$ defining a corner point, the derivative $\dot{x}(t)$ has left-hand limit $\dot{x}(c-)$ and right-hand limit $\dot{x}(c+)$. Geometrically the arc x is composed of a finite number of subarcs on each of which it has a continuously turning tangent, as indicated in Figure 4.1.

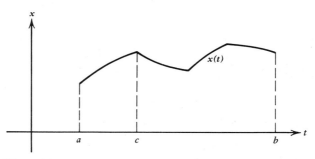

Figure 4.1

It should be noted that the symbol x is used in two senses. When we are concerned with a point (t,x) in tx-space, x is used to designate the x-coordinate of the point. When we are concerned with a function $x(t)$ $(a \leqslant t \leqslant b)$, we denote this function by x. This is analogous to using x to denote the point or vector $(x^1, \ldots, x^n)$ or x^i $(i = 1, \ldots, n)$. The ith component x^i of a vector x is often denoted by $x(i)$. Thus $x: x(i)$ $(i = 1, \ldots, n)$ is a description of an n-dimensional vector. Similarly a function $x: x(t)$ $(a \leqslant t \leqslant b)$ can be regarded as a vector having infinitely many components $x(t)$, one for each t in $[a,b]$. The functions in which we are interested can be interpreted geometrically as arcs or curves in tx-space. Accordingly we shall refer to the function x as the arc x.

The space $\mathcal{E}$ of all arcs x forms a real linear space. If x: $x(t)$ $(a \leqslant t \leqslant b)$ and y: $y(t)$ $(a \leqslant t \leqslant b)$ are two arcs in $\mathcal{E}$ and α, β are real numbers, the linear combination $\alpha x + \beta y$ is the arc

$$\alpha x + \beta y: \qquad \alpha x(t) + \beta y(t) \qquad (a \leqslant t \leqslant b).$$

The arc $x = 0$ is the arc having $x(t) \equiv 0$ on $a \leqslant t \leqslant b$.

The following lemma is called the *fundamental lemma* in the calculus of variations.

LEMMA 4.1

Let M(t) *and* N(t) *be piecewise continuous functions on* $a \leqslant t \leqslant b$. *If the relation*

$$L(y) = \int_a^b \left[M(t)y(t) + N(t)\dot{y}(t) \right] dt = 0 \tag{4.1}$$

holds for all arcs y *in* $\mathcal{E}$ *having* y(a) = y(b) = 0, *then*

$$N(t) = \int_a^t M(s)\, ds + N(a). \tag{4.2}$$

Conversely, if (4.2) *holds, then* (4.1) *holds for every arc* y *in* $\mathcal{E}$ *having* y(a) = y(b) = 0.

Suppose that equation (4.1) holds as stated. Let $\bar{t}$ be a point of continuity of $N(t)$ on $a < t \leqslant b$, and choose ϵ in the interval $\left(0, (\bar{t} - a)/2 \right)$. Let y be the arc shown in Figure 4.2. It is defined by the relations

$$y(t) = \frac{t - a}{\epsilon} \quad (a \leqslant t \leqslant a + \epsilon), \qquad y(t) = 1 \quad (a + \epsilon \leqslant t \leqslant \bar{t} + \epsilon),$$

$$y(t) = \frac{\bar{t} - t}{\epsilon} \quad (\bar{t} - \epsilon \leqslant t \leqslant \bar{t}), \qquad y(t) = 0 \quad (\bar{t} \leqslant t \leqslant b).$$

For this arc y equation (4.1) takes the form

$$\frac{1}{\epsilon} \int_a^{a+\epsilon} P(t)\, dt + \int_{a+\epsilon}^{\bar{t}-\epsilon} M(t)\, dt + \frac{1}{\epsilon} \int_{\bar{t}-\epsilon}^{\bar{t}} Q(t)\, dt = 0, \tag{4.3}$$

where

$$P(t) = M(t)(t - a) + N(t), \qquad Q(t) = M(t)(\bar{t} - t) - N(t).$$

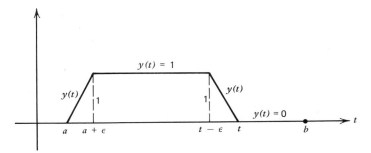

Figure 4.2

Observe that, if we set $t = a + \epsilon s$, then $dt = \epsilon \, ds$ and

$$\frac{1}{\epsilon} \int_a^{a+\epsilon} P(t)\, dt = \int_0^1 P(a + \epsilon s)\, ds.$$

Hence

$$\lim_{\epsilon \to 0} \frac{1}{\epsilon} \int_a^{a+\epsilon} P(t)\, dt = \int_0^1 P(a)\, ds = P(a) = N(a).$$

Similarly

$$\lim_{\epsilon \to 0} \frac{1}{\epsilon} \int_{\bar{t}-\epsilon}^{\bar{t}} Q(t)\, dt = Q(\bar{t}) = -N(\bar{t}).$$

Using these relations together with (4.3), we find that, as $\epsilon \to 0$, we obtain

$$N(a) + \int_a^{\bar{t}} M(t)\, dt - N(\bar{t}) = 0.$$

Consequently equation (4.2) holds at each point of continuity of $N(t)$. Since the right member in (4.2) is continuous, so also is $N(t)$ and (4.2) holds on $a \leqslant t \leqslant b$.

Conversely, if (4.2) holds and y is an arc having $y(a) = y(b) = 0$, then

$$\int_a^b (My + N\dot{y})\, dt = \int_a^b \left[\frac{d}{dt}(Ny) \right] dt = N(t) y(t) \Big|_a^b = 0,$$

as was to be proved.

5. QUADRATIC FORMS OF ARCS

Let $\mathscr{E}$ be the class of continuous arcs

$$x: \qquad x(t) \qquad (a \leqslant t \leqslant b)$$

in tx-space having piecewise continuous derivatives $\dot{x}(t)$ on $[a,b]$. It was seen in Section 4 that $\mathscr{E}$ is a linear space. In this section we shall be interested in two quadratic forms, J and K, on $\mathscr{E}$. They are defined by the formulas

$$J(x) = \int_a^b \left[r(t)\dot{x}(t)^2 - p(t)x(t)^2 \right] dt, \tag{5.1}$$

$$K(x) = \int_a^b x(t)^2 \, dt. \tag{5.2}$$

Here $r(t)$ is a positive function of class C' on $[a,b]$, and $p(t)$ is continuous on $[a,b]$. The corresponding bilinear forms are

$$J(x,y) = \int_a^b \left[r(t)\dot{x}(t)\dot{y}(t) - p(t)x(t)y(t) \right] dt, \tag{5.3}$$

$$K(x,y) = \int_a^b x(t)y(t) \, dt. \tag{5.4}$$

Observe that $J(x,y)$ and $K(x,y)$ are symmetric, that is,

$$J(x,y) = J(y,x), \qquad K(x,y) = K(y,x).$$

Moreover $J(x) = J(x,x)$ and $K(x) = K(x,x)$. The quadratic form $K(x)$ is positive on $\mathscr{E}$, that is, $K(x) > 0$ for all $x \neq 0$ in $\mathscr{E}$. However, $J(x)$ need not be positive.

Observe that

$$J(\alpha x + \beta y) = \alpha^2 J(x) + 2\alpha\beta J(x,y) + \beta^2 J(y) \tag{5.5}$$

is an identity in x,y and α,β. This identity remains valid when J is replaced by K.

We center our attention on the linear subspace $\mathscr{B}$ of all arcs x in $\mathscr{E}$ having $x(a) = x(b) = 0$. Proceeding in the manner described in Section 3, we say that an arc $x \neq 0$ in $\mathscr{B}$ is an *eigenvector* or *eigenfunction of J relative to K on* $\mathscr{B}$ if there is a number λ such that

$$J(x,y) = \lambda K(x,y) \tag{5.6}$$

for all arcs y in $\mathscr{B}$. The value λ is called the corresponding *eigenvalue of J relative to K on* $\mathscr{B}$. Moreover λ is given by the *Rayleigh quotient*:

$$\lambda = R(x) = \frac{J(x)}{K(x)}.$$

THEOREM 5.1

A nonnull arc

$$x: \qquad x(t) \qquad (a \leqslant t \leqslant b)$$

is an eigenvector of J relative to K on $\mathscr{B}$ *if and only if* $x(t)$ *is a solution of the equations*

$$\frac{d}{dt}[r(t)\dot{x}(t)] + [p(t) + \lambda]x(t) = 0, \tag{5.7a}$$

$$x(a) = x(b) = 0, \tag{5.7b}$$

for a suitable choice of λ.

EXAMPLE 5.1

Before establishing this result we shall illustrate it for the special case in which $a = 0$, $b = \pi$, $r(t) = 1$, and $p(t) = 0$. Here

$$J(x) = \int_0^\pi \dot{x}(t)^2 \, dt, \qquad K(x) = \int_0^\pi x(t)^2 \, dt.$$

Equations (5.7) take the form

$$\ddot{x} + \lambda x = 0, \qquad x(0) = 0, \qquad x(\pi) = 0.$$

This system has a nonnull solution if and only if $\lambda = k^2$, where k is an integer. We can choose k to be positive. The solutions corresponding to $\lambda = k^2$ are multiples of

$$x_k: \qquad x_k(t) = \sqrt{2/\pi} \, \sin kt \qquad (0 \leqslant t \leqslant \pi).$$

The arc x_k has been scaled so that

$$K(x_k) = \frac{2}{\pi} \int_0^\pi \sin^2 kt \, dt = 1.$$

The arc x_k is an eigenvector or eigenfunction of J relative to K corresponding to the eigenvalue $\lambda_k = k^2$. Observe that, if y is in $\mathscr{B}$, then

$$J(x_k,y) - k^2 K(x_k,y) = \sqrt{2/\pi} \int_0^\pi \left[k \cos kt \, \dot{y}(t) - k^2 \sin kt y(t) \right] dt$$

$$= k\sqrt{2/\pi} \int_0^\pi \frac{d}{dt} [y(t) \cos kt] dt = k\sqrt{2/\pi} \, [y(t) \cos kt]_0^\pi.$$

Since $y(0) = y(\pi) = 0$, it follows that

$$J(x_k,y) = k^2 K(x_k,y),$$

as stated in Theorem 5.1.

As a first step in the proof of Theorem 5.1, suppose that the arc x: $x(t)$ $(a \leqslant t \leqslant b)$ is a nonnull arc in $\mathscr{B}$ satisfying equations (5.7) with a constant λ. Select an arbitrary arc y in $\mathscr{B}$. We have

$$J(x,y) - \lambda K(x,y) = \int_a^b \{ r(t)\dot{x}(t)\dot{y}(t) - [p(t) + \lambda]x(t)y(t) \}. \quad (5.8)$$

Using (5.7a), we see that

$$\frac{d}{dt} [r(t)\dot{x}(t)y(t)] = r(t)\dot{x}(t)\dot{y}(t) - [p(t) + \lambda]x(t)y(t).$$

Integrating from a to b, we find that

$$r(t)\dot{x}(t)y(t)\big|_a^b = J(x,y) - \lambda K(x,y).$$

Since $y(a) = y(b) = 0$, it follows that

$$J(x,y) = \lambda K(x,y), \quad (5.9)$$

and hence that x is an eigenvector of J relative to K with λ as the corresponding eigenvalue.

To prove the converse, we make use of the fundamental lemma established in Section 4. Consider therefore an arc $x \neq 0$ in $\mathscr{B}$ having associated with it a number λ such that equation (5.9) holds for all arcs y in $\mathscr{B}$. Setting

$$L(y) = J(x,y) - \lambda K(x,y),$$

we see from (5.8) and (5.9) that

$$L(y) = \int_a^b \{-[p(t)+\lambda]x(t)y(t)+r(t)\dot{x}(t)\dot{y}(t)\} \, dt = 0$$

for all y in $\mathfrak{B}$. Setting

$$M(t) = -[p(t)+\lambda]x(t), \qquad N(t) = r(t)\dot{x}(t),$$

we find that this equation takes the form

$$L(y) = \int_a^b [M(t)y(t)+N(t)\dot{y}(t)] \, dt = 0.$$

By virtue of Lemma 4.3 we have

$$N(t) = \int_a^t M(s) \, ds + N(a),$$

that is,

$$r(t)\dot{x}(t) = -\int_a^t [p(s)+\lambda]x(s) \, ds + r(a)\dot{x}(a). \tag{5.10}$$

This equation tells us that $r(t)\dot{x}(t)$ is continuous, since the integral on the right is a continuous function of its upper limit. Moreover

$$\frac{d}{dt}[r(t)\dot{x}(t)] = -\frac{d}{dt}\int_a^t [p(s)+\lambda]x(s) \, ds = -[p(t)+\lambda]x(t).$$

Hence (5.7a) holds. Equation (5.7b) holds also in view of the fact that the arc x is in $\mathfrak{B}$. By virtue of our assumption that $r(t)$ is a *positive* function of class C', it follows from (5.10) that $\dot{x}(t)$ is the quotient of two functions of class C'. Hence $\dot{x}(t)$ is continuous and has a continuous derivative $\ddot{x}(t)$ on $[a,b]$. An eigenfunction $x: x(t)$ ($a \leqslant t \leqslant b$) is therefore of class C'' on $[a,b]$. This completes the proof of Theorem 5.1.

LEMMA 5.1

Let x_1 *and* x_2 *be two linearly independent eigenvectors of* J *relative to* K *on* $\mathfrak{B}$ *with* λ_1 *and* λ_2 *as their corresponding eigenvalues. Then* $\lambda_1 \neq \lambda_2$ *and*

$$J(x_1, x_2) = 0, \qquad K(x_1, x_2) = 0. \tag{5.11}$$

If $\lambda_1 = \lambda_2$, then x_1 and x_2 would satisfy equations (5.7) with $\lambda = \lambda_1$, and hence would be linearly dependent, which is not the case. Hence $\lambda_1 \neq \lambda_2$.

By virtue of our hypotheses we have

$$J(x_1,y) = \lambda_1 K(x_1,y), \qquad J(x_2,y) = \lambda_2 K(x_2,y) \qquad (5.12)$$

for all y in $\mathcal{B}$. Setting $y = x_2$ in the first equation and $y = x_1$ in the second, we see that

$$\lambda_1 K(x_1,x_2) = J(x_1,x_2) = J(x_2,x_1) = \lambda_2 K(x_2,x_1) = \lambda_2 K(x_1,x_2). \qquad (5.13)$$

Hence

$$(\lambda_1 - \lambda_2) K(x_1,x_2) = 0.$$

Since $\lambda_1 \neq \lambda_2$, we have $K(x_1,x_2) = 0$. Using (5.13) again, we see that $J(x_1,x_2) = 0$. This establishes relations (5.11).

EXAMPLE 5.1 (*Continued*)

Lemma 5.1 states that if $j \neq k$ the functions

$$x_j(t) = \sqrt{2/\pi} \,\sin jt, \qquad x_k(t) = \sqrt{2/\pi} \,\sin kt$$

satisfy the relations

$$J(x_j,x_k) = \int_0^{\pi} \dot{x}_j(t)\dot{x}_k(t)\,dt = \frac{2jk}{\pi} \int_0^{\pi} \cos jt \cos kt\,dt = 0,$$

$$K(x_j,x_k) = \int_0^{\pi} x_j(t)x_k(t)\,dt = \frac{2}{\pi} \int_0^{\pi} \sin jt \sin kt\,dt = 0.$$

The following lemma will be used to show that the eigenvalues of system (5.7) are bounded from below.

LEMMA 5.2

There is a number m *such that*

$$J(x) + mK(x) \geqslant 0 \qquad (5.14)$$

for all $x \neq 0$ *in* $\mathcal{B}$.

Observe that

$$J(x) + mK(x) = \int_a^b \{ r(t)\dot{x}(t)^2 + [m - p(t)]x(t)^2 \}\,dt.$$

Since $r(t) > 0$, the integrand will be nonnegative if m is chosen so that $m \geqslant p(t)$ on $[a,b]$. This proves the lemma.

If m is the smallest number such that (5.14) holds on $\mathcal{B}$, then $\lambda = -m$ is the least eigenvalue of J relative to K, as will be seen from the results given below.

As in the case of matrices, the eigenvectors and eigenvalues are determined by the *Rayleigh quotient*,

$$R(x) = \frac{J(x)}{K(x)}. \tag{5.15}$$

To see this we make use of identity (5.5) for J and a similar one for K to obtain the formula

$$R(x + \epsilon y) = \frac{J(x + \epsilon y)}{K(x + \epsilon y)} = \frac{J(x) + 2\epsilon J(x,y) + \epsilon^2 J(y)}{K(x) + 2\epsilon K(x,y) + \epsilon^2 K(y)}. \tag{5.16}$$

The derivative

$$R'(x,y) = \frac{d}{d\epsilon} R(x + \epsilon y)\Big|^{\epsilon=0}$$

is called the *directional derivative of R at x in the direction y*. It is also called the *first variation* of R. By the use of (5.16) we have

$$R'(x,y) = \frac{2}{K(x)} [J(x,y) - R(x)K(x,y)]. \tag{5.17}$$

An arc $x \neq 0$ in $\mathcal{B}$ will be said to be a *critical arc of R on* $\mathcal{B}$ if $R'(x,y) = 0$ for all y in $\mathcal{B}$. The value $R(x)$ at a critical arc x will be called a *critical value of R on* $\mathcal{B}$. By the use of (5.17), we see that an arc $x \neq 0$ is a critical arc of R on $\mathcal{B}$ if and only if

$$J(x,y) = R(x)K(x,y)$$

for all y in $\mathcal{B}$. This equation implies that x is an eigenvector of J relative to K on $\mathcal{B}$ with $\lambda = R(x)$ as the corresponding eigenvalue. We have accordingly the following result, analogous to that obtained in the finite dimensional case.

The eigenvectors of J *relative to* K *on* $\mathcal{B}$ *are the critical arcs of* R(x) *on* $\mathcal{B}$. *The eigenvalues of* J *relative to* K *on* $\mathcal{B}$ *are the critical values of* R *on* $\mathcal{B}$.

As in the finite dimensional case, the Rayleigh quotient R is homogeneous of degree zero, that is,

$$R(ax) = R(x) \qquad (a \neq 0).$$

Since $K(x) > 0$ whenever $x \neq 0$, we can select $a = K(x)^{-1/2}$. Then $K(ax) = a^2 K(x) = 1$. It follows that the values of $R(x)$ are completely determined by the vector x having $K(x) = 1$. In particular, eigenvectors x can be scaled so that $K(x) = 1$.

It should be noted further that by virtue of Lemma 5.2 we have

$$R(x) \geqslant -m$$

for all $x \neq 0$ in $\mathcal{B}$. If x is an eigenvector, its eigenvalue $\lambda = R(x) \geqslant -m$. This states that the eigenvalues of J relative to K on $\mathcal{B}$ are bounded from below.

As in the finite dimensional case, we have the following result.

THEOREM 5.2

There exists an arc $x_1 \neq 0$ *in* $\mathcal{B}$ *that minimizes the Rayleigh quotient,*

$$R(x) = \frac{J(x)}{K(x)}, \qquad (5.18)$$

on $\mathcal{B}$ *with* $x = 0$ *excluded. The arc* x_1 *is an eigenvector of* J *relative to* K *on* $\mathcal{B}$ *with* $\lambda_1 = R(x_1)$ *as the corresponding eigenvalue. The number* λ_1 *is the least eigenvalue of* J *relative to* K *on* $\mathcal{B}$. *The arc* x_1 *can be chosen so that* $K(x_1) = 1$.

We shall omit the proof of the existence of the minimizing arc x_1. Such a proof requires more background than we have developed.

Suppose therefore that we have an arc $x_1 \neq 0$ in $\mathcal{B}$ that minimizes $R(x)$ on $\mathcal{B}$. Choose a vector y in $\mathcal{B}$. For small values of ϵ the arc $x_1 + \epsilon y$ will be a nonnull arc in $\mathcal{B}$. It follows that the inequality

$$g(\epsilon) = R(x_1 + \epsilon y) \geqslant g(0) = R(x_1)$$

holds on an interval $-\delta < \epsilon < \delta$. The value $\epsilon = 0$ therefore affords a local minimum to $g(\epsilon)$. Consequently

$$g'(0) = R'(x_1, y) = 0.$$

Since y is an arbitrary arc in $\mathcal{B}$, the arc x_1 is a critical arc of R and hence is an eigenvector of J relative to K on $\mathcal{B}$, as was to be proved. We have accordingly

$$R(x) \geqslant R(x_1) = \lambda_1$$

for all $x \neq 0$ in $\mathcal{B}$ and, in particular, for every eigenvector x. Its corresponding eigenvalue $\lambda = R(x)$ therefore satisfies the relation $\lambda \geqslant \lambda_1$, that is, λ_1 is the least eigenvalue of J relative to K. Since $R(ax_1) = R(x_1)$ for all $a \neq 0$, we can replace x_1 by a multiple of x_1 to obtain a new minimizing vector, again called x_1, with the property that $K(x_1) = 1$. This proves the theorem.

THEOREM 5.3

Let $x_1, \ldots, x_{k-1}$ *be* $k-1$ *linearly independent arcs in* $\mathcal{B}$. *Let* $\mathcal{B}_k$ *be the class of all arcs* x *in* $\mathcal{B}$ *satisfying the relations*

$$K(x_\alpha, x) = 0 \qquad (\alpha = 1, \ldots, k-1). \tag{5.19}$$

There exists an arc $x_k \neq 0$ *in* $\mathcal{B}_k$ *which minimizes the Rayleigh quotient on* $\mathcal{B}_k$ *excluding* x = 0. *There exist multipliers* $\mu_1, \ldots, \mu_{k-1}$ *such that*

$$R'(x_k, y) = \mu_1 K(x_1, y) + \cdots + \mu_{k-1} K(x_{k-1}, y) \tag{5.20}$$

for all y *in* $\mathcal{B}$, *where* $R'(x, y)$ *is the directional derivative* (5.17) *of* R *at* x. *If* $x_1, \ldots, x_{k-1}$ *are eigenvectors of* J *relative to* K, *so also is* x_k *and* $\mu_\alpha = 0$ $(\alpha = 1, \ldots, k-1)$.

The proof of the existence of the arc x_k will be omitted. It can be obtained by essentially the same argument that can be used to prove the existence of the arc x_1 described in Theorem 5.2. As yet we have not developed the background required to prove the existence of x_k. We can, however, derive the properties of x_k described in Theorem 5.3.

Suppose therefore that we have a vector $x_k \neq 0$ in $\mathcal{B}_k$ that minimizes R on $\mathcal{B}_k$. If z is in $\mathcal{B}_k$, so also is $x_k + \epsilon z$ for all numbers ϵ. It follows that the function

$$g(\epsilon) = R(x_k + \epsilon z)$$

has the minimum value $g(0) = R(x_k)$ at $\epsilon = 0$. Consequently

$$g'(0) = R'(x_k, z) = 0 \tag{5.21}$$

for all z in $\mathcal{B}_k$, that is, for all z in $\mathcal{B}$ having

$$K(x_\alpha, z) = 0 \qquad (\alpha = 1, \ldots, k-1). \tag{5.22}$$

This result is equivalent to relation (5.20). To see this, we observe first that the determinant

$$|K(x_\alpha, x_\beta)| \neq 0 \qquad (\alpha, \beta = 1, \ldots, k-1)$$

by virtue of the linear independence of the arcs $x_1, \ldots, x_{k-1}$. Select $\mu_1, \ldots, \mu_{k-1}$ so that

$$R'(x_k, x_\beta) = \sum_{\alpha=1}^{k-1} \mu_\alpha K(x_\alpha, x_\beta). \qquad (5.23)$$

Given a vector y in $\mathfrak{B}$, select $b_1, \ldots, b_{k-1}$ so that

$$K(x_\alpha, y) = \sum_{\beta=1}^{k-1} K(x_\alpha, x_\beta) b_\beta. \qquad (5.24)$$

The arc $z = y - \sum_\beta x_\beta b_\beta$ satisfies equations (5.22), as can be seen by the computations

$$K(x_\alpha, z) = K\left(x_\alpha, y - \sum_\beta x_\beta b_\beta\right) = K(x_\alpha, y) - \sum_\beta K(x_\alpha, x_\beta) b_\beta = 0.$$

Consequently, by (5.21), (5.23), and (5.24),

$$0 = R'(x_k, z) = R'(x_k, y) - \sum_\beta R'(x_k, x_\beta) b_\beta$$

$$= R'(x_k, y) - \sum_\beta \left[\sum_\alpha \mu_\alpha K(x_\alpha, x_\beta) \right] b_\beta$$

$$= R'(x_k, y) - \sum_\alpha \left\{ \mu_\alpha \left[\sum_\beta K(x_\alpha, x_\beta) b_\beta \right] \right\}$$

$$= R'(x_k, y) - \sum_\alpha \mu_\alpha K(x_\alpha, y) = 0.$$

This establishes relation (5.20).

Suppose next that $x_1, \ldots, x_{k-1}$ are eigenvectors of J relative to K on $\mathfrak{B}$. Then

$$J(x_\beta, y) = \lambda_\beta K(x_\beta, y) \qquad (\beta = 1, \ldots, k-1)$$

for every vector y in $\mathfrak{B}$. Here $\lambda_\beta = R(x_\beta)$. Choosing $y = x_k$ and using the fact that $K(x_\beta, x_k) = 0$, we find that

$$J(x_k, x_\beta) = J(x_\beta, x_k) = \lambda_\beta K(x_\beta, x_k) = 0.$$

Consequently

$$R'(x_k, x_\beta) = \frac{2}{K(x_k)} [J(x_k, x_\beta) - R(x_k)K(x_k, x_\beta)] = 0.$$

Setting $y = x_\beta$ in (5.20), we find that

$$0 = \sum_\alpha \mu_\alpha K(x_\alpha, x_\beta).$$

This in turn implies that

$$0 = \sum_\beta \sum_\alpha \mu_\alpha K(x_\alpha, x_\beta) \mu_\beta = K(x, x) = K(x),$$

where $x = \sum_\alpha \mu_\alpha x_\alpha$. This is possible only if $x = \sum_\alpha \mu_\alpha x_\alpha = 0$, and hence only if $\mu_\alpha = 0$ ($\alpha = 1, \ldots, k-1$) by virtue of the linear independence of $x_1, \ldots, x_{k-1}$. It follows that $\mu_1 = \mu_2 = \cdots = \mu_{k-1} = 0$. By (5.20) we have $R'(x_k, y) = 0$ for all y in $\mathcal{B}$. The vector x_k is accordingly an eigenvector of J relative to K on $\mathcal{B}$, as was to be proved.

THEOREM 5.4

There exists an infinite sequence of eigenvectors $x_1, x_2, x_3, \ldots$ *of* J *relative to* K *on* $\mathcal{B}$ *such that* x_k *minimizes the Rayleigh quotient,*

$$R(x) = \frac{J(x)}{K(x)},$$

in the class of all vectors $x \neq 0$ *in* $\mathcal{B}$ *satisfying the relations*

$$K(x_\alpha, x) = 0 \qquad (\alpha = 1, \ldots, k-1). \tag{5.25}$$

The corresponding eigenvalues $\lambda_\alpha = R(x_\alpha)$ ($\alpha = 1, 2, 3, \ldots$) *satisfy the relations*

$$\lambda_1 < \lambda_2 < \cdots < \lambda_k < \lambda_{k+1} < \cdots. \tag{5.26}$$

These eigenvectors can be chosen so as to satisfy the first of the relations

$$K(x_\alpha, x_\beta) = \delta_{\alpha\beta}, \qquad J(x_\alpha, x_\beta) = \lambda_\beta \delta_{\alpha\beta} \tag{5.27}$$

and hence also the second.

This result is a simple consequence of Theorems 5.2 and 5.3. Its proof will be left to the reader. If this study is pursued further, it can be shown that at most a finite number of these eigenvalues are negative. In fact, it can be shown that $\lim_{k\to\infty}\lambda_k = +\infty$. If our eigenvectors have been chosen so that (5.27) holds, it is possible to prove the following statement: Given a vector y in $\mathcal{B}$, set

$$y_k = b_1 x_1 + \cdots + b_k x_k \qquad [\, b_\alpha = K(x_\alpha, y)\,].$$

Then

$$K(y_k) = b_1{}^2 + \cdots + b_k{}^2, \qquad J(y_k) = \lambda_1 b_1{}^2 \cdots + \lambda_k b_k{}^2.$$

Moreover

$$J(y) = \lim J(y_k) = \sum_{\alpha=1}^{\infty} \lambda_\alpha b_\alpha{}^2,$$

$$K(y) = \lim K(y_k) = \sum_{\alpha=1}^{\infty} b_\alpha{}^2.$$

In fact, $\lim y_k(t) = y(t)$ uniformly on $[a,b]$. The proofs of these results are beyond the scope of this book. They can be found in treatises on differential equations and on Hilbert space.

THEOREM 5.5

The k*th eigenvalue of* J *relative to* K *on* $\mathcal{B}$ *is given by the relation*

$$\lambda_k = \min_{\mathcal{C}^k}\left[\, \max_{\substack{x\in\mathcal{C}^k\\ x\neq 0}} R(x)\right],$$

where $\mathcal{C}^k$ *denotes a linear subspace of* $\mathcal{B}$ *of dimension* k.

The proof is like that of Theorem 9.6 in Chapter 1 and will be left to the reader.

EXERCISES

1. Let $x(t,\lambda)$ $(a \leqslant t \leqslant b)$ be a nonnull solution of the system

$$\frac{d}{dt}(r\dot{x}) + (p+\lambda)x = 0, \qquad x(a) = 0.$$

Show that λ is an eigenvalue of system (5.7) if and only if $x(b,\lambda) = 0$.

2. Use Theorem 5.3 and Example 5.1 to show that

$$\int_0^\pi \dot{x}(t)^2\, dt \geqslant k^2 \int_0^\pi x(t)^2\, dt$$

on the class of arcs x: $x(t)$ $(0 \leqslant t \leqslant \pi)$ having

$$x(0) = x(\pi) = 0, \qquad \int_0^\pi x(t)\sin jt\, dt = 0 \qquad (j=1,\ldots,k-1).$$

3. With the help of Theorem 5.2 and Example 5.1 show that

$$\int_a^b \dot{x}(t)^2\, dt \geqslant \frac{\pi^2}{(b-a)^2} \int_a^b x(t)^2\, dt$$

for all arcs x: $x(t)$ $(a \leqslant t \leqslant b)$ having $x(a) = x(b) = 0$.

6. FURTHER PROPERTIES OF QUADRATIC FORMS

We now return to the finite dimensional case in which P and Q are the quadratic forms

$$P(x) = x^*Ax, \qquad Q(x) = x^*Bx,$$

where A and B are symmetric matrices. In Section 2 it was seen that if B is a positive matrix, the least eigenvalue λ_1 of A relative to B is the minimum value of the Rayleigh quotient,

$$R(x) = \frac{P(x)}{Q(x)}.$$

Consequently, if $-\mu < \lambda_1$, we have $P(x)/Q(x) \geqslant -\mu$ or, equivalently,

$$P(x) + \mu Q(x) > 0 \tag{6.1}$$

for every vector $x \neq 0$. We now consider the question of whether or not inequality (6.1) will hold for some constant μ even if the quadratic form Q is not positive. It is clear that, whenever (6.1) holds, $P(x) > 0$ for all $x \neq 0$ such that $Q(x) = 0$. It is the purpose of this section to prove that the converse is also true, namely, that there is a constant μ such that (6.1) holds for all $x \neq 0$ if $P(x) > 0$ whenever $x \neq 0$ and $Q(x) = 0$. This result is given in

THEOREM 6.1

If $P(x)$ *is positive for all* $x \neq 0$ *such that* $Q(x) = 0$, *then there exists a constant* μ *such that*

$$P(x) + \mu Q(x) > 0$$

for all $x \neq 0$.

The proof of this theorem will be obtained by a sequence of three lemmas given below. Before considering these lemmas, we illustrate this result by

EXAMPLE 6.1

In the *xy*-plane with $z = (x, y)$ the quadratic form

$$P(z) = x^2 - 7xy + y^2$$

is positive whenever $z \neq 0$ and

$$Q(z) = xy = 0.$$

In this event we have

$$P(z) + \mu Q(z) = x^2 + (\mu - 7)xy + y^2.$$

This quadratic form is positive whenever $|\mu - 7| < 2$, that is, when $5 < \mu < 9$.

As a first lemma we have

LEMMA 6.1

Suppose that P *and* Q *are quadratic forms with the property that* $P(x) \leq 0$ *and* $Q(x) \leq 0$ *only if* $x = 0$. *If one of them is nonnegative, then there is a number* $\mu > 0$ *such that*

$$P(x) + \mu Q(x) > 0$$

for all $x \neq 0$.

Consider first the case in which $Q \geq 0$. If the conclusion in the lemma is false, then for every integer q there is a vector $x_q \neq 0$ such that

$$P(x_q) + qQ(x_q) \leq 0. \tag{6.2}$$

Inasmuch as

$$P\left(\frac{x}{|x|}\right) = \frac{P(x)}{|x|^2}, \qquad Q\left(\frac{x}{|x|}\right) = \frac{Q(x)}{|x|^2},$$

inequality (6.2) will hold when x_q is replaced by $x_q/|x_q|$. It follows that we can suppose that x_q has been chosen to be a unit vector. Then the sequence $\{x_q\}$, being bounded, has a convergent subsequence $\{x_{q_j}\}$. Since $Q \geqslant 0$ and $q_j \geqslant j$, we can replace x_q by x_{q_j} and q_j by j in (6.2). Accordingly we can suppose that our original sequence $\{x_q\}$ has been chosen to be a sequence of unit vectors converging to a vector x_0. Since $|x_q| = 1$, we have $|x_0| = \lim_{q \to \infty} |x_q| = 1$. Letting q become infinite in (6.2), we find that

$$P(x_0) + \limsup_{q \to \infty} qQ(x_q) \leqslant 0.$$

Since $Q(x_q) \geqslant 0$, this implies that

$$P(x_0) \leqslant 0, \qquad Q(x_0) = \lim_{q \to \infty} Q(x_q) = 0,$$

contrary to our hypothesis that $P(x) \leqslant 0$ and $Q(x) \leqslant 0$ only if $x = 0$. The lemma therefore holds when Q is nonnegative.

If P is nonnegative, then by interchanging the roles of P and Q we find that there is a positive number λ such that $Q + \lambda P$ is positive. The quadratic form $P + \mu Q$ having $\mu = 1/\lambda$ is therefore positive. This completes the proof of Lemma 6.1.

LEMMA 6.2

Let P *and* Q *be quadratic forms, neither of which is nonnegative. Suppose that* P(x) $\leqslant 0$ *and* Q(x) $\leqslant 0$ *only if* x = 0. *There exist positive numbers* a *and* b *with* a < b *such that*

$$P(x) + \mu Q(x) > 0$$

for all x $\neq 0$ *only if* a < μ < b.

In the proof of this result it will be convenient to introduce the notations

$$J(x, \mu) = P(x) + \mu Q(x), \qquad J(x, y, \mu) = P(x, y) + \mu Q(x, y),$$

where $P(x, y) = x^* A y$ and $Q(x, y) = x^* B y$ are the bilinear forms associated with P and Q, respectively. Clearly

$$J(x,y,\mu) = x^*(A + \mu B)y$$

is the bilinear form associated with $J(x,\mu)$ for each number μ.

Let S be the set of points $x \neq 0$ such that $Q(x) \leqslant 0$. By virtue of our hypotheses there exists a point x such that $Q(x) < 0$. The quadratic form $J(x,\mu)$ therefore cannot be nonnegative on S for large values of μ. However $J(x,0) = P(x) > 0$ on S. Let b be the least upper bound of the values μ such that $J(x,\mu) \geqslant 0$ on S. By continuity we have

$$J(x,b) = P(x) + bQ(x) \geqslant 0 \qquad (6.3)$$

for all x in S. In addition, for each integer q we can select a vector x_q in S such that

$$J\left(x_q, b + \frac{1}{q}\right) = P(x_q) + \left(b + \frac{1}{q}\right)Q(x_q) < 0. \qquad (6.4)$$

We can assume that $|x_q| = 1$. Moreover this sequence can be chosen so as to converge to a vector y, since this result can be obtained by replacing the original sequence by a convergent subsequence. In view of the relations

$$|y| = \lim |x_q| = 1, \qquad Q(y) = \lim Q(x_q) \leqslant 0,$$

it follows that y is in S. Using (6.3) and (6.4), we obtain the inequalities

$$J(y,b) \geqslant 0, \qquad J(y,b) = \lim J\left(x_q, b + \frac{1}{q}\right) \leqslant 0.$$

Consequently

$$J(y,b) = P(y) + bQ(y) = 0.$$

The relation $Q(y) = 0$ would imply that $P(y) = 0$, contrary to our hypotheses. Hence $Q(y) < 0$. Similarly the relation $b = 0$ is impossible. We have accordingly

$$b > 0, \qquad |y| = 1, \qquad P(y) > 0, \qquad Q(y) < 0, \qquad J(y,b) = 0. \quad (6.5)$$

We shall show next that $J(x,b) \geqslant 0$ not only on S but also on the whole space. To this end consider a vector $x \neq 0$. Since $Q(y) < 0$, there is a constant $\delta > 0$ such that $Q(y + tx) < 0$ whenever $|t| \leqslant \delta$. The points $y + tx$

having $|t| \leqslant \delta$ are therefore in S. Consequently, if $|t| \leqslant \delta$, we have

$$f(t) = J(y + tx, b) = J(y, b) + 2tJ(y, x, b) + t^2 J(x, b) \geqslant 0.$$

Since $f(0) = J(y, b) = 0$, the function f has a local minimum at $t = 0$. It follows that

$$f'(0) = 2J(y, x, b) = 0, \qquad f''(0) = 2J(x, b) \geqslant 0.$$

The quadratic form $J(x, b)$ is therefore a nonnegative quadratic form having

$$J(y, b) = 0, \qquad J(y, x, b) = 0$$

for all x in $\mathcal{E}^n$.

Interchanging the roles of P and Q, we see that there is a largest number c and a vector z such that

$$c > 0, \qquad |z| = 1, \qquad P(z) < 0, \qquad Q(z) > 0,$$

$$Q(z) + cP(z) = 0, \qquad Q(x) + cP(x) \geqslant 0, \qquad Q(z, x) + cP(z, x) = 0.$$

Setting $a = 1/c$, we have

$$J(z, a) = 0, \qquad J(x, a) \geqslant 0, \qquad J(z, x, a) = 0.$$

Since $Q(y) < 0$ and $Q(z) > 0$, there is a vector $x_0 = \alpha y + z \neq 0$ such that $Q(x_0) = 0$. Then

$$0 < P(x_0) = J(x_0, b) = J(z, b) = (b - a)Q(z).$$

Consequently $b > a$. Moreover, if $a < \mu < b$, we have

$$J(x, \mu) = J(x, a) + (\mu - a)Q(x) \geqslant (\mu - a)Q(x),$$

$$J(x, \mu) = J(x, b) - (b - \mu)Q(x) \geqslant -(b - \mu)Q(x).$$

It follows that $J(x, \mu) \geqslant 0$, the equality holding only if $Q(x) = 0$ and $P(x) = 0$, that is, only if $x = 0$. This proves Lemma 6.2.

LEMMA 6.3

Suppose that $P(x) > 0$ *whenever* $x \neq 0$ *and* $Q(x) = 0$; *then either* $Q(x)$ *or* $-Q(x)$ *is positive on the set of vectors* $x \neq 0$ *having* $P(x) \leqslant 0$.

Suppose there exist vectors x and y such that

$$P(x) \leqslant 0, \qquad Q(x) < 0, \qquad P(y) \leqslant 0, \qquad Q(y) > 0.$$

On the line $z = x + ty$ we have

$$P(z) = P(x) + 2tP(x,y) + t^2 P(y),$$

$$Q(z) = Q(x) + 2tQ(x,y) + t^2 Q(y).$$

Since $Q(x)Q(y) < 0$, there exist numbers $t' < 0 < t''$ such that $Q(z) = Q(x + ty)$ vanishes at the corresponding points $z' = x + t'y$ and $z'' = x + t''y$. By virtue of our hypotheses $P(z') > 0$ and $P(z'') > 0$. Since x lies between z' and z'', the quadratic equation

$$P(z) = P(x) + 2tP(x,y) + t^2 P(y) = 0$$

has two roots between t' and t''. This is impossible, however, if $P(y) = 0$. Hence $P(y) < 0$. But then $P(x + ty)$ would have an additional root exterior to $[t', t'']$, and this too is impossible. In view of this contradiction the lemma is established.

We are now in a position to prove Theorem 6.1. Since $P(x) > 0$ whenever $x \neq 0$ and $Q(x) = 0$, it follows from Lemma 6.3 that, by replacing Q by $-Q$ if necessary, we can suppose that $Q(x) > 0$ for all $x \neq 0$ such that $P(x) \leqslant 0$. There is accordingly no vector $x \neq 0$ such that $P(x) \leqslant 0$ and $Q(x) \leqslant 0$. In view of Lemmas 6.1 and 6.2 there is a number μ such that $P + \mu Q$ is positive, as was to be proved.

EXERCISES

In Exercises 1 to 3 determine whether or not a constant μ exists such that $P + \mu Q$ is positive.

1. $P = 2x^2 + xy, \qquad Q = xy + y^2$.

2. $P = x^2, \qquad Q = xy$.

3. $P = xy, \qquad Q = x^2 + y^2$.

4. Suppose that Q, R are two quadratic forms on $\mathcal{E}^n$ such that $\lambda Q + \mu R$ is indefinite for all $(\lambda, \mu) \neq (0,0)$. Suppose that a quadratic form P has the property that $P(x) > 0$ whenever $x \neq 0$, $Q(x) = 0$, and $R(x) = 0$. Show that λ, μ can be chosen so that $P + \lambda Q + \mu R$ is positive on $\mathcal{E}^n$.

5. Let $L_1, \ldots, L_m$ be linear forms. Show that, if P is a quadratic form such that $P(x) > 0$ for all $x \neq 0$ having $L_j(x) = 0$ $(j = 1, \ldots, m)$, there is a constant μ such that $P(x) + \mu[L_1(x)^2 + \cdots + L_m(x)^2] > 0$ for all $x \neq 0$.

7. RECTANGULAR MATRICES, NORMS, AND PRINCIPAL VALUES

We now turn to the study of rectangular matrices. In particular, we shall be concerned with an $(m \times n)$-dimensional matrix,

$$A = (a_{ij}) \qquad (i = 1, \ldots, m; j = 1, \ldots, n).$$

This matrix is associated with the linear transformation

$$y = Ax,$$

which maps a point x in an n-dimensional Euclidean space $\mathscr{E}^n$ to a point y in an m-dimensional Euclidean space $\mathscr{E}^m$. This transformation maps the unit sphere

$$|x| = 1$$

into an (normally degenerate) ellipsoid. The lengths

$$\mu_1 \geqslant \mu_2 \geqslant \cdots \geqslant \mu_r > 0$$

of the nonnull semiaxes of this ellipsoid are called the principal (or singular) values of A. The purpose of this section is to determine these principal values of A by analytic and algebraic methods.

The concept of a principal value of a matrix is closely associated with the concept of the norm of a matrix. The *norm* $\|A\|$ of a matrix A is defined by the formula

$$\|A\| = \max \frac{|Ax|}{|x|} = \max \left[\frac{x^* A^* A x}{x^* x} \right]^{1/2}$$

for all $x \neq 0$ in $\mathscr{E}^n$. Here A^* is the transpose of A. In view of this formula $\|A\|$ is the square root of the largest eigenvalue of $A^* A$.

Set $\mu_1 = \|A\|$, and select a vector x_1 such that

$$|x_1| = 1, \qquad \mu_1 = \frac{|Ax_1|}{|x_1|} = |Ax_1|.$$

Since x_1 maximizes the Rayleigh quotient

$$\frac{x^* A^* A x}{x^* x}$$

for $A^* A$, we have, by Theorem 2.1,

$$A^* A x_1 = \mu_1^2 x_1.$$

it follows that the vector

$$y_1 = \frac{1}{\mu_1} A x_1 \qquad (\mu_1 = |Ax_1|) \tag{7.1}$$

is a unit vector in $\mathscr{E}^m$ such that

$$A^* y_1 = \frac{1}{\mu_1} A^* A x_1 = \mu_1 x_1.$$

From this relation we see that

$$\|A\| = \mu_1 = |\mu_1 x_1| = |A^* y_1| = \frac{|A^* y_1|}{|y_1|} \leqslant \|A^*\|.$$

Interchanging the roles of A and A^*, we see that $\|A^*\| \leqslant \|A\|$. Hence $\|A\| = \|A^*\|$. A matrix and its transpose accordingly have the same norm. Moreover, if x_1 is a unit vector that maximizes

$$\frac{|Ax|}{|x|},$$

then the vector y_1 defined by (7.1) with $\mu_1 = \|A\|$ is a unit vector that maximizes the corresponding ratio,

$$\frac{|A^* y|}{|y|},$$

for A^*. The vectors x_1 and y_1 are connected by the relations

$$Ax_1 = \mu_1 y_1, \qquad A^* y_1 = \mu_1 x_1, \tag{7.2a}$$

$$\mu_1 = |Ax_1| = |A^* y_1|, \qquad |x_1| = |y_1| = 1. \tag{7.2b}$$

The number μ_1 described above is a principal value of A according to the following definition. By a *principal* (or *singular*) *value* μ of A will be meant a positive number μ such that there exist a vector $x \neq 0$ in $\mathscr{E}^n$ and a vector $y \neq 0$ in $\mathscr{E}^m$ satisfying the relations

$$Ax = \mu y, \qquad A^* y = \mu x. \tag{7.3}$$

The corresponding vectors x and y are called *principal* (or *singular*) *vectors of A and A^**, respectively. Observe that if (7.3) holds then

$$y^* Ax = \mu y^* y = \mu x^* x.$$

Consequently $y^*y = x^*x$, that is, $|x| = |y|$. Relations (7.3) therefore imply that x and y have the same length and that

$$\mu = \frac{|Ax|}{|x|} = \frac{|A^*y|}{|y|}. \tag{7.4}$$

Observe also that, by (7.3),

$$A^*Ax = \mu^2 x, \qquad AA^*y = \mu^2 y. \tag{7.5}$$

Hence μ^2 is an eigenvalue of A^*A, and x is a corresponding eigenvector. Furthermore μ^2 is also an eigenvalue of AA^*, and y is a corresponding eigenvector. Conversely, let λ be a nonnull eigenvalue of A^*A, and let x be a unit vector such that

$$A^*Ax = \lambda x.$$

Then $\lambda > 0$. Setting $\mu = \lambda^{1/2}$ and

$$y = \frac{1}{\mu} Ax,$$

we see that

$$A^*y = \frac{1}{\mu} A^*Ax = \frac{\lambda}{\mu} x = \mu x.$$

Consequently x is a principal vector of A if and only if x is an eigenvector of A^*A corresponding to a *nonnull* eigenvalue λ of A^*A. Moreover $\mu = \lambda^{1/2}$ is the corresponding principal value. Similarly a vector y is a principal vector of A^* if and only if y is an eigenvector of AA^* corresponding to a nonnull eigenvalue λ of AA^* and $\mu = \lambda^{1/2}$ is the corresponding principal value.

Recall that the *null space* $\mathfrak{N}_A$ of A is the class of all vectors x_0 such that $Ax_0 = 0$. A principal vector x of A is orthogonal to $\mathfrak{N}_A$, for, if x_0 is in $\mathfrak{N}_A$, then $x_0^* A^* = 0$ and by (7.3)

$$0 = x_0^* A^*y = \mu x_0^* x.$$

Since $\mu > 0$, we have $x_0^* x = 0$, as was to be proved. Similarly a principal vector y of A^* is orthogonal to the null space $\mathfrak{N}_{A^*}$ of A^*.

THEOREM 7.1

Let r *be the rank of* A. *There exists an orthonormal set of principal vectors* $x_1, \ldots, x_r$ *of* A *corresponding to a set of* r *principal values* $\mu_1, \ldots, \mu_r$ *satisfying the inequalities*

$$\mu \geqslant \mu_2 \geqslant \cdots \geqslant \mu_r.$$

The vectors $y_1, \ldots, y_r$, *defined by the formula*

$$y_\alpha = \frac{1}{\mu_\alpha} A x_\alpha \qquad (\alpha = 1, \ldots, r), \tag{7.6}$$

are corresponding orthonormal principal vectors of A^*. *Moreover*

$$\mu_k = \max \frac{|Ax|}{|x|} \text{ for all } x \neq 0 \text{ in } \mathcal{E}^n \text{ orthogonal to } x_1, \ldots, x_{k-1}. \tag{7.7}$$

Similarly

$$x_\alpha = \frac{1}{\mu_\alpha} A^* y_\alpha \tag{7.8}$$

and

$$\mu_k = \max \frac{|A^* y|}{|y|} \text{ for all } y \neq 0 \text{ in } \mathcal{E}^m \text{ orthogonal to } y_1, \ldots, y_{k-1}. \tag{7.9}$$

To prove this result we use, an orthonormal set of eigenvectors $x_1, \ldots, x_r$ corresponding to the r nonzero eigenvalues $\lambda_1, \ldots, \lambda_r$ of A^*A, which exist by virtue of Theorem 9.5 in Chapter 1. These can be ordered so that

$$\lambda_1 \geqslant \lambda_2 \geqslant \cdots \geqslant \lambda_r.$$

Setting $\mu_\alpha = \lambda_\alpha^{1/2}$, we obtain the first conclusion in the theorem from the remark made in the paragraphs preceding Theorem 7.1. In addition, we have $|y_\alpha| = |x_\alpha| = 1$ and

$$y_\alpha^* y_\beta = \frac{1}{\mu_\alpha \mu_\beta} x_\alpha^* A^* A x_\beta = \frac{\lambda_\alpha}{\mu_\alpha \mu_\beta} x_\alpha^* x_\beta = 0. \qquad (\alpha \neq \beta).$$

It follows that the vectors $y_1, \ldots, y_r$ are orthonormal. Relation (7.7) is equivalent to the statement that

$$\mu_k^2 = \lambda_k = \max \frac{x^* A^* A x}{x^* x} \qquad \text{for all } x \neq 0 \text{ orthogonal to } x_1, \ldots, x_{k-1}.$$

The remaining statement in the theorem follows by symmetry.

COROLLARY

A vector x *is in the null space of* A *if and only if it is orthogonal to the principal vectors of* A. *Similarly a vector* y *is in the null space of* A* *if and only if it is orthogonal to the principal vectors of* A*.

Clearly $Ax=0$ if and only if $A*Ax=0$. Hence a vector $x \neq 0$ is in the null space of A if and only if x is an eigenvector of $A*A$ corresponding to the eigenvalue $\lambda = 0$. Such an eigenvector is characterized by being orthogonal to all eigenvectors $x_1, \ldots, x_r$ of $A*A$ corresponding to the positive eigenvalues $\lambda_1 = \mu_1{}^2, \ldots, \lambda_k = \mu_k{}^2$. Since these eigenvectors are principal vectors of A, the first conclusion in the corollary follows. Replacing A by $A*$, we obtain the second conclusion.

EXAMPLE 7.1

Consider the matrix

$$A = \begin{bmatrix} 5 & 3 & 3 & 5 \\ 2 & 6 & 6 & 2 \\ 4 & 0 & 0 & 4 \end{bmatrix}.$$

Its principal values are $\mu_1 = 12$, $\mu_2 = 6$. The corresponding principal vectors of A and $A*$ are

$$x_1 = \begin{bmatrix} \frac{1}{2} \\ \frac{1}{2} \\ \frac{1}{2} \\ \frac{1}{2} \end{bmatrix}, \quad x_2 = \begin{bmatrix} \frac{1}{2} \\ -\frac{1}{2} \\ -\frac{1}{2} \\ \frac{1}{2} \end{bmatrix}, \quad y_1 = \begin{bmatrix} \frac{2}{3} \\ \frac{2}{3} \\ \frac{1}{3} \end{bmatrix}, \quad y_2 = \begin{bmatrix} \frac{1}{3} \\ -\frac{2}{3} \\ \frac{2}{3} \end{bmatrix}.$$

To verify this, observe that

$$Ax_1 = \begin{bmatrix} 8 \\ 8 \\ 4 \end{bmatrix} = 12y_1, \qquad A*y_1 = \begin{bmatrix} 6 \\ 6 \\ 6 \\ 6 \end{bmatrix} = 12x_1.$$

Similarly $Ax_2 = 6y_2$, $A*y_2 = 6x_2$. The vectors x_3 and x_4 having

$$2x_3^* = (1, -1, 1, -1), \qquad 2x_4^* = (1, 1, -1, -1)$$

are unit vectors generating the null space $\mathfrak{N}_A$ of A. Similarly the multiples of the vector y_3 having $3y_3^* = (-2, 1, 2)$ generate the null space of $A*$. It is easily verified that

$$A^*A = \begin{bmatrix} 45 & 27 & 27 & 45 \\ 27 & 45 & 45 & 27 \\ 27 & 45 & 45 & 27 \\ 45 & 27 & 27 & 45 \end{bmatrix}, \qquad AA^* = \begin{bmatrix} 68 & 56 & 40 \\ 56 & 80 & 16 \\ 40 & 16 & 32 \end{bmatrix}.$$

The vectors x_1, x_2, x_3, x_4 are orthonormal eigenvectors of A^*A corresponding to the eigenvalues $144, 36, 0, 0$. Similarly y_1, y_2, y_3 are orthonormal vectors of AA^* corresponding to the eigenvalues $144, 36, 0$. Observe that the matrices

$$U_1 = y_1 x_1^* = \begin{bmatrix} \frac{2}{3} \\ \frac{2}{3} \\ \frac{1}{3} \end{bmatrix} \begin{pmatrix} \frac{1}{2} & \frac{1}{2} & \frac{1}{2} & \frac{1}{2} \end{pmatrix} = \begin{bmatrix} \frac{1}{3} & \frac{1}{3} & \frac{1}{3} & \frac{1}{3} \\ \frac{1}{3} & \frac{1}{3} & \frac{1}{3} & \frac{1}{3} \\ \frac{1}{6} & \frac{1}{6} & \frac{1}{6} & \frac{1}{6} \end{bmatrix},$$

$$U_2 = y_2 x_2^* = \begin{bmatrix} \frac{1}{3} \\ -\frac{2}{3} \\ \frac{2}{3} \end{bmatrix} \begin{pmatrix} \frac{1}{2} & -\frac{1}{2} & -\frac{1}{2} & \frac{1}{2} \end{pmatrix} = \begin{bmatrix} \frac{1}{6} & -\frac{1}{6} & -\frac{1}{6} & \frac{1}{6} \\ -\frac{1}{3} & \frac{1}{3} & \frac{1}{3} & -\frac{1}{3} \\ \frac{1}{3} & -\frac{1}{3} & -\frac{1}{3} & \frac{1}{3} \end{bmatrix},$$

are matrices of rank 1 such that

$$U_1 U_1^* U_1 = y_1 x_1^* x_1 y_1^* y_1 x_1^* = y_1 x_1^* = U_1, \qquad U_2 U_2^* U_2 = U_2, \quad (7.10)$$

$$U_i U_j^* U_k = 0 \qquad \text{unless } i = j = k.$$

The matrices A and A^* are given by the formulas

$$A = 12U_1 + 6U_2, \qquad A^* = 12U_1^* + 6U_2^*, \quad (7.11)$$

as can readily be verified. In fact, this formula was used to construct the matrix A. By the use of the formulas for U_1 and U_2, we have

$$U = U_1 + U_2 = \begin{bmatrix} \frac{1}{2} & \frac{1}{6} & \frac{1}{6} & \frac{1}{2} \\ 0 & \frac{2}{3} & \frac{2}{3} & 0 \\ \frac{1}{2} & -\frac{1}{6} & -\frac{1}{6} & \frac{1}{2} \end{bmatrix}.$$

Observe that

$$UU^* = \begin{bmatrix} \frac{5}{9} & \frac{2}{9} & \frac{4}{9} \\ \frac{2}{9} & \frac{8}{9} & -\frac{2}{9} \\ \frac{4}{9} & -\frac{2}{9} & \frac{5}{9} \end{bmatrix}, \qquad UA^* = \begin{bmatrix} 6 & 4 & 4 \\ 4 & 8 & 0 \\ 4 & 0 & 4 \end{bmatrix}.$$

Using these results, we readily see that

$$U = UU^*U, \qquad A = UA^*U.$$

We term the matrix U to be a *unit associated with* A. It can be verified that the principal values $\mu_1 = 12$ and $\mu_2 = 6$ of of A are the eigenvalues of UA^*. They are also the eigenvalues of A^*U. Finally, if we set

$$A^{-*} = \tfrac{1}{12}U_1 + \tfrac{1}{6}U_2, \qquad A^{-1} = \tfrac{1}{12}U_1^* + \tfrac{1}{6}U_2^*,$$

then

$$A^{-*} = (A^{-1})^* = \begin{bmatrix} \frac{1}{18} & 0 & 0 & \frac{1}{18} \\ -\frac{1}{36} & \frac{1}{12} & \frac{1}{12} & -\frac{1}{36} \\ \frac{5}{72} & -\frac{1}{24} & -\frac{1}{24} & \frac{5}{72} \end{bmatrix}.$$

The matrices A^{-1} and $A^{-*} = (A^{-1})^*$ are the *pseudoinverses* of A and A^*, respectively. They have the property that

$$A = AA^{-1}A, \qquad A^{-1} = A^{-1}AA^{-1},$$

$$A^* = A^*A^{-*}A^*, \qquad A^{-*} = A^{-*}A^*A^{-*}.$$

These relations can be verified by carrying out the indicated multiplications. However, in the next section we shall establish these formulas by theoretical considerations.

The example just considered illustrates a general theory summarized in

THEOREM 7.2

Let $\mu_1 \geqslant \mu_2 \geqslant \cdots \geqslant \mu_r$ be the principal values of a matrix A. *Let* $x_1,\ldots,x_r$ *be a corresponding set of orthonormal principal vectors of* A, *and let* $y_1,\ldots,y_r$ *be the corresponding principal vectors of* A*, *defined by the formula*

$$y_\alpha = \frac{1}{\mu_\alpha}Ax_\alpha \qquad (\alpha = 1,\ldots,r). \tag{7.12}$$

The matrices

$$U_\alpha = y_\alpha x_\alpha^* \qquad (\alpha = 1,\ldots,r) \tag{7.13}$$

are matrices of rank 1 such that

$$U_\alpha = U_\alpha U_\alpha^* U_\alpha, \qquad U_\alpha U_\beta^* U_\gamma = 0 \qquad unless\ \alpha = \beta = \gamma. \tag{7.14}$$

The sum

$$U = U_1 + \cdots + U_r \qquad (7.15)$$

has the property that

$$y_\alpha = U x_\alpha, \qquad x_\alpha = U^* y_\alpha \qquad (\alpha = 1, \ldots, r). \qquad (7.16)$$

The matrix U *has the same null space as* A, *and its transpose* U* *has the same null space as* A*. *Moreover*

$$U = U U^* U, \qquad (7.17)$$

and

$$A = U A^* U = U U^* A = A U^* U = \mu_1 U_1 + \cdots + \mu_r U_r. \qquad (7.18)$$

Finally

$$A x_\alpha = \mu_\alpha U x_\alpha, \qquad A^* y_\alpha = \mu_\alpha U^* y_\alpha \qquad (\alpha = 1, \ldots, n) \qquad (7.19)$$

Inasmuch as the vectors $x_1, \ldots, x_r$ and $y_1, \ldots, y_r$ are orthonormal, we have

$$x_\alpha^* x_\beta = \delta_{\alpha\beta}, \qquad y_\alpha^* y_\beta = \delta_{\alpha\beta} \qquad (\alpha, \beta = 1, \ldots, r). \qquad (7.20)$$

From these relations it is seen, by (7.13), that

$$U_\alpha x_\alpha = y_\alpha x_\alpha^* x_\alpha = y_\alpha, \qquad U_\beta x_\alpha = y_\beta x_\beta^* x_\alpha = 0 \qquad (\alpha \neq \beta), \qquad (7.21)$$

$$U_\alpha U_\alpha^* = U_\alpha x_\alpha y_\alpha^* = y_\alpha y_\alpha^*, \qquad U_\beta U_\alpha^* = U_\beta x_\alpha y_\alpha^* = 0 \qquad (\alpha \neq \beta). \qquad (7.22)$$

Similarly

$$U_\alpha^* y_\alpha = x_\alpha, \qquad U_\beta^* y_\alpha = 0 \qquad (\alpha \neq \beta), \qquad (7.23)$$

$$U_\alpha^* U_\alpha = x_\alpha x_\alpha^*, \qquad U_\beta^* U_\alpha = 0. \qquad (\alpha \neq \beta). \qquad (7.24)$$

Finally

$$U_\alpha U_\alpha^* U_\alpha = y_\alpha y_\alpha^* U_\alpha = y_\alpha x_\alpha^* = U_\alpha, \qquad U_\alpha U_\beta^* U_\gamma = 0 \qquad \text{unless } \alpha = \beta = \gamma,$$

$$(7.25)$$

as described in (7.14). Using (7.21) and (7.23), we see that the matrix

$U = U_1 + \cdots + U_r$ has the property

$$Ux_\alpha = \sum_\beta U_\beta x_\alpha = U_\alpha x_\alpha = y_\alpha, \qquad U^* y_\alpha = \sum_\beta U_\beta^* y_\alpha = x_\alpha.$$

Combining this result with the relation

$$Ax_\alpha = \mu_\alpha y_\alpha, \qquad A^* y_\alpha = \mu_\alpha x_\alpha,$$

we find that

$$Ax_\alpha = \mu_\alpha Ux_\alpha, \qquad A^* y_\alpha = \mu_\alpha Uy_\alpha.$$

This proves (7.16) and (7.19). Recall that

$$Ax = 0 \qquad \text{if and only if } x_\alpha^* x = 0 \qquad (\alpha = 1, \dots, r).$$

Observe further that, since $y_1, \dots, y_r$ are linearly independent,

$$Ux = \sum_\alpha U_\alpha x = \sum_\alpha y_\alpha (x_\alpha^* x) = 0$$

if and only if the coefficients $x_\alpha^* x$ are zero. We have accordingly $Ax = 0$ if and only if $Ux = 0$. The matrices A and U accordingly have the same null space. Similarly A^* and U^* have the same null space.

The relation $UU^* U = U$ is a consequence of (7.25), as can be seen by the computations

$$UU^* U = \sum_\alpha \sum_\beta \sum_\gamma U_\alpha U_\beta^* U_\gamma = \sum_\alpha U_\alpha U_\alpha^* U_\alpha = \sum_\alpha U_\alpha = U.$$

To see that $A = \sum_\alpha \mu_\alpha U_\alpha$, observe that, since $x_1, \dots, x_r$ are orthonormal, a vector x in $\mathcal{E}^n$ is expressible uniquely in the form

$$x = \sum_\alpha x_\alpha x_\alpha^* x + x_0,$$

where x_0 is orthogonal to $x_1, \dots, x_r$ and hence is in the null space of A. We have accordingly

$$Ax = \sum_\alpha Ax_\alpha x_\alpha^* x + Ax_0 = \sum_\alpha \mu_\alpha y_\alpha x_\alpha^* x = \left(\sum_\alpha \mu_\alpha U_\alpha \right) x.$$

Since x is arbitrary, we have $A = \sum_\alpha \mu_\alpha U_\alpha$, as was to be proved.

Finally, by (7.25) again, we have

$$UA^*U = \sum_\alpha \sum_\beta \sum_\gamma \mu_\beta U_\alpha U_\beta^* U_\gamma = \sum_\alpha \mu_\alpha U_\alpha = A.$$

Moreover, since $UU^*U = U$, we have

$$A = UA^*U = UU^*UA^*U = UU^*A = UA^*UU^*U = AU^*U.$$

This completes the proof of Theorem 7.2.

From the relation $A = UA^*U$ it is seen that A is of the form $A = UP$, where

$$P = A^*U = (AU^*U)^*U = U^*UA^*U = U^*A$$

is symmetric. The matrix P has the same null space as A. In addition,

$$Px_\alpha = A^*Ux_\alpha = A^*y_\alpha = \mu_\alpha x_\alpha.$$

Hence $x_1,\ldots,x_r$ are the eigenvectors of P, and $\mu_1,\ldots,\mu_r$ are the corresponding eigenvalues. The matrix P is therefore nonnegative. Moreover

$$P^2 = A^*UU^*A = A^*A.$$

Consequently P is the square root of A^*A. In the same manner it is seen that $A = QU$, where $Q = UA^* = AU^*$ is the square root of AA^*. The eigenvectors of Q are $y_1,\ldots,y_r$ corresponding to $\mu_1,\ldots,\mu_r$ as eigenvalues of Q.

The connection between principal values and norms is given in

THEOREM 7.3

Let $\mu_1 \geqslant \mu_2 \geqslant \cdots \geqslant \mu_r$ be the principal values of A. Let $x_1,\ldots,x_r$ be corresponding orthonormal principal vectors of A, and let

$$y_\alpha = \frac{1}{\mu_\alpha} Ax_\alpha$$

be the corresponding principal vectors of A*. Set

$$A_1 = A, \qquad A_{\alpha+1} = A_\alpha - \mu_\alpha y_\alpha x_\alpha^* \qquad (\alpha = 1,\ldots,r-1).$$

Then μ_α is the norm of A_α. In fact,

$$\mu_\alpha = \|A_\alpha\| = \|A_\alpha^*\| = |Ax_\alpha| = |A^*y_\alpha|.$$

This result follows at once because

$$A_\alpha = \mu_\alpha U_\alpha + \cdots + \mu_r U_r,$$

from which we conclude that μ_α is the largest principal value of A_α and is accordingly its norm.

EXERCISES

1. Let A and B be $(m \times n)$-dimensional matrices, C an $(n \times p)$=dimensional matrix, and α a real number. Show that, in addition to the fact that $\|A\| > 0$ unless $A = 0$, we have

$$\|\alpha A\| = |\alpha| \|A\|, \qquad \|A + B\| \leqslant \|A\| + \|B\|, \qquad \|BC\| \leqslant \|B\| \|C\|.$$

2. Show that the principal values of A are the positive eigenvalues of the $[(m + n) \times (m + n)]$-dimensional symmetric matrix

$$\begin{pmatrix} 0 & A^* \\ A & 0 \end{pmatrix}.$$

3. Show that the function

$$f(x,y) = 2y^* A x - |x|^2 |y|^2$$

on $\mathcal{E}^n \times \mathcal{E}^m$ satisfies the relation

$$f\left(\alpha x, \frac{y}{\alpha} \right) = f(x,y) \qquad (\alpha \neq 0)$$

for real values $\alpha \neq 0$. Use this fact to show that this function possesses a maximum value λ_1 and that $\lambda_1 = \|A\|^2$. Show that, if $(x,y) \neq (0,0)$ is a critical point of f, so also is $(\alpha x, y/\alpha)$ $(\alpha \neq 0)$, and the corresponding critical value is $\mu^2 = |x| |y| = y^* A x$. Moreover μ is a principal value of A with $x/|x|$ and $y/|y|$ as corresponding principal unit vectors A and A^*, as described above.

4. Use the function f described in Exercise 3 to prove Theorem 7.1.

5. The number $\|A\|_E = (\Sigma_{i=1}^m \Sigma_{j=1}^n a_{ij}^2)^{1/2}$ is called the *Euclidean norm* of A. Show that

$$\|A\|_E^2 = \mu_1^2 + \cdots + \mu_r^2,$$

where $\mu_1, \ldots, \mu_r$ are the principal values of A. *Hint*: Observe that $\|A\|_E^2$ is the trace of $A^* A$.

6. Show that

$$F(x,y) = \|A - yx^*\|_E^2 = \|A\|_E^2 - f(x,y),$$

where f is the function described in Exercise 3. Hence show that there exist vectors x_1, y_1 which minimize $F(x,y)$ and that $\|A\|^2 = |x_1||y_1|$. Show that $\|A\|_E^2 - \|A\|^2$ is the minimum value of $F(x,y)$. Show that x_1, y_1 can be chosen so that $|x_1| = |y_1|$. Show further that, if $|x_1| = |y_1|$, then

$$Ax_1 = \mu_1 y_1, \qquad A^* y_1 = \mu_1 x_1, \qquad \mu_1 = \|A\|.$$

Hence x_1 is the principal vector for A, and y_1 is the associated principal vector for A^* corresponding to the largest principal value μ_1 of A.

7. Recall that a matrix M of rank 1 is expressible in the form $M = yx^*$, where x and y are vectors. Interpret the results described in Exercise 6 in terms of matrices of rank 1.

8. Let x_1, x_2, x_3 and y_1, y_2 be, respectively, the column vectors of the matrices

$$X = \begin{bmatrix} \dfrac{1}{\sqrt{3}} & \dfrac{1}{\sqrt{2}} & \dfrac{1}{\sqrt{6}} \\ \dfrac{1}{\sqrt{3}} & -\dfrac{1}{\sqrt{2}} & \dfrac{1}{\sqrt{6}} \\ \dfrac{1}{\sqrt{3}} & 0 & -\dfrac{2}{\sqrt{6}} \end{bmatrix}, \qquad Y = \begin{pmatrix} \frac{3}{5} & \frac{4}{5} \\ \frac{4}{5} & -\frac{3}{5} \end{pmatrix}.$$

Construct a (2×3)-dimensional matrix A having $\mu_1 = 10\sqrt{3}$ and $\mu_2 = 5\sqrt{2}$ as its principal values, and x_1, x_2 as corresponding principal vectors with y_1 and y_2 as the corresponding principal vectors of A^*. Construct the corresponding matrices U_1, U_2, and $U = U_1 + U_2$ described in Theorem 7.2, and verify that they are related to A as described in Theorem 7.2. Find the null space of A. Show that, if $B = \nu_1 U_1 + \nu_2 U_2$ and $C = \sigma_1 U_1 + \sigma_2 U_2$, then

$$AB^*C = \mu_1 \nu_1 \sigma_1 U_1 + \mu_2 \nu_2 \sigma_2 U_2.$$

Show that AB^*C is invariant under permutations of A, B, and C.

9. Let $x_1, \ldots, x_r$ be an orthonormal set of principal vectors of A corresponding to the principal values $\mu_1, \ldots, \mu_r$ of A as described in Theorem 7.1. Let $y_1, \ldots, y_r$ be the corresponding principal vectors of A^* defined by (7.6). Let X be the $(n \times r)$-dimensional matrix whose column vectors are $x_1, \ldots, x_r$. Let Y be the $(m \times r)$-dimensional matrix whose column vectors are $y_1, \ldots, y_r$. Show that

$$AX = YM, \qquad A^*Y = XM, \qquad X^*AY = M,$$

where M is the $(r \times r)$-dimensional diagonal matrix whose diagonal elements are $\mu_1, \ldots, \mu_r$.

10. Given a matrix A, let k be the least integer for which there exist numbers $c_1, \ldots, c_k$ such that

$$A = c_1 A(A^*A) + c_2 A(A^*A)^2 + \cdots + c_k A(A^*A)^k.$$

Show that, if μ is a principal value of A, then $\lambda = \mu^2$ is a zero of the polynomial

$$p(\lambda) = -1 + c_1\lambda + c_2\lambda^2 + \cdots + c_k\lambda^k.$$

Show conversely that, if $p(\lambda) = 0$, then $\lambda > 0$ and $\mu = \lambda^{1/2}$ is a principal value of A. Show that k is the number of distinct principal values of A.

11.   Show that the results given in this section are valid for a complex matrix A. In the complex case A^* denotes the conjugate transpose of A.

8.   PSEUDOINVERSES AND *-RECIPROCALS OF MATRICES

The purpose of this section is to show that every matrix A has an inverse in a generalized sense. This generalized inverse is called the *pseudoinverse* of A and will be denoted by A^{-1}. This notation is used because, if A is a nonsingular square matrix, A^{-1} is the ordinary inverse of A. The pseudoinverse of A is sometimes called the *general reciprocal* of A. The transpose $(A^{-1})^*$ of A^{-1} is the pseudoinverse of the transpose A^* of A. Hence $(A^{-1})^* = (A^*)^{-1}$. This suggests that we use the notation A^{-*} for the pseudoinverse of A^*. We shall call A^{-*} the *-reciprocal* of A. It should be observed that, if A is an $(m \times n)$-dimensional matrix, so also is A^{-*}. On the other hand, the matrices A^* and A^{-1} are $(n \times m)$-dimensional matrices. Since the theory of pseudoinverses plays no significant role in this book, we present it in condensed form.

Consider an $(m \times n)$-dimensional matrix A. This matrix is associated with a linear transformation

$$y = Ax, \tag{8.1}$$

which maps our n-dimensional Euclidean space $\mathcal{E}^n$ onto a linear subspace $\mathcal{R}_A$ of an m-dimensional Euclidean space $\mathcal{E}^m$. The linear subspace $\mathcal{R}_A$ is called the *range* of A. Every vector y in $\mathcal{E}^m$ is expressible uniquely in the form

$$y = \hat{y} + y_0 \qquad (\hat{y} \in \mathcal{R}_A, y_0 \in \mathcal{R}_A^\perp), \tag{8.2}$$

where $\hat{y}$ is in $\mathcal{R}_A$ and y_0 is in the orthogonal complement $\mathcal{R}_A^\perp$. The set of points x_0 in $\mathcal{E}^n$ such that $Ax_0 = 0$ forms a linear subspace $\mathcal{N}_A$ of $\mathcal{E}^n$ called the *null space of* A. Every vector x in $\mathcal{E}^n$ is expressible in the form

$$x = \hat{x} + x_0 \qquad (\hat{x} \in \mathcal{N}_A^\perp, x_0 \in \mathcal{N}_A), \tag{8.3}$$

where x_0 is in $\mathcal{N}_A$ and $\hat{x}$ is in the orthogonal complement, $\mathcal{N}_A^\perp$. We have

$$Ax = A\hat{x} + Ax_0 = A\hat{x}.$$

It follows that for each $\hat{y}$ in $\mathfrak{R}_A$ there is a unique $\hat{x}$ in $\mathfrak{N}_A^{\perp}$ such that $\hat{y} = A\hat{x}$. We denote the vector $\hat{x}$ corresponding to $\hat{y} = A\hat{x}$ in $\mathfrak{R}_A$ by $\hat{x} = A^{-1}\hat{y}$. The transformation $\hat{x} = A^{-1}\hat{y}$ is a linear transformation on $\mathfrak{R}_A$. We extend this transformation to all y in $\mathcal{E}^m$ by the formula

$$A^{-1}y = A^{-1}(\hat{y} + y_0) = A^{-1}\hat{y},$$

where $\hat{y}$ and y_0 are related to y as described in (8.2). If $y = y_0$ is in $\mathfrak{R}_A^{\perp}$, then $\hat{y} = 0$ and $A^{-1}y = 0$. The class $\mathfrak{R}_A^{\perp}$ is accordingly the nullspace $\mathfrak{N}_{A^{-1}}$ of A^{-1}. The transformation

$$x = A^{-1}y \tag{8.4}$$

so defined is called the pseudoinverse of transformation (8.1). The matrix A^{-1} associated with (8.4) is called pseudoinverse of A.

It remains to give a precise formula for the pseudoinverse A^{-1} of A. To this end, let $x_1, \ldots, x_r$ be a maximal set of orthonormal principal vectors of A in $\mathcal{E}^n$. Let $\mu_1, \ldots, \mu_r$ be the corresponding principal values of A. Let $y_1, \ldots, y_r$ be the corresponding principal vectors of A^*. We have the relations

$$Ax_\alpha = \mu_\alpha y_\alpha, \qquad A^* y_\alpha = \mu_\alpha x_\alpha \qquad (\alpha = 1, \ldots, r). \tag{8.5}$$

The vectors $x_1, \ldots, x_r$ form an orthonormal basis for the orthogonal complement $\mathfrak{N}_A^{\perp}$ of the null space $\mathfrak{N}_A$ of A. Similarly $y_1, \ldots, y_r$ form the corresponding orthonormal basis for the range $\mathfrak{R}_A$ of A. In Section 7 it was seen that the matrix A is expressible as the sum

$$A = \mu_1 y_1 x_1^* + \cdots + \mu_r y_r x_r^* \tag{8.6}$$

of matrices $\mu_\alpha U_\alpha = \mu_\alpha y_\alpha x_\alpha^*$ of rank 1. The matrix A^{-1} defined by the formula

$$A^{-1} = \frac{1}{\mu_1} x_1 y_1^* + \cdots + \frac{1}{\mu_r} x_r y_r^* \tag{8.7}$$

is the pseudoinverse of A described above. To verify this, consider a point y in $\mathcal{E}^m$, and select $\hat{y}$ in $\mathfrak{R}_A$ and y_0 in $\mathfrak{R}_A^{\perp}$ so that $y = \hat{y} + y_0$. Observe that $y_\alpha^* y_0 = 0$ and hence that $y_\alpha^* y = y_\alpha^* \hat{y}$. Clearly

$$\hat{y} = \sum_\alpha y_\alpha b_\alpha, \qquad b_\alpha = y_\alpha^* y = y_\alpha^* \hat{y}.$$

By the use of (8.7) we see that the vector

$$\hat{x}=A^{-1}y=\sum_\alpha \frac{1}{\mu_\alpha}x_\alpha y_\alpha^* y=\sum_\alpha x_\alpha a_\alpha=\sum_\alpha \frac{1}{\mu_\alpha}x_\alpha y_\alpha^* \hat{y}=A^{-1}\hat{y} \qquad \left(a_\alpha=\frac{1}{\mu_\alpha}b_\alpha\right)$$

is in $\mathfrak{N}_A^\perp$. It has the property that

$$A\hat{x}=\sum_\alpha Ax_\alpha a_\alpha=\sum_\alpha \mu_\alpha y_\alpha a_\alpha=\sum_\alpha y_\alpha b_\alpha=\hat{y}.$$

Consequently

$$AA^{-1}\hat{y}=\hat{y}, \qquad A^{-1}A\hat{x}=\hat{x} \qquad (8.8)$$

for all $\hat{y}$ in $\mathfrak{R}_A$ and all $\hat{x}$ in $\mathfrak{N}_A^\perp$. Furthermore $A^{-1}y_0=0$ for all y_0 in $\mathfrak{R}_A^\perp$. From these relations it is seen that the transformation $x=A^{-1}y$ is the pseudoinverse of the transformation $y=Ax$ in the sense described in the preceding paragraph.

In the same manner it is seen that the matrix

$$A^{-*}=\frac{1}{\mu_1}y_1 x_1^* + \cdots + \frac{1}{\mu_r}y_r x_r^* \qquad (8.9)$$

is the pseudoinverse $(A^*)^{-1}$ of the transpose

$$A^*=\mu_1 x_1 y_1^* + \cdots + \mu_r x_r y_r^* \qquad (8.10)$$

of A. Clearly A^{-*} is the transpose of A^{-1}, so that

$$A^{-*}=(A^*)^{-1}=(A^{-1})^*, \qquad A^{-1}=(A^{-*})^*=(A^*)^{-*}. \qquad (8.11)$$

It is easily verified that we also have the relations

$$(A^*)^*=A=(A^{-1})^{-1}=(A^{-*})^{-*}, \qquad A^*=(A^{-*})^{-1}=(A^{-1})^{-*}. \qquad (8.12)$$

Observe that, if $m=n$ and A is nonsingular, A^{-1} is the ordinary inverse of A. This follows from (8.8), since in this event $\mathfrak{N}_A=0$ and $\mathfrak{R}_A=\mathcal{E}^n=\mathfrak{N}_A^\perp$.

The following property of the pseudoinverse A^{-1} of A gives some indication of its importance in applications.

THEOREM 8.1

Let k be a given vector in $\mathcal{E}^m$. The vector $\hat{x}=A^{-1}k$ minimizes the function

$$E(x)=|k-Ax|^2.$$

Moreover $\hat{x}$ is the vector of minimum length having this property.

As was seen above, we may express k in the form $k = \hat{k} + k_0$, where $\hat{k}$ is in $\mathcal{R}_A$ and k_0 is orthogonal to $\mathcal{R}_A$. We have $\hat{x} = A^{-1}k = A^{-1}\hat{k}$ and hence $A\hat{x} = \hat{k}$. It follows that

$$E(\hat{x}) = |k - \hat{k}|^2 = |k_0|^2.$$

Since k_0 is orthogonal to $\mathcal{R}_A$, it follows that $E(\hat{x}) = |k_0|^2$ is the minimum of $E(x)$. If x is a second vector that minimizes $E(x)$, then $Ax = A\hat{x}$. The vector $x_0 = x - \hat{x}$ therefore has $Ax_0 = 0$ and is accordingly orthogonal to $\hat{x}$. Hence the vector $\hat{x}$ is the shortest vector minimizing $E(x)$, as was to be proved.

In formulas (8.7) and (8.9) for A^{-1} and A^{-*} a particular set of principal vectors of A and A^* was used. We shall show that as a consequence of these definitions the matrix $B = A^{-*}$ satisfies the relations

$$A = BA^*A, \qquad B = BB^*A. \tag{8.13}$$

We shall then show that this solution is unique. Since $B^* = A^{-1}$, it follows that formulas (8.7) and (8.9) for A^{-1} and A^{-*} are valid for any choice of orthonormal principal vectors $x_1,\ldots,x_r$ and $y_1,\ldots,y_r$ for A and A^*. To show that $B = A^{-*}$ satisfies (8.13), we set, as in Section 7,

$$U_\alpha = x_\alpha y_\alpha^* \qquad (\alpha = 1,\ldots,r).$$

Then, by (7.14),

$$U_\alpha U_\alpha^* U_\alpha = U_\alpha, \qquad U_\alpha U_\beta^* U_\gamma = 0 \qquad \text{unless } \alpha = \beta = \gamma.$$

Since

$$B = A^{-*} = \sum_\alpha \frac{1}{\mu_\alpha} U_\alpha, \qquad A^* = \sum_\beta \mu_\beta U_\beta^*, \qquad A = \sum_\gamma \mu_\gamma U_\gamma,$$

we have

$$BA^*A = \sum_\alpha \sum_\beta \sum_\gamma \frac{1}{\mu_\alpha} \mu_\beta \mu_\gamma U_\alpha U_\beta^* U_\gamma = \sum_\alpha \mu_\alpha U_\alpha = A,$$

$$BB^*A = \sum_\alpha \sum_\beta \sum_\gamma \frac{1}{\mu_\alpha} \frac{1}{\mu_\beta} \mu_\gamma U_\alpha U_\beta^* U_\gamma = \sum_\alpha \frac{1}{\mu_\alpha} U_\alpha = B = A^{-*}.$$

The matrix $B = A^{-*}$ therefore satisfies equations (8.13). The uniqueness of this solution of (8.13) is given in the proof of

THEOREM 8.2

*The *-reciprocal* $B = A^{-*}$ *of a matrix* A (*and hence also its pseudoinverse* $A^{-1} = B^*$) *is uniquely determined by the relations*

$$A = BA^*A = AB^*A = AA^*B, \qquad B = BB^*A = BA^*B = AB^*B. \quad (8.14)$$

In fact, $B = A^{-*}$ *is uniquely determined by the conditions*

$$A = BA^*A, \qquad B = BB^*A. \quad (8.15)$$

It is also uniquely determined by the conditions

$$A = AA^*B, \qquad B = AB^*B. \quad (8.16)$$

We have already seen that $B = A^{-*}$ satisfies (8.15). By the use of (8.15) we see that

$$A = BA^*A = B(BA^*A)^*A = (BA^*A)B^*A = AB^*A$$

$$= A(BB^*A)^*A = AA^*BB^*A = AA^*B,$$

$$B = BB^*A = BB^*(AA^*B) = B(AA^*B)^*B = BA^*B$$

$$= B(BA^*A)^*B = (BA^*A)B^*B = AB^*B.$$

It follows that (8.14) and (8.16) hold. In a similar manner it is seen that (8.16) implies (8.14) and (8.15).

If C is any matrix having

$$A = CA^*A, \qquad C = CC^*A,$$

then (8.14) holds with B replaced by C. Moreover

$$B = BB^*A = BB^*AA^*C = B(AA^*B)^*C = BA^*C$$

$$= B(CA^*A)^*C = BA^*AC^*C = AC^*C = C.$$

Consequently the solution B of (8.15) is unique. In the same manner it is seen that (8.16) has a unique solution. This proves Theorem 8.2.

Observe that, if A is a nonsingular square matrix, the relation $A = AB^*A$ implies that $B^*A = I$, the identity. Consequently in the nonsingular case the pseudoinverse $A^{-1} = B^*$ is the inverse of A. In the general case the relation $A = AB^*A$ is not sufficient to determine $A^{-1} = B^*$ uniquely. Additional requirements are needed, as indicated in Theorem 8.2. An alternative characterization of A^{-*} and hence also of $A^{-1} = (A^{-*})^*$ is given in

THEOREM 8.3

The *-reciprocal $B = A^{-*}$ of a matrix A (and hence also its pseudoinverse $A^{-1} = B^*$) is determined uniquely by the relations

$$A = AB^*A, \qquad B = BA^*B, \qquad BA^* = AB^*, \qquad B^*A = A^*B. \quad (8.17)$$

We have already seen that $B = A^{-*}$ satisfies the first two relations in (8.17). Recalling the formulas

$$A = \sum_{\alpha} \mu_{\alpha} U_{\alpha}, \qquad B = A^{-*} = \sum_{\alpha} \frac{1}{\mu_{\alpha}} U_{\alpha}$$

given above and the relations

$$U_{\alpha} U_{\beta}^* = 0 \quad (\alpha \neq \beta) \qquad \text{and} \qquad U_{\alpha}^* U_{\beta} = 0 \quad (\alpha \neq \beta)$$

found in (7.22) and (7.24), we see that

$$BA^* = \sum_{\alpha} \sum_{\beta} \frac{1}{\mu_{\beta}} \mu_{\beta} U_{\alpha} U_{\beta}^* = \sum_{\alpha} U_{\alpha} U_{\alpha}^* = \sum_{\alpha} \sum_{\beta} \mu_{\alpha} \frac{1}{\mu_{\beta}} U_{\alpha} U_{\beta}^* = AB^*.$$

Similarly $A^*B = B^*A$. The matrix $B = A^{-*}$ therefore satisfies (8.17).

Conversely, if B satisfies (8.17), B satisfies (8.15) in view of the computations

$$A = AB^*A = (AB^*)A = (BA^*)A = BA^*A, \qquad B = B(A^*B) = B(B^*A).$$

Consequently $B = A^{-*}$ by Theorem 8.2. This proves Theorem 8.3.

If we set $B^* = A^{-1}$ in (8.17), we obtain relations of the form

$$A = AA^{-1}A, \qquad A^{-1} = A^{-1}AA^{-1},$$

$$(AA^{-1})^* = AA^{-1}, \qquad (A^{-1}A)^* = A^{-1}A. \quad (8.18)$$

These relations are used by many authors as the definition of the pseudoinverse A^{-1} of A.

A further characterization of the *-reciprocal $B = A^{-*}$ of A is found in

THEOREM 8.4

*The *-reciprocal* $B = A^{-*}$ *of* A (*and hence also the pseudoinverse* $A^{-1} = B^*$) *is characterized by the following relations*:

$$A = AB^*A, \qquad B = BA^*B, \qquad \mathfrak{N}_A = \mathfrak{N}_B, \qquad \mathfrak{N}_{A^*} = \mathfrak{N}_{B^*}, \qquad (8.19)$$

where $\mathfrak{N}_C$ *denotes the null space of the matrix* C.

We have seen that (8.19) holds for the *-reciprocal $B = A^{-*}$. To see that there is only one solution B of (8.19), it is sufficient to show that (8.19) implies relations

$$A = BA^*A, \qquad B = BB^*A$$

given in (8.15). Suppose therefore that (8.19) holds, and set

$$D = A - BA^*A.$$

Since $A^* = A^*BA^*$ by (8.19), we have

$$A^*D = A^*A - A^*BA^*A = A^*A - A^*A = 0. \qquad (8.20)$$

In view of the relation $\mathfrak{N}_{B^*} = \mathfrak{N}_{A^*}$, we see that $B^*y = 0$ whenever $A^*y = 0$. It follows that

$$D^*y = A^*y - A^*AB^*y = 0 \qquad \text{whenever } A^*y = 0.$$

This relation tells us that the column vectors of D are orthogonal to the null space $\mathfrak{N}_{A^*}$ of A^*, whereas equation (8.20) tells us that the column vectors of D lie in $\mathfrak{N}_{A^*}$. This is possible only in the case $D = 0$. Hence $A = BA^*A$, as was to be proved.

Similarly, upon setting

$$E = B - BB^*A,$$

it is by virtue of the relations $B = BA^*B$ and $\mathfrak{N}_B = \mathfrak{N}_A$ that

$$BE^* = BB^* - BA^*BB^* = BB^* - BB^* = 0,$$
$$Ex = Bx - BB^*Ax = 0 \qquad \text{whenever } Bx = 0.$$

These relations imply, as above, that $E = B - BB^*A = 0$. Relations (8.19) therefore imply relations (8.15) and hence characterize the *-reciprocal $B = A^{-*}$ of A.

EXERCISES

1. Show that, if $m=1$ or $n=1$, that is, if A is a row vector or a column vector, then $A^{-1}=A^*/|A|^2$ is its pseudoinverse. Find the pseudoinverse of the vector $A=(2,2,1)$.

2. Show that the two matrices

$$\begin{pmatrix} 1 & 1 \\ 1 & 1 \\ 1 & -2 \end{pmatrix} \quad \text{and} \quad \begin{pmatrix} \frac{1}{3} & \frac{1}{3} & \frac{1}{3} \\ \frac{1}{6} & \frac{1}{6} & -\frac{1}{3} \end{pmatrix}$$

    are pseudoinverses of each other.

3. Show that, if $A=B+C$ and $B^*C=0$, $BC^*=0$, then $A^{-1}=B^{-1}+C^{-1}$.

4. Show that, if the column vectors of a matrix A are mutually orthogonal, the *-reciprocal A^{-*} of A can be found by dividing each nonnull column of A by the square of its length.

5. Show, by an example, that the formula $(AB)^{-1}=B^{-1}A^{-1}$ does not always hold for pseudoinverses.

6. Show that there is an integer k and constants $c_1,\dots,c_k$ such that

$$A = c_1 A(A^*A) + c_2 A(A^*A)^2 + \cdots + c_k A(A^*A)^k.$$

    Show that the *-reciprocal A^{-*} of A is given by the formula [†]

$$A^{-*} = c_1 A + c_2 A(A^*A) + \cdots + c_k A(A^*A)^{k-1}.$$

7. Show that $U=U^{-*}$ if and only if $U^*=U^{-1}$. Show also that $U=U^{-*}$ if and only if $U=UU^*U$. Show that, if $U=UU^*U$, then $|U|=1$ unless $U=0$. A matrix such that $U=UU^*U$ will be called a unit.

8. Given a matrix A, let $\mathfrak{M}$ be the class of all matrices B expressible in the form

$$B = b_0 A + b_1 A(A^*A) + b_2 A(A^*A)^2 + \cdots + b_q A(A^*A)^q,$$

    where $b_0, b_1, \dots, b_q$ are real numbers. Show that, if B, C, D are in $\mathfrak{M}$, so also is BC^*D. Show that the triple product BC^*D is unaltered under permutations of B, C, and D. Show that, if B is in $\mathfrak{M}$, so also is its *-reciprocal, B^{-*}. Show that there is a unit U in $\mathfrak{M}$ such that $B=UB^*U$ for every B in $\mathfrak{M}$.

9. Show that the results given in this section hold when A is a complex matrix. In this event A^* denotes the conjugate transpose of A.

[†]See M. R. Hestenes, "A Ternary Algebra with Applications to Matrices and Linear Transformations," *Archive for Rational Mechanics and Analysis*, Vol. 11 (1962), pp. 138–194.

3

THE LAGRANGE MULTIPLIER RULE FOR EQUALITY CONSTRAINTS

1. GENERAL REMARKS

In Chapter 1 we were concerned with the problem of minimizing a function f without constraints or with linear equality constraints. In the present chapter we seek to minimize a function f on a manifold S defined by equations of the form

$$g_\alpha(x) = 0 \qquad (\alpha = 1, \ldots, m < n). \tag{1.1}$$

Except in abnormal situations, this manifold is an $(n-m)$-dimensional manifold and is expressible locally in the parametric form

$$x^i = x^i(u^1, \ldots, u^{n-m}) \qquad (i = 1, \ldots, n).$$

Consequently, the problem of minimizing f on the manifold (1.1) is equivalent to the unconstrained problem of minimizing $f[x(u)]$. In some cases this is a suitable procedure. However, in many situations a better procedure is to use the Lagrange multiplier rule. This rule, which is developed in the present chapter, is based on the fact that at a local minimum point x_0 of f on the surface S defined by (1.1) the gradient ∇f of f must be normal to S.

An alternative development of the Lagrange multiplier rule for the case of equality constraints will be given in Sections 2, 3, and 4 in Chapter 5. There we consider the implications of the existence of multipliers $\lambda_1, \ldots, \lambda_m$

and a constant σ such that our solution x_0 minimizes an augmented function $H = f + \sum_\alpha (\lambda_\alpha g_\alpha + \frac{1}{2} \sigma g_\alpha^2)$ without constraints. This approach is independent of the development given in this chapter. Accordingly the reader who wishes to do so can proceed at once to Chapter 5. However, the approach given here is more intuitive and leads to a better understanding of the multiplier rule. In the development of this rule we make use of a standard implicit function theorem, and for completeness we include a proof of this implicit function theorem at the end of this chapter. The development of the multiplier rule given in Chapter 5 makes no use of implicit function theorems.

As an application of the theory of equality constrained minima we give in Section 4 a characterization of a nondegenerate critical point of a function. In Section 5 we study the concept of normality of constraints. Normality ensures the existence of suitable multipliers at a minimum point. Section 6 is concerned with the concept of the gradient of a function relative to constraints. This concept is useful in computational procedures.

Although the problem here considered is a special case of the minimum problem to be considered in the next chapter, it is desirable to discuss this case separately because it is simpler conceptually and because a large number of problems are of this type. It is an interesting fact that, by a simple device, the general problem considered in the next chapter involving inequality constraints can be reduced to one of the type here considered.

2. CONSTRAINED MINIMA

In Section 3 of Chapter 1 we were concerned with unconstrained minimum problems. These are the problems in which an interior point x_0 of a set S minimizes a function $f(x)$ on S. If a boundary point x_0 of S minimizes f on a set S, then x_0 is said to afford a *constrained minimum* to f on S. Linearly constrained problems were studied in Section 6 of Chapter 1. The present section is devoted to the case in which the constraints are nonlinear. The Lagrange multiplier rule will be derived first by a geometric argument, and later an analytic proof of the multiplier rule will be given.

We begin with the study of constrained minimum problems in the xy-plane. A simple example is that of finding the minimum of the function

$$f(x,y) = -2x^2 + 4xy + y^2 \qquad (2.1a)$$

on the circle

$$g(x,y) = 1 - x^2 - y^2 = 0. \qquad (2.1b)$$

It will be shown presently that f has a minimum value of -3 at each of the points $(2/\sqrt{5}, -1/\sqrt{5})$ and $(-2/\sqrt{5}, 1/\sqrt{5})$. This special example is of the following type: find a point (x_0, y_0) on the curve

$$g(x,y) = 0 \qquad (2.2)$$

which affords at least a local minimum on this curve to a prescribed function $f(x,y)$. Suppose that we have a minimum point (x_0, y_0) of this type. We shall show that, if the gradient ∇g of g is not zero at (x_0, y_0), then ∇f is a multiple of ∇g at this point, that is,

$$\nabla f + \lambda \nabla g = 0 \quad \text{at} \quad (x_0, y_0) \qquad (2.3a)$$

or, equivalently,

$$f_x + \lambda g_x = 0, \qquad f_y + \lambda g_y = 0 \quad \text{at} \quad (x_0, y_0). \qquad (2.3b)$$

This is the *Lagrange multiplier rule*. Incidentally we have assumed that f and g have continuous partial derivatives near (x_0, y_0). When second-order conditions are given, we assume the existence of continuous second derivatives for f and g.

The multiplier rule (2.3) can be obtained geometrically as follows. If $\nabla f = 0$ at (x_0, y_0), then (2.3) holds with $\lambda = 0$. Suppose therefore that $\nabla f \neq 0$ at this point. Let $c = f(x_0, y_0)$. Then, as indicated in Figure 2.1, on a circular neighborhood N of (x_0, y_0) the level curve

$$f(x,y) = c$$

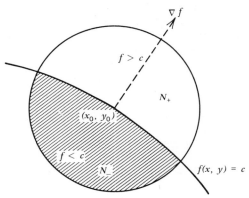

Figure 2.1

separates the set N_- of points in N at which $f(x,y)<c$ from the set N_+ of points at which $f(x,y)>c$. We suppose that N has been chosen so small that f has a minimum at (x_0,y_0) relative to all points in N on the curve γ defined by $g(x,y)=0$. We shall show that the gradients ∇f and ∇g are collinear. If ∇f and ∇g are not collinear, the curve γ must cross the curve $f(x,y)=c$ at (x_0,y_0) and hence must have points in common with N_-, as indicated in Figure 2.2. In this event there are points (x,y) of γ in N_-. These points have the property that $f(x,y)<c=f(x_0,y_0)$, contrary to the minimizing property of the point (x_0,y_0). It follows that at (x_0,y_0) the gradients of ∇f and ∇g are collinear, as expressed by equations (2.3). The gradient ∇f of f at (x_0,y_0) is therefore normal to the curve γ at (x_0,y_0).

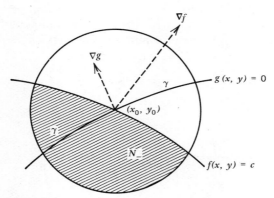

Figure 2.2

We summarize this result in

THEOREM 2.1: LAGRANGE MULTIPLIER RULE

Suppose that a point (x_0,y_0) *affords a local minimum to* $f(x,y)$ *subject to the constraint*

$$g(x,y)=0. \qquad (2.4)$$

Suppose further that $(g_x,g_y)\neq(0,0)$ *at* (x_0,y_0). *Then there is a multiplier* λ *such that, if we set*

$$F(x,y)=f(x,y)+\lambda g(x,y), \qquad (2.5)$$

then

$$F_x(x_0,y_0)=0, \qquad F_y(x_0,y_0)=0. \qquad (2.6)$$

In addition

$$F''(x_0,y_0;h,k) = F_{xx}(x_0,y_0)h^2 + 2F_{xy}(x_0,y_0)hk + F_{yy}(x_0,y_0)k^2 \geqslant 0 \quad (2.7a)$$

for all $(h,k) \neq (0,0)$ *such that*

$$g'(x_0,y_0;h,k) = g_x(x_0,y_0)h + g_y(x_0,y_0)k = 0. \quad\quad\quad (2.7b)$$

Equations (2.6) constitute the first-order multiplier rule. As remarked above, they state that the curves $f(x,y) = c$ and $g(x,y) = 0$ are tangent at the point (x_0,y_0). Tangency by itself is not sufficient to ensure that (x_0,y_0) is a solution to our problem. This is geometrically obvious from the three diagrams of Figure 2.3. In Figure 2.3(a) (x_0,y_0) maximizes f locally on the curve $g = 0$. In Figure 2.3(b) (x_0,y_0) affords a local minimum to f on $g = 0$. In Figure 2.3(c) (x_0,y_0) neither minimizes nor maximizes f on the curve

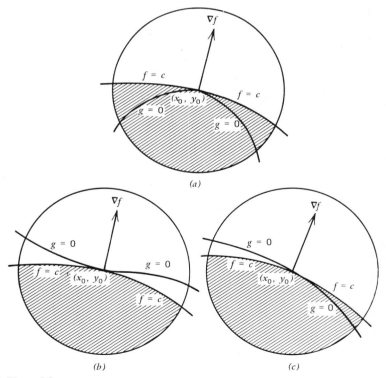

(a)

(b)   (c)

Figure 2.3

$g=0$. It is clear from these diagrams that the situation indicated in Figure 2.3(b) must prevail if (x_0,y_0) is to be a solution to our minimum problem. When this result is expressed analytically, the second-order condition (2.7) is obtained. A proof of this condition is given in the proof of the next theorem.

EXAMPLE 2.1

Return now to the example given by (2.1), in which $f(x,y)= -2x^2+4xy+y^2$ was minimized subject to the constraint

$$g(x,y)=1-x^2-y^2=0.$$

In this case

$$F(x,y)= -2x^2+4xy+y^2+\lambda(1-x^2-y^2).$$

Consequently at a minimum point we have

$$F_x = 2[(-2-\lambda)x+2y]=0, \tag{2.8a}$$

$$F_y = 2[2x+(1-\lambda)y]=0, \tag{2.8b}$$

$$0= x^2+y^2-1. \tag{2.8c}$$

Observe that, if these equations hold at a point (x,y), then

$$0= \tfrac{1}{2}(xF_x+yF_y)= -2x^2+4xy+y^2-\lambda(x^2+y^2)=f(x,y)-\lambda.$$

Hence the multiplier λ is the minimum value of f on the unit circle about the origin. To find λ, observe that since $(x,y)\neq(0,0)$ equations (2.8a) and (2.8b) tell us that

$$\begin{vmatrix} -2-\lambda & 2 \\ 2 & 1-\lambda \end{vmatrix}=\lambda^2+\lambda-6=0$$

and hence that $\lambda=2$ or $\lambda= -3$. The value $\lambda=2$ is the maximum of f on the circle, and $\lambda= -3$ is its minimum. Setting $\lambda= -3$ in (2.8), we see that $(x,y)=(2/\sqrt{5},-1/\sqrt{5})$ and $(-2/\sqrt{5},1/\sqrt{5})$ are solutions to our problem.

The argument given above can be extended to the n-dimensional case to obtain the following result, in which we are concerned with functions that are of class C'' on the set of points considered.

THEOREM 2.2: LAGRANGE MULTIPLIER RULE

Suppose that x_0 affords a local minimum to $f(x)$ subject to the constraints

$$g_\alpha(x) = 0 \qquad (\alpha = 1, \ldots, m < n). \tag{2.9}$$

Suppose further that x_0 is a normal point in the sense that the matrix

$$\left(\frac{\partial g_\alpha(x_0)}{\partial x^i} \right) \qquad (\alpha = 1, \ldots, m; \; i = 1, \ldots, n) \tag{2.10}$$

has rank m. *Then there exist unique multipliers* $\lambda_1, \ldots, \lambda_m$ *such that, if we set*

$$F = f + \lambda_1 g_1 + \cdots + \lambda_m g_m, \tag{2.11}$$

then $\nabla F(x_0) = 0$, *that is,*

$$\frac{\partial F}{\partial x^i} = \frac{\partial f}{\partial x^i} + \sum_{\alpha=1}^{m} \lambda_\alpha \frac{\partial g_\alpha}{\partial x^i} = 0 \qquad at \; x = x_0. \tag{2.12}$$

Furthermore, the inequality

$$F''(x_0, h) \geqslant 0 \tag{2.13}$$

holds for all solutions $h \neq 0$ *of the equation*

$$g'_\alpha(x_0, h) = \langle \nabla g_\alpha(x_0), h \rangle = 0 \qquad (\alpha = 1, \ldots, m). \tag{2.14}$$

The multipliers $\lambda_1, \ldots, \lambda_m$ are called *Lagrange multipliers*, and *F* is termed a *Lagrange function* or a *Lagrangian*. The result can be obtained also by an analytic argument, which proceeds as follows. Observe that the condition that the matrix (2.10) be of rank *m* assures us that a solution *h* of equations (2.14) is a tangent vector of the surface (2.9) at $x = x_0$. This means that, if a vector *h* satisfies equations (2.14), there is a curve

$$x(t) \qquad (-\delta < t < \delta)$$

on the surface (2.9) such that $x(0) = x_0$ and $\dot{x}(0) = h$, where $\dot{x} = dx/dt$. An analytic proof of this fact will be given in Theorem 5.1. It will be shown further that this curve can be chosen to be of class C''. Along this curve the function *f* is a function

$$w(t) = f[x(t)]$$

of t. Since $w(0) = f(x_0)$, the function $w(t)$ has a local minimum at $t = 0$. Hence $w'(0) = 0$. The value of $w'(0)$ in terms of f is given by the formula

$$w'(0) = f'[x(0), \dot{x}(0)] = f'(x_0, h) = \langle \nabla f(x_0), h \rangle = 0. \qquad (2.15)$$

This equation holds for all tangent vectors h, that is, for all vectors h such that

$$g'_\alpha(x_0, h) = \langle \nabla g_\alpha(x_0), h \rangle = 0 \qquad (\alpha = 1, \ldots, m). \qquad (2.16)$$

The result just obtained states that the gradient $\nabla f(x_0)$ is orthogonal to all tangent vectors h and hence is normal to the surface (2.9) at x_0. Since the tangent space to this surface is defined by the solution h of equations (2.16), the gradients $\nabla g_1(x_0), \ldots, \nabla g_m(x_0)$ generate the normal space to our surface at $x = x_0$. It follows that $\nabla f(x_0)$ is a linear combination

$$\nabla f(x_0) = \mu_1 \nabla g_1(x_0) + \mu_2 \nabla g_2(x_0) + \ldots + \mu_m \nabla g_m(x_0)$$

of the normals $\nabla g_1(x_0), \ldots, \nabla g_m(x_0)$. To conform with notations to be used later, we set $\lambda_\alpha = -\mu_\alpha$ and write the last equation in the form

$$\nabla f(x_0) + \lambda_1 \nabla g_1(x_0) + \cdots + \lambda_m \nabla g_m(x_0) = 0.$$

Setting $F = f + \sum_\alpha \lambda_\alpha g_\alpha$, we find that

$$\nabla F(x_0) = \nabla f(x_0) + \sum_\alpha \lambda_\alpha \nabla g_\alpha(x_0) = 0. \qquad (2.17)$$

Consequently equations (2.12) hold. Since matrix (2.10) has rank m, the gradients $\nabla g_1(x_0), \ldots, \nabla g_m(x_0)$ are linearly independent. It follows that these multipliers are unique. A fuller account of tangent spaces and normal spaces will be given in Section 5.

To prove the last conclusion in the theorem, let h be a vector satisfying the conditions

$$g'_\alpha(x_0, h) = 0,$$

and choose $x(t)$ $(-\delta \leqslant t \leqslant \delta)$ as above so that $x(0) = x_0$, $\dot{x}(0) = h$, and

$$g_\alpha[x(t)] = 0.$$

Then the function

$$w(t) = f[x(t)] = F[x(t)]$$

has a minimum at $t=0$. Hence $w'(0)=0$ and $w''(0)\geqslant 0$. We complete the proof by showing that

$$w''(0)=F''(x_0,h).$$

To this end we use Taylor's formula and the relation $\nabla F(x_0)=0$ to obtain

$$\frac{w(t)-w(0)}{t^2}=\frac{F[x(t)]-F(x_0)}{t^2}=\tfrac{1}{2}F''\left[\bar{x}(t),\frac{x(t)-x_0}{t}\right],$$

where $\bar{x}(t)=x_0+\theta(t)[x(t)-x_0]$ for a suitable choice of $\theta(t)$ on $0<\theta<1$. Taking the limit at $t=0$, we find that

$$\tfrac{1}{2}w''(0)=\lim_{t\to 0}\frac{w(t)-w(0)}{t^2}=\tfrac{1}{2}F''(x_0,h)\geqslant 0,$$

as was to be proved.

The conditions described in Theorem 2.2 are necessary conditions for a constrained local minimum. Sufficient conditions for a constrained local minimum will be given in the next section.

EXAMPLE 2.2

Observe that in the xy-plane the point $(x_0,y_0)=(0,0)$ satisfies the Lagrange multiplier rule in Theorem 2.1 with $\lambda=1$ when $f(x,y)=x^3+xy-y$ and the constraint is $g(x,y)=y=0$. Obviously (x_0,y_0) fails to minimize $f(x,y)$ subject to the constraint $g(x,y)=0$. This example illustrates the fact that a necessary condition for a minimum need not be a sufficient condition for a minimum.

EXAMPLE 2.3

As an application of Theorem 2.2 let us establish the relation

$$(a_1a_2\cdots a_n)^{1/n}<\frac{a_1+\cdots+a_n}{n} \tag{2.18}$$

between the geometric mean and the arithmetic mean of n positive numbers $a_1,\dots,a_n$. This can be obtained by minimizing the function

$$f(x)=\frac{x^1+\cdots+x^n}{n}$$

subject to the constraint

$$g(x)=1-x^1x^2\cdots x^n=0$$

on the set of points having $x^j > 0$ $(j = 1, \ldots, n)$. To see that a minimum point exists, observe that, for each constant $c > 0$, the set of points satisfying the relations

$$f(x) \leqslant c, \qquad g(x) = 0, \qquad x^j > 0 \qquad (j = 1, \ldots, n)$$

is bounded and closed. Hence f attains its minimum by Theorem 2.2 in Chapter 1. There is accordingly a multiplier λ such that the equations

$$0 = \frac{\partial f}{\partial x^i} + \lambda \frac{\partial g}{\partial x^i} = \frac{1}{n} - \lambda \frac{x^1 \ldots x^n}{x^i} = \frac{1}{n} - \frac{\lambda}{x^i} \qquad (i = 1, \ldots, n)$$

hold at the minimum point. These equations hold only if $x^i = x^j$ for all indices i and j. It follows that the point $x_0 = (1, 1, \ldots, 1)$ minimizes f. Consequently $f(x) \geqslant f(x_0) = 1$ on the set $g(x) = 0$. Given a set of positive numbers $a_1, \ldots, a_n$, we see that the point x having

$$x^i = \frac{a_i}{G}, \qquad G = (a_1 a_2 \cdots a_n)^{1/n}$$

satisfies the relation $g(x) = 0$. Hence

$$\frac{1}{n} \left(\frac{a_1}{G} + \cdots + \frac{a_n}{G} \right) \geqslant 1.$$

This inequality yields the desired inequality (2.18).

EXAMPLE 2.4

The multiplier rule can be applied to the case of inequality constraints by a simple device. Consider the problem of minimizing

$$f(x,y) = (x - 3)^2 + (y - 4)^2$$

subject to the constraint

$$x^2 + y^2 - 1 \leqslant 0.$$

By introducing an auxiliary variable z, we can see that this problem is equivalent to that of minimizing $f(x,y)$ on the class of points (x,y,z) satisfying the relation

$$g(x,y,z) = x^2 + y^2 + z^2 - 1 = 0.$$

To apply the Lagrange multiplier rule, we construct the function

$$F = f + \lambda g = (x-3)^2 + (y-4)^2 + \lambda(x^2 + y^2 + z^2 - 1).$$

At the minimum point we have

$$F_x = 2(x-3) + 2\lambda x = 0, \qquad F_y = 2(y-4) + 2\lambda y = 0, \qquad F_z = 2\lambda z = 0,$$

$$x^2 + y^2 + z^2 = 1.$$

Since $\lambda z = 0$, we have $\lambda = 0$ or else $z = 0$. It is easily verified that $\lambda = 0$ is impossible. Hence $z = 0$, and

$$x = \frac{3}{1+\lambda}, \qquad y = \frac{4}{1+\lambda}, \qquad x^2 + y^2 = 1.$$

From this result $1 + \lambda = \pm 5$ and $\lambda = 4$ or $\lambda = -6$. The case $\lambda = -6$ can be excluded by an application of the second-order condition (2.13) subject to (2.14). For the case here considered, this becomes

$$2(1+\lambda)\xi^2 + 2(1+\lambda)\eta^2 + 2\lambda\zeta^2 \geqslant 0 \qquad (2.19)$$

for all $h = (\xi, \eta, \zeta)$ satisfying the relation

$$2x\xi + 2y\eta + 2z\zeta = 0.$$

Since $z = 0$, the variable ζ is arbitrary. Hence we may choose $(\xi, \eta, \zeta) = (0, 0, 1)$ in (2.19) to obtain the inequality $\lambda \geqslant 0$. This excludes the case $\lambda = -6$. Consequently $\lambda = 4$ and $x = 3/5$, $y = 4/5$ is the solution to our problem. This fact could have been obtained by inspection, since the nearest point to $(3, 4)$ in the circle must lie on the line segment joining $(3, 4)$ to the center $(0, 0)$ of the circle.

EXAMPLE 2.5

As a further application of the Lagrange multiplier rule, consider the problem of minimizing the quadratic form

$$f(x) = x^* A x \qquad (A^* = A) \qquad (2.20)$$

subject to the constraint

$$g(x) = 1 - |x|^2 = 0. \qquad (2.21)$$

This problem was discussed in Section 9 of Chapter 1 by the use of the

Rayleigh quotient,

$$R(x) = \frac{x^*Ax}{x^*x}$$

Observe that, since $\nabla g(x) = -2x$, every point on the sphere $g(x) = 0$ has $\nabla g(x) \neq 0$. Hence the Lagrange multiplier rule is applicable: setting

$$F(x) = f(x) + \lambda g(x) = x^*Ax + \lambda(1 - x^*x)$$

it is seen that a solution x_1 to our problem must satisfy the equations

$$\tfrac{1}{2}\nabla F(x_1) = Ax_1 - \lambda x_1 = 0$$

and hence must be a unit eigenvector of A. Moreover the corresponding minimum value

$$f(x_1) = x_1^* Ax_1 = \lambda x_1^* x_1 = \lambda$$

of f is the smallest eigenvalue λ_1 of A.

EXERCISES

1. Find the shortest distance and the longest distance from the origin to a point on the ellipse

$$5x^2 + 4xy + y^2 = 10$$

What is the geometrical interpretation of these distances?

2. Find the maximum and minimum values of

$$f(x,y,z) = 2x^2 + 5y^2 + 11z^2 + 20xy - 4xz + 16yz$$

on the unit sphere $x^2 + y^2 + z^2 = 1$.

Answer: 18 and -9.

3. Find the points within the circle $x^2 + y^2 \leqslant 1$ that are at the greatest and the least distances from the line $x + y = 5$.

4. Find the parallelopiped of maximum volume that can be inscribed in an ellipsoid $x^2/a^2 + y^2/b^2 + z^2/c^2 = 1$. Assume that the parellelopiped is centered at the origin and its edges are parallel to the axes.

5. Find the path of a ray of light from P_1 to P_2 in case these points are on opposite sides of the x-axis, the velocity of light being v_1 from P_1 to the axis and v_2 from the axis to P_2. Assume that the path is such as to make the time from P_1 to P_2 a minimum. Show that the multiplier rule yields "Snell's law" of diffraction.

6. Find the shortest distance from the origin to the surface $xyz = 1$.
7. Find the points on the sphere $x^2 + y^2 + z^2 = 1$ that are nearest to the plane $x + y + z = 5$ and those that are farthest from it.
8. Determine the rectangular box of greatest volume having a fixed surface area.
9. Determine the triangle of greatest area having a fixed perimeter.
10. Solve the following constrained problem:

$$f(x,y,z) = 1/(x^2 + y^2 + z^2) = \min,$$

$$g_1(x,y,z) = 1 - (x^2 + 2y^2 + 3z^2) = 0,$$

$$g_2(x,y,z) = x + y + z = 0.$$

Compare your results with those of Exercise 15, Section 9 of Chapter 1.

Answer: $f_{\min} = 1/(8 + 4\sqrt{3})$ at $x = \sqrt{2} + 2\sqrt{6}/3$, $y = -\sqrt{2} - \sqrt{6}/3$, $z = -\sqrt{6}/3$.

11. (a) Show that the following problem:

$$f(x,y,z) = 4a - x - 3y - 20z = \min; \quad a > 0, \quad \text{constant},$$

$$g(x,y,z) = x^2 + 3y^2 - 20z^2 + a^2 = 0,$$

has two multipliers λ_1, λ_2 and two corresonding points at which the gradient Lagrangian $F = f + \lambda g$ vanishes. Investigate the matrix of second derivatives of F at these points, apply condition (2.13) of Theorem 2.2, and show that a local solution of the problem is $(a/4, a/4, -a/4)$ with the corresponding multiplier $\lambda = 2/a$.
(b) Investigate the problem $g(x,y,z) = \min$ as above, but with constraint $f(x,y,z) = 0$.
12. Show that the product $(x + a)(y + b)(z + c)$, where a, b, c are positive constants, subject to the condition that $xyz = d^3$, d a positive constant, is a minimum when $x = ad/\mu$, $y = bd/\mu$, $z = cd/\mu$, $\mu = (abc)^{1/3}$.
13. Show that the minimum value of $x + y + z$ on the surface $xyz = 1$ is 3.
14. Show that the minimum value of $x^2 + y^2 + z^2$ on the surface $xyz = 1$ is 3, and that this value is attained at four distinct points.
15. Suppose that $g(x,y,z) = c$ defines a smooth surface S in 3-space, and (x_0, y_0, z_0) is a fixed point not on S; assume that (x_1, y_1, z_1) is a point on S which minimizes the distance from (x_0, y_0, z_0) to S. Why must the line through (x_0, y_0, z_0), (x_1, y_1, z_1) be perpendicular to S at (x_1, y_1, z_1)?
16. Find the points which furnish local minima to $f(x,y) = \sin^2 x + \sin^2 y$ subject to the constraint $y - x = \pi/4$.

Answer: $(7\pi/8 + k\pi, \ 9\pi/8 + k\pi)$, $k = 0, 1, 2 \ldots$; $(-\pi/8 - k\pi, \pi/8 - k\pi)$, $k = 0, 1, 2 \ldots$.

17. Interpret the problem

$$f(x,y,z) = (\tfrac{1}{2})(x^2 + y^2 + z^2) = \min, \qquad g(x,y,z) = z - xy - 5 = 0$$

geometrically. Let $F(x,y,z,\lambda) = f(x,y,z) + \lambda g(x,y,z)$ be the Lagrangian. Find all quadruples (x,y,z,λ) such that

$$\nabla F = 0, \qquad g = 0$$

hold simultaneously. Locate local minima and global minima of the constrained problem.

Answer: $(0,0,5, -5)$, $(2, -2, 1, -1)$, $(-2, 2, 1, -1)$; global min $= 9/2$.

18. Show that the solution of the problem

$$f(x,y,z) = x + y + z = \min, \qquad g(x,y,z) = \frac{a^2}{x} + \frac{b^2}{y} + \frac{c^2}{z} - 1 = 0,$$

for $x > 0$, $y > 0$, $z > 0$, where a, b, c are nonzero constants, is $x = as$, $y = bs$, $z = cs$, $s = a + b + c$.

19. Let $x_1, \ldots, x_m$ be eigenvectors of a symmetric matrix A. With the help of the Lagrange multiplier rule show that if $m < n$ the minimum point x_0 of $f(x) = x^* A x$ subject to the constraints $1 - x^* x = 0$, $x_j^* x = 0$ $(j = 1, \ldots, m)$ is an eigenvector of A and that $f(x_0)$ is the corresponding eigenvalue.

20. Use the results given in Example 2.5 and Exercise 19 to establish Theorem 9.5 of Chapter 1.

3. SUFFICIENT CONDITIONS FOR A LOCAL CONSTRAINED MINIMUM

The multiplier rule given in Theorem 2.2 when suitably strengthened yields sufficient conditions for a local constrained minimum, as described in the following theorem. We assume, of course, that all functions encountered are of class C''.

THEOREM 3.1

Suppose that for a point x_0 *on the surface*

$$g_\alpha(x) = 0 \qquad (\alpha = 1, \ldots, m) \tag{3.1}$$

there is a Lagrange function

$$F(x) = f(x) + \lambda_1 g_1(x) + \ldots + \lambda_m g_m(x) \tag{3.2}$$

such that

$$\nabla F(x_0) = 0 \tag{3.3}$$

and such that the inequality

$$F''(x_0, h) > 0 \tag{3.4a}$$

holds for all vectors $h \neq 0$ *satisfying the tangential constraints*

$$g'_\alpha(x_0, h) = 0. \tag{3.4b}$$

Then there exists a neighborhood N *of* x_0 *and a constant* $m > 0$ *such that the inequality*

$$f(x) \geqslant f(x_0) + m|x - x_0|^2 \tag{3.5}$$

holds for all points x *in* N *satisfying constraints* (3.1).

To establish this result, suppose that the conclusion is false. Then for every integer q there is a point x_q such that

$$g_\alpha(x_q) = 0, \qquad t_q = |x_q - x_0| < \frac{1}{q}, \qquad f(x_q) < f(x_0) + \left(\frac{1}{q}\right) t_q^2. \tag{3.6}$$

By virtue of the last inequality we see that $t_q > 0$. If necessary, we can replace $\{x_q\}$ by a subsequence, again denoted by $\{x_q\}$, so that the sequence

$$h_q = \frac{x_q - x_0}{t_q} = \frac{x_q - x_0}{|x_q - x_0|}$$

of unit vectors converges to a vector h. Clearly h is a unit vector. From the relations $g_\alpha(x_q) = 0$, $g_\alpha(x_0) = 0$ we find that

$$0 = \lim_{q \to \infty} \frac{g_\alpha(x_q) - g_\alpha(x_0)}{t_q} = g'_\alpha(x_0, h).$$

Consequently h satisfies conditions (3.4b) and (3.4a). In as much as $f(x_q) = F(x_q)$ and $f(x_0) = F(x_0)$, where $F = f + \Sigma \lambda_\alpha g_\alpha$, we have, by (3.6),

$$\frac{F(x_q) - F(x_0)}{t_q^2} < \frac{1}{q}$$

3. SUFFICIENT CONDITIONS

Using the fact that $\nabla F(x_0)=0$, we have, by Taylor's theorem,

$$\frac{F(x_q)-F(x_0)}{t_q^2}=\tfrac{1}{2}F''\left(\bar{x}_q,\frac{x_q-x_0}{t_q}\right)=\tfrac{1}{2}F''(\bar{x}_q,h_q),$$

where $\bar{x}_q=x_0+\theta_q(x_q-x_0)$ $(0<\theta_q<1)$. It follows that

$$\lim_{q\to\infty}\frac{F(x_q)-F(x_0)}{t_q^2}=\tfrac{1}{2}F''(x_0,h)\leqslant 0,$$

contrary to relation (3.4a). This proves the theorem.

A point x_0 will be called a *critical point of* f *relative to the constraints*

$$g_\alpha(x)=0 \qquad (\alpha=1,\ldots,m) \tag{3.7}$$

if it satisfies these constraints and has associated with it a Lagrange function

$$F=f+\lambda_1 g_1+\cdots+\lambda_m g_m \tag{3.8}$$

such that $\nabla F(x_0)=0$. If in addition the determinant

$$\begin{vmatrix} F_{x^ix^j}(x) & g_{\beta x^i}(x) \\ g_{\alpha x^j}(x) & 0 \end{vmatrix} \qquad (i,j=1,\ldots,n;\alpha,\beta=1,\ldots,m) \tag{3.9}$$

is different from zero, x_0 is said to be a *nondegenerate* critical point of f relative to these constraints. Since the matrix $(g_{\alpha x^j}(x))$ is of rank m whenever determinant (3.9) is different from zero, it follows that a nondegenerate critical point is a normal point of the set S defined by equations (3.7).

THEOREM 3.2

Suppose that x_0 *is a nondegenerate critical point of* f *relative to constraints* (3.7). *Let* F *be the Lagrange function* (3.8) *associated with* x_0. *The point* x_0 *affords a strict local minimum for* f *relative to these constraints if and only if the inequality*

$$F''(x_0,h)\geqslant 0 \tag{3.10a}$$

holds for every vector h *satisfying the tangential constraints*

$$g'_\alpha(x_0,h)=0 \qquad (\alpha=1,\ldots,m). \tag{3.10b}$$

The necessity of condition (3.10) follows from Theorem 2.2. To establish the sufficiency of conditions (3.10) for a strict minimum, it suffices, by Theorem 3.1, to show that the strict inequality

$$F''(x_0, h) > 0 \tag{3.11}$$

holds for every solution $h \neq 0$ of equations (3.10b). Suppose therefore that there is a solution $h_0 \neq 0$ of equations (3.10) such that $F''(x_0, h_0) = 0$. Then the function

$$\hat{f}(h) = F''(x_0, h)$$

has a minimum at $h = h_0$ relative to the constraints

$$\hat{g}_\alpha(h) = g_\alpha'(x_0, h) = 0.$$

Since matrix (2.10) has rank m, the point h_0 is a normal point for the auxiliarly minimum problem. It follows from Theorem 2.2 that there exists a Lagrange function

$$\hat{F}(h) = \hat{f}(h) + \Sigma \hat{\lambda}_\alpha \hat{g}_\alpha(h)$$

such that $\nabla \hat{F}(h_0) = 0$. Hence we have

$$\frac{\partial \hat{F}}{\partial h^i}(h_0) = 2 \sum_j F_{x^i x^j}(x_0) h_0^j + \sum_\beta \hat{\lambda}_\beta g_{\beta x^i}(x_0) = 0,$$

$$2\hat{g}_\alpha(h_0) = 2 \sum_j g_{\alpha x^j}(x_0) h_0^j = 0.$$

Since $h_0 \neq 0$, this is possible only if determinant (3.9) is zero at $x = x_0$, contrary to our assumption. It follows that (3.11) holds for every solution $h \neq 0$ of equations (3.10). This completes the proof of Theorem 3.2.

In applications of optimization theory to problems in economics, engineering, and other fields, the multipliers have interpretations which may be of greater importance than the geometric one given elsewhere in this text. In such problems the constraints are generally written in the form

$$g_\alpha(x) = b_\alpha \qquad (\alpha = 1, \dots, m),$$

where $b_1, \dots, b_m$ is an "input" vector that may represent parameters of input data, estimates, or control data, of critical importance to the model which the problem

$$f(x) = \min, \qquad g(x) = b$$

describes or approximates. Then the multiplier λ_β measures the "sensitivity" of the "objective" (or "performance") function f to a change in the constraint parameter b_β. If λ_β is large in magnitude, a small change in the constraint value b_β results in a relatively large change in the objective function f, at least in a neighborhood of the optimal solution. This result can be established as follows. Consider the Lagrangian

$$F(x,\lambda,b) = f(x) + \sum_{\alpha=1}^{m} \lambda_\alpha [b_\alpha - g_\alpha(x)].$$

Let (x_0, λ_0, b_0) be an optimal triple. It satisfies the multiplier rule

$$\nabla F(x,\lambda,b) = \nabla f(x) - \sum_{\beta=1}^{m} \lambda_\beta \nabla g_\beta(x) = 0 \qquad (i=1,\ldots,n), \quad (3.12\text{a})$$

$$g_\alpha(x) - b_\beta = 0 \qquad (\alpha = 1,\ldots,m). \qquad\qquad (3.12\text{b})$$

Here ∇F is the gradient of F with respect to x. We assume that this triple is nondegenerate in the sense that the Jacobian

$$\begin{vmatrix} F_{x^i x^j} & -g_{\beta x^i} \\ g_{\alpha x^j} & 0 \end{vmatrix} \qquad \begin{array}{l} (i,j=1,\ldots,n) \\ (\alpha,\beta=1,\ldots,m) \end{array}$$

of system (3.12) with respect to x and λ is different from zero at (x,λ) $=(x_0,\lambda_0)$. By the implicit function theorem given in Section 7 equations (3.12) have solutions $x(b), \lambda(b)$ such that $x(b_0) = x_0$, $\lambda(b_0) = \lambda_0$. Along these solutions the Lagrangian F is a function

$$\hat{F}(b) = F[x(b),\lambda(b),b] = f[x(b)] + \sum_{\beta=1}^{n} \lambda_\beta(b)\{b_\beta - g_\beta[x(b)]\} = f[x(b)]$$

of the control parameters b. For each α, $1 \leqslant \alpha \leqslant m$, we have

$$\frac{\partial \hat{F}}{\partial b_\alpha} = \sum_{i=1}^{n} \frac{\partial F}{\partial x^i} [x(b),\lambda(b),b] \frac{\partial x^i}{\partial b_\alpha}(b)$$

$$+ \sum_{\beta=1}^{m} \{b_\beta - g_\alpha[x(b)]\} \frac{\partial \lambda_\beta}{\partial b_\alpha}(b) + \lambda_\alpha(b) = \frac{\partial}{\partial b_\alpha} f[x(b)]$$

Setting $b = b_0$, we find that

$$\frac{\partial \hat{F}}{\partial b_\alpha}(b_0) = \lambda_\alpha(b_0) = \lambda_{\alpha 0} = \frac{\partial}{\partial b_\beta} f[x(b)]\Big|_{b=b_0}.$$

The multiplier $\lambda_{\alpha 0}$ therefore measures the sensitivity of the minimum of f to small changes in the parameter b_α.

EXERCISES

1. In the xy-plane the origin minimizes $f(x,y) = x^2 + ay$ subject to the constraint $g(x,y) = y = 0$. Show that if $a > 0$ the origin maximizes g subject to the constraint $f(x,y) = 0$. Show further that if $a < 0$ the origin minimizes g subject to the constraint $f(x,y) = 0$.

2. Generalize the result given in Exercise 1 as follows. Suppose that a point x_0 satisfies the hypotheses described in Theorem 3.1 with a set of multipliers $\lambda_1, \ldots, \lambda_m$. Show that, if $\lambda_\beta > 0$ (β fixed), x_0 affords a strict local minimum to g_β subject to the constraints $f(x) = f(x_0)$, $g_\alpha(x) = 0$ ($\alpha \neq \beta$, $\alpha = 1, \ldots, m$). What can be said if $\lambda_\beta < 0$? This result is called the *principle of reciprocity*.

3. In the xy-plane the origin affords a global minimum to $f(x,y) = x^2 - y^2 - 2y$ subject to the constraint $g(x,y) = y = 0$. Show that, although the origin affords a local minimum to g subject to the constraint $f = 0$, it does not afford a global minimum of g subject to $f = 0$.

4. Show that the origin minimizes $f(x,y) = x^2 - 7xy + y^2$ subject to the constraint $g(x,y) = xy = 0$. Show that the multiplier rule in Theorem 3.1 is satisfied with λ on the interval $5 < \lambda < 9$. Show that if $5 < \lambda < 9$ then $F = f + \lambda g$ has an unconstrained minimum at the origin.

5. Show that the origin minimizes every function $f(x,y)$ subject to the constraint $g(x,y) = x^2 + y^2 = 0$. In this situation excluded in Theorem 3.1?

6. Establish the following extension of Theorem 3.1. Suppose that $g_\alpha(x_0) = 0$ ($\alpha = 1, \ldots, m$). Suppose that, for each solution $h \neq 0$ of the equations $g_\alpha'(x_0, h) = 0$ ($\alpha = 1, \ldots, m$) there is a set of multipliers $\lambda_1, \ldots, \lambda_m$ such that $\nabla F(x_0) = 0$ and $F''(x_0, h) > 0$, where $F = f + \Sigma \lambda_\alpha g_\alpha$. Then x_0 affords a proper local minimum for f subject to the constraints $g_\alpha(x) = 0$ ($\alpha = 1, \ldots, m$).

7. Choose p so that $1 < p < \infty$. In the xyz-space the minimum m of $f(x,y,z) = |x|^p + |y|^p + |z|^p$ subject to the constraint $ax + by + cz = 1$ is attained at a point (x_0, y_0, z_0). Here $(a,b,c) \neq (0,0,0)$. Let (pA, pB, pC) be the gradient of f at (x_0, y_0, z_0). What are the values of A, B, and C? Show that $A = ma$, $B = mb$, $C = mc$, and $|A|^q + |B|^q + |C|^q = m$, where $q = p/(p-1)$. Find formulas for m, x_0, y_0, z_0 in terms of a, b, c. Show that (x_0, y_0, z_0) minimizes $f(x,y,z) - pm(ax + by + cz)$. Show further that (x_0, y_0, z_0) maximizes $ax + by + cz$ subject to $f(x,y,z) = m$. Observe that, because of convexity, second-order conditions are not needed. In fact, if $p < 2$, second derivatives of f fail to exist at points having one or more zero coordinates.

8. Extend the results given in Exercise 7 to the n-dimensional case.

4. CLASSIFICATION OF CRITICAL POINTS

Consider a function f of class C'' on an open set S. Recall that a point x_0 in S is a critical point of f if $\nabla f(x_0) = 0$. It is a *nondegenerate* critical point if the determinant

$$|f_{x^i x^j}(x_0)| \qquad (i,j=1,\ldots,n) \tag{4.1}$$

is different from zero. As a first result we have

THEOREM 4.1

A critical point x_0 that is nondegenerate is isolated.

Suppose that x_0 is not an isolated critical point. Then for every integer q there is a critical point $x_q \neq x_0$ such that $|x_q - x_0| < 1/q$. This sequence $\{x_q\}$ of critical points can be chosen so that the limit

$$h = \lim_{q \to \infty} \frac{x_q - x_0}{t_q}, \qquad t_q = |x_q - x_0|$$

exists. Clearly $|h| = 1$. Moreover, since $\nabla f(x_q) = \nabla f(x_0) = 0$, we have

$$0 = \lim_{q \to \infty} \frac{f_{x^i}(x_q) - f_{x^i}(x_0)}{t_q} = \sum_{j=1}^{n} f_{x^i x^j}(x_0) h^j.$$

This implies that determinant (4.1) is zero, contrary to our hypotheses. It follows that x_0 is an isolated critical point, as was to be proved.

By the *index* or *signature* k of a nondegenerate critical point x_0 will be meant the number of negative eigenvalues of the matrix

$$(f_{x^i x^j}(x_0)),$$

each counted a number of times equal to its multiplicity. If $k = 0$, then

$$f''(x_0, h) = \sum_{i,j} f_{x^i x^j}(x_0) h^i h^j > 0$$

for all $h \neq 0$. In this event x_0 affords a local minimum to f. If $k = n$, then

$$f''(x_0, h) < 0$$

for all $h \neq 0$ and x_0 affords a local maximum to f. If $0 < k < n$, then x_0 is a *saddle point* of f.

Consider now a nondegenerate critical point x_0 of f. We can assume that $x_0 = 0$. The Taylor expansion of f about $x_0 = 0$ takes the form

$$f(x) = f(0) + \tfrac{1}{2} x^* A x + r(x), \tag{4.2}$$

where A is the Hessian matrix

$$A = \left(\frac{\partial^2 f(0)}{\partial x^i \partial x^j} \right) \tag{4.3}$$

and $r(x)$ has the property that

$$\lim_{x \to 0} \frac{r(x)}{|x|^2} = 0. \tag{4.4}$$

Since $x_0 = 0$ is nondegenerate, the matrix A is nonsingular. Under a nonsingular transformation $x = By$ we find that

$$f(By) = f(0) + \tfrac{1}{2} y^* B^* A B y + r(By).$$

If we select the columns of B to be an orthonormal set of eigenvectors of A, then $B^* A B$ will be a diagonal matrix whose diagonal elements are the eigenvalues $\lambda_1, \lambda_2, \ldots, \lambda_n$ of A. These can be ordered so that $\lambda_1 \leqslant \lambda_2 \leqslant \ldots \leqslant \lambda_n$. If we rename $(y^1, \ldots, y^n)$ to be $(x^1, \ldots, x^n)$, we obtain

THEOREM 4.2

Under a suitable choice of axes the Taylor expansion of f *about a nondegenerate critical point* $x_0 = 0$ *of* f *takes the form*

$$f(x) = f(0) + \tfrac{1}{2}\left[\lambda_1 (x^1)^2 + \ldots + \lambda_n (x^n)^2 \right] + r(x), \tag{4.5}$$

where

$$\lambda_1 \leqslant \lambda_2 \leqslant \ldots \leqslant \lambda_n \tag{4.6}$$

and the remainder r(x) *satisfies condition* (4.4). *The number* k *of negative elements in the set* $\lambda_1, \ldots, \lambda_n$ *is the index of* $x_0 = 0$ *as a critical point of* f.

In sufficiently small neighborhood of $x_0 = 0$ the function f "behaves" like the quadratic

$$f(0) + \lambda_1 (x^1)^2 + \ldots + \lambda_n (x^n)^2.$$

In particular, if $\lambda_1, \ldots, \lambda_k$ are negative and $\lambda_{k+1}, \ldots, \lambda_n$ are positive, f has a local maximum at $x_0 = 0$ on the k-plane defined by the relation

$$x^{k+1} = 0, \qquad x^{k+2} = 0, \qquad \ldots, \qquad x^n = 0.$$

Moreover this is not true on any $(k+1)$-plane through x_0. This yields the first conclusion in the following theorem. The second conclusion follows similarly.

THEOREM 4.3

Let x_0 *be a nondegenerate critical point of* f. *The index of* x_0 *is equal to the greatest integer* k *for which there exists a* k*-plane through* x_0 *on which* f *has a strict local maximum at* x_0. *Alternatively, the index* k *of* x_0 *is the least integer* k *for which there is an* $(n-k)$*-plane through* x_0 *on which* f *has a strict local minimum at* x_0.

The results given above can be generalized to constrained problems. We shall give a sketch of how this can be done. Recall that a point x_0 is a *critical point* of f on the set

$$g_\alpha(x)=0 \qquad (\alpha=1,\ldots,m) \tag{4.7}$$

if there exist multipliers $\lambda_1,\ldots,\lambda_m$ such that $\nabla F(x_0)=0$, where $F=f+\lambda_1 g_1+\cdots+\lambda_m g_m$. It is *nondegenerate* if the $(n+m)$-dimensional determinant

$$\begin{vmatrix} F_{x^i x^j}(x_0) & g_{\beta x^i}(x_0) \\ g_{\alpha x^j}(x_0) & 0 \end{vmatrix} \qquad \begin{matrix} (i,j=1,\ldots,n) \\ (\alpha,\beta=1,\ldots,m) \end{matrix} \tag{4.8}$$

is different from zero. Here i and α are row indices, and j and β are column indices. By the *index* k of a nondegenerate critical point x_0 of f on the constraint surface (4.7) will be meant the number of negative eigenvalues of the quadratic form

$$F''(x_0,h)=\sum_{i,j} F_{x^i x^j}(x_0)h^i h^j \tag{4.9}$$

on the $(n-m)$-plane defined by the relations

$$g_\alpha'(x_0,h)=0 \qquad (\alpha=1,\ldots,m). \tag{4.10}$$

Clearly $k \le n-m$. Let $h_1,\ldots,h_k$ be eigenvectors corresponding to these negative eigenvalues. They can be chosen to be orthonormal. Since determinant (4.8) is nonnull, the quadratic form $F''(x_0,h)$ has no zero eigenvalue. It follows that

$$F''(x_0,h)>0$$

for all $h \neq 0$ satisfying the constraints

$$g'_\alpha(x_0,h)=0 \quad (\alpha=1,\dots,m), \qquad \langle h_\gamma,h \rangle=0 \quad (\gamma=1,\dots,k).$$

By virtue of Theorem 3.1 this implies that x_0 affords a local minimum to f subject to the constraints

$$g_\alpha(x)=0 \quad (\alpha=1,\dots,m), \qquad \langle h_\gamma, x-x_0 \rangle=0 \quad (\gamma=1,\dots,k).$$

In fact, x_0 is a nondegenerate critical point of f relative to these constraints.

In a similar way it is seen that, if $h_{k+1},\dots,h_{n-m}$ are orthonormal eigenvectors for $F''(x,h)$ relative to (4.10) and corresponding to the positive eigenvalues of $F''(x_0,h)$ on this set, then x_0 affords a local maximum to f subject to the constraints

$$g_\alpha(x)=0 \quad (\alpha=1,\dots,m), \qquad \langle h_\rho, x-x_0 \rangle=0 \quad (\rho=k+1,\dots,n-m).$$

The results given in this section are basic in the theory of critical points developed by Marston Morse.[†]

EXERCISES

1. Classify the critical points of the following functions:
   (a) $f(x,y)=(x^2-1)^2+y^2$,
   (b) $f(x,y)=(x^2-1)^2+(y^2-1)^2$.
2. Let A be a symmetric matrix. Show that the critical points of $f(x)=x^*Ax$ on the unit sphere $x^*x=1$ are unit eigenvectors of A.
3. Let A be an $(n \times n)$-dimensional symmetric matrix, and let D be an $(r \times n)$-dimensional matrix of rank $r<n$. Let $\mathcal{B}$ be all vectors x such that $Dx=0$. Show that a unit vector x is a eigenvector of A relative to $\mathcal{B}$ if and only if x is a critical point of $f(x)=x^*Ax$ subject to the constraints $Dx=0, x^*x=1$.
4. Show that the index k of a nondegenerate critical point x_0 of f is the dimension of a maximal linear subspace on which $f''(x_0,h) \leqslant 0$.
5. Let x_0 be a nondegenerate critical point of f. Suppose that x_0 minimizes f subject to a set of normal constraints $g_\alpha(x)=0$ $(\alpha=1,\dots,m)$. Show that the index k of x_0 cannot exceed m. Can k equal m?
6. Generalize the results given in Exercises 4 and 5 to nondegenerate constrained critical points of f.

[†]See, for example, M. Morse, "Calculus of Variations in the Large," Chapter VI in *Colloquium Publications*, Vol. XVIII, The American Mathematical Society, Providence, R.I.

5. TANGENT VECTORS AND NORMALITY

Let x_0 be a point on a surface S defined by a set of equations of the form

$$g_\alpha(x) = 0 \qquad (\alpha = 1, \ldots, m). \qquad (5.1)$$

It is assumed that the functions $g_\alpha(x)$ are of class C' on a neighborhood of x_0. A vector h will be said to be a *tangent vector of S at x_0* if there is a curve $x(t)$ $(0 \leqslant t \leqslant \delta)$ in S such that $x(0) = x_0$ and $\dot{x}(0) = h$. Here $\dot{x}(0)$ denotes the derivative of $x(t)$ at $t = 0$. Differentiating the identity

$$g_\alpha[x(t)] = 0$$

at $t = 0$, we find that

$$0 = g'_\alpha[x(0), \dot{x}(0)] = \sum_{i=1}^{n} \frac{\partial g_\alpha(x_0)}{\partial x^i} \dot{x}^i(0) = g'_\alpha(x_0, h).$$

It follows that every tangent vector h must satisfy the equations

$$g'_\alpha(x_0, h) = 0. \qquad (5.2)$$

The converse, however, is not always true. For example, in the xy-plane the equation

$$g(x,y) = (x^2 + y^2 - 1)^2 = 0$$

represents the unit circle about the origin. At the point $(x_0, y_0) = (0, 1)$ its tangent vectors (h, k) are of the form $(h, 0)$, where h is arbitrary. We have

$$g'(x,y; h,k) = 2(x^2 + y^2 - 1)(2xh + 2yk).$$

Consequently at $(0, 1)$ we have $g'(0, 1; h, k) \equiv 0$ for all vectors (h, k). This equation therefore does not determine the tangent vectors to the circle. In this event we can redefine $g(x,y)$ to be $g(x,y) = x^2 + y^2 - 1$. Then the equations $g'(0, 1; h, k) = 2k = 0$ determine the tangent vectors $(h, 0)$ to the circle at the point $(0, 1)$. A somewhat different situation arises when $g(x,y) = x^2 - y^3$. At the origin $(0, 0)$ the curve $g(x,y) = 0$ has a cusp, as shown in Figure 5.1. In this case the vectors $(0, k)$ with $k \geqslant 0$ are the tangent vectors at the origin. Inasmuch as $g'(x,y; h,k) = 2xh - 3y^2k$, we have $g'(0, 0; h, k) = 0$ for all vectors (h, k). Consequently again this equation does not determine the tangent vectors to our curve.

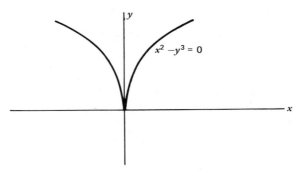

Figure 5.1

A point x_0 in S will be said to be a *normal point* of S if the linear equations

$$g_\alpha'(x_0, h) = \langle \nabla g_\alpha(x_0), h \rangle = \sum_{j=1}^{n} \frac{\partial g_\alpha(x_0)}{\partial x^j} h^j = 0 \qquad (\alpha = 1, \ldots, m) \quad (5.3)$$

in h are linearly independent. This is equivalent to requiring that the gradients $\nabla g_1(x_0), \ldots, \nabla g_m(x_0)$ be linearly independent. It is also the criterion that the matrix

$$\left(\frac{\partial g_\alpha(x_0)}{\partial x^j} \right) \qquad (\alpha = 1, \ldots, m) \tag{5.4}$$

be of rank m. At a normal point x_0 of S every solution h of equations (5.3) is a tangent vector of S at x_0, as will be seen in the next theorem.

The concept of normality can be obtained from another point of view. By a *normal k* of S at x_0 is meant a vector k that is perpendicular to every tangent vector h of S at x_0. The class $\mathcal{K}$ of all normals to S forms a linear manifold orthogonal to S at x. Since every tangent vector h satisfies equation (5.3), it follows that the gradients $\nabla g_1(x_0), \ldots, \nabla g_m(x_0)$ are normals to S at x_0. So also is every linear combination

$$k = \lambda_1 \nabla g_1(x_1) + \ldots + \lambda_m \nabla g_m(x_0) \tag{5.5}$$

of these gradients. The converse is true when x_0 is a normal point of S, as stated in the following proposition.

The condition for normality of x_0 is the condition that the gradients $\nabla g_1(x_0), \ldots, \nabla g_m(x_0)$ form a basis for the normal space $\mathcal{K}$ of S at x_0.

This result justifies the term "normality". A basis for $\mathcal{K}$ is of course a set of *linearly independent* generators of $\mathcal{K}$.

The proof of this proposition is based on the result given in the next theorem, which states that the class $\mathcal{K}$ of all tangent vectors to S at x_0 is composed of all solutions h of *tangential constraints* (5.3). Since these equations are linearly independent, the dimension of $\mathcal{K}$ is $n - m$. The orthogonal complement $\mathcal{K}^\perp$ of $\mathcal{K}$ is the normal space $\mathcal{K}$ of S at x_0. Its dimension is m. Since the gradients $\nabla g_1(x_0), \ldots, \nabla g_m(x_0)$ are a set of m linearly independent vectors in $\mathcal{K}$ they form a basis for $\mathcal{K}$, as was to be proved.

The fact that in the normal case the tangent space $\mathcal{K}$ is determined by tangential constraints (5.3) is verified in the following theorem.

THEOREM 5.1

Let x_0 *be a normal point of the surface* S *defined by the equations*

$$g_\alpha(x) = 0 \qquad (\alpha = 1, \ldots, m).$$

Let h *be a vector satisfying the tangential constraints*

$$g'_\alpha(x_0, h) = 0 \qquad (\alpha = 1, \ldots, m). \tag{5.6}$$

There exists a curve $x(t)$ $(-\delta \leqslant t \leqslant \delta)$ *in* S *of class* C' *on* S *such that* $x(0) = x_0$ *and* $\dot{x}(0) = h$, *where* $\dot{x}(t)$ *is the derivative of* $x(t)$. *If the functions* $g_\alpha(x)$ *are of class* C^k *near* x_0, *then* $x(t)$ *is of class* C^k *also.*

This result is obtained from the following theorem by choosing h so that (5.6) holds.

THEOREM 5.2

Let $g_\alpha(x)$ $(\alpha = 1, \ldots, m < n)$ *be a set of* m *real-valued functions of class* C^k $k \geqslant 1)$ *on a neighborhood of a point* x_0. *Suppose further that the matrix*

$$\left(\frac{\partial g_\alpha}{\partial x^i} \right) \qquad (\alpha = 1, \ldots, m; i = 1, \ldots, n) \tag{5.7}$$

has rank m *at* $x = x_0$. *Then for a given vector* h, *the equations*

$$g_\alpha(x) = g_\alpha(x_0) + t g'_\alpha(x_0, h) \qquad (\alpha = 1, \ldots, m) \tag{5.8}$$

have a solution

$$x(t) \qquad (-\delta \leqslant t \leqslant \delta) \tag{5.9}$$

of class C^k *such that* $x(0) = x_0$ *and* $\dot{x}(0) = h$, *where* $\dot{x}(t)$ *is the derivative of* $x(t)$ *with respect to* t.

Let h_α be the gradient ∇g_α of g_α at $x = x_0$. Then for each fixed α the vector h_α is the transpose

$$h_\alpha = \begin{bmatrix} \dfrac{\partial g_\alpha(x_0)}{\partial x^1} \\ \vdots \\ \dfrac{\partial g_\alpha(x_0)}{\partial x^n} \end{bmatrix} \qquad (\alpha = 1, \ldots, m)$$

of the αth row of matrix (5.7). Since matrix (5.7) has rank m, the vectors $h_1, \ldots, h_m$ are linearly independent. It follows that the determinant

$$\left| g'_\alpha(x_0, h_\beta) \right| = \left| \langle h_\alpha, h_\beta \rangle \right| \neq 0.$$

Let h be an arbitrary vector. The equations

$$G_\alpha(b, t) = g_\alpha(x_0 + h_1 b_1 + \cdots + h_m b_m + th) - g_\alpha(x_0) - t g'_\alpha(x_0, h) = 0 \quad (5.10)$$

have the initial solution $(b, t) = (0, 0)$. Moreover at this point we have

$$\left| \frac{\partial G_\alpha}{\partial b_\beta} \right| = \left| g'_\alpha(x_0, h_\beta) \right| \neq 0. \tag{5.11}$$

It follows from the implicit function theorem (see Theorem 7.1) that equations (5.10) have solutions

$$b_\beta = B_\beta(t) \qquad (-\delta \leqslant t \leqslant \delta)$$

of class C^k such that $B_\beta(0) = 0$. The function

$$x(t) = x_0 + \sum_{\beta=1}^{m} h_\beta B_\beta(t) + th \qquad (-\delta \leqslant t \leqslant \delta) \tag{5.12}$$

is of class C^k, has $x(0) = x_0$, and satisfies equation (5.8). We have accordingly the identity

$$g_\alpha[x(t)] = g_\alpha\left[x_0 + \sum_\beta h_\beta B_\beta(t) + th \right] = g_\alpha(x_0) + t g'_\alpha(x_0, h)$$

on $-\delta \leqslant t \leqslant \delta$. Differentiating with respect to t and setting $t = 0$, we obtain the relations

$$\sum_\beta g'_\alpha(x_0, h_\beta) \dot{B}_\beta(0) + g'_\alpha(x_0, h) = g'_\alpha(x_0, h).$$

Hence

$$\sum_\beta g'_\alpha(x_0, h_\beta) \dot{B}_\beta(0) = 0.$$

Since determinant (5.11) is different from zero, we have $\dot{B}_\beta(0) = 0$ ($\beta = 1, \ldots, m$). Consequently, by (5.12),

$$\dot{x}(0) = \sum_\beta h_\beta \dot{B}_\beta(0) + h = h.$$

This completes the proof of Theorem 5.2.

The condition of normality for x_0 is a sufficient condition for the tangent space $\mathcal{H}$ to be determined by the tangential constraints $g'_\alpha(x_0, h) = 0$. It is however, by no means necessary. For example, if the functions $g_\alpha(x)$ are linear, the surface

$$g_\alpha(x) = \sum_{i=1}^n a_{\alpha i} x^i + b_\alpha = 0 \qquad (\alpha = 1, \ldots, m) \qquad (5.13)$$

is a k-plane $\pi_k (k \geqslant n - m)$ and the tangential constraints take the simpler form

$$g'_\alpha(x_0, h) = \sum_{i=1}^n a_{\alpha i} h^i = 0. \qquad (5.14)$$

If x_0 is in the k-plane π_k and h satisfies equation (5.14), then

$$g_\alpha(x_0 + th) = g_\alpha(x_0) + t g'_\alpha(x_0, h) = 0$$

for all values of t. Hence the solutions h of equations (5.14) are tangent vectors of π_k at x_0. Observe that the tangent space $\mathcal{H}$ is independent of x_0 in this case. Of course equations (5.13) can be replaced by a smaller set in which the equations are linearly independent.

In view of this result we define a point x_0 to be a *regular point* of S if every solution h of the tangential constraints $g'_\alpha(x_0, h) = 0$ is actually tangent to S at x_0. This implies that *the normal space* $\mathcal{H}$ *of* S *at* x_0 *is generated by the gradients* $\nabla g_1(x_0), \ldots, \nabla g_m(x_0)$. A normal point of S is a regular point of S. If the functions $g_\alpha(x)$ are linear, every point of S is a regular point of S. Apart from these two cases it is difficult to test for regularity. However, the Lagrange multiplier rule is valid for regular points, as can be seen by a careful analysis of the proof of the Lagrange multiplier rule given in Theorem 2.2. In the regular case the Lagrange multipliers may not be unique.

In the interest of generality we state without proof the following extension of Theorem 5.2.

THEOREM 5.3

Suppose that the real-valued functions $g_\alpha(x)$ $(\alpha = 1, \ldots, m)$ *are continuous on a neighborhood of* x_0 *and are differentiable at* x_0. *Suppose further that their functional matrix*

$$\left(\frac{\partial g_\alpha(x_0)}{\partial x^i} \right) \qquad (\alpha = 1, \ldots, m; \ i = 1, \ldots, n)$$

at x_0 *has rank* m. *Then, for a given vector* h, *the equation*

$$g_\alpha(x) = g_\alpha(x_0) + t g'_\alpha(x_0, h)$$

has a solution

$$x(t) \qquad (-\delta \leqslant t \leqslant \delta)$$

such that x_0 *and* $\dot{x}(0) = h$.

The function $x(t)$ is continuous at $t = 0$ but need not be continuous elsewhere. The proof of this theorem will be given in Section 12 of Chapter 6. This result tells us that a normal point of S is a regular point of S under the weaker assumption that the functions $g_\alpha(x)$ are differentiable only at the point x_0. Moreover by the use of this result the Lagrange multiplier rule given in Theorem 2.2 can be established under the weaker assumption that the functions $f, g_1, \ldots, g_n$ are twice differentiable at x_0. They may fail, however, to be differentiable elsewhere.

EXERCISES

1. Show that the equations $g_\alpha(x) = 0$ $(\alpha = 1, \ldots, m)$ are equivalent to the single equation

$$G(x) = \sum_{\alpha=1}^{m} g_\alpha(x) g_\alpha(x) = 0.$$

Show further that a point x_0 on $G(x)=0$ is abnormal relative to the constraint $G(x)=0$.

2. Let x_0 be a normal point satisfying the constraints $g_\alpha(x)=0$ $(\alpha=1,\ldots,m)$. Let $g_{m+1}(x)=G[g_1(x),\ldots,g_m(x)]$, where G is of class C' and $G(0)=0$. Show that x_0 is a regular point relative to the constraints $g_\beta(x)=0$ $(\beta=1,\ldots,m+1)$ but is not a normal point relative to these constraints.

3. In the xy-plane let $g(0,y)=y$, $g(x,y)=y-x^2\sin(1/x)$ $(x\neq0)$. Show that the origin is a normal point relative to the constraint $g(x,y)=0$ but is not normal relative to the constraints $y=0$, $g(x,y)=0$. Show that under the definition given above the origin is not a regular point relative to the constraints $y=0$, $g(x,y)=0$. In the next chapter we shall modify the concept of regularity so that the origin is regular in this case.

4. Suppose that a curve $x(t)$ $(0\leqslant t\leqslant\delta)$ on the surface

$$g_\alpha(x)=0 \qquad (\alpha=1,\ldots,m)$$

has $x(0)=x_0$ and $\dot{x}(0)=h$. Show that, if the functions $g_\alpha(x)$ are differentiable at x_0, then

$$g'_\alpha(x_0,h)=0 \qquad (\alpha=1,\ldots,m).$$

Show that, if $g_\alpha[x(t)]\leqslant0$ on $0\leqslant t\leqslant\delta$, then $g'_\alpha(x_0,h)\leqslant0$.

5. Suppose that the functions $g_\alpha(x)$ are differentiable at x_0 and that $g_\alpha(x_0)=0$. Let $\{x_q\}$ be a sequence of points having

$$g_\alpha(x_q)\leqslant0 \qquad (\alpha=1,\ldots,m;\ q=1,2,3,\ldots)$$

and converging to x_0 in such a way that the limit

$$\lim_{q\to0}\frac{x_q-x_0}{t_q}=h, \qquad t_q=|x_q-x_0|>0$$

exists. Show that

$$g'_\alpha(x_0,h)\leqslant0 \qquad (\alpha=1,\ldots,m).$$

Show that, if $g_\alpha(x_q)=0$ $(q=1,2,3,\ldots)$, then $g'_\alpha(x_0,h)=0$.

6.   GRADIENT OF A FUNCTION RELATIVE TO CONSTRAINTS

In the preceding pages we associated Lagrange multipliers only with critical points of f relative to constraints

$$g_\alpha(x)=0 \qquad (\alpha=1,\ldots,m). \qquad (6.1)$$

However, the concept of Lagrange multipliers can be extended in a meaningful way to an arbitrary *normal* point x_0 on the surface S defined by constraints (5.1). To this end observe that for any set of multipliers the function

$$F(x) = f(x) + \lambda_1 g_1(x) + \ldots + \lambda_m g_m(x) \qquad (6.2)$$

is equivalent to f on S in the sense that $F(x) = f(x)$ on S. At a normal point x_0 on S there is a unique set of multipliers $\lambda_1, \ldots, \lambda_m$, called *Lagrange multipliers*, such that gradient

$$\nabla F(x) = \nabla f(x) + \lambda_1 \nabla g(x) + \ldots + \lambda_m \nabla g_m(x) \qquad (6.3)$$

of F is tangent to S at $x = x_0$. The corresponding function $F(x)$ will be called the *Lagrange function* for f at x_0. Its gradient $\nabla F(x_0)$ is the orthogonal projection of the gradient $\nabla f(x_0)$ of f at x_0 on the tangent space of S at x_0, as indicated in Figure 6.1.

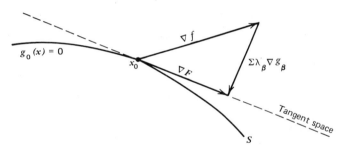

Figure 6.1

Since the vectors $\nabla g_1(x_0), \ldots, \nabla g_m(x_0)$ are normal to S at x_0 the vector $\Sigma \lambda_\beta \nabla g_\beta(x_0)$ is also normal to S at x_0. Consequently $\nabla F(x_0)$ is the orthogonal projection of $\nabla f(x_0)$ on the tangent space of S at x_0. The multipliers $\lambda_1, \ldots, \lambda_m$ are determined by the linear equations

$$0 = \langle \nabla g_\alpha(x_0), \nabla F(x_0) \rangle = \langle \nabla g_\alpha(x_0), \nabla f(x_0) \rangle$$
$$+ \sum_\beta \langle \nabla g_\alpha(x_0), \nabla g_\beta(x_0) \rangle \lambda_\beta, \qquad (6.4)$$

which state that $\nabla F(x_0)$ is a tangent vector to S at x_0. In these equations the Grammian matrix

$$(\langle \nabla g_\alpha(x), \nabla g_\beta(x)\rangle) \tag{6.5}$$

of the gradients $\nabla g_1, \ldots, \nabla g_m(x)$ is nonsingular at x_0 since these gradients are linearly independent. Let $G(x) = (G_{\alpha\beta}(x))$ $(\alpha, \beta = 1, \ldots, m)$ denote the inverse of the Grammian matrix (6.5). In terms of this inverse the solutions $\lambda_1, \ldots, \lambda_m$ of equations (6.5) are given by the formula $\lambda_\alpha = \Lambda_\alpha(x_0)$, where

$$\Lambda_\alpha(x) = - \sum_{\beta=1}^{m} G_{\alpha\beta}\langle \nabla g_\beta, \nabla f\rangle = - \sum_{\beta=1}^{m} \sum_{i=1}^{n} G_{\alpha\beta}\frac{\partial g_\beta}{\partial x^i}\frac{\partial f}{\partial x^i}. \tag{6.6}$$

Formula (6.6) can be written in the alternative form

$$\Lambda_\alpha(x) = - \sum_{i=1}^{n} \Gamma_{\alpha i}(x)\frac{\partial f(x)}{\partial x^i} \qquad (\alpha = 1, \ldots, m), \tag{6.7}$$

where

$$\Gamma_{\alpha i}(x) = \sum_{\beta=1}^{m} G_{\alpha\beta}(x)\frac{\partial g_\beta(x)}{\partial x^i} \qquad (\alpha = 1, \ldots, m; i = 1, \ldots, n). \tag{6.8}$$

In matrix notations

$$\Lambda(x) = -\Gamma(x)\nabla f(x). \tag{6.9}$$

The matrix

$$\Gamma(x) = (\Gamma_{\alpha i}(x)) \qquad (\alpha = 1, \ldots, m; i = 1, \ldots, n) \tag{6.10}$$

is the *transpose of the pseudoinverse* of the matrix

$$\left(\frac{\partial g_\alpha(x)}{\partial x^i}\right) \qquad (\alpha = 1, \ldots, m; i = 1, \ldots, n) \tag{6.11}$$

whose row vectors are the gradients $\nabla g_1(x), \ldots, \nabla g_m(x)$.

The gradient $\nabla F(x_0)$ of the Lagrange function F of f at x_0 will be called the *gradient of* f *relative to the constraints* $g_\alpha(x) = 0$. The justification for this definition is given by the following theorem, which states that $\nabla F(x_0)$ is in the direction of fastest ascent of f on S at x_0.

THEOREM 6.1

Let x_0 *be a normal point of* S, *and let* F *be the corresponding Lagrange function. If* $\nabla F(x_0) \neq 0$, *the vector* $h_0 = \nabla F(x_0)/|\nabla F(x_0)|$ *maximizes the directional derivative* $f'(x_0, h)$ *amongst all unit tangent vectors* h *of* S *at* x_0. *If* $\nabla F(x_0) = 0$, *then* $f'(x_0, h) = 0$ *for all tangent vectors* h.

If $\nabla F(x_0) = 0$, then $\nabla f(x_0)$ is normal to S at x_0. Consequently $f'(x_0, h) = \langle \nabla f(x_0), h \rangle = 0$ for all tangent vectors h. Suppose therefore that $\nabla F(x_0) \neq 0$. Let h_0 be a solution to the problem

$$f'(x_0, h) = \max, \qquad g'_\alpha(x_0, h) = 0, \qquad |h|^2 - 1 = \sum_1^n h^i h^i - 1 = 0.$$

The point h_0 is a normal point relative to this problem, as can readily be verified. By the Lagrange multiplier rule there exist multipliers $\lambda_1, \ldots, \lambda_m$, $\lambda_{m+1} = -(\sigma/2)$ such that the gradient of the function

$$\hat{F}(h) = f'(x_0, h) + \sum_{\alpha=1}^m \lambda_\alpha g'_\alpha(x_0, h) - \frac{\sigma}{2}[|h|^2 - 1]$$

with respect to h vanishes at $h = h_0$, that is,

$$\nabla f(x_0) + \sum_{\alpha=1}^m \lambda_\alpha \nabla g_\alpha(x_0) - \sigma h_0 = 0.$$

This equation tells us that σh_0 is the projection $\nabla F(x_0)$ of $\nabla f(x_0)$ on the tangent space of S at x_0. If follows that $\sigma = |\nabla F(x_0)|$ and hence that $h_0 = \nabla F(x_0)/|\nabla F(x_0)|$, as was to be proved.

The Lagrange function F at x_0 can be characterized alternatively by the following criterion.

THEOREM 6.2

Let x_0 *be a normal point of* S. *The Lagrange function* F *for* f *at* x_0 *relative to* S *is the function of the form*

$$F = f + \lambda_1 g_1 + \ldots + \lambda_m g_m$$

whose gradient ∇F *at* x_0 *is of minimum length.*

The multipliers $\lambda_1, \ldots, \lambda_m$, which afford a minimum to the function

$$\phi(\lambda) = \tfrac{1}{2}|\nabla F(x_0)|^2 = \tfrac{1}{2}\left|\nabla f(x_0) + \sum_\beta \lambda_\beta \nabla g_\beta(x_0)\right|^2,$$

must satisfy the equations $\partial\phi/\partial\lambda_\alpha = 0$ $(\alpha = 1,\ldots,m)$. When these derivatives are evaluated, equations (6.4) are obtained. Consequently these multipliers are the Lagrange multipliers for f at x_0, as was to be proved.

EXERCISES

1. In the xy-plane find the gradient of the function $f(x,y) = 2x + 3y$ at (x_0,y_0) $= (3,4)$ subject to the constraint $g(x,y) = x^2 + y^2 - 25 = 0$.

2. Let $f(x) = \frac{1}{2}x^* Ax - k^*x$, where $A = A^* > 0$. Given a point x_1, set $p_1 = -\nabla f(x_1)$. Let $x_2 = x_1 + a_1 p_1$ be the minimum point of f on the line $x = x_1 + \alpha p_1$. Show that $p_1^* \nabla f(x_2) = 0$. Show that $\nabla f(x_2) = \nabla f(x_1) + a_1 A p_1$ and hence that $\nabla f(x_2)$ $= a_1 A p_1 - p_1$. Set $b_1 = |\nabla f(x_2)|^2/|\nabla f(x_1)|^2$. Show that apart from a positive scale factor the vector $\nabla f(x_2) + b_1 \nabla f(x_1)$ is the gradient of f at x_2 relative to the $(n-1)$-plane $p_1^*(Ax - k) = 0$. The vector $p_2 = -\nabla f(x_2) + b_1 p_1$ is in the direction of steepest descent for f at x_2 on this $(n-1)$-plane. Show that $p_2^* A p_1 = 0$.

3. Continuing with Exercise 2, let $x_3 = x_2 + a_2 p_2$ be the minimum of $f(x)$ on the line $x = x_2 + \alpha p_2$. Show that $p_2^* \nabla f(x_3) = 0$. Show that $\nabla f(x_3) = \nabla f(x_2) + a_2 A p_2$. Set $b_2 = |\nabla f(x_3)|^2/|\nabla f(x_2)|^2$. Show that $p_3 = -\nabla f(x_3) + b_2 p_2$ is in the direction of steepest descent for f at x_3 on the $(n-2)$-plane defined by the equations $p_1^*(Ax - k) = 0$, $p_2^*(Ax - k) = 0$.

4. Exercises 2 and 3 suggest the following algorithm. Starting at a point x_1, set $p_1 = -\nabla f(x_1)$. Having obtained the point x_k and the direction p_k, find the minimum point x_{k+1} on the line $x_{k+1} = x_k + \alpha p_k$. Set $p_{k+1} = -\nabla f(x_{k+1}) + b_k p_k$, where $b_k = |\nabla f(x_{k+1})|^2/|\nabla f(x_k)|^2$, and continue. This algorithm is called the *conjugate gradient algorithm* for minimizing f. It minimizes f in $m \leqslant n$ steps.[†] It can be applied to nonquadratic functions by restarting after each cycle of n steps.[‡]

5. Apply the algorithm given in Exercise 4 to the minimum problem described in Exercise 5, Section 7 of Chapter 1.

7. IMPLICIT FUNCTION THEOREMS

The proof of the Lagrange multiplier rule given in Theorem 2.2 makes use of an implicit function theorem. Such a theorem is concerned with the conditions under which a set of equations

$$f_i(t,x) = f_i(t^1,\ldots,t^m,x^1,\ldots,x^n) = 0 \qquad (i = 1,\ldots,n) \qquad (7.1)$$

can be solved for $x = (x^1,\ldots,x^n)$ as a function $x(t) = (x^1(t),\ldots,x^n(t))$ of

[†]See M. R. Hestenes and E. Stiefel, "Methods of Conjugate Gradients for Solving Linear Systems,"*Journal of Research of the National Bureau of Standards*, Vol. 49(1952); No. 6.
[‡]See, for example, R. Fletcher and C. M. Reeves, "Function Minimization by Conjugate Gradients," *Computer Journal*, Vol. 7 (1964), 149.

$t=(t^1,\ldots,t^m)$. Normally these equations can be solved by holding t fixed and minimizing the function

$$F(t,x)= \sum_{i=1}^{n} f_i(t,x)f_i(t,x)=f_1(t,x)^2+ \cdots +f_n(t,x)^2. \qquad (7.2)$$

However, a minimum point $x(t)$ of $F(t,x)$ for fixed t need not be a solution to system (7.1). For example, if $m=n=1$ and

$$f(t,x)=1+t^2+x^2,$$

the equation $f(t,x)=0$ has no solution $x(t)$ for any value of t even though the point $x(t)=0$ affords a minimum to

$$F(t,x)=f(t,x)^2=(1+t^2+x^2)^2$$

for each fixed t. It follows that suitable criteria are needed to ensure that the minimum of F will yield a solution of system (7.1). To this end we assume that the functions $f_i(t,x)$ are continuous and have continuous partial derivatives with respect to x^j ($j=1,\ldots,n$) on an open set S in the $(m \times n)$-dimensional space of points $p=(t^1,\ldots,t^m,\ x^1,\ldots,x^n)$. We denote by $D(t,x)$ the functional determinant

$$D(t,x)= \left| \frac{\partial f_i}{\partial x^j}(t,x) \right|. \qquad (7.3)$$

Under these assumptions we have the following implicit function theorem.

THEOREM 7.1

Suppose that the relations

$$f_i(a,b)=0 \quad (i=1,\ldots,n), \qquad D(a,b)\neq0 \qquad (7.4)$$

hold at a point $(t,x)=(a,b)$ *in* S. *There exist continuous functions*

$$x^i(t)=x^i(t^1,\ldots,t^m) \qquad (i=1,\ldots,n)$$

on a neighborhood T *of* $t=a$ *and a constant* $\varepsilon>0$ *such that*

$$x^i(a)=b^i, \qquad f_i[t,x(t)]=0 \qquad (i=1,\ldots,n;\ t \in T) \qquad (7.5)$$

and such that the relations

$$f_i(t, x) = 0, \qquad |x - x(t)| < \varepsilon \quad (t \, \varepsilon \, T) \qquad (7.6)$$

hold only in the case $x = x(t)$. *If the functions* $f_i(t, x)$ *are of class* $C^{(k)}$ *on S, then the functions* $x(t)$ *are of class* $C^{(k)}$ *on T.*

This theorem is a well-known one in mathematical analysis. Proofs can be found in the standard books on this subject. For the sake of completeness we include a proof of the theorem based on optimization techniques. However, the reader may wish to accept this result as being well known and continue with the study of constrained optimization theory. A large part of this theory is independent of implicit function theorems.

To prove Theorem 7.1 we can assume without loss of generality that the set S is convex in x. This means that the point $(t, x + \theta(y - x))$ $(0 \leqslant \theta \leqslant 1)$ is in S whenever (t, x) and (t, y) are in S. We then have the formula

$$f_i(t, y) - f_i(t, x) = \sum_j B_{ij}(t, x, y)(y^j - x^j) \qquad (7.7)$$

where

$$B_{ij}(t, x, y) = \int_0^1 \frac{\partial f_i}{\partial x^j}[t, x + \theta(y - x)] d\theta$$

whenever (t, x) and (t, y) are in S. Set

$$D(t, x, y) = |B_{ij}(t, x, y)|.$$

Since $D(a, b, b) = D(a, b) \neq 0$, we can choose positive number ε such that

$$D(t, x, y) \neq 0$$

for all (t, x, y) in the set P defined by the inequalities

$$|t - a| \leqslant 2\varepsilon, \qquad |x - b| \leqslant 2\varepsilon, \qquad |y - b| \leqslant 2\varepsilon.$$

It follows from (7.7) that, if (t, x, y) is in P and $f_i(t, x) = f_i(t, y)$, then $y = x$.

Since $f_i(a, b) = 0$, the function $F = \sum f_i f_i$ has $F(a, b) = 0$. In view of the result described in the last paragraph we have $F(a, x) > 0$ for all x having $|x - b| = \varepsilon$. By Theorem 2.5 in Chapter 1 there are positive number m and δ such that

$$F(t, x) > m > 0 \qquad \text{whenever} \qquad |t - a| \leqslant \delta, |x - b| = \varepsilon. \qquad (7.8)$$

Since $F(a,b)=0$, we can diminish δ if necessary so that

$$F(t,x)<m \qquad \text{whenever} \quad |t-a|\leqslant\delta, |x-b|\leqslant\delta. \tag{7.9}$$

Let T be the open sphere $|t-a|<\delta$ in t-space, and let X be the closed sphere $|x-b|\leqslant\varepsilon$ in x-space. Select t in T. Since X is compact and $F(t,x)$ is continuous on X, there is a point $x(t)$ in X at which $F(t,x)$ assumes a minimum value. By virtue of (7.8) and (7.9) the point $x(t)$ is interior to X. Consequently

$$\frac{\partial F}{\partial x^j}=2\sum_i f_i\frac{\partial f_i}{\partial x^j}=0 \qquad \text{at } x=x(t).$$

Since $D[t,x(t)]\neq 0$, this implies that $f_i[t,x(t)]=0$. If (t,x) is a point having

$$f_i(t,x)=0, \qquad |x-x(t)|<\varepsilon,$$

then $|x-b|\leqslant|x-x(t)|+|x(t)-b|<2\varepsilon$. Hence $x=x(t)$, by virtue of the uniqueness result obtained in the last paragraph.

To establish the continuity of $x(t)$, let t and $t+\Delta t$ be points in T, and set

$$\Delta x=x(t+\Delta t)-x(t).$$

By (7.7) with t replaced by $t+\Delta t$, y by $x(t+\Delta t)$, and x by $x(t)$, we see that

$$f_i[t+\Delta t,x(t+\Delta t)]-f_i[t+\Delta t,x(t)]=\sum_j B_{ij}[t+\Delta t,x(t),x(t+\Delta t)]\Delta x^j.$$

Inasmuch as $f_i[t+\Delta t,x(t+\Delta t)]=0$, we have

$$-f_i[t+\Delta t,x(t)]=\sum_j B_{ij}[t+\Delta t,x(t),x(t+\Delta t)]\Delta x^j. \tag{7.10}$$

Since $D[t,x(t),x(t+\Delta t)]\neq 0$ and $f_i[t,x(t)]=0$, it follows from this relation that $\Delta x\to 0$ as $\Delta t\to 0$. Consequently $x(t)$ is continuous on T.

Suppose next that the functions f_i are of class C' and S. Select t in T, $\Delta t^h=0(h\neq k)$, and $\Delta t^k\neq 0$. Since $f_i[t,x(t)]=0$, we have

$$\lim_{\Delta t\to 0}\frac{f_i[t+\Delta t,x(t)]}{\Delta t^k}=\lim_{\Delta t\to 0}\frac{f_i[t+\Delta t,x(t)]-f_i[t,x(t)]}{\Delta t^k}=\frac{\partial f_i}{\partial t^k}$$

at $(t,x(t))$. Dividing each member of (7.10) by Δt^k, we see that the limits

$$\frac{\partial x^j}{\partial t^k} = \lim_{\Delta t^k \to 0} \frac{\Delta x^j}{\Delta t^k}$$

exist and satisfy the equation

$$-\frac{\partial f_i}{\partial t^k} = \sum_j \frac{\partial f_i}{\partial x^j}\frac{\partial x^j}{\partial t^k}$$

at $(t,x(t))$. From this formula it follows by induction that, if f_i is of class $C^{(k)}$ on S, then $x^j(t)$ is of class $C^{(k)}$ on T. This completes the proof of Theorem 7.1.

By essentially the same argument we can prove the following extension of Theorem 7.1.

THEOREM 7.2

Suppose that there exist functions

$$x_0^i(t) \qquad (i=1,\ldots,n)$$

on a compact set T_0 *such that if t is in* T_0 *then* $(t,x_0(t))$ *is in S and*

$$f_i[t,x_0(t)]=0, \qquad D[t,x_0(t)]\neq 0.$$

Then there exist continuous functions

$$x^i(t)$$

defined on a neighborhood T *of* T_0 *and a constant* $\varepsilon>0$ *such that*

$$x^i(t)=x_0^i(t) \quad (t\ in\ T_0), \qquad f_i[t,x(t)]=0. \quad (t\ in\ T)$$

and such that (7.6) holds only in the case $x=x(t)$. *If the functions* f_i *are of class* $C^{(k)}$ *on S, the functions* $x^j(t)$ *are of class* $C^{(k)}$ *on T.*

EXERCISES

1. Verify that the hypotheses of Theorem 7.1 are satisfied in each of the following situations. What can be said about the size of the neighborhood T mentioned in the conclusion of Theorem 7.1?
   (a) $n=1$, $m=1$, $f(t,x)=x^2+t^2-\sin(x+t)$, $(a,b)=(0,0)$.

(b) $f_1(t^1, t^2, x^1, x^2) = t^1 - a_{11}x^1 - a_{12}x^2, f_2(t_1, t_2, x_1, x_2) = t^2 - a_{21}x^1 - a_{22}x^2, (a, b)$
$= (0, 0, 0, 0)$; assume $a_{11}a_{22} - a_{12}a_{21} \neq 0$.

(c) $f_i(\lambda, t^1, \ldots, t^n, x_1, \ldots, x_n) = \lambda t^i - \sum_{j=1}^{n} a_{ij}x^j (i = 1, \ldots, n), (a, b) = (0, 0, \ldots, 0, \ldots, 0)$;

assume matrix $A = (a_{ij})$ is symmetric and nonsingular.

(d) $f(t^1, t^2, x) = [(t^1)^2 + (t^2)^2]x + 1 + x^3, (a, b) = (0, 0, -1)$.

2. Consider the equation $f(x, y) = x^2 e^y + y^2 = 0$. Is it possible that this equation defines a function $y = g(x)$ in the neighborhood of some value x_0?

3. Consider the equation $f(x, y) = x^2 + y^2 - x^3 = 0$. Given a point (x_0, y_0) such that $f(x_0, y_0) = 0$, does there always exist a neighborhood T of x_0 and a function $y = g(x)$ on T such that $f[x, g(x)] = 0$, x in T?

4

GENERAL CONSTRAINED
MINIMUM PROBLEMS

1. INTRODUCTION

In the preceding pages we were concerned primarily with the problem of minimizing a function f on an open set S or else on a set S defined by a set of equality constraints

$$g_\alpha(x) = 0 \qquad (\alpha = 1, \ldots, m).$$

In the present chapter we shall discuss the problem of minimizing f on more general sets S. In particular, we will consider sets S defined by inequality constraints of the type

$$g_\alpha(x) \leqslant 0 \qquad (\alpha = 1, \ldots, p).$$

We shall be concerned mainly with the nonlinear case. The case in which the functions f and g_α are linear is a very important one and belongs to the theory of linear programming. More detailed treatments of the linear constraint case are given in books on linear programing.[†] Our discussion of linear programming is limited mainly to showing its connection with the general case.

There are several approaches to the study of constrained minima. This chapter will be devoted to extensions of the methods used in Chapter 3. It is in the spirit of the classical theory of the calculus of variations. In the next chapter we alter our approach and obtain the multiplier rule by

---

[†]See, for example, George B. Dantzig, *Linear Programming and Extensions*, Princeton University Press, Princeton, N. J., 1963.

177

suitably augmenting the function to be minimized. In the final chapter we introduce still another approach to constrained minima, which has the advantage that it is immediately applicable to infinite dimensional problems. It is useful in the modern theory of optimal control.

The underlying principles in optimization are simple. At a minimum point x_0 of a function f on a set S its one-sided tangential derivatives must be nonnegative. This implies that the negative gradient $-\nabla f$ must be an outer normal of S at x_0. This fact is expressed by an appropriate Lagrange multiplier rule. Second-order conditions, when appropriate, are expressed in terms of the second derivatives of the Lagrange function. Although this theory has a long history in variational theory,[†] its significance for the finite dimensional case was brought to the attention of the general public by Kuhn and Tucker[‡] and accordingly is known as the Kuhn-Tucker theory in the finite dimensional case. An earlier account of the finite dimensional case can be found in a master's dissertation by W. E. Karush.[§] The infinite dimensional analogue is often referred to as optimal control theory or as the Euler-Lagrange-Weierstrass theory.

Our analysis is based on the theory of cones. As we shall see presently, the tangent space of a set S at a point x_0 in S is a cone. Its dual cone consists of the outer normals of S at x_0. At a minimum point x_0 of f on S, the negative gradient $-\nabla f$ is an outer normal of S and hence is in the dual cone of the tangent cone. This fact yields the Lagrange multiplier rule. When the set S is defined by constraints of the form

$$g_\alpha(x) \leqslant 0 \quad (\alpha = 1, \ldots, p), \qquad g_\beta(x) = 0 \quad (\beta = p+1, \ldots, m),$$

[†]See, for example, O. Bolza, "Über Variationsprobleme mit Ungleichungen als Nebenbedingungen," *Mathematische Abhandlungen*, H. A. Schwartz, 1914, pp. 1–18. In this paper Bolza obtains the Euler-Lagrange multiplier rule for a very general variational problem with equality and inequality constraints. Although it is not immediately obvious, the finite dimensional case is a special instance of this general problem. Sufficient conditions for a minimum for a general problem of this type were given by F. A. Valentine, "The problem of Lagrange with Differential Inequalities as Added Side Conditions" (1937), *Contributions to the Calculus of Variations* 1933–37, University of Chicago Press. His methods are applicable to the finite dimensional case. An improved sufficiency theorem for the general variational problem, as well as for the finite dimensional one, was given by L. L. Pennisi, "An Indirect Sufficiency Proof for the Problem of Lagrange with Differential Inequalities as Side Conditions," dissertation, University of Chicago, Chicago, Ill., 1952. See also *Transactions of the American Mathematical Society*, Vol. 74 (1953), 177–198. The hypotheses made in these papers are somewhat stronger than those currently used.

[‡]H. W. Kuhn and A. W. Tucker, "Nonlinear Programming," *Proceedings of the Second Berkeley Symposium on Mathematical Statistics and Probability*, University of California Press, Berkeley, Calif., 1950, pp. 487–492. See also H. W. Kuhn, "Nonlinear Programming—A Historical View," to appear in SIAM-AMS Proceedings, No. 9, 1976.

[§]W. E. Karush "Minima of Functions of Several Variables with Inequalities as Side Conditions," master's dissertation, University of Chicago, Chicago, Ill., December 1939.

a tangent vector h of S at x_0 satisfies the linearized constraints

$$g'_\alpha(x_0, h) \leqslant 0 \quad \text{if } g_\alpha(x_0) = 0, \qquad g'_\beta(x_0, h) = 0.$$

If the converse is true, we say that our problem is *regular*. In the regular case the outer normal cone of S at x_0 is generated by the gradients of $g_1, \ldots, g_m$ corresponding to the active constraints at x_0. The condition of regularity, when slightly strengthened, becomes the *Kuhn-Tucker constraint qualification condition*. This condition was also used by Karush. "Normality" criteria for regularity are given in Section 10. The case of infinitely many inequality constraints is treated briefly in Section 11. We conclude the chapter with an application to the minimization of integrals.

2. THE LAGRANGE MULTIPLIER RULE

Consider the problem of minimizing a function f on a given set S. We assume that the function f has a local minimum at a point x_0 in S. This means that there is a spherical neighborhood N of x_0 such that the inequality

$$f(x) \geqslant f(x_0) \tag{2.1}$$

holds for every point $x \neq x_0$ in $S \cap N$. To interpret this situation geometrically, set $c = f(x_0)$. If the gradient ∇f of f is not zero at x_0, we have the situation shown schematically in Figure 2.1 in the two-dimensional case. The level surface $f(x) = c$ divides N into two parts, N^+ and N^-, according as $f(x) \geqslant c$ or $f(x) < c$. The shaded portion is the set N^-. The inequality $f(x) \geqslant c = f(x_0)$ on $S \cap N$ implies that the set $S \cap N$ must lie in N^+, as indicated in Figure 2.2. In this figure the boundary of S is smooth and hence must be tangent to the level surface $f(x) = c$. This signifies that the

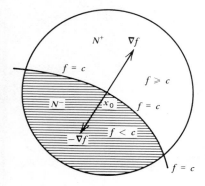

Figure 2.1

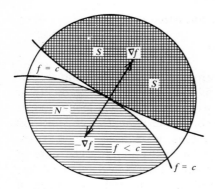

Figure 2.2

negative gradient $-\nabla f$ of f at x_0 is an outer normal of the set S. The situation just described arises when the set S is defined by an inequality of the form

$$g(x) \leqslant 0 \tag{2.2}$$

and the gradient ∇g of g at x_0 is not zero. In this event ∇g is an outer normal of the set S. The vectors ∇g and $-\nabla f$ are both outer normals of S at x_0, so that ∇g is directed in the opposite direction to ∇f, as shown in Figure 2.3. Consequently, there is a *positive* multiplier λ such that

$$-\nabla f(x_0) = \lambda \nabla g(x_0) \qquad \text{or} \qquad \nabla f(x_0) + \lambda \nabla g(x_0) = 0. \tag{2.3}$$

This is the *Lagrange multiplier rule*. It differs from the multiplier rule involving equality constraints in that the sign of the multiplier is a significant part of the rule. It is clear that the multiplier rule (2.3) is not

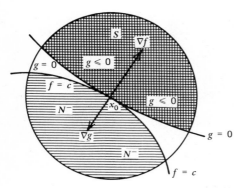

Figure 2.3

sufficient to ensure that x_0 minimizes f subject to the constraint $g \leqslant 0$ because this situation prevails even if the surface $g(x)=0$ lies in the set N^- except at x_0, at which point it is tangent to the surface $f(x)=c$.

In general, the boundary of S need not be smooth. A situation of this type is indicated schematically in Figure 2.4. Again, the negative gradient $-\nabla f(x_0)$ is an outer normal to S at x_0 in the sense that it makes an angle of at least 90° with any tangent vector of S at x_0. This situation and more complicated ones will be studied in this chapter. We do so by considering the behavior of f near x_0 relative to the set S. This involves the notion of derivatives of f in directions that lead into S. Directions of this type are determined by the tangent vectors. The notions of tangent vectors and outer normals of S at x_0 will be described in Section 4.

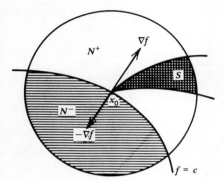

Figure 2.4

We continue to illustrate these ideas with specific examples.

EXAMPLE 2.1

Consider the two-dimensional problem of finding the point (x_0, y_0) in the disk

$$x^2 + y^2 \leqslant 1$$

that is nearest to the point $(5, 0)$. In this case the function to be minimized can be taken to be of the form

$$f(x,y) = (x-5)^2 + y^2.$$

The disk is given by the constraint

$$g(x,y) = x^2 + y^2 - 1 \leqslant 0.$$

It is clear geometrically that the solution is given by the point $(1,0)$, as shown in Figure 2.5. The gradients ∇f, ∇g of f, g at an arbitrary point (x,y) are $\nabla f = (2x - 10, 2y)$, $\nabla g = (2x, 2y)$. At the point $(1,0)$ we have $\nabla f = (-8, 0)$ and $\nabla g = (2, 0)$. Consequently at the point $(1,0)$ we have $\nabla f + \lambda \nabla g = 0$ with $\lambda = 4$. It should be noted that in this event the solution $(x_0, y_0) = (1,0)$ also affords an unconstrained minimum to the function

$$F(x,y) = f + 4g = 5(x-1)^2 + 5y^2 + 16.$$

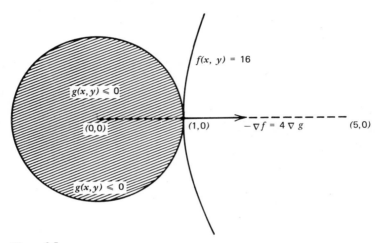

Figure 2.5

EXAMPLE 2.2

Consider next the problem of finding the distance from the point (x_0, y_0) in the set S defined by the inequalities

$$g_1(x,y) = -y + x^2 \leqslant 0, \qquad g_2(x,y) = y - x \leqslant 0 \qquad (2.4)$$

which is nearest to the point $(2,1)$. The set S is shown in Figure 2.6. The point $(x_0, y_0) = (1,1)$ is obviously the nearest point in S to the point $(2,1)$. Analytically the problem is that of minimizing the function

$$f(x,y) = (x-2)^2 + (y-1)^2$$

subject to constraints (2.4). At the minimum point $(1,1)$ we have $\nabla f = (-2, 0)$,

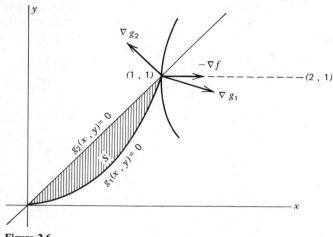

Figure 2.6

$\nabla g_1 = (2, -1)$, $\nabla g_2 = (-1, 1)$. Consequently

$$\nabla f + \lambda_1 \nabla g_1 + \lambda_2 \nabla g_2 = (-2 + 2\lambda_1 - \lambda_2, -\lambda_1 + \lambda_2) = (0, 0)$$

if and only if $\lambda_1 = \lambda_2 = 2$. In this event the Lagrange multipliers λ_1 and λ_2 are positive. Observe that ∇g_1 and ∇g_2 at $(1, 1)$ are outer normals of S which make angles of 90° with S. Every outer normal of S at $(1, 1)$ is of the form $\mu_1 \nabla g_1 + \mu_2 \nabla g_2$, where $\mu_1 \geqslant 0$ and $\mu_2 \geqslant 0$. In this case also the point $(1, 1)$ affords an unconstrained minimum to the Lagrange function

$$F = f + 2g_1 + 2g_2 = 3(x-1)^2 + (y-1)^2 + 1.$$

As we shall see in Chapter 6, this is a consequence of the convexity of the functions f, g_1, and g_2.

EXAMPLE 2.3

Consider the set S in the xy-plane defined by inequalities of the following form:

$$g_1(x,y) = \quad x - 2y + \quad 1 \leqslant 0,$$
$$g_2(x,y) = \quad x + 4y - 23 \leqslant 0,$$
$$g_3(x, 1) = -2x + \quad y + \quad 1 \leqslant 0,$$
$$g_4(x,y) = \quad -x - 9y + 10 \leqslant 0.$$

The set S is a triangle whose vertices are the points $(1, 1)$, $(7, 4)$, and $(3, 5)$, as shown in Figure 2.7. Observe that the inequality $g_4(x, y) \leq 0$ plays no role in defining S and hence could be deleted. However, we shall not do so.

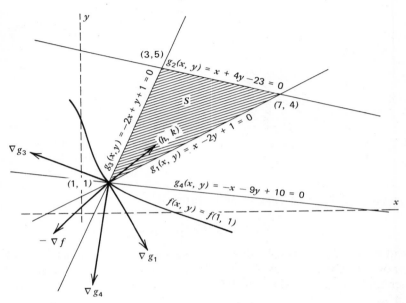

Figure 2.7

We shall center our attention on the vertex $(x_0, y_0) = (1, 1)$ of S. Intuitively a tangent vector of S at the point $(1, 1)$ is a vector (h, k) that leads into S from the point $(1, 1)$, as indicated in Figure 2.7. For example, the vector $(h, k) = (2, 1)$ is a tangent vector lying in the boundary $g_1 = 0$ of S and is accordingly perpendicular to the gradient $\nabla g_1 = (1, -2)$ of g_1 at the point $(1, 1)$. Similarly the vector $(h, k) = (1, 2)$ is a tangent vector of S at $(1, 1)$ and is perpendicular to the gradient $\nabla g_3 = (-2, 1)$ of g_3 at the point $(1, 1)$. It is clear from the figure that each of the vectors ∇g_1 and ∇g_3 makes an obtuse angle with every tangent vector (h, k) of S at the point $(1, 1)$. Right angles are considered to be obtuse angles. A vector making an obtuse angle with every tangent vector of S at the point $(1, 1)$ will be called an *outer normal* of S at the point $(1, 1)$. If $\mu_1 \geq 0$ and $\mu_3 \geq 0$, the nonnegative linear combination $\mu_1 \nabla g_1 + \mu_3 \nabla g_3$ of the outer normals ∇g_1 and ∇g_3 is again an outer normal. Moreover every outer normal of S at $(1, 1)$ is expressible in this form. Observe further that the gradient $\nabla g_4 = (-1, -9)$ is also an outer normal. We have

$$\nabla g_4 = \tfrac{19}{3} \nabla g_1 + \tfrac{11}{3} \nabla g_3.$$

In view of the relation

$$\mu_1 \nabla g_1 + \mu_3 \nabla g_3 + \mu_4 \nabla g_4 = \left(\mu_1 + \tfrac{19}{3} \mu_4 \right) \nabla g_1 + \left(\mu_3 + \tfrac{11}{3} \mu_4 \right) \nabla g_3,$$

a nonnegative linear combination of the vectors $\nabla g_1, \nabla g_3,$ and ∇g_4 is an outer normal of S at $(1,1)$. In fact, if $\mu_1, \mu_2, \mu_3, \mu_4$ are nonnegative numbers such that

$$\mu_1 g_1(1,1) + \mu_2 g_2(1,1) + \mu_3 g_3(1,1) + \mu_4 g_4(1,1) = -18\mu_2 = 0,$$

then $\mu_2 = 0$, and the vector

$$\mu_1 \nabla g_1 + \mu_2 \nabla g_2 + \mu_3 \nabla g_3 + \mu_4 \nabla g_4$$

is an outer normal of S at the point $(1,1)$. Moreover every outer normal is expressible in this form.

It was shown above by an intuitive argument that, if a function f has a minimum on S at the point $(1,1)$, the negative gradient $-\nabla f$ of f at $(1,1)$ must be an outer normal of S at this point. It follows from the remarks made in the last paragraph that there exist multipliers $\lambda_1 \geqslant 0,\ \lambda_2 \geqslant 0,\ \lambda_3 \geqslant 0,$ $\lambda_4 \geqslant 0$ with $\lambda_2 = 0$ such that

$$-\nabla f = \lambda_1 \nabla g_1 + \lambda_2 \nabla g_2 + \lambda_3 \nabla g_3 + \lambda_4 \nabla g_4$$

or, equivalently, such that, if we set

$$F = f + \lambda_1 g_1 + \lambda_2 g_2 + \lambda_3 g_3 + \lambda_4 g_4,$$

then

$$\nabla F = \nabla f + \lambda_1 \nabla g_1 + \lambda_2 \nabla g_2 + \lambda_3 \nabla g_3 + \lambda_4 \nabla g_4 = 0$$

at the minimum point $(1,1)$. This is the Lagrange multiplier rule.

The function $f(x,y) = x^3 + y^3$ has a minimum on S at the point $(1,1)$. Its gradient at this point is $\nabla f = (3,3)$. In this event the multipliers $\lambda_1 = 3,$ $\lambda_2 = 0,\ \lambda_3 = 3,\ \lambda_4 = 0$ have the property described above. The Lagrangian

$$F = f + \Sigma \lambda_\alpha g_\alpha = x^3 + y^3 - 3x - 3y + 6$$

has $\nabla F = (3x^2 - 3, 3y^2 - 3) = (0,0)$ at the point $(1,1)$. It should be noted that the point $(1,1)$ does not afford an unconstrained minimum to F. However, the point $(1,1)$ minimizes F on S.

The foregoing discussions suggest that the Lagrange multiplier rule given in Chapter 3 can be extended as follows.

THEOREM 2.1: LAGRANGE MULTIPLIER RULE

Suppose that x_0 *minimizes a function* $f(x)$ *locally on the set* S *defined by the constraints*

$$g_\alpha(x) \leq 0 \quad (\alpha = 1,\ldots,p), \qquad g_\beta(x) = 0 \quad (\beta = p+1,\ldots,m). \quad (2.5)$$

If x_0 *is a regular point of* S, *then there exist multipliers* $\lambda_1,\ldots,\lambda_m$ *such that*

$$\lambda_\alpha \geq 0 \quad (\alpha = 1,\ldots,p) \quad with \; \lambda_\gamma = 0 \quad if \; g_\gamma(x_0) < 0 \quad (2.6)$$

and such that

$$\nabla F = 0, \qquad where \; F = f + \lambda_1 g_1 + \cdots + \lambda_m g_m. \quad (2.7)$$

In addition,

$$F(x) \leq f(x) \quad on \; S, \qquad F(x_0) = f(x_0). \quad (2.8)$$

This theorem is also known as the *Kuhn-Tucker theorem*. As will be seen in Section 7, the condition of regularity of $g_1,\ldots,g_m$ at x_0 is the condition that the outer normals of S at x_0 are determined by the active gradients $\nabla g_{\gamma_1},\ldots,\nabla g_{\gamma_r}$ at x_0. Here $\gamma_1,\ldots,\gamma_r$ are the indices γ such that $g_\gamma(x_0) = 0$. These ideas will be developed in Section 7. The condition of regularity is always satisfied when the functions g_γ are linear. It is also satisfied when the functions $g_1,\ldots,g_p$ are concave and $g_{p+1},\ldots,g_m$ are linear. The fact that $\lambda_\gamma = 0$ when $g_\gamma(x_0) < 0$ is a consequence of the fact that the constraint $g_\gamma(x) \leq 0$ plays no active role in determining the nature of S near x_0. It implies the condition $F(x_0) = f(x_0)$ in (2.8). The inequality $F(x) \leq f(x)$ on S follows from the fact that $\lambda_1,\ldots,\lambda_p$ are nonnegative.

The Lagrange multiplier rule is a necessary condition for a minimum of f at a regular point x_0. In special cases it is sufficient; for example, it is sufficient if the function F turns out to be convex. Normally further necessary conditions are needed. They involve the second-order directional derivative $F''(x_0, h)$ of F at x_0. Sufficient conditions for a local minimum of f on S are obtained by suitably strengthening the necessary conditions for a minimum. These results will be developed later in this chapter.

EXERCISES

In Exercises 1–12 sketch the set S in the xy-plane defined by the exhibited constraints. In each case determine whether or not a solution for the problem exists. Determine the active and inactive constraints at the solution. Find the corresponding Lagrange multipliers when they exist. Are these multipliers unique? Which constraints, if any, are redundant?

1. $(x-a)^2+(y-b)^2=\min$, $0\leqslant x\leqslant 1$, $0\leqslant y\leqslant 1$, for the cases $a\leqslant 0$, $b\leqslant 0$; $a\leqslant 0$, $0<b<1$; $a\leqslant 0$, $b\geqslant 1$.
2. $x^2+(y+1)^2=\min$, $x^2+y^2\leqslant 4$, $1+y^2-x\leqslant 0$, $-x-2y+1\leqslant 0$.
3. Add the constraint $-x-y+1\leqslant 0$ to the problem in Exercise 2.
4. $x+3y=\min$, $-x+y-1\leqslant 0$, $x+y-2\leqslant 0$, $-x\leqslant 0$, $-y\leqslant 0$.
5. $x+y=\min$, $y-x^3\leqslant 0$, $-y\leqslant 0$, $1-x\leqslant 0$.
6. $x^2+2x+y^4=\min$, $xy-x\leqslant 0$, $|y|\leqslant 0.5$.
7. $(x-5)^2+y^2=\min$, $x^2+y^2\leqslant 4$, $x^2-2x+y^2\leqslant 0$, $x+y^2\leqslant 2$.
8. $x+y=\min$, $x^2+y^2\leqslant 2$, $x+2y+3\leqslant 0$.
9. $x+y=\min$, $x^2+y^2\leqslant 2$, $xy\leqslant 1$.
10. $x+y=\min$, $xy\leqslant 1$.
11. $2x+5y=\max$, $x\geqslant 0$, $y\geqslant 0$, $x+y\leqslant 9$, $x+4y\leqslant 24$, $3x+y\leqslant 21$.
12. $2x+y=\max$, $x\geqslant 0$, $y\geqslant 0$, $x-2y\leqslant 2$, $y-x\leqslant 1$.
13. In xyz-space minimize $x^2+y^2+z^2+2x-4z$ subject to the constraints $x\geqslant 0$, $y\geqslant 0$, $z\geqslant 0$, and $x-y+z=1$.
14. Find the minimum value of $f(x)=|x|^2$ subject to the constraints $x^i\geqslant 0$ $(i=1,\ldots,n)$, $x^1+\cdots+x^n=1$. Interpret the result geometrically.
15. Let A be a positive definite symmetric matrix. Given a vector y, show that $\langle y, A^{-1}y\rangle^{1/2}$ is the maximum value of $f(x)=\langle y,x\rangle$ subject to the constraint $\langle x,Ax\rangle\leqslant 1$. Establish the inequality $|\langle x,y\rangle|^2\leqslant\langle x,Ax\rangle\langle y,A^{-1}y\rangle$.
16. Let $L(x)=\langle b,x\rangle$, where b is a fixed nonnull vector. Let $N(x)=\sum_{i=1}^{n}|x^i|^p$, where $1<p<\infty$. Find the point x_0 that maximizes $L(x)$ subject to the constraint $N(x)\leqslant 1$. Set $m=L(x_0)$. Show that $\lambda=m/p$ is the Lagrange multiplier associated with x_0. Show that x_0 maximizes $L(x)-\lambda N(x)$. Show that x_0 minimizes $N(x)$ subject to the constraint $L(x)\leqslant m$. Find a formula for m in terms of b.

3. CONVEX CONES AND THEIR DUALS

The Lagrange multiplier rule described in Section 2 follows from the theory of convex cones because, as will be seen later, the tangent vectors of a set S at a point x_0 normally form a convex cone and the outer normals to S at x_0 belong to the dual of the tangent cone. In view of this fact we devote this section to the study of cones and their duals. Later the tangent and normal cones of S will be given a precise meaning.

Intuitively a cone is a collection of half lines emanating from the origin. A half line can be considered to be the set of nonnegative multiples of a vector. Accordingly we shall define a *cone* $\mathcal{C}$ to be a class of vectors in $\mathcal{E}^n$ such that if x is a vector in $\mathcal{C}$ so also is αx for all numbers $\alpha \geqslant 0$. Observe that $x = 0$ is in $\mathcal{C}$. A *convex cone* is of course a cone that is convex, that is, a cone $\mathcal{C}$ such that, if x and y are vectors in $\mathcal{C}$, every vector of the form $z = (1-\theta)x + \theta y$ with $0 \leqslant \theta \leqslant 1$ is also in $\mathcal{C}$. It should be noted that a *cone $\mathcal{C}$ is convex if and only if the sum* x+y *of any two vectors* x *and* y *in* $\mathcal{C}$ *is in* $\mathcal{C}$. To see this, consider two vectors, x and y, in $\mathcal{C}$. If $\mathcal{C}$ is convex, the vector $z = \frac{1}{2}(x+y)$ is in $\mathcal{C}$. Since $\mathcal{C}$ is a cone, the vector $2z = x+y$ is in $\mathcal{C}$. Consequently the sum of two vectors in $\mathcal{C}$ is in $\mathcal{C}$ whenever $\mathcal{C}$ is convex. Conversely, if the sum of every pair of vectors in $\mathcal{C}$ is in $\mathcal{C}$, then $\mathcal{C}$ is convex, for, if x and y are in $\mathcal{C}$ and $0 \leqslant \theta \leqslant 1$, the vectors $(1-\theta)x$ and θy are in $\mathcal{C}$ as well as their sum $(1-\theta)x + \theta y$, as was to be proved.

It is clear that a linear subspace $\mathcal{L}$ of $\mathcal{E}^n$ is a convex cone. It is a convex cone with the property that if x is in $\mathcal{L}$ so also is $-x$.

If $\mathcal{C}$ is a cone, so also is the class $-\mathcal{C}$, consisting of the negatives $-x$ of the vectors x in $\mathcal{C}$. If $\mathcal{C}$ is convex, so also is $-\mathcal{C}$. If $\mathcal{C}$ is convex, then $\mathcal{C} = -\mathcal{C}$ if and only if $\mathcal{C}$ is a linear subspace of $\mathcal{E}^n$.

EXAMPLE 3.1

In the case $n = 2$ let $\mathcal{C}$ be all vectors $x = (u,v)$ such that $u > 0$, $v > 0$, together with the vector $x = (0,0)$. The cone $\mathcal{C}$ is convex but is not closed. For example, $(1,0)$ is not in $\mathcal{C}$. The closure $\bar{\mathcal{C}}$ of $\mathcal{C}$ consists of all vectors $x = (u,v)$ with nonnegative components. The cone $-\mathcal{C}$ is the class of all vectors x having negative components together with the origin. The set of vectors $\mathcal{D}$ consisting of all nonnegative multiples of vectors $x = (u,v)$ having $u \geqslant 0$ and $v = mu$ ($m = 1, 2, 3, \ldots$) is a cone which is neither convex nor closed.

EXAMPLE 3.2

Various cones in $\mathcal{E}^2$ are given schematically in Figures 3.1 and 3.2. The bounding rays of $\mathcal{C}_8$ do not belong to $\mathcal{C}_8$. The reader may wish to consider the following questions. Which cones are convex? Which cones are closed? Is $\mathcal{C}_1 \cup \mathcal{C}_4$ a cone? What is the smallest convex cone containing $\mathcal{C}_1$ and $\mathcal{C}_3$? $\mathcal{C}_1$ and $\mathcal{C}_4$? $\mathcal{C}_2$ and $\mathcal{C}_3$? $\mathcal{C}_5$? $\mathcal{C}_6$ and $\mathcal{C}_8$? Where is $-\mathcal{C}_3$ and $-\mathcal{C}_5$?

Given a class $\mathcal{B}$ of vectors, the class $\mathcal{C}$ of all nonnegative linear combinations

$$x = a_1 x_1 + \cdots + a_N x_N \qquad (a_j \geqslant 0; j = 1, \ldots, N) \qquad (3.1)$$

of vectors $x_1, \ldots, x_N$ selected from $\mathcal{B}$ is a convex cone. If x is of form (3.1)

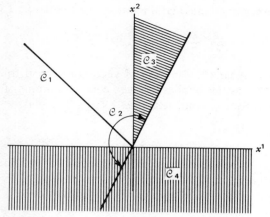

Figure 3.1

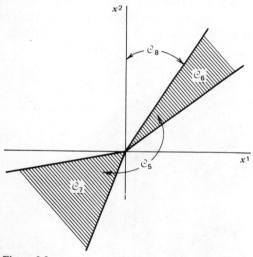

Figure 3.2

so also is

$$\alpha x = (\alpha a_1)x_1 + \cdots + (\alpha a_N)x_N$$

for every nonnegative number α. Hence $\mathcal{C}$ is a cone. If

$$y = b_1 y_1 + \cdots + b_M y_M$$

is a second nonnegative linear combination of vectors $y_1,\ldots,y_M$ in $\mathcal{B}$, then

$$x+y = a_1x_1 + \cdots + a_N x_N + b_1 y_1 + \cdots + b_M y_M$$

is a nonnegative linear combination of vectors in $\mathcal{B}$. It follows that $\mathcal{C}$ is convex. In fact, $\mathcal{C}$ is the smallest convex cone containing $\mathcal{B}$. The class $\mathcal{C}$ is said to be the convex cone *generated* by $\mathcal{B}$. The class $\mathcal{B}$ *generates* $\mathcal{C}$.

EXAMPLE 3.3

In uv-space let $\mathcal{B}$ be the class of all unit vectors in the first quadrant of the form $x=(\cos\theta,\sin\theta)$ with $\tan\theta=q$ or $\tan\theta=1/q$, where q is an arbitrary integer. The class $\mathcal{B}$ generates the convex cone $\mathcal{C}$ (see Example 3.1) whose nonnull vectors are the vectors $x=(u,v)$ having $u>0$ and $v>0$. The cone $\mathcal{C}$ is also generated by the class of vectors of the form $x=(1,2^q)$, where $q=\pm 1, \pm 2, \pm 3, \ldots$. The cone $\mathcal{C}$ cannot be generated by a finite set of vectors. Its closure $\bar{\mathcal{C}}$, however, is generated by the vectors $(1,0)$ and $(0,1)$. The situation is illustrated in Figure 3.3. The vectors $x_1=(1,\frac{1}{4})$ and $x_2=(1,2)$ generate the closed cone $\mathcal{C}_1$.

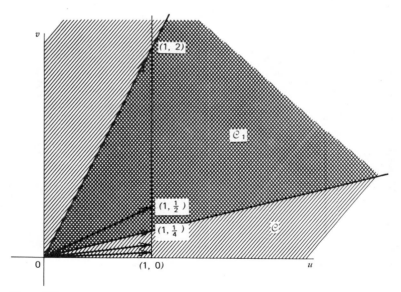

Figure 3.3

EXAMPLE 3.4

In the case $n=3$ let $\mathcal{B}$ be the class of all vectors $x=(u,v,w)$ having $w=\sqrt{u^2+v^2}$. The class $\mathcal{B}$ is a closed cone, but it is not convex. The class $\mathcal{B}$ generates the closed convex cone $\mathcal{C}$ of vectors $x=(u,v,w)$ having $\sqrt{u^2+v^2} \leqslant w$. Describe the cones $-\mathcal{B}$ and $-\mathcal{C}$. The class $\mathcal{D}$ of vectors $x=(u,v,w)$ having $\sqrt{u^2+v^2} < w$ unless $u=v=w=0$ is a convex cone having the cone $\mathcal{B}$ as its boundary and the cone $\mathcal{C}$ as its closure. The cone $\mathcal{D}$ is not closed. See Figure 3.4.

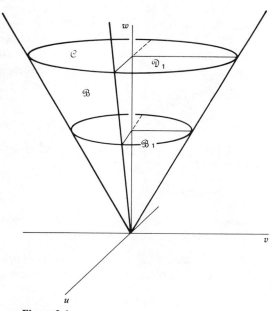

Figure 3.4

Observe that, if $x_1=(u_1,v_1,w_1)$ and $x_2=(u_2,v_2,w_2)$ are in $\mathcal{C}$, then

$$\pm(u_1u_2+v_1v_2) \leqslant \sqrt{u_1^2+v_1^2}\ \sqrt{u_2^2+v_2^2} \leqslant w_1w_2.$$

Hence we have the inequality

$$\langle x_1,x_2\rangle = u_1u_2+v_1v_2+w_1w_2 \geqslant 0 \qquad (3.2)$$

for every pair of vectors x_1 and x_2 in $\mathcal{C}$. In fact, if x_2 is any vector such that inequality (3.2) holds for all x_1 in $\mathcal{C}$, then x_2 is also in $\mathcal{C}$, for if we select $x_1 = (0, 0, 1)$ we see that $\langle x_1, x_2 \rangle = w_2 \geqslant 0$. Hence x_2 is in $\mathcal{C}$ if $u_2 = v_2 = 0$. If we select $u_1 = -u_2$, $v_1 = -v_2$, and $w_1 = \sqrt{u_1{}^2 + v_1{}^2}$, we find that

$$\langle x_1, x_2 \rangle = -u_2{}^2 - v_2{}^2 + w_2 \sqrt{u_2{}^2 + v_2{}^2} \geqslant 0.$$

Consequently

$$w_2 \geqslant \sqrt{u_2{}^2 + v_2{}^2} \qquad \text{and} \qquad x_2 \text{ is in } \mathcal{C}.$$

From this result we conclude that $-\mathcal{C}$ consists of all vectors z such that $\langle y, z \rangle = -\langle y, -z \rangle \leqslant 0$ for all vectors y in $\mathcal{C}$. The cone $\mathcal{B}_1$ is all $x = (u, v, w)$ in $\mathcal{B}$ having $u \geqslant 0$ and $v \geqslant 0$. The cone $\mathcal{D}_1$ is all $x = (u, v, w)$ in $\mathcal{D}$ having $u \geqslant 0$ and $v \geqslant 0$. What is the cone generated by $\mathcal{B}_1$?

The following lemma will be useful.

LEMMA 3.1

Let $\mathcal{C}$ be the convex cone generated by a class $\mathcal{B}$ of vectors. Let $\overline{\mathcal{C}}$ be the closure of $\mathcal{C}$. Given a vector z, the inequality

$$\langle y, z \rangle \leqslant 0 \tag{3.3}$$

holds for every vector y in $\mathcal{C}$ if and only if it holds for every vector y in $\mathcal{B}$ and in fact if and only if it holds for every vector y in $\overline{\mathcal{C}}$.

Suppose first that inequality (3.3) holds for every vector y in $\mathcal{B}$. Since every vector y in $\mathcal{C}$ is expressible as a nonnegative linear combination

$$y = a_1 y_1 + \cdots + a_N y_N$$

of vectors $y_1, \ldots, y_N$ in $\mathcal{B}$, we have

$$\langle y, z \rangle = a_1 \langle y_1, z \rangle + \cdots + a_N \langle y_N, z \rangle \leqslant 0.$$

This follows from the inequalities $a_j \geqslant 0$ and $\langle y_j, z \rangle \leqslant 0$ $(j = 1, \ldots, N)$. If y is the limit of a sequence $\{y_q\}$ of vectors in $\mathcal{C}$, we have

$$\lim_{q \to \infty} \langle y_q, z \rangle = \langle y, z \rangle.$$

Consequently, if $\langle y_q, z \rangle \leqslant 0$ $(q = 1, 2, 3, \ldots)$, we have $\langle y, z \rangle \leqslant 0$ also. It follows that (3.3) holds for all y in $\bar{\mathcal{C}}$ if it holds for all y in $\mathcal{C}$. Conversely, since $\bar{\mathcal{C}} \supset \mathcal{C} \supset \mathcal{B}$, inequality (3.3) holds for all y in $\mathcal{B}$ if it holds for all y in $\mathcal{C}$ or in $\bar{\mathcal{C}}$. This proves the lemma.

LEMMA 3.2

Let $\mathcal{B}$ be a class of vectors, and let $\mathcal{B}$ * be the class of all vectors z such that the inequality

$$\langle y, z \rangle \leqslant 0$$

holds for all y *in* $\mathcal{B}$. *The class* $\mathcal{B}$ * *is a closed convex cone. The cone* $\mathcal{B}$ * *is called the dual cone of* $\mathcal{B}$.

Let y be a vector in $\mathcal{B}$. If z_1 and z_2 are in $\mathcal{B}$ * and $a_1 \geqslant 0$, $a_2 \geqslant 0$, then

$$\langle y, a_1 z_1 + a_2 z_2 \rangle = a_1 \langle y, z_1 \rangle + a_2 \langle y, z_2 \rangle \leqslant 0.$$

Hence $a_1 z_1 + a_2 z_2$ is in $\mathcal{B}$ *. It follows that $\mathcal{B}$ * is a convex cone. If z is the limit of the sequence of vectors $\{z_q\}$ in $\mathcal{B}$ *, we have

$$\langle y, z \rangle = \lim_{q \to \infty} \langle y, z_q \rangle \leqslant 0$$

for all vectors y in $\mathcal{B}$. The convex cone $\mathcal{B}$ * is therefore closed, as was to be proved.

As an example, if $\mathcal{B}$ is a half line, $\mathcal{B}$ * is a closed half space. If $\mathcal{B}$ is a line, $\mathcal{B}$ * is a $(n-1)$-space.

Combining Lemmas 3.1 and 3.2, we obtain

LEMMA 3.3

If $\mathcal{C}$ *is the convex cone generated by a class* $\mathcal{B}$, *then* $\mathcal{B}$, $\mathcal{C}$, *and the closure* $\bar{\mathcal{C}}$ *of* $\mathcal{C}$ *possess the same dual cone.*

It should be noted that, if the cone $\mathcal{C}$ is a linear space, its dual is its orthogonal complement. If $\mathcal{B}$ is the set of coordinate vectors

$$e_1 = (1, 0, \ldots, 0), \quad e_2 = (0, 1, 0, \ldots, 0), \ldots, e_n = (0, \ldots, 0, 1)$$

then $\mathcal{B}$ generates the cone $\mathcal{C}$ of all vectors x whose components are nonnegative. The dual cone $\mathcal{C}$ * of $\mathcal{C}$ and hence of $\mathcal{B}$ consists of all vectors y whose components are nonpositive.

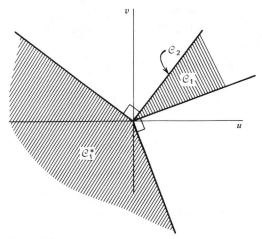

Figure 3.5

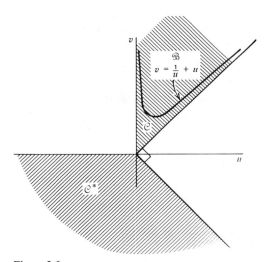

Figure 3.6

EXAMPLE 3.5

Two-dimensional dual cones $\mathcal{C}$, and $\mathcal{C}_1^*$ are shown in Figure 3.5. What is the dual of $\mathcal{C}_2$? In Figure 3.6 the curve $\mathcal{B}$ generates a cone $\mathcal{C}$ that is not closed. The cone $\mathcal{C}^*$ is the dual of $\mathcal{B}$, of $\mathcal{C}$, and of the closure $\overline{\mathcal{C}}$ of $\mathcal{C}$.

The following theorem is basic.

THEOREM 3.1

Let $\mathcal{C}$ be a closed convex cone, and let $\mathcal{C}^*$ be its dual. Every vector x in $\mathcal{E}^n$ is expressible uniquely in the form $x = y + z$, where y and z are orthogonal vectors with y in $\mathcal{C}$ and z in $\mathcal{C}^*$.

Consider a vector x_0 in $\mathcal{E}^n$, and let y_0 be the vector in $\mathcal{C}$ nearest to x_0. The vector y_0 minimizes the function

$$F(y) = |x_0 - y|^2$$

on $\mathcal{C}$. If y is in $\mathcal{C}$, then $y_0 + ty$ $(0 \leqslant t < \infty)$ is in $\mathcal{C}$. If we set $z_0 = x_0 - y_0$, it follows that the function

$$\varphi(t) = F(y_0 + ty) = |z_0 - ty|^2 = |z_0|^2 - 2t\langle z_0, y\rangle + t^2|y|^2$$

of t on $0 \leqslant t < \infty$ has a minimum at $t = 0$. Hence

$$\varphi'(0) = -2\langle z_0, y\rangle \geqslant 0.$$

Since y is an arbitrary vector in $\mathcal{C}$, it follows that z_0 is in the dual $\mathcal{C}^*$ of $\mathcal{C}$. If $y_0 = 0$, then z_0 is orthogonal to y_0. If $y_0 \neq 0$, we can choose $y = y_0$ in the formula for $\varphi(t)$. In this event $y_0 + ty_0$ is in $\mathcal{C}$ whenever $t > -1$. Hence the function $\varphi(t)$ on $-1 \leqslant t < \infty$ has a local minimum at $t = 0$. Consequently

$$\varphi'(0) = -2\langle z_0, y_0\rangle = 0,$$

that is, y_0 and z_0 are orthogonal. The vector x_0 is therefore the sum of orthogonal vectors y_0 in $\mathcal{C}$ and z_0 in $\mathcal{C}^*$. To see that y_0 and z_0 are unique, let y in $\mathcal{C}$ and z in $\mathcal{C}^*$ be orthogonal vectors such that $x_0 = y + z$. We then have

$$|y|^2 = \langle y, x_0\rangle = \langle y, y_0\rangle + \langle y, z_0\rangle \leqslant \langle y, y_0\rangle$$

since $\langle y, z_0\rangle \leqslant 0$. Similarly $|y_0|^2 \leqslant \langle y, y_0\rangle$. These two inequalities are possible only if $y = y_0$. Consequently $y = y_0$ and $z = z_0$. This completes the proof of Lemma 3.3.

THEOREM 3.2

Let $\mathcal{C}$ be a convex cone, and let $\mathcal{C}^*$ be its dual. The dual $\mathcal{C}^{**} = (\mathcal{C}^*)^*$ of $\mathcal{C}^*$ is the closure $\bar{\mathcal{C}}$ of $\mathcal{C}$. If $\mathcal{C}$ is closed, then $\mathcal{C}^{**} = \mathcal{C}$.

The second conclusion follows from the first. To establish the first conclusion, observe that $\mathcal{C} \subset \mathcal{C}^{**}$ and hence that $\bar{\mathcal{C}} \subset \mathcal{C}^{**}$. Consider a vector x in $\mathcal{C}^{**}$. By Theorem 3.1 x is expressible as the sum $x = y + z$ of orthogonal vectors y in $\overline{\mathcal{C}}$ and z in $\mathcal{C}^*$. Since x is in $\mathcal{C}^{**}$ and y is orthogonal to z, we have

$$0 \geqslant \langle x, z \rangle = \langle y, z \rangle + \langle z, z \rangle = |z|^2.$$

Hence $z = 0$ and $x = y$ is in $\overline{\mathcal{C}}$, as was to be proved.

For two cones $\mathcal{C}$ and $\mathcal{D}$, the *sum* $\mathcal{C} + \mathcal{D}$ consists of all vectors $x = y + z$ with y in $\mathcal{C}$ and z in $\mathcal{D}$. If $\mathcal{C}$ and $\mathcal{D}$ are convex, so also is the sum $\mathcal{C} + \mathcal{D}$ and the difference $\mathcal{C} - \mathcal{D} = \mathcal{C} + (-\mathcal{D})$. The difference $\mathcal{C} - \mathcal{C}$ is the smallest linear subspace of $\mathcal{E}^n$ containing a given convex cone $\mathcal{C}$.

If $\mathcal{C}$ and $\mathcal{D}$ are closed convex cones, their sum $\mathcal{C} + \mathcal{D}$ need not be closed. This phenomenon is illustrated by

EXAMPLE 3.5

Let $\mathcal{C}$ be the set of vectors in 3-space consisting of all vectors of the form $x = (u, v, w)$ such that $u \geqslant 0$, $v \geqslant 0$, $w \geqslant 0$, $uv \geqslant w^2$. If x is in $\mathcal{C}$ and $\alpha \geqslant 0$, then $\alpha x = (\alpha u, \alpha v, \alpha w)$ is also in $\mathcal{C}$. Hence $\mathcal{C}$ is a cone. Moreover $\mathcal{C}$ is convex, for let $x = (u, v, w)$ and $\bar{x} = (\bar{u}, \bar{v}, \bar{w})$ be vectors in $\mathcal{C}$. Since $w^2 \leqslant uv$ and $\bar{w}^2 \leqslant \bar{u}\bar{v}$, it follows that

$$2w\bar{w} \leqslant 2\sqrt{u\bar{v}\bar{u}v} \leqslant u\bar{v} + \bar{u}v$$

and hence that

$$(w + \bar{w})^2 = w^2 + 2w\bar{w} + \bar{w}^2 \leqslant (u + \bar{u})(v + \bar{v}).$$

The vector $x + \bar{x} = (u + \bar{u}, v + \bar{v}, w + \bar{w})$ is therefore in $\mathcal{C}$. Consequently $\mathcal{C}$ is convex.

Consider now a second cone $\mathcal{D}$ of vectors of the form $y = \alpha(-1, 0, 0)$ ($\alpha \geqslant 0$). Clearly $\mathcal{D}$ is convex. The sum $\mathcal{C} + \mathcal{D}$ consists of all vectors of the form

$$x + y = (u - \alpha, v, w),$$

where $\alpha \geqslant 0$, $u \geqslant 0$, $v \geqslant 0$, $w \geqslant 0$, $uv \geqslant w^2$. Observe that if $w = 1$ then $u > 0$, $v > 0$. The point $(0, 0, 1)$ is therefore not in $\mathcal{C} + \mathcal{D}$. By selecting $u = \alpha = q$ and $v = 1/q$, it is seen that the points $(0, 1/q, 1)$ are in $\mathcal{C} + \mathcal{D}$ and have $(0, 0, 1)$ as their limit as q becomes infinite. Hence $\mathcal{C} + \mathcal{D}$ is not closed, as was to be shown.

A criterion which ensures the closure of the sum $\mathcal{C} + \mathcal{D}$ of two closed cones $\mathcal{C}$ and $\mathcal{D}$ is given in

LEMMA 3.4

Let $\mathcal{C}$ and $\mathcal{D}$ be two closed cones. If there is no vector $z \neq 0$ in $\mathcal{D}$ such that $y = -z$ is in $\mathcal{C}$, then $\mathcal{C} + \mathcal{D}$ is closed. Equivalently, if there is a constant $m > -1$ such that the inequality

$$\langle y, z \rangle \geqslant m|y|\|z| \tag{3.4}$$

holds for all y in $\mathcal{C}$ and z in $\mathcal{D}$, then $\mathcal{C} + \mathcal{D}$ is closed.

We shall show first that the two criteria given in the lemma are equivalent. Suppose first that there is no vector $z \neq 0$ in $\mathcal{D}$ such that $y = -z$ is in $\mathcal{C}$. The classes $\mathcal{C}_1$ and $\mathcal{D}_1$ of unit vectors in $\mathcal{C}$ and $\mathcal{D}$, respectively, are bounded and closed. It follows that the function

$$f(y, z) = \langle y, z \rangle$$

on the Cartesian product $\mathcal{C}_1 \times \mathcal{D}_1$ attains its minimum value m at a point (y_0, z_0). Clearly $m = \langle y_0, z_0 \rangle \geqslant -1$ since $|y_0| = |z_0| = 1$. If $m = -1$, then $y_0 = -z_0$, which is impossible. Hence $m > -1$. It follows that, if y and z are nonnull vectors in $\mathcal{C}$ and $\mathcal{D}$, we have

$$\langle y, z \rangle = \left\langle \frac{y}{|y|}, \frac{z}{|z|} \right\rangle |y|\|z| \geqslant m|y|\|z|,$$

as was to be proved.

Conversely, if (3.4) holds as stated with $m > -1$, the relation $y = -z$ is impossible for nonnull vectors y in $\mathcal{C}$ and z in $\mathcal{D}$.

We are now in a position to prove that $\mathcal{C} + \mathcal{D}$ is closed whenever condition (3.4) holds with $m > -1$. To do so, let x_0 be a point in the closure of $\mathcal{C} + \mathcal{D}$. Select a sequence $\{x_q\}$ in $\mathcal{C} + \mathcal{D}$ converging to x_0, and choose y_q in $\mathcal{C}$ and z_q in $\mathcal{D}$ so that $x_q = y_q + z_q$. By the use of (3.4) it is seen that

$$|x_q|^2 = |y_q|^2 + 2\langle y_q, z_q \rangle + |z_q|^2 \geqslant [|y_q| - |z_q|]^2 + 2(1 + m)|y_q|\|z_q|.$$

Since the sequence $\{x_q\}$ is bounded and $1 + m > 0$, it follows from this inequality that the sequences $\{y_q\}$ and $\{z_q\}$ are also bounded. There is accordingly a subsequence $\{y_{q_j}\}$ of $\{y_q\}$ which converges to a point y_0.

Then

$$z_{q_j} = x_{q_j} - y_{q_j} \to x_0 - y_0 = z_0.$$

Since $\mathcal{C}$ and $\mathcal{D}$ are closed, we have y_0 in $\mathcal{C}$ and z_0 in $\mathcal{D}$. Consequently $x_0 = y_0 + z_0$ is in $\mathcal{C} + \mathcal{D}$. The cone $\mathcal{C} + \mathcal{D}$ is therefore closed, as was to be proved.

The following theorem will be useful.

THEOREM 3.3

A convex cone having a finite set of generators is closed.

The proof will be obtained by induction. A cone generated by a single vector is obviously closed. Suppose that the theorem is true for a cone possessing N generators. Consider a cone $\mathcal{B}$ having $N+1$ generators $y_1, \ldots, y_{N+1}$. Two cases arise. In the first case the vectors $-y_1, \ldots, -y_{N+1}$ are in $\mathcal{B}$. In this event $\mathcal{B}$ coincides with $-\mathcal{B}$ and is accordingly a linear space. It is therefore closed. In the second case the negative of one of the vectors, say $-y_{N+1}$, is not in $\mathcal{B}$ and hence is not in the closed cone $\mathcal{C}$ generated by $y_1, \ldots, y_N$. Let $\mathcal{D}$ be the cone generated by y_{N+1}. It is closed. Moreover there is no vector $z = \beta y_{N+1} \neq 0$ in $\mathcal{D}$ such that $y = -z$ is in $\mathcal{C}$. It follows from Lemma 3.4 that $\mathcal{C} + \mathcal{D} = \mathcal{B}$ is closed, and the theorem is established.

As a consequence of this result we have

THEOREM 3.4

Let $b_1, \ldots, b_m$ be a set of m vectors. The class $\mathcal{C}$ of vectors y such that

$$\langle b_\alpha, y \rangle \leqslant 0 \quad (\alpha = 1, \ldots, p), \qquad \langle b_\beta, y \rangle = 0 \quad (\beta = p+1, \ldots, m) \quad (3.5)$$

is a convex cone. The dual cone $\mathcal{C}^*$ of $\mathcal{C}$ is generated by the vectors $b_1, \ldots, b_m, -b_{p+1}, \ldots, -b_m$. If b is a vector such that

$$\langle b, y \rangle \leqslant 0 \tag{3.6}$$

for all y in $\mathcal{C}$, then b is representable in the form

$$b = \lambda_1 b_1 + \cdots + \lambda_m b_m \tag{3.7}$$

where $\lambda_1, \ldots, \lambda_p$ are nonnegative. If $b_1, \ldots, b_m$ are linearly independent and $m - p < n$, there is a vector $y \neq 0$ in $\mathcal{C}$.

Relations (3.5) are equivalent to the inequalities

$$\langle b_\gamma, y \rangle \leqslant 0 \quad (\gamma = 1, \ldots, m), \qquad -\langle b_\beta, y \rangle \leqslant 0 \quad (\beta = p+1, \ldots, m).$$

In view of this fact the cone $\mathcal{C}$ is the dual $\mathcal{B}^*$ of the convex cone $\mathcal{B}$ generated by the vectors $b_1, \ldots, b_m, -b_{p+1}, \ldots, -b_m$. By virtue of Theorem 3.3 the cone $\mathcal{B}$ is closed. It follows that $\mathcal{B}^{**} = \mathcal{B}$ is the dual $\mathcal{C}^*$ of the cone $\mathcal{C}$. If b is a vector such that (3.6) holds, then b is in $\mathcal{C}^* = \mathcal{B}$. There are accordingly nonnegative numbers $\mu_1, \ldots, \mu_m, \nu_{p+1}, \ldots, \nu_m$ such that

$$b = \mu_1 b_1 + \cdots + \mu_m b_m + \nu_{p+1}(-b_{p+1}) + \cdots + \nu_m(-b_m).$$

This relation is of form (3.7) with $\lambda_\alpha = \mu_\alpha (\alpha = 1, \ldots, p)$ and $\lambda_\beta = \mu_\beta - \nu_\beta$ $(\beta = p+1, \ldots, m)$.

Suppose next that the vectors $b_1, \ldots, b_m$ are linearly independent. Then $m \leqslant n$. If $m < n$, there is a vector $y \neq 0$ orthogonal to $b_1, \ldots, b_m$. This vector is in $\mathcal{C}$. If $m = n$ and $p > 0$, then $m - p < n$. Select a vector $y \neq 0$ orthogonal to $b_2, \ldots, b_m$ such that $\langle b_1, y \rangle = -1$. This vector y is also in $\mathcal{C}$. Hence in either case the cone $\mathcal{C}$ contains a vector $y \neq 0$. This completes the proof of Theorem 3.4.

LEMMA 3.5

A convex cone $\mathcal{C}$ coincides with $\mathcal{E}^n$ if and only if its dual $\mathcal{C}^*$ consists of the null vector $x = 0$.

This result is an immediate consequence of Lemma 3.4 and

LEMMA 3.6

A convex cone $\mathcal{C}$ and its closure $\overline{\mathcal{C}}$ have the same interior points.

It is sufficient to show that an interior point of $\overline{\mathcal{C}}$ is also an interior point of $\mathcal{C}$. Of course a cone need not possess interior points.

Consider therefore an interior point x of $\overline{\mathcal{C}}$. For a sufficiently small positive constant ϵ the points $x_j = (x_j^1, \ldots, x_j^n)$ $(j = 1, \ldots, n)$ defined by the formulas

$$x_j^j = x^j + \epsilon, \qquad x_j^i = x^i \quad (i \neq j)$$

are in $\overline{\mathcal{C}}$. So also is the vector x_0 having

$$x_0^j = x^j - \epsilon \quad (j = 1, \ldots, n).$$

We have

$$(n+1)x = x_0 + x_1 + \cdots + x_n. \tag{3.8}$$

Since x_j is in the closure $\bar{\mathcal{C}}$ of $\mathcal{C}$, there is a sequence of vectors $\{x_{jq}\}$ in $\mathcal{C}$ converging to x_j. For q sufficiently large, the matrix

$$\left(x_{jq}{}^i - x^i\right) \qquad (j=0,1,\ldots,n;\ i=1,\ldots,n)$$

has rank n since it has rank n in the limit. Consequently for large values of q the equations

$$\sum_{j=0}^{n} a_j \left(x_{jq}{}^i - x^i\right) = 0, \qquad \sum_{j=0}^{n} a_j = 1$$

have solutions $a_j = a_{jq}$. By virtue of (3.8) we have

$$\lim_{q\to\infty} a_{jq} = \frac{1}{n+1}.$$

It follows that if q is large then $a_{jq} > 0$ and

$$x = \sum_j x_{jq} a_{jq}$$

is interior to $\mathcal{C}$, as was to be proved.

A useful application of the theory of cones is found in the following theorem, in which the real linear space $\mathcal{E}$ need not be finite dimensional.

THEOREM 3.5

Let $L_1,\ldots,L_m$ *be linear forms on a real linear space* $\mathcal{E}$ *. Let S be the set of points defined by the inequalities* $L_j(x) \leqslant 0$ $(j=1,\ldots,m)$. *If the linear forms* $L_1,\ldots,L_m$ *vanish identically on S, there exist positive multipliers* $\lambda_1,\ldots,\lambda_m$ *such that*

$$\lambda_1 L_1(x) + \cdots + \lambda_m L_m(x) = 0 \tag{3.9}$$

for all x *in* $\mathcal{E}$ *.*

Let $\mathcal{C}$ be the cone in $\mathcal{E}^m$ consisting of all vectors $y=(y^1,\ldots,y^m)$ for which there is a point x in $\mathcal{E}$ such that

$$y^j \geqslant L_j(x) \qquad (j=1,\ldots,m). \tag{3.10}$$

Setting $x=0$, we see that the vectors $e_1=(1,0,\ldots,0)$, $e_2=(0,1,0,\ldots,0),\ldots,e_m=(0,\ldots,0,1)$ are in $\mathcal{C}$. Since the linear forms $L_1,\ldots,L_m$

vanish simultaneously whenever $L_j(x) \leqslant 0$ $(j=1,\ldots,m)$, the vectors $-e_1,\ldots,-e_m$ are not in $\mathcal{C}$. The image $\mathcal{C}_1$ of $\mathcal{E}$ under the transformation $y^j = L_j(x)$ $(j=1,\ldots,m)$ is a linear manifold in $\mathcal{C}$. Every vector y in $\mathcal{C}$ is expressible in the form $y = y_1 + a_1 e_1 + \cdots + a_m e_m$, where y_1 is in $\mathcal{C}_1$ and $a_1,\ldots,a_m$ are nonnegative numbers. Since the cone $\mathcal{C}_1$ has a finite number of generators, so also has $\mathcal{C}$. Hence $\mathcal{C}$ is a closed cone. Inasmuch as e_j is in $\mathcal{C}$, we have $\langle e_j, z \rangle = z^j \leqslant 0$ for every vector z in the dual cone $\mathcal{C}*$ of $\mathcal{C}$. The vectors z in $\mathcal{C}*$ therefore have nonpositive components. By Theorem 3.1 the vector $-e_j$ is expressible as the sum $-e_j = y_j + z_j$ of orthogonal vectors with y_j in $\mathcal{C}$ and z_j in $\mathcal{C}*$. We have

$$-z_j{}^j = \langle -e_j, z_j \rangle = \langle y_j + z_j, z_j \rangle = |z_j|^2.$$

Since $-e_j$ is not in $\mathcal{C}$, we have $z_j \neq 0$ and hence $z_j{}^j < 0$. The vector $z = z_1 + \cdots + z_m$ is a vector in $\mathcal{C}*$ whose components are all negative. Given a vector x in $\mathcal{E}$, the vector y having $y^j = L_j(x)$ $(j=1,\ldots,m)$ is in $\mathcal{C}$. The inequality $\langle z, y \rangle \leqslant 0$ takes the form

$$z^1 L_1(x) + \cdots + z^m L_m(x) \leqslant 0.$$

Replacing x by $-x$, we see that the equality holds for all x in $\mathcal{E}$. The multipliers $\lambda_j = -z^j$ $(j=1,\ldots,m)$ are positive multipliers such that (3.9) holds on $\mathcal{E}$. This proves Theorem 3.5.

COROLLARY

If the linear forms $L_1,\ldots,L_m$ *vanish identically of the set* S *defined by the constraints*

$$L_i(x) \leqslant 0 \quad (i=1,\ldots,p), \qquad L_k(x) = 0 \quad (k=p+1,\ldots,m), \qquad (3.11)$$

there exist multipliers $\lambda_1,\ldots,\lambda_m$ *with* $\lambda_1,\ldots,\lambda_p$ *positive such that (3.9) holds on* $\mathcal{E}$.

This result follows from Theorem 3.5 if constraints (3.11) are replaced by the equivalent constraints

$$L_j(x) \leqslant 0 \quad (j=1,\ldots,m), \qquad -L_k(x) \leqslant 0 \quad (k=p+1,\ldots,m).$$

EXERCISES

1. Find the dual cones for each of the following cones in xy-space:
    (a) $x \geqslant 0, y \geqslant 0$,
    (b) $x+y \geqslant 0, 2x+3y \geqslant 0$,

    (c) $2x+3y \geqslant 0$,

    (d) $2x+3y = 0$.

2. Determine a closed cone in xy-space having

    (a) one generator,

    (b) two generators but not one,

    (c) three generators but not two,

    (d) four generators but not three.

3. Construct a closed cone in xyz-space which does not have a finite set of generators. Construct a closed cone that is not convex.

4. Prove Lemma 3.5.

5. Show that a vector $y_0 \neq 0$ is an interior point of a convex cone $\mathcal{C}$ if and only if there is a number $r > 0$ such that the inequality $\langle y_0, z \rangle \leqslant -r|y_0||z|$ holds for every vector z in the dual $\mathcal{C}^*$ of $\mathcal{C}$.

6. Show that if, in Theorem 3.5, we replace the assumption that the linear forms $L_1, \ldots, L_m$ vanish identically on S by the assumption that $L_1, \ldots, L_r$ $(r \leqslant m)$ vanish identically on S, there exist positive multipliers $\lambda_1, \ldots, \lambda_r$ and nonnegative multipliers $\lambda_{r+1}, \ldots, \lambda_m$ such that $\lambda_1 L_1 + \cdots + \lambda_m L_m$ vanishes identically on $\mathcal{S}$. Is the converse true? *Hint*: The proof is like that of Theorem 3.5 except that we now know only that $-e_1, \ldots, -e_r$ are not in $\mathcal{C}$. Consequently in this case the multipliers $\lambda_1, \ldots, \lambda_m$ are determined by the vector $z = z_1 + \cdots + z_r$, where z_j is the vector described in the proof of Theorem 3.5.

7. Let $\mathcal{S}$ be a linear space, and let $L, L_1, \ldots, L_p$ be linear forms on $\mathcal{S}$. Suppose that $L(x) \geqslant 0$ for all x in $\mathcal{S}$ satisfying the relations $L_\alpha(x) \leqslant 0$ $(\alpha = 1, \ldots, p)$. Show that there are nonnegative multipliers $\lambda_1, \ldots, \lambda_p$ such that $L(x) + \lambda_1 L_1(x) + \cdots + \lambda_p L_p(x) = 0$ for all x in $\mathcal{S}$. *Hint*: Use Exercise 6.

8. Let $L, L_1, \ldots, L_m$ be linear forms on a linear space $\mathcal{S}$. Suppose that $L(x) \geqslant 0$ for all x in $\mathcal{S}$ having $L_\alpha(x) \leqslant 0$ $(\alpha = 1, \ldots, p)$, $L_\beta(x) = 0$ $(\beta = p+1, \ldots, m)$. Show that there exist nonnegative multipliers $\lambda_1, \ldots, \lambda_p$ and multipliers $\lambda_{p+1}, \ldots, \lambda_m$ such that $L(x) + \lambda_1 L_1(x) + \cdots + \lambda_m L(x) = 0$ for all x in $\mathcal{S}$. *Hint*: Use Exercise 7 with the conditions $L_\gamma(x) \leqslant 0$ $(\gamma = 1, \ldots, m)$, $-L_\beta(x) \leqslant 0$ $(\beta = p+1, \ldots, m)$.

9. Let $x_1, \ldots, x_k$ be a set of vectors in $\mathcal{S}^n$. Show that a vector x is expressible in the form $x = a_1 x_1 + \cdots + a_k x_k$ with $a_j \geqslant 0$ if and only if we have $\langle x, y \rangle \leqslant 0$ for all vectors y such that $\langle x_j, y \rangle \leqslant 0$ $(j = 1, \ldots, k)$. Restate this result in terms of the cone $\mathcal{C}$ generated by $x_1, \ldots, x_k$.

10. Let $\mathcal{C}$ be the cone generated by a set $\mathcal{B}$ of vectors. Show that, given a vector $x \neq 0$ in $\mathcal{C}$, there exist linearly independent vectors $x_1, \ldots, x_k$ in $\mathcal{B}$ such that x is in the cone generated by the vectors $x_1, \ldots, x_k$. *Hint*: Let k be the least integer such that x is a nonnegative linear combination of k vectors in $\mathcal{B}$.

11. Given m distinct nonnull vectors $x_1, \ldots, x_m$ having associated with them positive numbers $a_1, \ldots, a_m$ such that $a_1 x_1 + \cdots + a_m x_m = 0$, show that there exist a subset $y_1, \ldots, y_k$ of these vectors and positive numbers $b_1, \ldots, b_k$ such that $b_1 y_1 + \cdots + b_k y_k = 0$ and $k \leqslant n+1$. *Hint*: Let $\mathcal{C}$ be the cone generated by the set $\mathcal{B}$ of vectors $x_2, \ldots, x_m$. Then $-x_1$ is in $\mathcal{C}$. Apply the result given in Exercise 10 to $x = -x_1$.

12. Let $\mathcal{C}$ be the cone generated by a bounded closed set $\mathcal{B}$ in $\mathcal{E}^n$. Show that, if $\mathcal{C}$ is not closed, there exist $k \leqslant n$ vectors $x_1, \ldots, x_k$ in $\mathcal{B}$ and nonnegative numbers $a_1, \ldots, a_k$, not all zero, such that $a_1 x_1 + \cdots + a_k x_k = 0$. *Hint*: Let y be a vector in the closure of $\mathcal{C}$ which is not in $\mathcal{C}$. Then y is the limit of a sequence $\{y_q\}$ of vectors in $\mathcal{C}$. By Exercise 10 we can express y_q in the form $y_q = a_{1q} x_{1q} + \cdots + a_{nq} x_{nq}$, where $a_{jq} > 0$ $(j = 1, \ldots, n)$ and $x_{1q}, \ldots, x_{nq}$ (repetitions allowed) are in $\mathcal{B}$. Set $b_q = a_{1q} + \cdots + a_{nq}$. Show that these sequences can be chosen so that $\{x_{jq}\}$ converges to x_j and $\{a_{jq}/b_q\}$ converges to a_j. Show that

$$\lim_{q \to \infty} b_q = \infty, \qquad a_1 x_1 + \cdots + a_n x_n = 0, \qquad a_1 + \cdots + a_n = 1.$$

13. Suppose that a set $\mathcal{B}$ in $\mathcal{E}^n$ generates a closed cone $\mathcal{C}$. Assume that there is a vector $x \neq 0$ in $\mathcal{C}$ whose negative $-x$ is also in $\mathcal{C}$. Show that there exist $k \leqslant n+1$ vectors $x_1, \ldots, x_k$ in $\mathcal{B}$ and positive numbers $a_1, \ldots, a_k$ such that $a_1 x_1 + \cdots + a_k x_k = 0$. *Hint*: Express x and $-x$ in the forms $x = b_1 y_1 + \cdots + b_p y_p$, $-x = b_{p+1} y_{p+1} + \cdots + b_m y_m$, where $y_1, \ldots, y_m$ are in $\mathcal{B}$ and $b_1, \ldots, b_m$ are positive. Add and use Exercise 11.

14. Let $\mathcal{C}$ be a closed cone in $\mathcal{E}^n$. Show that the following two conditions are equivalent: (i) there is no $x \neq 0$ in $\mathcal{C}$ such that $-x$ is in $\mathcal{C}$; (ii) there is a vector y such that $\langle y, x \rangle < 0$ for every $x \neq 0$ in $\mathcal{C}$. *Hint*: Show that (ii) implies (i). Suppose that (i) holds. Let $\mathcal{D}$ be the class of vectors in the dual cone $\mathcal{C}*$ of $\mathcal{C}$ whose negatives are in $\mathcal{C}*$. Show that $\mathcal{D}$ is a linear manifold orthogonal to $\mathcal{C}$. Let $\hat{\mathcal{C}}$ be the class of vectors in $\mathcal{C}*$ orthogonal to $\mathcal{D}$. Let $y_1, \ldots, y_r$ be a maximal set of linearly independent vectors in $\hat{\mathcal{C}}$. Show that $y = y_1 + \cdots + y_r$ has the property described in (ii).

15. Let $\mathcal{B}$ be a compact set in $\mathcal{E}^n$. Suppose that there is a vector y such that $\langle y, x \rangle < 0$ for every vector x in $\mathcal{B}$. Show that the cone $\mathcal{C}$ generated by $\mathcal{B}$ is closed and that $\langle y, x \rangle < 0$ for every $x \neq 0$ in $\mathcal{C}$. *Hint*: Use Exercise 12.

16. Let $\mathcal{B}$ be a compact set in $\mathcal{E}^n$. Show that there is no set of vectors $x_1, \ldots, x_k$ in $\mathcal{B}$ and positive numbers $a_1, \ldots, a_k$ such that $a_1 x_1 + \cdots + a_k x_k = 0$ if and only if there is a vector y such that $\langle y, x \rangle < 0$ for all x in $\mathcal{B}$. *Hint*: Use Exercises 12 to 15.

4. TANGENT CONES AND NORMAL CONES

Consider a point x_0 belonging to a set S. Intuitively a vector h will be considered to be a tangent vector of S at x_0 if it leads us from x_0 into S. For example, if a vector h has the property that a line segment of the form $x = x_0 + th$ $(0 \leqslant t \leqslant \delta)$ is in S for a positive number δ, then h leads us into S and is accordingly a tangent vector of S at x_0. Such a tangent vector h will be called a *linear tangent vector* of S at x_0. It is also called a *feasible direction*. This concept of a tangent vector is too limited for our purposes. For example, a circle fails to have nonnull tangent vectors of this type. It does, however, have a curvilinear tangent. By a *curvilinear tangent* vector will be meant a vector h such that h is the derivative $\dot{x}(0) = h$ at $t = 0$ of continuous arc $x(t)$ $(0 \leqslant t \leqslant \delta)$ in S having $x(0) = x_0$ as its initial point. Obviously linear tangent vectors are curvilinear tangent vectors, but even this concept is sometimes too restrictive. Accordingly we shall generalize the concept of tangent vectors by replacing a curve by a directionally convergent sequence of points. This leads to the concept of a sequential tangent. A vector h will be called a *sequential tangent* of S at x_0 if there are a sequence $\{x_q\}$ of points in S and a sequence of positive numbers $\{t_q\}$ such that

$$\lim_{q \to \infty} \frac{x_q - x_0}{t_q} = h, \qquad \lim_{q \to \infty} t_q = 0. \tag{4.1}$$

Every curvilinear tangent h is a sequential tangent, for, if $x(t)$ $(0 \leqslant t \leqslant \delta)$ is an arc in S having $x(0) = x_0$ and $\dot{x}(0) = h$, then (4.1) holds with $t_q = \delta / q$ and $x_q = x(t_q)$. It is a simple matter to exhibit sequential tangents that are not curvilinear tangents. However, in most of the applications with which we are concerned the two concepts are equivalent. *In what follows sequential tangent vectors will be called tangent vectors.*

In defining tangent vectors we used the concept of directionally convergent sequences. A sequence $\{x_q\}$ will be said *to converge to x_0 in a direction h*, written $x_q \to x_0$ in direction h, if there is a sequence of positive numbers $\{t_q\}$ such that relations (4.1) hold. If (4.1) holds, we have

$$\lim_{q \to \infty} x_q = x_0, \qquad \lim_{q \to \infty} \frac{|x_0 - x_q|}{t_q} = |h|. \tag{4.2}$$

Consequently, if $h \neq 0$ and (4.1) holds, $x_q \neq x_0$ for large values of q and

$$\lim_{q \to \infty} \frac{x_q - x_0}{|x_q - x_0|} = \lim_{q \to \infty} \frac{x_q - x_0}{t_q} \lim_{q \to \infty} \frac{t_q}{|x_q - x_0|} = \frac{h}{|h|}. \tag{4.3}$$

It follows that, if h is a unit vector and $x_q \to x_0$ in the direction h, we can choose $t_q = |x_q - x_0|$ in (4.1). Observe further that, if (4.1) holds and $\alpha > 0$, then

$$\lim_{q \to \infty} \frac{x_q - x_0}{t_q / \alpha} = \alpha h, \qquad \lim_{q \to \infty} \frac{x_q - x_0}{t_q^{1/2}} = 0.$$

Consequently, if $x_q \to x_0$ in the direction h, then $x_q \to x_0$ in the direction αh for each $\alpha \geqslant 0$. Finally, if $x_q \to x_0$ in the usual sense, $x_q \to x_0$ in the null direction $h = 0$. This can be seen by selecting $t_q = |x_q - x_0|^{1/2}$ if $x_q \neq x_0$ and $t_q = 1/q$ otherwise.

It should be noted that we made use of directionally convergent sequences in the proof given in Section 3 of Chapter 3.

The following lemma will be useful.

LEMMA 4.1

Let $\{y_q\}$ be a sequence of points distinct from x_0 which converges to x_0. There are a subsequence $\{x_q\}$ of $\{y_q\}$ and a unit vector h such that $\{x_q\}$ converges to x_0 in the direction h.

The vectors

$$k_q = \frac{y_q - x_0}{|y_q - x_0|} \quad (q = 1,2,3,\dots)$$

are unit vectors. By the Bolzano-Weierstrass theorem the sequence $\{k_q\}$ has a subsequence $\{h_q\}$ converging to a vector h. Since $|h_q| \to |h|$ and $|h_q| = 1$, it follows that $|h| = 1$. The corresponding subsequence $\{x_q\}$ of $\{y_q\}$ has the property that

$$h_q = \frac{x_q - x_0}{|x_q - x_0|} \to h.$$

This proves Lemma 4.1.

Consider now a point x_0 in a set S in $\mathcal{E}^n$. According to the definition given above, a vector h is a tangent vector of S at x_0 if there is a sequence $\{x_q\}$ of points in S converging to x_0 in the direction h. Since a sequence converging to x_0 in the direction h also converges to x_0 in the direction αh for all $\alpha \geqslant 0$, it follows that the class $\mathcal{K}$ of tangent vectors h of S at x_0 is a cone. Accordingly the class $\mathcal{K}$ will be called the *tangent cone* of S at x_0. The class $\mathcal{K}$ will also be called the *tangent space* of S at x_0. It should be noted that $\mathcal{K}$ is the null cone (consisting only of the vector $h=0$) if and only if x_0 is an isolated point of S.

Since the nonnegative multiples of a nonnull vector h can be identified with a ray (half line), we can interpret $\mathcal{K}$ as the collection of rays. Each ray L in $\mathcal{K}$ can be determined as follows. There exists a sequence of points $\{x_q\}$ in S distinct from x_0 and converging to x_0 such that, if L_q is the ray through x_q emanating from x_0, then L is the limit of the sequence of rays $\{L_q\}$. The rays L_q need not be in $\mathcal{K}$.

In this context the ordinary tangent line to a curve through x_0 consists of two half rays which are oppositely oriented. It consists of all nonnegative multiples of a vector h and of its negative $-h$.

If x_0 is an interior point of S, the tangent space $\mathcal{K}$ of S at x_0 coincides with $\mathcal{E}^n$. If x_0 is a point on the spherical surface

$$|x|=r,$$

$\mathcal{H}$ consists of all vectors $h=x-x_0$ such that

$$\langle x_0,h\rangle=\langle x_0,x-x_0\rangle=0$$

and is the usual tangent space. If S is the closed ball

$$|x|\leqslant r$$

and x_0 is a point on the boundary of S, the tangent space $\mathcal{H}$ of S at x_0 consists of all vectors h such that

$$\langle x_0,h\rangle\leqslant 0$$

and hence is a half space. The tangent space of the interval

$$0\leqslant x^i\leqslant 2 \qquad (i=1,\ldots,n)$$

at the origin is defined by the inequalities

$$0\leqslant h^i \qquad (i=1,\ldots,n).$$

Let S be the square $0\leqslant x\leqslant 2$, $0\leqslant y\leqslant 2$ in the xy-plane. The tangent space of S at $(0,0)$ is the first quadrant, at the point $(1,0)$ is the upper half plane, and at $(1,1)$ is the whole plane. If S is the set of points (x,y) such that $x^3\geqslant y^2$, the tangent space of S at $(0,0)$ is the positive x-axis.

LEMMA 4.2

The tangent space $\mathcal{H}$ of a set S at a point x_0 in S is closed.

Clearly $h=0$ is in $\mathcal{H}$. Consider a vector $h\neq 0$ which is a limit of a sequence $\{h_q\}$ of vectors in $\mathcal{H}$. Since $\{h_q/|h_q|\}$ is a sequence in $\mathcal{H}$ converging to $h/|h|$, it is sufficient to consider the case in which $|h|=|h_q|=1$. For each q we can select a vector x_q in S such that

$$0<t_q=|x_q-x_0|<\frac{1}{q}, \qquad \left|\frac{x_q-x_0}{t_q}-h_q\right|<\frac{1}{q}.$$

We then have

$$\left|\frac{x_q-x_0}{t_q}-h\right|\leqslant\left|\frac{x_q-x_0}{t_q}-h_q\right|+|h_q-h|<\frac{1}{q}+|h_q-h|.$$

Hence

$$\lim_{q \to \infty} \frac{x_q - x_0}{t_q} = h.$$

This implies that h is in $\mathcal{K}$, as was to be proved.

An important case in which the tangent vectors defined by sequences are also defined by arcs is the one in which S is convex. In this case the tangent space $\mathcal{K}$ of S at a point x_0 is a convex cone, that is, a cone $\mathcal{K}$ such that the sum $h_1 + h_2$ of two vectors in $\mathcal{K}$ is in $\mathcal{K}$. Recall that a *linear tangent* of S at x_0 is a vector h such that line segment $x_0 + th$ $(0 \leqslant t \leqslant \delta)$ is in S if δ is sufficiently small.

LEMMA 4.3

Let x_0 be a point in a convex set S. The tangent space $\mathcal{K}$ of S at x_0 is a convex cone. The class of all linear tangents of S at x_0 forms a convex cone $\hat{\mathcal{K}}$ whose closure is $\mathcal{K}$. Each tangent vector $h \neq 0$ is defined by an arc in S and is therefore a curvilinear tangent of S at x_0.

If h_1 and h_2 are nonnull linear tangent vectors at x_0, there exist points x_1 and x_2 in S and positive numbers α_1 and α_2 such that

$$h_1 = \alpha_1(x_1 - x_0), \qquad h_2 = \alpha_2(x_2 - x_0).$$

Hence upon setting

$$\alpha = \alpha_1 + \alpha_2, \qquad x = \frac{\alpha_1}{\alpha} x_1 + \frac{\alpha_2}{\alpha} x_2,$$

we see that

$$h = h_1 + h_2 = \alpha(x - x_0).$$

Since S is convex, the point x is in S. Consequently h is a linear tangent vector of S at x_0, and $\hat{\mathcal{K}}$ is convex. Since $\mathcal{K}$ is the closure of $\hat{\mathcal{K}}$, it too is convex.

The last statement in the lemma will be established in Section 11, Chapter 6.

The dual cone $\mathcal{K}^*$ of the tangent cone $\mathcal{K}$ of S at x_0 will be called the *normal cone* or *the normal space of S at x_0*. The vectors in $\mathcal{K}^*$ will be called *outer normals of S at x_0* or simply the *normals of S at x_0*. An outer normal of S at x_0 makes an obtuse angle with each tangent of S at x_0. In this connection we consider right angles to be obtuse angles. If the tangent cone $\mathcal{K}$ is a linear space, the normal space is the orthogonal complement of $\mathcal{H}$. If the tangent space is a half space, the normal cone consists of a single ray. If the tangent cone is a ray, the normal cone is a half space. Tangent and normal cones are illustrated in Figures 4.1 and 4.2. In these figures $\mathcal{H}$ is the tangent cone, and $\mathcal{H}^*$ is the outer normal cone of S at x_0. In Figure 4.3, what are the tangent cones and the normal cones at O of the shaded region and of the unshaded region?

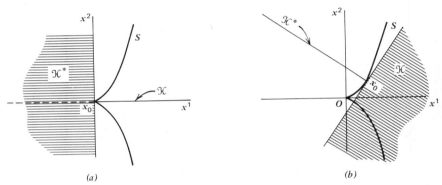

(a)   (b)

Figure 4.1

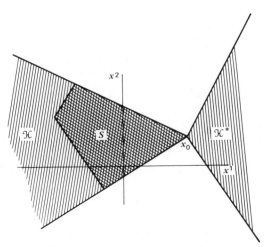

Figure 4.2

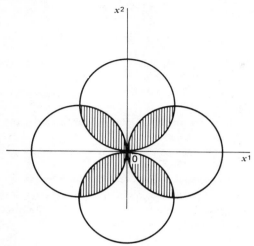

Figure 4.3

EXERCISES

1. Show that if x_0 is a point in a convex set S the tangent space $\mathcal{H}$ of S at x_0 is the closure of the class $\tilde{\mathcal{K}}$ of linear tangents of S at x_0.

2. Let $h_1, \ldots, h_m$ be a set of m vectors. Show that the set $\mathcal{H}$ of all vectors h expressible in the form

$$h = a_1 h_1 + \cdots + a_m h_m,$$

where $a_i \geqslant 0$ $(i = 1, \ldots, m)$, is a convex cone. The vectors in the set $h_1, \ldots, h_m$ are called *generators* of $\mathcal{H}$.

3. Let S be the set in the xy-plane defined by the inequalities

$$y \geqslant x(x-1), \qquad y \geqslant x(1-x).$$

Find the tangent and normal spaces of S at $(0,0)$ and at $(1,0)$. Show that, if (x_0, y_0) is any other boundary point of S, its tangent space is a half plane. Discuss the case in which S is determined by the inequalities

$$y \geqslant x(1-x), \qquad y \leqslant x(x+1).$$

In each case find a set of generators of the tangent space.

4. Give an example of set S for which there is a point x_0 in S whose tangent space is not convex.

5. In xyz-space find the tangent space at $(x,y,z) = (0,0,0)$ of the set S, defined by

the inequalities

$$x+y \geqslant 0, \qquad x+z \geqslant 0, \qquad y+z \geqslant 0.$$

Also discuss the case in which S is defined by the inequalities

$$x^2+(z-1)^2 \geqslant 1, \qquad z^2+(y-1)^2 \geqslant 1, \qquad x \geqslant 0, \qquad y \geqslant 0, \qquad z \geqslant 0.$$

6. Let S be the set of points in the xy-plane determined by the inequalities

$$1 - x^2 - (y-1)^2 \leqslant 0, \qquad x^2+(y-2)^2-4 \leqslant 0, \qquad -y^2-x \leqslant 0.$$

Describe the tangent spaces at the boundary points of S.

7. In the xy-plane let S be the set of points (x,y) having $y=0$ and $g(x,y)=0$, where $g(0,y)=y$, $g(x,y)=y-x^2\sin(1/x)$ $(x \neq 0)$. Show that $(h,k)=(1,0)$ is a tangent vector of S at $(x_0,y_0)=(0,0)$ but is not a curvilinear tangent vector of S at (x_0,y_0).

8. With g defined as in Exercise 7, let S be the set of points (x,y) defined by the constraints $y \leqslant 0$, $g(x,y) \geqslant 0$. Determine the tangent space and the normal space at the origin. Are there any nonnull curvilinear tangent vectors of S at the origin?

5. REMARKS ON DIFFERENTIATION

In the following pages we shall have occasion to differentiate functions with the help of directionally convergent sequences. To this end let $\{x_q\}$ be a sequence converging to x_0 in a direction h. Let $\{t_q\}$ be a sequence of positive numbers such that

$$t_q \to 0, \qquad \frac{x_q-x_0}{t_q} \to h \quad \text{as } q \to \infty. \tag{5.1}$$

In a moment we shall show that, if f is of class C' on a neighborhood of x_0, then

$$\lim_{q \to \infty} \frac{f(x_q)-f(x_0)}{t_q} = f'(x_0,h). \tag{5.2}$$

We shall show in addition that, if f is of class C'', then

$$\lim_{q \to \infty} \frac{f(x_q)-f(x_0)-f'(x_0,x_q-x_0)}{t_q^2} = \tfrac{1}{2}f''(x_0,h). \tag{5.3}$$

In fact, (5.2) holds if f is differentiable at x_0 and (5.3) holds if f is twice differentiable at x_0.

Consider first the case in which f is differentiable at x_0. By this we mean that f is defined on a neighborhood of x_0 and has a differential

$$f'(x_0, h) = \sum_{i=1}^{n} f_i'(x_0) h^i \qquad (5.4)$$

at x_0 in the sense that

$$\lim_{x \to x_0} \frac{r_1(x_0, x - x_0)}{|x - x_0|} = 0, \qquad (5.5)$$

where $r_1(x_0, h)$ is the remainder term in the Taylor expansion

$$f(x) = f(x_0) + f'(x_0, x - x_0) + r_1(x_0, x - x_0). \qquad (5.6)$$

It is clear that the coefficients $f_i'(x_0)$ in (5.4) is the partial derivative of f with respect to x^i at x_0. It is accordingly the ith component of the gradient $\nabla f(x_0)$ of f at x_0. As is shown in the appendix, a function f is differentiable at x_0 if it is of class C' on a neighborhood of x_0.

To establish formula (5.2), it is sufficient to treat the case in which $x_q \neq x_0$ ($q = 1, 2, 3, \ldots$). Then by (5.6) we have

$$\frac{f(x_q) - f(x_0)}{t_q} = f'\left(x_0, \frac{x_q - x_0}{t_q}\right) + \frac{r_1(x_0, x_q - x_0)}{t_q}. \qquad (5.7)$$

Since recalling that $|x_q - x_0|/t_q \to |h|$, it follows from (5.5) that

$$\lim_{q \to \infty} \frac{r_1(x_0, x_q - x_0)}{t_q} = \lim_{q \to \infty} \frac{r_1(x_0, x_q - x_0)}{|x_q - x_0|} \lim_{q \to \infty} \frac{|x_q - x_0|}{t_q} = 0.$$

Combining this result with the relation

$$\lim_{q \to \infty} f'\left(x_0, \frac{x_q - x_0}{t_q}\right) = f'(x_0, h),$$

we see, by (5.7), that (5.2) holds, as was to be proved.

Consider next relation (5.3). Recall that, if f is of class C'' in a neighborhood of x_0, we have the Taylor formula

$$f(x) = f(x_0) + f'(x_0, x - x_0) + \tfrac{1}{2} f''(x_0, x - x_0) + r_2(x_0, x - x_0), \qquad (5.8)$$

where

$$\lim_{q \to \infty} \frac{r_2(x_0, x - x_0)}{|x - x_0|^2} = 0. \tag{5.9}$$

Accordingly we say that f is twice differentiable at x_0 if it is differentiable at x_0 and there is a quadratic form

$$f''(x_0, h) = \sum_{i,j=1}^{n} f''_{ij}(x_0) h^i h^j \tag{5.10}$$

such that (5.9) holds with $r_2(x_0, h)$ defined by formula (5.8). Using (5.8), we find that

$$\frac{f(x_q) - f(x_0) - f'(x_0, x_q - x_0)}{t_q^2} = \tfrac{1}{2} f''\left(x_0, \frac{x_q - x_0}{t_q}\right) + \frac{r_2(x_0, x_q - x_0)}{t_q^2}.$$

$$\tag{5.11}$$

By (5.9) the last term on the right has the limit

$$\lim_{q \to \infty} \frac{r_2(x_0, x_q - x_0)}{|x_q - x_0|^2} \lim_{q \to \infty} \frac{|x_q - x_0|^2}{t_q^2} = 0,$$

provided that $x_q \neq x_0$, as we can assume. In view of the relation

$$\lim_{q \to \infty} f''\left(x_0, \frac{x_q - x_0}{t_q}\right) = f''(x_0, h)$$

it is seen, by (5.11), that formula (5.3) holds. The coefficient $f''_{ij}(x_0)$ appearing in (5.10) is the partial derivative $f_{x^i x^j}$ of f at x_0.

There is a fine distinction between directional derivatives and differentials. In general, $f'(x_0, h)$ is called a *directional derivative of* f *at* x_0 *in the direction* h if zero relation (5.2) holds whenever (5.1) holds. Observe that, if $x_0 = 0$ and $f(x) = |x|$, then $f'(x_0, h) = |h|$ is the directional derivative of f at $x_0 = 0$. Since $f'(x_0, h) = |h|$ is not of form (5.4), it is not a differential of f at x_0. The linearity of $f'(x_0, h)$ as a function of h is an essential part of the definition of a differential. In the pages that follow we shall be concerned only with directional derivatives determined by differentials. Accordingly we assume throughout that $f'(x_0, h)$ is a differential of f at x_0, even though its principal use is that of a directional derivative.

It should be noted that in the definition $f'(x_0,h)$ we assumed that f was defined on a neighborhood of x_0, but this assumption is not essential. Let x_0 be a limit point of the domain D of a function f. Then the linear form $f'(x_0,h)$ defined by (5.4) is called a *differential of* f *at* x_0 if limit (5.5) holds when x is restricted to D. We shall use this extended definition of a differential in the definition of derived sets given in Section 9, Chapter 6. The definition of second differentials can be extended similarly.

EXERCISES

1. Suppose that f is differentiable at x_0 and that h is a unit vector. Show that, if $\{x_q\}$ converges to x_0 in the direction h, then

$$\lim_{q\to\infty}\frac{x_q-x_0}{|x_q-x_0|}=h,\qquad \lim_{q\to\infty}\frac{f(x_q)-f(x_0)}{|x_q-x_0|}=f'(x_0,h).$$

2. Suppose that f is twice differentiable at x_0. Show that, if $\{x_q\}$ converges to x_0 in the direction of a unit vector h, then

$$\lim_{q\to\infty}\frac{f(x_q)-f(x_0)-f'(x_0,x_q-x_0)}{|x_q-x_0|^2}=\tfrac{1}{2}f''(x_0,h).$$

3. Suppose that f has a directional derivative $f'(x_0,h)$ at x_0 in the sense that (5.2) holds whenever (5.1) holds. Show that $f'(x_0,h)$ is a continuous positively homogeneous function of h of degree 1. Show further that

$$\lim_{t\to0+}\frac{f(x_0+th)-f(x_0)}{t}=f'(x_0,h). \tag{5.12}$$

4. Formula (5.12) is used as an alternative definition of a directional derivative of f at x_0 in the direction h. Let f be a discontinuous function on the unit sphere $|x|=1$. Extend the definition of f to the whole space by the formula $f(tx)=tf(x)$, where $t\geqslant0$ and $|x|=1$. Show that relation (5.12) holds with $x_0=0$ and $f'(x_0,h)=f(h)$. Show that f fails to have a directional derivative at $x_0=0$ in the sense described in Exercise 3.

6. MINIMUM OF A FUNCTION ON AN ARBITRARY SET S

We are now in a position to study the roles of the tangent space $\mathcal{K}$ and the normal space $\mathcal{K}^*$ of S at a minimum point x_0 of a function f on S. The results here given will be used to establish the Lagrange multiplier rule given in Section 2. We assume that f is differentiable at x_0, and when

second derivatives occur we assume that f is twice differentiable at x_0.
As a first result we have

THEOREM 6.1

Let x_0 *be a local minimum point of a function* f *on a set* S. *Then the negative gradient* $-\nabla f(x_0)$ *is an outer normal of* S *at* x_0. *Equivalently, the inequality*

$$f'(x_0, h) = \langle \nabla f(x_0), h \rangle \geq 0 \tag{6.1}$$

holds for all vectors h *in the tangent space* $\mathcal{K}$ *of* S *at* x_0. *Furthermore, if* $\mathcal{K}$ *is convex and possesses a finite number of generators* $h_1, \ldots, h_r$, *inequality* (6.1) *holds on* $\mathcal{K}$ *if and only if*

$$f'(x_0, h_j) \geq 0 \qquad (j = 1, \ldots, r). \tag{6.2}$$

Intuitively, the directional derivative of f at x_0 in directions h "leading into S" cannot be negative. This ensures that no nearby points of S can furnish smaller values of f than $f(x_0)$.

The first conclusion follows from the second and the definition of an outer normal. To establish the second conclusion, let h be a vector in $\mathcal{K}$. Select a sequence $\{x_q\}$ of points in S and a sequence $\{t_q\}$ of positive numbers such that

$$\lim_{q \to \infty} t_q = 0, \qquad \lim_{q \to \infty} \frac{x_q - x_0}{t_q} = h.$$

Then, as was seen in Section 5,

$$\lim_{q \to \infty} \frac{f(x_q) - f(x_0)}{t_q} = f'(x_0, h). \tag{6.3}$$

Since $x_q \to x_0$, we have $f(x_q) \geq f(x_0)$ for large values of q. When this fact is used, it follows from (6.3) that (6.1) holds, as was to be proved.

If $\mathcal{K}$ is convex and is generated by vectors $h_1, \ldots, h_r$, a vector h in $\mathcal{K}$ is expressible in the form

$$h = a_1 h_1 + \cdots + a_r h_r \qquad (a_j \geq 0; j = 1, \ldots, r). \tag{6.4}$$

We then have

$$f'(x_0, h) = a_1 f'(x_0, h_1) + \cdots + a_r f'(x_0, h_r). \tag{6.5}$$

It follows that in this event inequality (6.1) holds on S if and only if relations (6.2) hold. This proves the theorem.

For the sake of completeness we restate basic Theorem 5.2 of Chapter 1 in the following form.

THEOREM 6.2

Suppose that S *is convex and that* f *is convex on* S. *Then a point* x_0 *in* S *minimizes* f *on* S *if and only if the inequality*

$$f'(x_0, h) \geqslant 0 \tag{6.6}$$

holds for every tangent vector h *of* S *at* x_0 *or, equivalently, if and only if* $-\nabla f(x_0)$ *is an outer normal of* S *at* x_0.

Since S is convex, the tangent space $\mathcal{H}$ of S at x_0 is determined by the vectors h of the form $h = x - x_0$, where x is in S. Using this fact, we see that inequality (6.6) holds on $\mathcal{H}$ if and only if the inequality

$$f'(x_0, x - x_0) \geqslant 0$$

holds for every point x in S. Combining this result with Theorem 5.2 of Chapter 1, we obtain Theorem 6.2.

THEOREM 6.3

Let x_0 *be a point on* S *at which* f *is differentiable. If*

$$f'(x_0, h) > 0 \tag{6.7}$$

for all $h \neq 0$ *in the tangent space* $\mathcal{H}$ *of* S *at* x_0, *then there are a neighborhood* N *of* x_0 *and a positive number* m *such that*

$$f(x) \geqslant f(x_0) + m|x - x_0|$$

for all x *in* S∩N. *If* $\mathcal{H}$ *is a convex cone and possesses a finite number of nonnull generators* $h_1, \ldots, h_r$, *then* (6.7) *holds for all* $h \neq 0$ *in* $\mathcal{H}$ *if and only if it holds for each of the generators* $h_1, \ldots, h_r$.

Suppose that the conclusion is false. Then there is a sequence $\{x_q\}$ of points in S such that

$$t_q = |x_q - x_0| < \frac{1}{q}, \qquad f(x_q) - f(x_0) < \frac{1}{q}|x_q - x_0|.$$

Clearly $t_q > 0$. Since we can replace our original sequence by a subsequence without disturbing these inequalities, we can suppose, by Lemma 4.1, that the sequence $\{x_q\}$ has been chosen so that the sequence of unit vectors

$$\frac{x_q - x_0}{t_q}$$

converges to a vector h. Then $|h| = 1$, h is in $\mathcal{K}$, and

$$\lim_{q \to \infty} \frac{f(x_q) - f(x_0)}{t_q} = f'(x_0, h) \leqslant 0,$$

contrary to our assumption that (6.7) holds for all $h \neq 0$ in $\mathcal{K}$. The last conclusion follows from relations (6.4) and (6.5), which hold when $\mathcal{K}$ is convex.

EXAMPLE 6.1

As a simple illustration of an application of Theorems 6.1 and 6.2, we turn to the case in which S is the set of points (x, y) in the xy-plane satisfying the inequalities

$$x \geqslant 0, \qquad y \geqslant x, \qquad y \leqslant 2x,$$

as indicated in Figure 6.1. In this case the tangent space $\mathcal{K}$ of S at the origin coincides with S. It is generated by the vectors $h_1 = (1, 1)$ and $h_2 = (1, 2)$. A function f on S having a minimum at the origin must satisfy the relation

$$f_x + f_y \geqslant 0, \qquad f_x + 2f_y \geqslant 0 \tag{6.8}$$

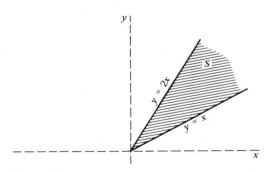

Figure 6.1

at the origin. If the equality fails to hold in each case, f has a local minimum at the origin. For example, each of the functions

$$3x-y, \qquad 3x-y+xy, \qquad 3x-y-x^3$$

satisfies conditions (6.8) at $(0,0)$ with the equality excluded and hence has a local minimum relative to S at $(0,0)$.

Similarly, if a function $f(x,y,z)$ has a minimum at the origin subject to the constraints $x \geqslant 0$, $y \geqslant 0$, $z \geqslant 0$, then $f_x \geqslant 0$, $f_y \geqslant 0$, $f_z \geqslant 0$ at the origin. Conversely, if $f_x > 0$, $f_y > 0$, $f_z > 0$ at the origin, f has a local minimum at the origin subject to these constraints.

In many examples with inequality constraints we have $f'(x_0,h)=0$ for some tangent vectors h and $f'(x_0,h)>0$ for other tangent vectors h at x_0. In many situations in which this occurs there is associated with f an auxiliary function F having the same differentiability properties as f at x_0 and satisfying the relations

$$F(x) \leqslant f(x) \quad \text{on } S, \qquad F(x_0)=f(x_0), \qquad \nabla F(x_0)=0. \qquad (6.9)$$

Such a function F will be called a *lower support function for* f *at* x_0. If f possesses a lower support function F at x_0, then, by (6.9), the function $G(x)=f(x)-F(x)$ satisfies the relations

$$G(x) \geqslant 0 \quad \text{on } S, \qquad G(x_0)=0, \qquad G'(x_0,h)=f'(x_0,h) \geqslant 0 \qquad (6.10)$$

for every vector h in the tangent space $\mathcal{H}$ of S at x_0. The last inequality can be established as follows. Given a vector h in $\mathcal{H}$, select a sequence $\{x_q\}$ in S and a sequence $\{t_q\}$ of positive numbers such that

$$t_q \to 0, \qquad \frac{x_q-x_0}{t_q} \to h \quad \text{as } q \to \infty.$$

Since $G(x_q) \geqslant G(x_0)=0$ and $\nabla F(x_0)=0$, we have

$$0 \leqslant \lim \frac{G(x_q)}{t_q} = \lim \frac{G(x_q)-G(x_0)}{t_q}$$

$$= G'(x_0,h)=f'(x_0,h)-F'(x_0,h)=f'(x_0,h),$$

as stated in (6.10).

It should be noted that the functions $F=f+\Sigma \lambda_\gamma g_\gamma$ appearing in Theorem 2.1 of this chapter and in Theorems 2.1, 3.1, and 3.2 of Chapter 3 are lower support functions of this type. In general, the support functions we shall encounter are constructed with the help of the Lagrange multiplier rule.

Lower support functions are associated with minima. The corresponding function F for a maximum point x_0 of f on S will be called an *upper support function F*. It is defined by the relations

$$F(x) \geqslant f(x) \quad \text{on } S, \qquad F(x_0) = f(x_0), \qquad \nabla F(x_0) = 0.$$

In this event the function $G = f - F$ has the properties

$$G(x) \leqslant 0 \quad \text{on } S, \qquad G(x_0) = 0, \qquad G'(x_0, h) = f'(x_0, h) \leqslant 0$$

for tangent vectors h of S at x_0. As before, we shall normally restrict ourselves to the consideration of minimum points and leave to the reader the translation of the results to maximum points.

The following theorem gives some indication of the usefulness of the concept of a support function. In this theorem we assume that f is twice differentiable at $x = x_0$.

THEOREM 6.4

Let x_0 be a point in S, and suppose that there is a vector $h \neq 0$ in the tangent space $\mathcal{H}$ of S at x_0 such that

$$f'(x_0, h) = 0. \tag{6.11}$$

Suppose further that for each vector $h \neq 0$ in $\mathcal{H}$ satisfying relation (6.11) there is a lower support function F such that

$$F''(x_0, h) > 0. \tag{6.12}$$

Then there are a neighborhood N of x_0 and a constant $m > 0$ such that the inequality

$$f(x) \geqslant f(x) + m|x - x_0|^2 \tag{6.13}$$

holds for x in $N \cap S$.

Observe that we do not require F to be the same for every $h \neq 0$ in $\mathcal{H}$ satisfying equations (6.11). In most applications F can be chosen to be independent of h.

As a first step in the proof of this result, observe that the inequality

$$f'(x_0, h) \geqslant 0 \tag{6.14}$$

holds for all h in $\mathcal{H}$. This follows from (6.10) and the existence of a lower support function F. As a next step we assume that the conclusion in the theorem is false. Then there exists for every integer q a point x_q in S such that

$$t_q = |x_q - x_0| < \frac{1}{q}, \qquad f(x_q) - f(x_0) < \frac{t_q^2}{q}. \qquad (6.15)$$

These inequalities imply that $t_q > 0$. Since we can replace our original sequence $\{x_q\}$ by any one of its subsequences without violating inequality (6.15), we can suppose, by Lemma 4.1, that the sequence $\{x_q\}$ has been chosen so that the sequence

$$h_q = \frac{x_q - x_0}{t_q} \qquad (q = 1, 2, 3, \dots)$$

of unit vectors converges to a vector h. Clearly h is a unit vector in the tangent space $\mathcal{H}$ of S at x_0. By virtue of (6.15) we have

$$\frac{f(x_q) - f(x_0)}{t_q} < \frac{t_q}{q} < \frac{1}{q^2}$$

and hence also

$$f'(x_0, h) = \lim_{q \to \infty} \frac{f(x_q) - f(x_0)}{t_q} \leqslant 0.$$

Combining this result with (6.14), we find that $f'(x_0, h) = 0$.

We next select a lower support function F of f at x_0 such that (6.12) holds for the unit vector h just obtained. We have the relations

$$f(x) = F(x) + G(x), \qquad f(x_0) = F(x_0), \qquad \nabla F(x_0) = 0,$$

where $G(x) = f(x) - F(x) \geqslant 0$ on S. Using these functions, we obtain from (6.15) the inequality

$$\frac{F(x_q) - F(x_0)}{t_q^2} + \frac{G(x_q)}{t_q^2} < \frac{1}{q}.$$

Since $G(x_q) \geqslant 0$ and $\nabla F(x_0) = 0$, these relations imply that

$$\lim_{q \to \infty} \frac{F(x_q) - F(x_0)}{t_q^2} = \tfrac{1}{2} F''(x_0, h) \leqslant 0,$$

contrary to inequality (6.12). This proves Theorem 6.4.

As a partial converse to the last theorem we have

THEOREM 6.5

Let x_0 *be a point of* S, *and suppose there is a lower support function* F *of* f *such that* $F(x) = f(x)$ *on* S. *If* x_0 *affords a local mimimum to* f *on* S, *then*

$$F''(x_0, h) \geqslant 0 \qquad\qquad (6.16)$$

holds for every tangent vector h *of* S *at* x_0.

Let h be a tangent vector of S at x_0, and let $\{x_q\}$ be a sequence in S converging to x_0 in the direction h. Let $\{t_q\}$ be a sequence of positive numbers such that

$$t_q \to 0, \qquad \frac{x_q - x_0}{t_q} \to h \qquad \text{as } q \to \infty.$$

Since $\nabla F(x_0) = 0$ and $F(x_q) - F(x_0) = f(x_q) - f(x_0) \geqslant 0$, it follows, by (5.3), that

$$\lim_{q \to \infty} \frac{F(x_q) - F(x_0)}{t_q^2} = \tfrac{1}{2} F''(x_0, h) \geqslant 0,$$

as was to be proved.

EXERCISES

1. Suppose that x_0 minimizes a function f of class C' on S. Show that $f'(x_0, h) \geqslant 0$ for all h in the closure of the convex cone $\hat{\mathfrak{K}}$ generated by tangent space $\mathfrak{K}$ of S at x_0. The cone $\hat{\mathfrak{K}}$ consists of all vectors h expressible in the form $h = a_1 h_1 + \cdots + a_N h_N$, where $a_j \geqslant 0$ and h_j is in $\mathfrak{K}$ for $j = 1, \ldots, N$.

2. Show that, if S is convex and x_0 minimizes f on S, then $F(x) = f(x) - f'(x_0, x - x_0)$ is a lower support function for f on S at x_0. Show further that, if f is convex on S, then x_0 minimizes F on S. The function F appears in a modified form in the theory of convex functions.

3. Suppose that x_0 minimizes f on S. Suppose further that for each x in S the vector $h = x - x_0$ is in the closure of the cone $\mathcal{K}$ described in Exercise 1. Show that $F(x) = f(x) - f'(x_0, x - x_0)$ is a lower support function for f on S at x_0.

4. Show that, if x_0 is not an isolated point of S, there is a nonzero tangent h of S at x_0.

7. MINIMA SUBJECT TO NONLINEAR CONSTRAINTS

We now turn our attention to the case in which the set S of points on which a function f is to be minimized is determined by constraints

$$g_\alpha(x) \leqslant 0 \quad (\alpha = 1, \ldots, p), \qquad g_\beta(x) = 0 \quad (\beta = p+1, \ldots, m), \qquad (7.1)$$

where $g_1, \ldots, g_m$ are, in general, nonlinear. If $p = 0$, we disregard statements involving g_α. Similarly, if $p = m$, we disregard statements regarding g_β. In this section we are concerned with the nature of these constraints in a neighborhood of a point x_0 in S. To this end we assume that the functions $f, g_1, \ldots, g_m$ are of class C' near x_0 when only first derivatives are involved and of class C'' near x_0 when second derivatives are used. Actually the essential results are valid if we merely assume differentiability at x_0. We tacitly assume that x_0 is not an isolated point of S.

We distinguish between active and inactive constraints in (7.1). A constraint $g_\alpha(x) \leqslant 0$ will be said to be *active* at x_0 if $g_\alpha(x_0) = 0$ and to be *inactive* if $g_\alpha(x_0) < 0$. An index α will be said to be *active* or *inactive* according as the constraint $g_\alpha(x) \leqslant 0$ is active or inactive. It will be convenient to consider the constraints $g_\beta(x) = 0$ ($\beta = p+1, \ldots, m$) as active constraints and the indices $p+1, \ldots, m$ as active indices. Let $\alpha_1, \ldots, \alpha_r$ be the active indices $\leqslant p$. We shall show that, if h is a tangent vector of S at x_0, then h satisfies the relations

$$g_\alpha'(x_0, h) = \langle \nabla g_\alpha(x_0), h \rangle \leqslant 0 \quad (\alpha = \alpha_1, \ldots, \alpha_r), \qquad (7.2\text{a})$$

$$g_\beta'(x_0, h) = \langle \nabla g_\beta(x_0), h \rangle = 0 \quad (\beta = p+1, \ldots, m). \qquad (7.2\text{b})$$

Accordingly we shall term constraints (7.2) on h as the *tangential constraints* at x_0. However, a vector h can satisfy tangential constraints (7.2) without being a tangent vector, as will be seen in Example 7.1. In view of this fact we shall say that constraints (7.1) are *regular* at x_0 if every solution h of tangential constraints (7.2) is a tangent vector h of S at x_0. We shall use the abbreviation "x_0 is a regular point of S" to signify that constraints (7.1) are regular at x_0. If the functions $g_\gamma(x)$ are linear (affine) functions of x, every point in S is a regular point of S. This follows from the fact that solutions of the tangential constraints are linear tangents of S at x_0.

To see that a tangent vector h of S at x_0 satisfies constraints (7.2), let $\{x_q\}$ be a sequence of points in S and $\{t_q\}$ be a sequence of positive numbers such that

$$t_q \to 0, \qquad \frac{x_q - x_0}{t_q} \to h \quad \text{as } q \to \infty.$$

Then

$$\lim_{q \to \infty} \frac{g_\gamma(x_q) - g_\gamma(x_0)}{t_q} = g_\gamma'(x_0, h).$$

If $\gamma > p$, then $g_\gamma(x_q) = g_\gamma(x_0) = 0$. In this event $g_\gamma'(x_0, h) = 0$. If γ is an active index $\leqslant p$, we have $g_\gamma(x_0) = 0$ and $g_\gamma(x_q) \leqslant 0$. Consequently $g_\gamma'(x_0, h) \leqslant 0$ if γ is active. It follows that h satisfies conditions (7.2), as was to be proved.

Incidentally from this result it follows that, if x_0 is not an isolated point of S, there is a vector $h \neq 0$ satisfying constraints (7.2). Consequently, if there is no vector $h \neq 0$ satisfying the tangential constraints, x_0 must be an isolated point of S.

Observe that, in our definition of regularity, sequential tangent vectors are used. If the definition of regularity is modified so as to require a solution h of tangential constraints (7.2) to be a curvilinear tangent vector, we obtain a modified regularity condition known as the *Kuhn-Tucker constraint qualification condition*. A sequential tangent vector of S at x_0 need not be a curvilinear tangent vector of S at x_0, as was seen in Exercises 7 and 8 of Section 4. In each of these cases the origin is a regular point of S which does not satisfy the Kuhn-Tucker constraint qualification condition. These cases, however, are exceptional. Usually we establish regularity by showing that the Kuhn-Tucker constraint qualification condition is satisfied.

LEMMA 7.1

If a point x_0 *in* S *is a regular point of* S, *then every outer normal* w *of* S *at* x_0 *is expressible in the form*

$$w = \lambda_1 \nabla g_1(x_0) + \cdots + \lambda_m \nabla g_m(x_0), \tag{7.3}$$

where $\lambda_1, \ldots, \lambda_p$ *are nonnnegative and* $\lambda_\alpha = 0$ *whenever* $g_\alpha(x_0) < 0$.

Recall that a vector w is an outer normal of S at x_0 if it is in dual cone $\mathcal{H}^*$ of the tangent cone $\mathcal{H}$ of S at x_0. By virtue of Theorem 3.4 we see that, if x_0 is a regular point of S, the vectors $\nabla g_\gamma(x_0)$ ($\gamma = 1, \ldots, m; \gamma$ active) and $-\nabla g_\beta(x_0)$ $(\beta = p+1, \ldots, m)$ generate the normal cone $\mathcal{K}^*$. By Theorem 3.4 a vector w is in $\mathcal{K}^*$ if and only if w is expressible in form (7.3). This proves Lemma 7.1.

EXAMPLE 7.1

Consider the set S in the xy-plane defined by the constraints

$$g_1(x,y) = -x^3 \leqslant 0, \qquad g_2(x,y) = -y^3 \leqslant 0.$$

The set S is the first quadrant in the xy-plane.
The tangent space $\mathcal{K}$ of S at $(x_0, y_0) = (0,0)$ consists of all vectors (h,k) having $h \geqslant 0$, $k \geqslant 0$. The inequalities

$$g_1'(x_0, y_0; h, k) = -3x_0^2 h \leqslant 0, \qquad g_2'(x_0, y_0; h, k) = -3y_0^2 k \leqslant 0$$

corresponding to (7.2) take the form

$$g_1'(0, 0; h, k) = 0, \qquad g_2'(0, 0; h, k) = 0.$$

These equations hold for all vectors (h,k). Consequently in this event equations (7.2) do not determine the tangent space $\mathcal{K}$ of S at (x_0, y_0). Observe, however, that if we had replaced the constraints given above the set

$$g_1(x,y) = -x \leqslant 0, \qquad g_2(x,y) = -y \leqslant 0,$$

the set S would be unaltered and x_0 would be a regular point of S in relation to the new set of constraints.

As will be seen below, the Lagrange multiplier rule holds at x_0 whenever the outer normals of S at x_0 are expressible in form (7.3). Accordingly we shall say that x_0 is a *quasiregular point of* S if the outer normals of S are generated in this manner. This is equivalent to the condition that the convex closure of the tangent space $\mathcal{K}$ of S at x_0 consists of the solutions h of tangential constraints (7.2).

Except in special cases it is difficult to test for regularity and quasiregularity. In Section 10 we shall describe certain types of "normality" conditions which imply regularity. In the meantime we shall impose regularity or quasiregularity conditions whenever these conditions play significant roles in our proofs. The following simple example shows that a quasiregular point of S need not be a regular point of S.

EXAMPLE 7.2

Let S be the set of points in the xy-plane satisfying the constraints $x \leqslant 0$, $x + y \leqslant 0$, $x^2 - y^2 = 0$. It consists of the two rays defined by the relations $x \leqslant 0$, $y = \pm x$. It is easily verified that the origin is a quasiregular point of S but fails to be a regular point of S.

One of the principal results of this section is given in

THEOREM 7.1

If x_0 *is a quasiregular minimum point of* S, *there exist multipliers* $\lambda_1, \ldots, \lambda_m$ *such that*

$$\lambda_\alpha \geqslant 0 \quad (\alpha = 1, \ldots, p) \quad \text{with } \lambda_\alpha = 0 \text{ if } g_\alpha(x_0) < 0, \quad (7.4a)$$

$$\nabla F(x_0) = 0, \quad \text{where } F = f + \lambda_1 g_1 + \cdots + \lambda_m g_m. \quad (7.4b)$$

By Theorem 6.1 the negative gradient $-\nabla f(x_0)$ is an outer normal of S at x_0. By quasiregularity the outer normal $w = -\nabla f(x_0)$ is expressible in the form

$$-\nabla f(x_0) = \lambda_1 \nabla g_1(x_0) + \cdots + \lambda_m \nabla g_m(x_0)$$

subject to relations (7.4a). This equation yields (7.4b).

Relations (7.4) constitute the first-order *Lagrange multiplier rule* for the problem here considered. The function F is called a *Lagrangian*, and the multipliers $\lambda_1, \ldots, \lambda_m$ are termed *Lagrange multipliers*. Observe that Lagrange multipliers are constrained by relations (7.4a). As remarked earlier, conditions (7.4) are also known as the *Kuhn-Tucker conditions*.

LEMMA 7.2

If the Lagrange multiplier rule (7.4) *holds at* x_0, *the Lagrangian* F *is a lower support function for* S *at* x_0 *in the sense that*

$$F(x) \leqslant f(x) \text{ on } S, \quad F(x_0) = f(x_0), \quad \nabla F(x_0) = 0. \quad (7.5)$$

Observe that, by (7.4a), we have $\lambda_\alpha = 0$ for inactive indices α. Consequently $F(x_0) = f(x_0)$. Since the sum $\Sigma_\alpha \lambda_\alpha g_\alpha(x)$ is nonpositive on S, it follows that $F(x) \leqslant f(x)$ on S. Consequently (7.5) holds. In view of relations (7.4b) and (7.5) it follows that F is a lower support function for f at x_0 in the sense described in Section 6.

LEMMA 7.3

The inequality

$$f'(x_0, h) = \langle \nabla f(x_0), h \rangle \geqslant 0 \tag{7.6}$$

holds for every solution h *of tangential constraints* (7.2) *if and only if* x_0 *satisfies the Lagrange multiplier rule* (7.4).

This result follows from Theorem 3.4.

LEMMA 7.4

Suppose that x_0 *satisfies the Lagrange multiplier rule* (7.4) *with a set of multipliers* $\lambda_1, \ldots, \lambda_m$. *Let* $\gamma_1, \ldots, \gamma_s$ *be the indices* $\gamma \leqslant p$ *such that* $\lambda_\gamma > 0$. *Then a vector* $h \neq 0$ *satisfying tangential constraints* (7.2) *has*

$$f'(x_0, h) = 0 \tag{7.7}$$

if and only if

$$g'_\gamma(x_0, h) = 0 \qquad (\gamma = \gamma_1, \ldots, \gamma_s). \tag{7.8}$$

This follows because, if $h \neq 0$ satisfies tangential constraints (7.2), condition (7.4b) yields the relation

$$0 = F'(x_0, h) = f'(x_0, h) + \sum_{\gamma = \gamma_1}^{\gamma_s} \lambda_\gamma g'_\gamma(x_0, h) = 0. \tag{7.9}$$

Consequently, if (7.8) holds, we have $f'(x_0, h) = 0$. Conversely, if $f'(x_0, h) = 0$, it follows from (7.9) and the relations $\lambda_\gamma > 0$, $g'_\gamma(x_0, h) \leqslant 0$ that (7.8) holds. This proves the lemma.

THEOREM 7.2

Suppose that x_0 *satisfies the Lagrange multiplier rule* (7.4). *Suppose further that there is no vector* $h \neq 0$ *satisfying tangential constraints* (7.2) *having*

$$f'(x_0, h) = 0.$$

Then x_0 *affords a strict local minimum to* f *on S.*

This result follows from Theorem 6.3 in view of the fact that by virtue of Lemma 7.2 our hypotheses imply that $f'(x_0, h) > 0$ for every vector $h \neq 0$ satisfying tangential constraints (7.2) and hence for every tangent vector $h \neq 0$ of S at x_0.

In the following theorem we assume that f and $g_1, \ldots, g_m$ are twice differentiable at x_0.

THEOREM 7.3

Let x_0 *be a point of* S, *and suppose that there is a vector* $h \neq 0$ *satisfying tangential constraints* (7.2) *such that*

$$f'(x_0, h) = 0. \tag{7.10}$$

Suppose that for each vector $h \neq 0$ *of this type there is a Lagrange function* F *defined by* (7.4) *such that*

$$F''(x_0, h) > 0.$$

Then there are a neighborhood N *of* x_0 *and a constant* $m > 0$ *such that the inequality*

$$f(x) \geqslant f(x_0) + m|x - x_0|^2$$

holds for all x *in* N *belonging to* S.

This result is an immediate consequence of Theorem 6.4, since every Lagrange function F defined by (7.4) is a lower support function of f at x_0.

The results given in Theorems 7.2 and 7.3 can be combined with Lemma 7.4 to give

THEOREM 7.4

Suppose that there exists a set of multipliers $\lambda_1, \ldots, \lambda_m$ *such that*

$$\lambda_\alpha \geqslant 0 \qquad (1 \leqslant \alpha \leqslant p, \text{ with } \lambda_\alpha = 0 \text{ if } g_\alpha(x_0) < 0),$$

$$\nabla F(x_0) = 0, \qquad \text{where } F = f + \lambda_1 g_1 + \cdots + \lambda_m g_m, \tag{7.11}$$

and such that

$$F''(x_0, h) > 0 \tag{7.12}$$

for all $h \neq 0$ *satisfying the modified tangential constraints*

$$g'_\alpha(x_0, h) \leqslant 0 \text{ if } 1 \leqslant \alpha \leqslant p, g_\alpha(x_0) = 0, \text{ and } \lambda_\alpha = 0,$$

$$g'_\alpha(x_0, h) = 0 \text{ if } 1 \leqslant \alpha \leqslant p, g_\alpha(x_0) = 0, \text{ and } \lambda_\alpha > 0, \tag{7.13}$$

$$g'_\beta(x_0, h) = 0 \text{ if } p < \beta \leqslant m.$$

Then there are a neighborhood N *of* x_0 *and a constant* m > 0 *such that*

$$f(x) \geqslant f(x_0) + m|x - x_0|^2$$

for all points x *in* S$\cap$N. *The function* F *is a lower support function for* F *at* x_0 *on* S.

If there is a vector $h \neq 0$ satisfying the tangential constraints such that $f'(x_0, h) = 0$, the conclusion follows from Theorem 7.3. Otherwise we have $f'(x_0, h) > 0$ for all solutions $h \neq 0$ satisfying the tangential constraints. In this event there are by Theorem 6.3 a number $\hat{m} > 0$ and a neighborhood N of x_0 such that

$$f(x) - f(x_0) \geqslant \hat{m}|x - x_0|$$

on $S \cap N$. Selecting $m > 0$ such that $\hat{m}|x - x_0| \geqslant m|x - x_0|^2$ on N, we obtain the desired result.

Theorems 7.3 and 7.4 give sufficient conditions for a local minimum at x_0. We now give a second-order necessary condition for a local minimum of f at x_0.

THEOREM 7.5

Let x_0 *be a minimum point of* f *satisfying the Lagrange multiplier rule* (7.11) *with a Lagrangian* $F = f + \lambda_1 g_1 + \cdots + \lambda_m g_m$. *Let* S_1 *be the subset of all points* x *in* S *having* f(x) = F(x). *Then* S_1 *is defined by the constraints*

$$g_\alpha(x) \leqslant 0 \quad \text{if } \lambda_\alpha = 0, \qquad g_\alpha(x) = 0 \quad \text{if } \lambda_\alpha > 0,$$

$$g_\beta(x) = 0 \quad (\beta = p + 1 \cdots m). \tag{7.14}$$

If x_0 *is a regular point of* S_1, *then the inequality*

$$F''(x_0, h) \geqslant 0 \tag{7.15}$$

holds for all vectors h *satisfying tangential constraints* (7.13) *for* S_1 *at* x_0.

Observe that on S we have

$$F(x) - f(x) = \lambda_{\alpha_1} g_{\alpha_1}(x) + \cdots + \lambda_{\alpha_s} g_{\alpha_s}(x)$$

where $\alpha_1, \ldots, \alpha_s$ are the indices $\alpha \leqslant p$ such that $\lambda_\alpha > 0$. Since $g_\alpha(x) \leqslant 0$ on S, it follows that $f(x) = F(x)$ at a point x in S if and only if x satisfies conditions (7.14). Relations (7.13) are accordingly the tangential constraints for S_1. If x_0 is a regular point of S_1, the tangent space $\mathcal{K}_1$ of S_1 at

x_0 constitutes the solutions h of (7.13). Since $f(x) = F(x)$ on S_1 the point x_0 minimizes $F(x)$ on S_1. Since $\nabla F(x_0) = 0$, we have $F''(x_0, h) \geqslant 0$ for all h in $\mathcal{H}_1$, by Theorem 6.5, as was to be proved.

EXAMPLE 7.3

The point $(x_0, y_0) = (2, 0)$ in the xy-plane minimizes the function $f(x,y) = x + y^2$ on the set S determined by the concave constraints

$$g_1(x,y) = 4 - x^2 - y^2 \leqslant 0, \qquad g_2(x,y) = -x \leqslant 0,$$

$$g_3(x,y) = -6 + 7x - 2x^2 - 2y^2 \leqslant 0.$$

The set S is the shaded portion shown in Figure 7.1. Observe that the constraint $g_3(x,y) \leqslant 0$ plays no role in determining S. However, the index $\alpha = 3$ is an active index at the point $(x_0, y_0) = (2, 0)$. So also is the index $\alpha = 1$. The index $\alpha = 2$, however, is inactive. A vector (h, k) is tangent to S at $(2, 0)$ if and only if $h \geqslant 0$. The tangent vectors (h, k) of S at $(2, 0)$ accordingly are determined by the tangential constraints

$$g_1'(2, 0; h, k) = -4h \leqslant 0, \qquad g_3'(2, 0; h, k) = -h \leqslant 0.$$

Consequently x_0 is a regular point of S, and the Lagrange multiplier rule (7.4) holds at x_0 with nonnegative multipliers $\lambda_1, \lambda_2, \lambda_3$. Since $\alpha = 2$ is inactive, we have $\lambda_2 = 0$. The case $\lambda_1 = \lambda_3 = 0$ is impossible. Accordingly we can suppose that $\lambda_1 \geqslant 0$, $\lambda_2 = 0$, $\lambda_3 \geqslant 0$, $4\lambda_1 + \lambda_3 = 1$. Then the Lagrangian F

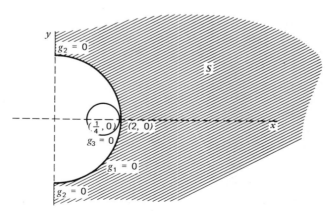

Figure 7.1

takes the form

$$F(x,y)=f(x,y)+\lambda_1 g_1(x,y)+\lambda_3 g_3(x,y)$$
$$=6\lambda_3+(1+7\lambda_3)x-(\lambda_1+2\lambda_3)x^2+(1-\lambda_1-2\lambda_3)y^2.$$

We have $\nabla F(2,0)=0$. Moreover

$$F''(2,0;h,k)=-2(\lambda_1+2\lambda_3)h^2+2(1-\lambda_1-2\lambda_3)k^2.$$

If $\lambda_1=0$, $\lambda_3=1$, constraints (7.13) take the form

$$g_1'(2,0;h,k)=-4h\leq 0, \qquad g_3'(2,0;h,k)=-h=0.$$

Hence $h=0$ and

$$F''(2,0;0,k)=-2k^2<0$$

if $k\neq 0$. The conclusion in Theorem 7.5 is therefore invalid for the case $\lambda_1=\lambda_2=0$, $\lambda_3=1$. However, if we choose $\lambda_1=\frac{1}{4}$, $\lambda_2=0$, $\lambda_3=0$, conditions (7.13) again imply that $h=0$ and $F''(2,0;h,k)=\frac{3}{2}k^2>0$ if $k\neq 0$. For this choice the conclusion in Theorem 7.5 is valid. Compare this result with that given in Theorem 10.4 in Chapter 6.

EXERCISES

In these exercises x_0 is a point in the set S defined by constraints (7.1). We assume that there is a least one active index $\leq p$.

1. Let $\mathcal{H}$ be the class of vectors h satisfying tangential constraints (7.2). Let $\hat{\mathcal{H}}$ be a dense set in $\mathcal{H}$, that is, a set whose closure is $\mathcal{H}$. Show that, if every vector h in $\hat{\mathcal{H}}$ is a tangent vector of S at x_0, then x_0 is a regular point of S. *Hint:* Use the fact that the tangent cone is closed.

2. Suppose that $p=m$ so that there are no equality constraints. Show that, if $\hat{h}$ is a vector such that $g_\alpha'(x_0,\hat{h})<0$ for every active index α at x_0, then $\hat{h}$ is a linear tangent of S at x_0. Show that, if there exists a vector $\hat{h}$ of this type, x_0 is a regular point of S. *Hint:* Show that, if $g_\alpha'(x_0,h)\leq 0$ (α active), then for $t>0$ we have $g_\alpha'(x_0,h+t\hat{h})<0$. Apply Exercise 1.

3. Suppose that $p=m$ and that for each active index α there is a vector h_α such that $g_\alpha'(x_0,h_\alpha)<0$, $g_\gamma'(x_0,h_\alpha)\leq 0$ (γ active, $\gamma\neq\alpha$). Show that x_0 is a regular point of S. *Hint:* Choose $h=\Sigma_\alpha h_\alpha$ (α active) in Exercise 2.

4. Suppose that $p=m$ and that the functions $g_1,\ldots,g_p$ are convex. Show that, if none of the functions $g_1,\ldots,g_p$ is identically zero on S, then x_0 is a regular point of S. *Hint:* If x is in S, $g_\alpha(x)<0$, and $g_\alpha(x_0)=0$, show by convexity that $0>g_\alpha(x)>g_\alpha'(x_0,x-x_0)$. Take $h_\alpha=x-x_0$ in Exercise 3.

5. Extend the results given in Exercises 2, 3, and 4 to the case in which the functions g_β ($\beta = p+1, \ldots, m$) are linear (affine) functions of x.

6. Suppose that the functions $f, g_1, \ldots, g_m$ are convex and that $g_{p+1}, \ldots, g_m$ are linear. Suppose that none of the functions $g_1, \ldots, g_p$ is identically zero on S. Show that x_0 minimizes f on S if and only if there exist multipliers $\lambda_1, \ldots, \lambda_m$ such that $\lambda_1, \ldots, \lambda_p$ are nonnegative with $\lambda_\alpha = 0$ if $g_\alpha(x_0) < 0$, and such that x_0 minimizes $F = f + \lambda_1 g_1 + \cdots + \lambda_m g_m$ without constraints.

7. Suppose that $p = m$ and that $g_1, \ldots, g_p$ are convex. Show that, if there exist nonnegative multipliers $\lambda_1, \ldots, \lambda_p$, not all zero, such that $\lambda_\alpha = 0$ if $g_\alpha(x_0) < 0$, and such that $\lambda_1 \nabla g_1(x_0) + \cdots + \lambda_p \nabla g_p(x_0) = 0$, then at least one of the functions $g_1, \ldots, g_p$ is identically zero on S.

8. Find the smallest circle in the xy-plane that encloses the points $(a, 0)$, $(-a, 0)$, (b, c), where $a > 0$, $c > 0$. Hint: Minimize z subject to the constraints $(x - a)^2 + y^2 - z \leq 0$, $(x + a)^2 + y^2 - z \leq 0$, $(x - b)^2 + (y - c)^2 - z \leq 0$. Show that the minimum point (x_0, y_0, z_0) has $x_0 = 0$, $y_0 = cd$, and $z_0 = a^2 + c^2 d^2$, where $2c^2 d = c^2 + b^2 - a^2$. What are the values of the Lagrange multipliers? Is the Lagrangian F minimized by the point (x_0, y_0, z_0)?

9. Find the smallest sphere in $\mathcal{E}^n$ which encloses a given set of distinct points $y_1, \ldots, y_p$, that is, minimize z subject to the constraints $|x - y_\alpha|^2 - z \leq 0$ ($\alpha = 1, \ldots, p$). Why does a solution (x_0, z_0) exist? Establish the relations $x_0 = \Sigma \lambda_\alpha y_\alpha$, $z_0 = \Sigma \lambda_\alpha |y_\alpha|^2 - |x_0|^2$, $\Sigma \lambda_\alpha = 1$, where $\lambda_1, \ldots, \lambda_p$ are the Lagrange multipliers. Show that the Lagrangian can be put into the form $F(x) = |x - x_0|^2 + z_0$. Is the solution unique? Are the multipliers unique? Can one expect to have inactive constraints? Carry out some special cases in detail.

10. Let $f(x) = S_2 S_4 - S_3^2$, where S_k is the sum of the kth powers of the components of x. Determine the global and local maximum points of f on the unit cube $0 \leq x^i \leq 1$ ($i = 1, \ldots, n$). See P. Wolfe, "Explicit Solution of an Optimization Problem," *Mathematical Programming*, Vol. 2 (1972), 258–260.

8. CONCAVE AND LINEAR CONSTRAINTS

One of the significant special cases of the general problem considered in Section 7 is the problem of minimizing a function f on the set S defined by constraints of the form

$$g_\alpha(x) \leq 0 \qquad (\alpha = 1, \ldots, p), \tag{8.1}$$

where the functions $g_1, \ldots, g_p$ are concave. Since linear functions are concave, this contains the important case in which the functions $g_1, \ldots, g_p$ are linear. It also contains the case in which the set S is defined by relations of the form

$$g_\alpha(x) \leq 0 \quad (\alpha = 1, \ldots, p), \qquad g_\beta(x) = 0 \quad (\beta = p+1, \ldots, m), \tag{8.2}$$

in which $g_1, \ldots, g_p$ are concave and $g_{p+1}, \ldots, g_m$ are linear. This follows because constraints (8.2) are equivalent to the concave inequality constraints,

$$g_\alpha(x) \leqslant 0, \qquad g_\beta(x) \leqslant 0, \qquad -g_\beta(x) \leqslant 0 \qquad (\alpha = 1, \ldots, p; \beta = p+1, \ldots, m).$$

$$(8.3)$$

Let x_0 be a point in the set S defined by concave constraints of form (8.1). The tangential constraints for S at x_0 are given by the inequalities

$$g_\alpha'(x_0, h) = \langle \nabla g_\alpha(x_0), h \rangle \leqslant 0 \qquad (\alpha = \alpha_1, \ldots, \alpha_r), \qquad (8.4)$$

where $\alpha_1, \ldots, \alpha_r$ are the active indices at x_0. In the next lemma it will be shown that every solution h of tangential constraints (8.4) is a linear tangent vector of S at x_0. Consequently x_0 is a regular point of S whenever the functions $g_1, \ldots, g_p$ are concave. We assume, of course, that the functions $f, g_1, \ldots, g_p$ have the usual continuity and differentiability properties.

LEMMA 8.1

Let $\alpha_1, \ldots, \alpha_r$ be the active indices at a point x_0 in S. Given a vector $h \neq 0$ satisfying tangential constraints (8.4) for S at x_0, there is a constant $\delta > 0$ such that the line segment $x_0 + th (0 \leqslant t \leqslant \delta)$ is in S.

Let $h \neq 0$ satisfy tangential constraints (8.4). Consider the functions

$$\phi_\alpha(t) = g_\alpha(x_0 + th) \qquad (0 \leqslant t \leqslant \delta),$$

where δ is so small that $x_0 + th$ is in the domain of g_α. If $g_\alpha(x_0) < 0$, we can select δ so small that $\phi_\alpha(t) \leqslant 0$ on the interval $0 \leqslant t \leqslant \delta$. If α is one of the active indices $\alpha_1, \ldots, \alpha_r$, then $\phi_\alpha(t)$ is a concave function of t on $0 \leqslant t \leqslant \delta$. Since

$$\phi_\alpha'(0) = g_\alpha'(x_0, h) \leqslant 0,$$

the function $\phi_\alpha(t)$ has a maximum value at $t = 0$. Hence on $0 \leqslant t \leqslant \delta$ we have

$$\phi_\alpha(t) = g_\alpha(x_0 + th) \leqslant \phi_\alpha(0) = 0 \qquad (\alpha = \alpha_1, \ldots, \alpha_r).$$

This proves the lemma.

COROLLARY

If S *is the set of points defined by constraints of form* (8.2), *if the functions* $g_1, \ldots, g_p$ *are concave, and if the functions* $g_{p+1}, \ldots, g_m$ *are linear, then a point* x_0 *in* S *is a regular point of* S.

We summarize in the following theorems the results given earlier for the case considered here.

THEOREM 8.1

Suppose that a point x_0 *affords a local minimum to* f *on the set* S *defined by concave constraints* (8.1). *Then the inequality*

$$f'(x_0, h) = \langle \nabla f(x_0), h \rangle \geq 0 \qquad (8.5)$$

holds for all solutions h *of tangential constraints* (8.4). *Equivalently, the negative gradient* $- \nabla f(x_0)$ *is an outer normal of* S *at* x_0. *Equivalently, there exist nonnegative multipliers* $\lambda_1, \ldots, \lambda_p$ *such that the Lagrange function*

$$F = f + \lambda_1 g_1 + \cdots \lambda_p g_p \qquad (8.6a)$$

has

$$\nabla F(x_0) = 0, \qquad F(x_0) = f(x_0), \qquad \lambda_\alpha \geq 0 \qquad (\alpha = 1, \ldots, p). \qquad (8.6b)$$

This result follows from Theorem 7.1 in view of the fact that x_0 is a regular point of S, as was proved in Lemma 8.1. Observe that the condition $F(x_0) = f(x_0)$ implies that

$$\lambda_1 g_1(x_0) + \lambda_2 g_2(x_0) + \cdots + \lambda_p g_p(x_0) = 0.$$

Since $\lambda_\alpha \geq 0$ and $g_\alpha(x_0) \leq 0$, we have $\lambda_\alpha = 0$ whenever $g_\alpha(x_0) < 0$, as stated in (7.4a).

THEOREM 8.2

If the constraints in (8.1) *are linear and if* f *is convex on the set* S, *then the point* x_0 *in* S *minimizes* f *on* S *if and only if the conditions described in Theorem* 8.1 *hold at* x_0.

This result follows from Theorems 6.2 and 8.1. Using Theorem 6.3, together with the fact that a point x_0 in S is a regular point of S, we obtain

THEOREM 8.3

If the inequality

$$f'(x_0, h) > 0$$

holds for all solutions $h \neq 0$ *of tangential constraints* (8.4), *then* x_0 *affords a proper local minimum to* f *on* S.

The conditions for a minimum involving second-order conditions are given in

THEOREM 8.4

If x_0 *affords a local minimum on* S, *then*

$$f''(x_0, h) \geqslant 0$$

holds for every solution h *of tangential constraints* (8.4) *orthogonal to* $\nabla f(x_0)$. *Conversely, if constraints* (8.1) *are linear, then a point* x_0 *in* S *affords a strict local minimum to* f *on* S *if* $-\nabla f(x_0)$ *is an outer normal of* S *at* x_0 *and* $f''(x_0, h) > 0$ *for every solution* $h \neq 0$ *of tangential constraints* (8.4) *that is orthogonal to* $\nabla f(x_0)$.

Let h be a solution of tangential constraints (8.4) that is orthogonal to $\nabla f(x_0)$. By Lemma 8.1 there is a constant δ such that the line segment $x_0 + th$ $(0 \leqslant t \leqslant \delta)$ is in S. If x_0 affords a local minimum to f on S, then $t = 0$ affords a local minimum to the function

$$\phi(t) = f(x_0 + th)$$

on $0 \leqslant t \leqslant \delta$. Since $\phi(0) = f'(x_0, h) = \langle \nabla f(x_0, h \rangle = 0$, we have

$$\phi(0) = f''(x_0, h) \geqslant 0,$$

as was to be proved.

Conversely suppose that constraints (8.1) are linear. If $-\nabla f(x_0)$ is an outer normal, x_0 has associated with it a Lagrange function F such that (8.6) holds. Since the functions g_α are linear, we have $F''(x_0, h) = f''(x_0, h)$. Using this result, we find that the last statement in Theorem 8.4 follows from Theorem 7.4.

The last conclusion fails to hold, however, if constraints (8.1) are concave but not linear, as can be seen in

EXAMPLE 8.1

Let S be the set of points in the xy-plane determined by the constraints

$$g_1(x,y) = -6 + 7x - 2x^2 - 2y^2 \leqslant 0, \qquad g_2(x,y) = -x \leqslant 0.$$

At the point $(x_0, y_0) = (2,0)$ we have $g_1(2,0) = 0$, $g_2(2,0) = -2$. Hence $\alpha = 1$ is an active index and $\alpha = 2$ is inactive. Since these constraints are concave, a vector (h,k) is a tangent vector to S at (x_0,y_0) if and only if

$$g_1(2,0;h,k) = -h \leqslant 0.$$

The function $f(x,y) = x + y^2$ has $\nabla f = (1,0)$ as its gradient at $(x_0,y_0) = (2,0)$. It follows that $-\nabla f = (-1,0)$ is an outer normal. If $k \neq 0$, the vector $(0,k)$ is a tangent vector of S at $(2,0)$ that is orthogonal to $\nabla f = (1,0)$ and has

$$f''(2,0;0,k) = 2k^2 > 0.$$

However, the point $(2,0)$ fails to afford a local minimum to f on S as can readily be verified.

EXERCISES

In the two-dimensional case set $g(x,y,a) = 2ax - x^2 - y^2$. In Exercices 1 to 8 sketch the set S determined by the given constraints. Verify that in each case the origin is a regular point of S and that the tangent vectors of S at the origin are linear tangent vectors. Is Lemma 8.1 applicable in every case?

1. $g(x,y,1) \leqslant 0$.
2. $g(x,y,1) \leqslant 0$, $g(x,y,-1) \leqslant 0$.
3. $g(x,y,1) \leqslant 0$, $g(x,y,2) \leqslant 0$, $g(x,y,-1) \leqslant 0$, $g(x,y,-2) \leqslant 0$.
4. $g(x,y,1) \leqslant 0$, $g(x,y,-1) \leqslant 0$, $g(y,x,-1) \leqslant 0$.
5. $g(x,y,1) \leqslant 0$, $g(y,x,-1) \leqslant 0$.
6. $g(x,y,1) \leqslant 0$, $g(y,x,-1) \leqslant 0$, $x^2 - y \leqslant 0$.
7. $x^2 - y^2 \leqslant 0$.
8. $x^2 - y^2 \leqslant 0$, $-y \leqslant 0$.
9. Discuss the case in which the functions $g_1, \ldots, g_m$ are linear and f is quadratic. The study of problems of this type is called *quadratic programming*. An elegant algorithm for solving quadratic programming problems has been given by P. Wolfe, "The Simplex Method for Quadratic Programming," *Econometrica*, Vol. 27 (1959), 382–397.

9. LINEAR PROGRAMMING

Linear programming is a very important branch of optimization theory. A large class of significant problems in economics and engineering can be formulated as linear programming problems or can be approximated by such problems. An important feature of linear programming is its numerical solvability even when the number of variables is very large. As in all numerical procedures, considerable skill is needed to master the numerical difficulties that arise from nearly singular systems. There are many excellent books concerned with linear programming and with the associated theory of games. The most comprehensible treatise on this subject is the book by George Dantzig,[†] who is largely responsible for the development of this field. The list of contributors to the linear programming field is very long. An account of the earlier contributions can be found in Dantzig's book. Here we shall limit ourselves to a brief description of certain relationships that exist between linear programming and the general nonlinear problem which is our main concern.

Throughout this section matrix notations will be used. Let A be an $(m \times n)$-dimensional matrix. The vectors x, x_0, c will denote n-dimensional column vectors; the vectors y, y_0, b, m-dimensional column vectors. The corresponding row vectors are their transposes, $x^*, x_0^*, c^*, y^*, y_0^*, b^*$. Similarly the symbol $x \geqslant 0$ signifies that each component of x is nonnegative. If each component of x is positive, we write $x > 0$. The inequality $Ax \leqslant b$ signifies that $b - Ax \geqslant 0$.

A standard linear programming problem is that of maximizing a linear function c^*x on the set of points $x \geqslant 0$ satisfying constraints of the form $Ax \leqslant b$. This problem is abbreviated as follows:

$$c^*x = \max \text{ subject to } Ax \leqslant b \text{ and } x \geqslant 0. \tag{9.1}$$

A corresponding minimum problem is

$$b^*y = \min \text{ subject to } A^*y \geqslant c \text{ and } y \geqslant 0. \tag{9.2}$$

These problems are said to be *duals* of each other. It is customary to call one of these problems the *primal problem* and the other the *dual problem*. We shall consider problem (9.1) to be the primal one and problem (9.2) to be the dual.

The set S, defined by the constraints $Ax \leqslant b$, $x \geqslant 0$, is the intersection of half spaces. Accordingly the set S, if not empty, is a convex polyhedron. A point x in S is called a *feasible solution* for the primal problem (9.1). A point x_0 in S that maximizes c^*x on S is called an *optimum solution*. Similar terminology is used for the dual problem (9.2).

In view of Theorem 8.2 we find that a point x_0 satisfying the relations

$$Ax_0 \leqslant b, \qquad x_0 \geqslant 0 \tag{9.3}$$

is an optimum solution of the primal problem (9.1) if and only if it satisfies the Lagrange multiplier rule (8.6) for the problem of minimizing $f(x) = -c^*x$ subject to the constraints

$$Ax - b \leqslant 0, \qquad -x \leqslant 0.$$

[†]George B. Dantzig, *Linear Programming and Extensions*, Princeton University Press, Princeton, N.J., 1963.

The multiplier rule (8.6) for this problem requires the existence of an m-vector y_0 and an n-vector z_0 such that

$$y_0 \geqslant 0, \qquad z_0 \geqslant 0, \qquad y_0^*(Ax_0 - b) = 0, \qquad z_0^* x_0 = 0, \qquad (9.4a)$$

$$-c + A^* y_0 = z_0. \qquad (9.4b)$$

Conditions (9.4) are equivalent to conditions (8.6b) for our problem. Condition (9.4b) states that the gradient with respect to x of the function

$$-c^* x + y_0^*(Ax - b) + z_0^*(-x)$$

must vanish at x_0. This is the condition, $\nabla F(x_0) = 0$, in the multiplier rule (8.6). Eliminating the variable z_0 in equations (9.4), we see that conditions (9.3) and (9.4) are equivalent to the relations

$$x_0 \geqslant 0, \qquad y_0 \geqslant 0, \qquad Ax_0 \leqslant b, \qquad A^* y_0 \geqslant c, \qquad (9.5a)$$

$$b^* y_0 = y_0^* A x_0 = c^* x_0. \qquad (9.5b)$$

Summing up these results, we see that:

An n-vector x_0 is an optimum solution to problem (9.1) if and only if there exists an m-vector y_0 with which it satisfies relations (9.5).

By symmetry it is seen that:

An m-vector y_0 is an optimum solution to problem (9.2) if and only if there is an n-vector x_0 with which it satisfies relations (9.5).

In view of (9.5b) the optimum (maximum) value of $c^* x$ in problem (9.1) is the same as the optimum (minimum) value of $b^* y$ in problem (9.2).

These results can be summarized as follows.

If either of problems (9.1) and (9.2) admits an optimum solution, so does the other and the optimum value is the same in each case. These problems admit optimum solutions if and only if relations (9.5) possess a solution (x_0, y_0).

EXERCISES

1. Show that, if a feasible solution exists for primal problem (9.1) and the criterion function $c^* x$ is bounded from above on the class of feasible solutions, then an optimum solution x_0 exists for the primal problem.
2. Show that, if the primal and dual problems have feasible solutions x and y, then $c^* x \leqslant y^* A x \leqslant b^* y$. Show that in this event the primal and dual problems have optimum solutions x_0 and y_0.
3. Show that, if the dual problem has no feasible solution, either there is no feasible solution for the primal problem or else there is a sequence $\{x_q\}$ of feasible solutions for the primal problem such that $\lim_{q \to \infty} c^* x_q = \infty$.

4. Show that the set of optimum solutions of the primal problem, if not empty, is a convex polyhedron.

5. State the analogous results for the dual problem.

6. What is meant by a vertex or an extreme point of a convex polyhedron? Show that an optimum solution of a linear programming problem, if it exists, can be found in the class of vertices of the convex polyhedron defined by the feasible solutions.

10. CRITERIA FOR REGULARITY

We return now to the problem considered in Section 7, in which the set S under consideration is defined by constraints of the form

$$g_\alpha(x) \leqslant 0, \qquad g_\beta(x) = 0 \qquad (\alpha = 1,\ldots,p; \ \beta = p+1,\ldots,m). \quad (10.1)$$

Let x_0 be a point in S. Since inactive constraints at x_0 remain inactive on a neighborhood of x_0, they play no role in the determination of the tangent and outer normal cones of S at x_0. Accordingly we shall assume that all constraints are active at x_0. We then have $g_\gamma(x_0)=0$ $(\gamma = 1,\ldots,m)$ and the tangential constraints for S at x_0 take the form

$$g'_\alpha(x_0,h) \leqslant 0, \qquad g'_\beta(x_0,h) = 0 \qquad (\alpha = 1,\ldots,p; \ \beta = p+1,\ldots,m). \quad (10.2)$$

As was seen in Section 7, every tangent vector h of S at x_0 satisfies these constraints. If the converse is true, we said that *constraints* (10.1) *were regular* at x_0 or, briefly, that x_0 was a *regular point* of S.

Let $\mathcal{H}$ be the class of all vectors h satisfying tangential constraints (10.2). The class $\mathcal{H}$ is a closed convex cone. Its dual cone $\mathcal{H}^*$ is composed of all vectors h^* expressible in the form

$$h^* = \sum_{\gamma=1}^{m} \lambda_\gamma \nabla g_\gamma(x_0), \qquad \lambda_\alpha \geqslant 0 \quad (\alpha = 1,\ldots,p). \quad (10.3)$$

As was seen in Section 7, the tangent cone of S at x_0 is a subcone of $\mathcal{H}$. The outer normal cone, being the dual of the tangent cone, therefore contains the dual cone $\mathcal{H}^*$ of $\mathcal{H}$. It follows that every vector h^* in $\mathcal{H}^*$ is an outer normal of S at x_0. Moreover in the regular case $\mathcal{H}$ is the tangent cone of S at x_0, and $\mathcal{H}^*$ is the outer normal cone of S at x_0.

An index γ will be called an *active index for a vector* h in $\mathcal{H}$ if $g'_\gamma(x_0,h)=0$. It is *inactive for* h if $g'_\gamma(x_0,h)<0$. The number r of indices that are inactive for some vector h in $\mathcal{H}$ will be called the h-inactivity *index* of S at x_0. Clearly $0 \leqslant r \leqslant p$. We can assume without loss of generality that the constraints have been indexed so that each of the indices $1,\ldots,r$ is inactive for some vector h in $\mathcal{H}$. We then have $g'_\sigma(x_0,h)=0$ $(\sigma > r)$ for all vectors h in $\mathcal{K}$. Tangential constraints (10.2) are then equivalent to the constraints

$$g'_\rho(x_0,h) \leqslant 0, \qquad g'_\sigma(x_0,h)=0 \qquad (\rho=1,\ldots,r;\ \sigma=r+1,\ldots,m) \quad (10.4)$$

with the obvious interpretation when $r=0$. Consequently a vector h^* in the dual cone $\mathcal{K}^*$ of $\mathcal{K}$ has the alternative representation

$$h^* = \sum_{\gamma=1}^m \lambda_\gamma \nabla g_\gamma(x_0), \qquad \lambda_\rho \geqslant 0 \quad (\rho=1,\ldots,r). \quad (10.5)$$

Relations (10.4) are the tangential constraints at x_0 associated with the set S_0 defined by the constraints

$$g_\rho(x) \leqslant 0, \qquad g_\sigma(x_0)=0 \qquad (\rho=1,\ldots,r;\ \sigma=r+1,\ldots,m). \quad (10.6)$$

It follows that, *if x_0 is a regular point of S_0, then x_0 is a regular point of S.* However, x_0 can be a regular point of S without being a regular point of S_0. For example, in the one-dimensional case the constraint $-x^2 \leqslant 0$ is regular at $x=0$ whereas the constraint $-x^2=0$ is not. If $r=p$, then $S_0 \equiv S$.

Observe that, if we select for each index $\rho \leqslant r$ a vector h_ρ in $\mathcal{K}$ such that $g'_\rho(x_0,h_\rho)<0$, the vector $\hat{h}=h_1+\cdots+h_r$ satisfies the relations

$$g'_\rho(x_0,h)<0, \qquad g'_\sigma(x_0,h)=0 \qquad (\rho=1,\ldots,r;\ \sigma=r+1,\ldots,m). \quad (10.7)$$

The class $\hat{\mathcal{K}}$ composed of $h=0$ and all solutions h of relations (10.7) is a convex cone whose closure is $\mathcal{K}$. In fact, if h is in $\mathcal{K}$ and $\hat{h}$ is in $\hat{\mathcal{K}}$, then $h+t\hat{h}$ is in $\hat{\mathcal{K}}$ if t is positive. Since the tangent space of S at x_0 is closed, it follows that *x_0 is a regular point of S if and only if every vector h in $\hat{\mathcal{K}}$ is a tangent vector of S at x_0.*

One other observation should be made, namely, that if $r<p$ a vector h *satisfies the constraints*

$$g'_\tau(x_0,h) \leqslant 0, \qquad g'_\beta(x_0,h)=0 \qquad (\tau=r+1,\ldots,p;\ \beta=p+1,\ldots,m) \quad (10.8)$$

if and only if

$$g'_\sigma(x_0,h)=0 \qquad (\sigma=r+1,\ldots,m). \quad (10.9)$$

If $r=0$, then (10.4) is of the desired form (10.9). If $r>0$, consider a vector $h \neq 0$ satisfying (10.8). Select a vector $\hat{h} \neq 0$ in $\hat{\mathcal{K}}$, and select $t>0$ so large that

$$g'_\rho(x_0,h+t\hat{h}) = g'_\rho(x_0,h)+tg'_\rho(x_0,\hat{h}) \leqslant 0 \qquad (\rho=1,\ldots,r).$$

Observing that

$$g'_\tau(x_0, h + t\hat{h}) = g'_\tau(x_0, h) \leqslant 0, \qquad g'_\beta(x_0, h + t\hat{h}) = 0,$$

we find that $h + t\hat{h}$ is in $\mathcal{H}$ and hence, by (10.7), that

$$g'_\sigma(x_0, h + t\hat{h}) = g'_\sigma(x_0, h) = 0 \qquad (\sigma = r+1, \dots, m).$$

This proves our assertion that constraints (10.8) and (10.9) are equivalent.

It should be noted that, if $r < p$, then, by virtue of the corollary to Theorem 3.5 applied to constraints (10.8), there exist multipliers $\lambda_{r+1}, \dots, \lambda_m$ such that

$$\lambda_{r+1} g'_{r+1}(x_0, h) + \cdots + \lambda_m g'_m(x_0, h) = 0, \qquad \lambda_\tau > 0 \qquad (\tau = r+1, \dots, p)$$

for all vectors h, and hence such that

$$\lambda_{r+1} \nabla g_{r+1}(x_0) + \cdots + \lambda_m \nabla g_m(x_0) = 0, \qquad \lambda_\tau > 0 \qquad (\tau = r+1, \dots, p).$$

$$(10.10)$$

Hence, if $r < p$, the gradients $\nabla g_{r+1}(x_0), \dots, \nabla g_m(x_0)$ are linearly dependent.

Relations (10.8) are the tangential constraints at x_0 for the set T defined by the constraints

$$g_\tau(x) \leqslant 0, \qquad g_\beta(x) = 0 \qquad (\tau = r+1, \dots, p; \beta = 1, \dots, m). \quad (10.11)$$

Similarly, equations (10.9) are the tangential constraints at x_0 of the corresponding set T_0 defined by the conditions

$$g_\sigma(x) = 0 \qquad (\sigma = r+1, \dots, m). \qquad (10.12)$$

The following lemma will be useful.

LEMMA 10.1

If x_0 is a regular point of T, then x_0 is a regular point of S. If x_0 is a regular point of T_0, then x_0 is a regular point of T, of S_0, and of S.

The second conclusion follows from the first and from the result given above. Of course, if $p = r$, then $T = T_0$ and $S = S_0$.

Suppose that x_0 is a regular point of T. To show that x_0 is a regular point of S, it is sufficient to show that a vector h in the class $\mathcal{H}$ defined by (10.7) is a tangent vector of S at x_0. Consider therefore a vector $h \neq 0$ in $\mathcal{H}$. Since it satisfies constraints (10.8), it is a tangent vector of T at x_0. There is accordingly a sequence of points $\{x_q\}$ in T converging to x_0 in the direction h, that is, there is a sequence $\{x_q\}$ in T and a sequence $\{t_q\}$ of positive numbers such that

$$\lim_{q \to \infty} t_q = 0, \qquad \lim_{q \to \infty} \frac{x_q - x_0}{t_q} = h.$$

Then

$$\lim_{q \to \infty} \frac{g_\gamma(x_q)}{t_q} = \lim_{q \to \infty} \frac{g_\gamma(x_q) - g_\gamma(x_0)}{t_q} = g'_\gamma(x_0, h) \qquad (\gamma = 1, \ldots, m)$$

Since $g'_\rho(x_0, h) < 0$ ($\rho = 1, \ldots, r$), there is a number q_0 such that $g_\rho(x_q) < 0$ ($q > q_0$). By choice, the point x_q satisfies the remaining constraints (10.11). Consequently, when $q > q_0$, the point x_q satisfies constraints (10.1) and hence is in S. It follows that every vector h in $\mathcal{K}$ is a tangent vector of S at x_0, as was to be proved.

THEOREM 10.1

If the functions $g_{r+1}, \ldots, g_m$ *are linear or, more generally, if the functions* $g_{r+1}, \ldots, g_p$ *are concave and* $g_{p+1}, \ldots, g_m$ *are linear, then* x_0 *is a regular point of* S. *In particular, if* $r = p$ *and* $g_{p+1}, \ldots, g_m$ *are linear, then* x_0 *is a regular point of* S.

In this event the point x_0 is a regular point of T and hence also of S by virtue of the results established in Section 8.

If the functions $g_{r+1}, \ldots, g_m$ are linear, we have $T = T_0$ and $S = S_0$, as is readily verified.

THEOREM 10.2

Suppose that the functions $g_{p+1}, \ldots, g_m$ *are linear and that the functions* $g_1, \ldots, g_p$ *are convex on a spherical neighborhood* N *of* x_0. *If the functions* g_α *that vanish identically on* S∩N *are linear, then* x_0 *is a regular point of* S.

If x_0 is an isolated point of S in N, all functions vanish identically on $S \cap N$ and accordingly are linear. In this event x_0 is a regular point of S. Suppose therefore that there is a point $x \neq x_0$ in $S \cap N$. Because the set $S \cap N$ is convex, the line segment joining x to x_0 is in S. The vector $h = x - x_0$ is therefore a nonnull linear tangent vector of S at x_0. By virtue of the convexity of g_α ($\alpha \leqslant p$) we have the relations

$$0 \geqslant g_\alpha(x) = g_\alpha(x) - g_\alpha(x_0) \geqslant g'_\alpha(x_0, x - x_0) = g'_\alpha(x_0, h).$$

If $g_\alpha(x) < 0$, then $g'_\alpha(x_0, h) < 0$ and hence $\alpha \leqslant r$. It follows that, if $\alpha > r$, the function g_α must vanish identically on $S \cap N$ and accordingly must be linear. The functions $g_{r+1}, \ldots, g_m$ are therefore linear, and x_0 is a regular point of S, by Theorem 10.1. This establishes Theorem 10.2.

Criteria for regularity involving gradients are given in

THEOREM 10.3

If the gradients $\nabla g_{r+1}, \ldots, \nabla g_m$ *at* x_0 *are linearly independent, then* $r = p$ *and* x_0 *is a regular point of* S. *If* $r = p$ *and the gradients* $\nabla g_{p+1}, \ldots, \nabla g_m$ *at* x_0 *are linearly independent, then* x_0 *is a regular point of* S. *If the gradients* $\nabla g_1, \ldots, \nabla g_m$ *are linearly independent at* x_0, *then* x_0 *is a regular point of* S.

The last two conclusions in the theorem are simple consequences of the first conclusion. Suppose therefore that the gradients $\nabla g_{r+1}(x_0), \ldots, \nabla g_m(x_0)$ are linearly independent. By virtue of the statement following relation (10.10) we have $r = p$. By Theorem 5.1 (or by Theorem 5.3) in Chapter 3, the point x_0 is a regular point of T_0 and hence also of T, S_0, and S, as was to be proved.

It will be conveneint to admit inactive constraints in the statement of the following theorem.

THEOREM 10.4

The following two conditions are equivalent:
(i) *The gradients* $\nabla g_{p+1}, \ldots, \nabla g_m$ *at* x_0 *are linearly independent and, if* $p > 0$, *there exists a vector* h *such that*

$$g'_\alpha(x_0, h) < 0 \quad (\alpha \leqslant p; \ g_\alpha(x_0) = 0), \qquad g'_\beta(x_0, h) = 0 \quad (\beta > p). \quad (10.13)$$

(ii) *There exists no set of multipliers* $\lambda_1, \ldots, \lambda_m$, *not all zero, such that*

$$\sum_{\gamma=1}^{m} \lambda_\gamma \nabla g_\gamma(x_0) = 0, \qquad \lambda_\alpha \geqslant 0 \quad (\alpha \leqslant p), \qquad \lambda_\alpha = 0 \quad \text{if } g_\alpha(x_0) < 0. \quad (10.14)$$

If these conditions hold, then x_0 *is a regular point of* S.

In the proof we suppose that all constraints are active. Then condition (10.13) is the condition that $r = p$. By Theorem 10.3 the point x_0 is a regular point of S whenever (i) holds.

Suppose that condition (i) is satisfied and that $\lambda_1, \ldots, \lambda_m$ are multipliers satisfying relations (10.14). Choose a vector h such that (10.13) holds. Since

$g'_\beta(x_0, h) = 0$, we have

$$\sum_{\gamma=1}^{m} \lambda_\gamma g'_\gamma(x_0, h) = \sum_{\alpha=1}^{p} \lambda_\alpha g'_\alpha(x_0, h) = 0, \qquad \lambda_\alpha \geqslant 0 \quad (\alpha \leqslant p).$$

Inasmuch as $g'_\alpha(x_0, h) < 0$, this is possible only if $\lambda_\alpha = 0$ $(\alpha = 1, \ldots, p)$. Condition (10.14) becomes

$$\lambda_{p+1} \nabla g_{p+1}(x_0) + \cdots + \lambda_m \nabla g_m(x_0) = 0. \tag{10.15}$$

Since the gradients appearing in this expression are linearly independent, the multipliers $\lambda_{p+1}, \ldots, \lambda_m$ are also zero. It follows that condition (ii) is satisfied when condition (i) holds.

Suppose next that condition (ii) holds. Then (10.15) cannot be satisfied unless $\lambda_{p+1} = \cdots = \lambda_m = 0$. The gradients $\nabla g_{p+1}(x_0), \ldots, \nabla g_m(x_0)$ are therefore linearly independent. If $p = 0$, then (i) holds. If $p > 0$, then, by virtue of the statement involving relation (10.10), we see that $r = p$ and hence that there is a vector h satisfying relation (10.13). Consequently (i) holds and the two conditions are equivalent, as was to be proved.

In deriving these results, it was assumed that our functions are of class C'. However, these results remain valid under the weaker assumption that the functions $g_1, \ldots, g_m$ are continuous near x_0 and are differentiable at x_0. For the sake of completeness we state in the next theorem a further condition for regularity, which will be established in Section 8 of the next chapter. In this theorem we suppose that our functions are of class C' in a neighborhood of x_0.

THEOREM 10.5

The point x_0 *is a regular point of* S *if there exists no set of multipliers* $\lambda_1, \ldots, \lambda_m$, *not all zero satisfying the following two conditions:*

$$\lambda_\alpha \geqslant 0 \quad (\alpha = 1, \ldots, p), \qquad \sum_{\gamma=1}^{m} \lambda_\gamma \nabla g_\gamma(x_0) = 0; \tag{10.16a}$$

In every neighborhood of x_0 *there is a point* x *such that*

$$\text{if } \lambda_\gamma \neq 0 \text{ then } \lambda_\gamma g_\gamma(x) > 0. \tag{10.16b}$$

This result will be established in Section 8 of the next chapter.

In Theorem 7.5 we had occasion to consider a subset S_1 of S defined by conditions of the form

$$g_\gamma(x) = 0 \quad (\gamma \text{ in } \Gamma), \qquad g_\gamma(x) \leqslant 0 \quad (\gamma \text{ not in } \Gamma), \tag{10.17}$$

where Γ is a subset of the indices $1,\ldots,m$ containing the indices $p+1,\ldots,m$. The tangential constraints for S_1 take the form

$$g'_\gamma(x_0,h)=0 \quad (\gamma \text{ in } \Gamma), \qquad g'_\gamma(x_0,h) \leqslant 0 \quad (\gamma \text{ not in } \Gamma). \qquad (10.18)$$

The point x_0 will be called a *completely regular point* of S if x_0 is a regular point of every subset S_1 of S of this type. It follows from Theorem 10.3 that x_0 is a completely regular point if the gradients $\nabla g_1(x_0),\ldots,\nabla g_m(x_0)$ are linearly independent. However, this condition is too restrictive. A less restrictive condition is given in

THEOREM 10.6

Given a vector h *in* $\mathcal{H}$, *let* $\Gamma(h)$ *denote the set of indices* γ *for which* $g'_\gamma(x_0,h)=0$. *If for every vector* $h \neq 0$ *in* $\mathcal{H}$, *the gradients* $\nabla g_\gamma(x_0)$ [γ *in* $\Gamma(h)$] *are linearly independent, then* x_0 *is a completely regular point of* S.

Consider a subset Γ of the indices $1,\ldots,m$ containing the indices $p+1,\ldots,m$. Let S_1 be the set defined by constraints (10.17). If there is no $h \neq 0$ satisfying tangential constraints (10.18) at x_0, then x_0 is an isolated point of S_1 and is a regular point of S_1. Suppose therefore that there is a vector $h \neq 0$ satisfying relations (10.18). Then Γ is a subset of the set $\Gamma(h)$ of the indices γ such that $g'_\gamma(x_0,h)=0$. Since the gradients $\nabla g_\gamma(x_0)$ [γ in $\Gamma(h)$] are linearly independent, the hypotheses of Theorem 10.3 hold when S is replaced by S_1. It follows from Theorem 10.3 that x_0 is a regular point of S_1, as was to be proved.

It is customary in the calculus of variations to call a condition on the gradients $\nabla g_1(x_0),\ldots,\nabla g_m(x_0)$ a *normality condition* if it implies regularity at x_0. This terminology is appropriate, since a normality condition implies that the gradients $\nabla g_1(x_0),\ldots,\nabla g_m(x_0)$ generate the outer normal space $\mathcal{H}^*$ of S at x_0 via formula (10.3). We have given various normality criteria, namely, the criteria specified in Theorems 10.3, 10.4, and 10.6. In the case of equality constraints these conditions are the same. If they are satisfied, x_0 is called a *normal point* of S. For the case in which inequality constraints are present, these criteria are not equivalent. We select condition (ii) in Theorem 10.4 as our basic criterion for normality. Accordingly we say that x_0 is a *normal point of* S if there exists no set of multipliers $\lambda_1,\ldots,\lambda_m$, not all zero, such that

$$\sum_{\gamma=1}^{m} \lambda_\gamma \nabla g_\gamma(x_0)=0, \qquad \lambda_\alpha \geqslant 0 \qquad [\alpha \leqslant p \text{ with } \lambda_\alpha=0 \text{ if } g_\alpha(x_0)<0]. \qquad (10.19)$$

Of course, the equivalent condition (i) in Theorem 10.4 can be used to define normality. In particular, in the case $p = m$ *the point* x_0 *is a normal point of* S *if and only if there is a vector* h *such that* $g'_\alpha(x_0, h) < 0$ *for all active indices* α *at* x_0. It will be seen in Exercise 12 that, if $p = m$ and the functions $g_1, \ldots, g_m$ are convex, x_0 is a normal point of S if none of the functions $g_1, \ldots, g_m$ is identically zero on S.

Inasmuch as the condition given in Theorem 10.6 implies that x_0 is a completely regular point of S, we shall say that x_0 is a *completely normal point of* S if the criterion given in Theorem 10.6 is satisfied. *If* $m \leqslant n$, *it can be shown that* x_0 *is a completely normal point if and only if the gradients* $\nabla g_1(x_0), \ldots, \nabla g_m(x_0)$ *are linearly independent.*

The criteria of normality and complete normality are point conditions. The criterion given in Theorem 10.5, which will be discussed in the next chapter, is not a pure point condition, since it involves the behavior of the functions $g_1, \ldots, g_m$ at neighboring points of x_0. However, the condition is mainly a condition on the outer normals $\nabla g_1(x_0), \ldots, \nabla g_m(x_0)$. For this reason we shall call the condition given in Theorem 10.5 a *quasinormality condition*. In particular, we shall say that x_0 is a *quasinormal point of* x_0 if the criterion for regularity given in Theorem 10.5 is satisfied. It will be seen in Section 8 in the next chapter that this criterion is satisfied when the functions $g_1, \ldots, g_p$ are concave and the functions $g_{p+1}, \ldots, g_m$ are linear.

EXERCISES

In these exercises x_0 is a point of a set S defined by constraints of form (10.1), where $g_1, \ldots, g_m$ are of class C'.
Give examples illustrating the following phenomena.

1. A nonregular point x_0.

2. A regular point that is not completely regular.

3. A quasinormal point that is not normal.

4. A regular point that is not normal.

5. A normal point that is not completely normal.

6. A regular point that is not quasinormal. *Hint:* See Exercise 7, Section 4.

7. A completely normal point x_0 at which the gradients $\nabla g_1(x_0), \ldots, \nabla g_m(x_0)$ are linearly dependent.

Establish the following results.

8. Show that if $m \leqslant n$ a point x_0 is a completely normal point of S if and only if the gradients $\nabla g_1(x_0), \ldots, \nabla g_m(x_0)$ are linearly independent.

9. Show that x_0 is a normal point of S if and only if it is a normal point of the set T appearing in Lemma 10.1.

10. Show that, if x_0 is a normal point of S, there is a neighborhood N of x_0 such that every point in $S \cap N$ is a normal point of S.

11. Show that, if x_0 is a completely normal point of S, there is a neighborhood N of x_0 such that every point in $S \cap N$ is a completely normal point of S.

12. Suppose that $p = m$ and that $g_1, \ldots, g_m$ are convex. Show that, if none of the functions $g_1, \ldots, g_m$ is identically zero on S, then x_0 is a normal point of S.

11. INFINITELY MANY INEQUALITY CONSTRAINTS

The main results given in the preceding pages can be extended to the case in which the set S is defined by constraints of the form

$$g_\alpha(x) \leqslant 0 \qquad (\alpha \text{ in } A), \tag{11.1}$$

where the index set A is a compact set in an Euclidean space or, more generally, where A is a compact metric space. If A is composed of a finite number of elements, these constraints are of form (8.1) with no equality constraints. As is to be expected, the results obtained in this section will be consistent with those given in the preceding pages for the case in which no equality constraints occur.

We suppose that we are given a point x_0 in S which affords a local minimum to a prescribed function $f(x)$ on S. It is assumed that $f(x)$ is of class C' on a closed neighborhood N of x_0. The functions $g_\alpha(x)$ and their gradients $\nabla g_\alpha(x)$ are assumed to be continuous in x and α for x in N and α in A.

Let A_0 be the set of active indices at x_0, that is, the set of indices α in A such that $g_\alpha(x_0) = 0$. Since $g_\alpha(x_0)$ is a continuous function of α on A, the set A_0 is a compact subset of A. By the argument given in Section 7 it is seen that a tangent vector h of S at x_0 satisfies the constraints

$$g_\alpha'(x_0, h) \leqslant 0 \qquad (\alpha \text{ in } A_0). \tag{11.2}$$

Accordingly these constraints will be called the *tangential constraints for* S *at* x_0. As before, the class of vectors h satisfying these constraints will be denoted by $\mathcal{H}$. The point x_0 will be called a *regular point of* S if $\mathcal{H}$ is the tangent cone of S at x_0 and if, in addition, the cone $\mathcal{N}$ generated by the gradients $\nabla g_\alpha(x_0)$ (α in A_0) is closed. If x_0 is a regular point of S, then $\mathcal{N}$ is the dual cone of the tangent cone $\mathcal{H}$ and is accordingly the outer normal cone of S at x_0. It should be noted that the set $\mathcal{B}$ of gradients $\nabla g_\alpha(x_0)$ (α in A_0) is a compact set in $\mathcal{E}^n$, by virtue of the continuity of $\nabla g_\alpha(x_0)$ as a function of α on the compact set A_0. However, the compactness of $\mathcal{B}$ does not guarantee the closure of $\mathcal{N}$ unless $\mathcal{B}$ is a finite set of vectors.

The first-order Lagrange multiplier rule is given in

THEOREM 11.1

If a regular point x_0 *minimizes* f *on* S, *then either* $\nabla f(x_0) = 0$ *or else there exist* $r \leqslant n$ *indices* $\alpha_1, \ldots, \alpha_r$ *in* A_0 *and a set of positive multipliers* $\lambda_1, \ldots, \lambda_r$

such that

$$\nabla f(x_0) + \lambda_1 \nabla g_{\alpha_1}(x_0) + \cdots + \lambda_r \nabla g_{\alpha_r}(x_0) = 0. \tag{11.3}$$

The gradients $\nabla g_\alpha(x_0)$ $(\alpha = \alpha_1, \ldots, \alpha_r)$ *can be chosen to be linearly independent.*

By Theorem 6.1 the negative gradient $-\nabla f(x_0)$ is an outer normal of S at x_0 and hence is in the outer normal cone of S at x_0. By regularity this cone is the cone $\mathcal{R}$ generated by the gradients $\nabla g_\alpha(x_0)$ (α in A_0). If $\nabla f(x_0) \neq 0$, then, in view of the result given in Exercise 10 of Section 3, the vector $-\nabla f(x_0)$ is a positive linear combination of linearly independent gradients $\nabla g_{\alpha_1}(x_0), \ldots, \nabla g_{\alpha_r}(x_0)$ with $\alpha_1, \ldots, \alpha_r$ in A_0, as stated in the theorem.

The following lemma will be useful in the determination of regularity.

LEMMA 11.1

If a vector h *satisfies the condition*

$$g_\alpha'(x_0, h) < 0 \qquad (\alpha \text{ in } A_0), \tag{11.4}$$

then h *is a linear tangent of* S *at* x_0. *In fact, there is a constant* $\delta > 0$ *such that*

$$g_\alpha(x_0 + th) < 0 \qquad (0 < t \leq \delta; \ \alpha \text{ in } A). \tag{11.5}$$

To prove this result, observe that, by the continuity of $g_\alpha'(x, h)$ as a function of x and α, condition (11.4) implies that there is a neighborhood N of x_0 and a neighborhood A_1 of A_0 in A such that

$$g_\alpha'(x_0, h) < 0 \qquad (x \text{ in } N; \ \alpha \text{ in } A_1). \tag{11.6}$$

Since $g_\alpha(x_0) < 0$ when α is in the compact set $A - A_1$, we can diminish N so that $g_\alpha(x) < 0$ when x is in N and α is in $A - A_1$. Choose $\delta > 0$ so that $x_0 + th$ is in N when $0 \leq t \leq \delta$. We then have $g_\alpha(x_0 + th) < 0$ $(0 \leq t \leq \delta;\ \alpha$ in $A - A_1)$. If α is in A_1, then, since $g_\alpha(x_0) \leq 0$, we have, by (11.6) and Taylor's theorem,

$$g_\alpha(x_0 + th) \leq g_\alpha(x_0 + th) - g_\alpha(x_0) = tg_\alpha'(x_0 + t_\alpha h, h) < 0 \qquad (0 < t_\alpha < t \leq \delta).$$

It follows that (11.5) holds and that h is a linear tangent of S at x_0, as was to be proved.

The point x_0 will be said to be a *normal point of* S if there is a vector h such that $g_\alpha'(x_0, h) < 0$ (α in A_0). This definition of normality is consistent with the concept of normality introduced in Section 10. We have the following alternative criterion for normality.

LEMMA 11.2

The point x_0 *is a normal point of* S *if and only if for every set of* $k \leqslant n + 1$ *indices* $\alpha_1, \ldots, \alpha_k$ *in* A_0 *there is no set of nonnegative numbers* $\lambda_1, \ldots, \lambda_k$, *not all zero, such that*

$$\lambda_1 \nabla g_{\alpha_1}(x_0) + \cdots + \lambda_k \nabla g_{\alpha_k}(x_0) = 0.$$

This result, with $\mathscr{B}$ as the set of gradients $\nabla g_\alpha(x_0)$ (α in A_0), was given in Exercise 16 of Section 3. The verification of this result will be left to the reader.

THEOREM 11.2

A normal point of S *is a regular point of* S.

Let x_0 be a normal point of S. Then the class $\hat{\mathscr{H}}$ of vectors h satisfying conditions (11.4) is not empty. By Lemma 11.1 the vectors in $\hat{\mathscr{H}}$ are tangent vectors of S at x_0. Let h be a vector in $\hat{\mathscr{H}}$. Select a vector h_0 satisfying the tangential constraints $g_\alpha'(x_0, h) \leqslant 0$ (α in A_0). Inasmuch as

$$g_\alpha'(x_0, h_0 + th) = g_\alpha'(x_0, h_0) + t g_\alpha'(x_0, h) < 0 \qquad (0 < t \leqslant 1; \ \alpha \text{ in } A_0),$$

the vectors $h_0 + th$ ($0 < t \leqslant 1$) are in $\hat{\mathscr{H}}$ and hence are tangent vectors of S at x_0. Since the tangent cone of S at x_0 is closed, the vector h_0 is also a tangent vector of S at x_0. The tangent cone of S at x_0 is therefore determined by tangential constraints (11.2). In addition, by virtue of the result given in Exercise 15 of Section 3, the cone $\mathscr{N}$ generated by the compact set $\mathscr{B}$ of gradients $\nabla g_\alpha(x_0)$ (α in A_0) is closed. The point x_0 therefore is a regular point of S, as was to be proved.

COROLLARY

A normal minimizing point x_0 *of* f *on* S *satisfies the Lagrange multiplier rule given in Theorem 11.1.*

In the convex case we have the following special criterion for normality.

THEOREM 11.3

Suppose that the functions g_α *(* α *in* A*) are convex on a neighborhood* N *of* x_0. *Then the point* x_0 *is a normal point of* S *if and only if there is a point* x_1 *in* N *such that* $g_\alpha(x_1) < 0$ *for all* α *in* A_0.

In view of Lemma 11.1 such a point x_1 exists if x_0 is a normal point of S. Conversely, if a point x_1 of this type exists, we have, by convexity, for α in A_0

$$0 > g_\alpha(x_1) = g_\alpha(x_1) - g_\alpha(x_0) \geqslant g_\alpha'(x_0, x_1 - x_0) = g_\alpha'(x_0, h),$$

where $h = x_1 - x_0$. Consequently x_0 is a normal point of S, and the theorem is established.

EXAMPLE 11.1

Let A be a compact set in $\mathcal{E}^n$. Then there is a smallest sphere enclosing A. This sphere is obtained by minimizing z subject to the constraints

$$g_\alpha(x, z) = |x - \alpha|^2 - z \leqslant 0 \qquad (\alpha \text{ in } A).$$

Obviously a minimum point (x_0, z_0) exists. Moreover, this point is a normal point of the set S defined by these constraints, as can be seen by application of Theorem 11.3. By Theorem 11.1 there exist $r \leqslant n+1$ points $\alpha_1, \ldots, \alpha_r$ in A and multipliers $\lambda_1, \ldots, \lambda_r$ such that the gradient of the Lagrangian

$$F(x, z) = \sum_{j=1}^r \lambda_j |x - \alpha_j|^2 - (\lambda_1 + \cdots + \lambda_r - 1)z$$

is zero at (x_0, z_0). This yields the relations

$$x_0 = \lambda_1 \alpha_1 + \cdots + \lambda_r \alpha_r, \qquad \lambda_1 + \cdots + \lambda_r = 1, \tag{11.7}$$

$$F(x_0, z_0) = z_0 = \sum_{j=1}^r \lambda_j |x_0 - \alpha_j|^2 = \sum_{j=1}^r \lambda_j |\alpha_j|^2 - |x_0|^2.$$

By a simple computation it is seen that

$$F(x, z) = |x - x_0|^2 + z_0.$$

Consequently the solution is unique. The number $R = \sqrt{z_0}$ is the radius of the sphere about x_0 which encloses A. The diameter $d = \max |\alpha_i - \alpha_j|$ of the set $\{\alpha_1, \ldots, \alpha_r\}$ satisfies the relation

$$d \geqslant R \left(\frac{2r}{r-1} \right)^{1/2} \tag{11.8}$$

To obtain this result, set $D_{ij} = |\alpha_i - \alpha_j|^2$. Observe that

$$D_{ij} = |\alpha_i - \alpha_j|^2 = |(\alpha_i - x_0) - (\alpha_j - x_0)|^2 = 2R^2 - 2\langle \alpha_i - x_0, \alpha_j - x_0 \rangle.$$

By the use of (11.7) it is seen that

$$\sum_{i,j=1}^{r} \lambda_i D_{ij} \lambda_j = 2R^2 = \sum_{i \neq j} \lambda_i D_{ij} \lambda_j \leqslant d^2 \sum_{i \neq j} \lambda_i \lambda_j$$

In as much as $\sum_{i=1}^{r} \lambda_i = 1$, we have $\sum_i \lambda_i^2 \geqslant 1/r$ and

$$\sum_{i \neq j} \lambda_i \lambda_j = 1 - \sum_i \lambda_i^2 \leqslant 1 - \frac{1}{r} = \frac{r-1}{r}.$$

Hence

$$2R^2 \leqslant d^2 \left(\frac{r-1}{r} \right),$$

as was to be proved.[†]

As a final result we have the following theorem, due to F. John.[†]

THEOREM 11.4

If x_0 *minimizes* f *on* S, *there exist indices* $\alpha_1, \ldots, \alpha_r$ *in* A_0 *and nonnegative multipliers* $\lambda_0, \lambda_1, \ldots, \lambda_r$, *not all zero, such that*

$$\lambda_0 \nabla f(x_0) + \lambda_1 \nabla g_{\alpha_1}(x_0) + \cdots + \lambda_r \nabla g_{\alpha_r}(x_0) = 0. \qquad (11.7)$$

If x_0 is a regular point of S, this result holds with $\lambda_0 = 1$, by Theorem 11.1. If x_0 is not a regular point of S, it is not a normal point of S. In this event it follows from Lemma 11.2 that a relation of form (11.7) holds with $\lambda_0 = 0$. This proves Theorem 11.4.

12. A SIMPLE INTEGRAL PROBLEM

The results given above have an interesting application to the problem of minimizing integrals of the type appearing in problems of optimal control.

[†]F. John, "Extremum Problems with Inequalities as Subsidiary Conditions," *Studies and Essays: Courant Anniversary Volume*, Interscience, New York, 1951.

To this end consider the problem of minimizing an integral

$$J(u) = \int_a^b F\left[t, u(t)\right] dt$$

in a class $\mathcal{C}$ of functions

$$u: \qquad u^k(t) \qquad (a \leqslant t \leqslant b; \, k = 1, \ldots, q)$$

The class $\mathcal{C}$ is assumed to be the class of all piecewise continuous functions $u(t) = (u^1(t), \ldots, u^k(t))$ on a fixed interval $a \leqslant t \leqslant b$ whose elements $(t, u(t))$ are constrained to lie in a prescribed set $\mathcal{R}_0$ of points $(t, u) = (t, u^1, \ldots, u^k)$. It is assumed that the set $\mathcal{R}_0$ has the property that, given a point $(\bar{t}, \bar{u})$ in $\mathcal{R}_0$, there is a continuous function $\bar{u}(t)$ on an interval $|t - \bar{t}| \leqslant \delta$ such that $\bar{u}(\bar{t}) = \bar{u}$ and such that $(t, \bar{u}(t))$ is in $\mathcal{R}_0$ whenever $|t - \bar{t}| \leqslant \delta$. A set $\mathcal{R}_0$ of this type will be said to be *admissible*. Its elements (t, u) will be called *admissible elements*. A function $u : u(t)$ $(a \leqslant t \leqslant b)$ will be said to be *admissible* if its elements $(t, u(t))$ are admissible. The class $\mathcal{C}$ is accordingly the class of admissible functions u. We assume that the integrand $F(t, u)$ is continuous on $\mathcal{R}_0$.

The basic theorem to be established is

THEOREM 12.1

A function

$$u_0: \qquad u_0(t) \qquad (a \leqslant t \leqslant b)$$

minimizes J(u) *on the class* $\mathcal{C}$ *of admissible functions, if and only if the inequality*

$$F(t, u) \geqslant F[t, u_0(t)] \qquad (a \leqslant t \leqslant b)$$

holds, whenever the element (t, u) *is admissible. If* u_0 *minimizes* J, *then* $F[t, u_0(t)]$ *is continuous on* $a \leqslant t \leqslant b$.

Briefly the theorem states that the integral will be minimized on $\mathcal{C}$ if we minimize $F(t, u)$ on $\mathcal{R}_0$ for each t on $a \leqslant t \leqslant b$.

Before establishing this result, we consider several examples.

EXAMPLE 12.1

Consider the problem of minimizing the integral

$$J(u) = \int_0^2 \left[u(t)^2 - 2tu(t)\right] dt$$

on the class $\mathcal{C}$ of all admissible functions $u: u(t)$ $(0 \leqslant t \leqslant 2)$ for the case in which $\mathcal{R}_0$ consists of all elements (t, u). If t is fixed, then $u^2 - 2tu$ has a minimum value when $u = u_0(t) = t$. The function $u_0: u_0(t) = t$ $(0 \leqslant t \leqslant 2)$ therefore minimizes $J(u)$ on $\mathcal{C}$.

EXAMPLE 12.2

In this case we modify Example 12.1 by restricting $\mathcal{R}_0$ to be the class of points (t, u) having $|u| \leqslant 1$. In this event the solution is $u_0: u_0(t)$ $(0 \leqslant t \leqslant 2)$, where

$$u_0(t) = t \quad (0 \leqslant t \leqslant 1), \qquad u_0(t) = 1 \quad (1 \leqslant t \leqslant 2),$$

as is readily verified.

EXAMPLE 12.3

Minimize the integral

$$J(u) = \int_0^2 (t-1)u(t)\,dt$$

in the class of admissible functions $u: u(t)$ $(0 \leqslant t \leqslant 2)$ having $|u(t)| \leqslant 1$. In this event $\mathcal{R}_0$ consists of all points (t, u) having $|u| \leqslant 1$. For t on the interval $0 \leqslant t \leqslant 1$ the minimum of $(t-1)u$ subject to the constraint $|u| \leqslant 1$ is given by $u_0(t) = -1$. On the interval $1 < t \leqslant 2$ the minimum of $(t-1)u$ with $|u| \leqslant 1$ is given by $u_0(t) = 1$. The minimizing function u_0 is therefore given by

$$u_0(t) = -1 \quad (0 \leqslant t \leqslant 1), \qquad u_0(t) = 1 \quad (1 \leqslant t \leqslant 2).$$

To prove Theorem 11.1 suppose that a function $u_0: u_0(t)$ $(a \leqslant t \leqslant b)$ minimizes $J(u)$ on $\mathcal{C}$. Let $\bar{t}$ be a point in $a < t < b$ which is a point of continuity of $u_0(t)$. Choose $\bar{u}$ such that $(\bar{t}, \bar{u})$ is in $\mathcal{R}_0$. Let $\bar{u}(t)$ $(|t - \bar{t}| \leqslant \delta)$ be a continuous function such that $\bar{u}(\bar{t}) = \bar{u}$ and $(t, \bar{u}(t))$ is in $\mathcal{R}_0$ if $|t - \bar{t}| \leqslant \delta$. We can suppose that $\delta < b - \bar{t}$. Suppose that

$$F\big[\bar{t}, u_0(\bar{t})\big] > F(\bar{t}, \bar{u});$$

then by continuity we can diminish δ so that

$$F\big[t, u_0(t)\big] > F\big[t, \bar{u}(t)\big] \qquad (|t - \bar{t}| \leqslant \delta).$$

Let $u: u(t)$ $(a \leqslant t \leqslant b)$ be the admissible function such that $u(t) = \bar{u}(t)$

$(\bar{t} \leqslant t \leqslant \bar{t} + \delta)$, $u(t) = u_0(t)$ elsewhere. Then

$$J(u) - J(u_0) = \int_{\bar{t}}^{\bar{t}+\delta} \{ F[t, \bar{u}(t)] - F[t, u_0(t)] \}\, dt < 0,$$

contrary to the minimizing property of u_0. Consequently

$$F(t, u) \geqslant F[t, u_0(t)]$$

for all (t, u) in $\mathcal{R}_0$ whenever t is a point of continuity of $u_0(t)$ on $a < t < b$. By continuity it holds for the remaining points t on $a \leqslant t \leqslant b$. At a point of discontinuity of $u_0(t)$ this inequality holds when $u_0(t)$ is the right- and left-hand limits, $u_0(t+0)$ and $u_0(t-0)$. Accordingly we have

$$F[t, u_0(t+0)] \geqslant F[t, u_0(t-0)] \geqslant F[t, u_0(t+0)].$$

Consequently $F[t, u_0(t)]$ is continuous on $a \leqslant t \leqslant b$.

Conversely, if

$$F(t, u) \geqslant F[t, u_0(t)] \qquad (a \leqslant t \leqslant b)$$

wherever (t, u) is in $\mathcal{R}_0$, then

$$J(u) - J(u_0) = \int_a^b \{ F[t, u(t)] - F[t, u_0(t)] \}\, dt \geqslant 0$$

for every admissible function u. Consequently u_0 minimizes J on $\mathcal{C}$, as was to be proved.

5

AUGMENTABILITY AND LAGRANGE MULTIPLIERS

1. INTRODUCTION

Occasionally one encounters the following derivation of the Lagrange multiplier rule. To minimize a function $f(x)$ subject to a constraint $g(x)=0$, minimize a function F of the form $F(x)=f(x)+\lambda g(x)$ without constraints. This yields the Lagrange multiplier rule $\nabla F(x)=\nabla f(x)+\lambda\nabla g(x)=0$ at the minimum point, in addition to the original condition $g(x)=0$. Although this procedure may be a good device for remembering the first-order multiplier rule, it is unsatisfactory because the class of problems to which it can be applied is limited. For example, in the xy-plane, it does not apply to the problem of minimizing the function $f(x,y)=x^2-3y-y^2$ subject to the constraint $g(x,y)=y=0$. The origin is the solution to this problem. The corresponding Lagrangian, $F(x,y)=f(x,y)+\lambda g(x,y)=x^2+(\lambda-3)y-y^2$, fails to have an unconstrained minimum no matter how λ is chosen. However, $\nabla F=0$ at the origin when λ is the correct Lagrange multiplier, $\lambda=3$. The procedure fails because there is no provision for convexifying the function F. In general, convexity is determined by the second-order terms. Second order terms can be modified by using the augmented function $H=f+\lambda g+(\sigma/2)g^2$. In the example given above,

$$H(x,y)=x^2+(\lambda-3)y+\left(\frac{\sigma-2}{2}\right)y^2.$$

The choice $\lambda=3$ ensures the vanishing of the gradient at the origin. The choice $\sigma>2$ convexifies the augmented function H.

The foregoing remarks suggest that, if a point x_0 is a local solution of the problem $f(x) = \min$, $g(x) = 0$, there is a constant λ and a number σ such that x_0 affords an unconstrained local minimum to the function $H = f + \lambda g + (\sigma/2) g^2$. If this is the case, the constrained problem will be said to be *augmentable*. Except in unusual cases a constrained minimum problem is augmentable. It is always augmentable when the standard sufficiency conditions for a constrained minimum hold at x_0.

The present chapter will be devoted mainly to the study of augmentability. It will be shown that the Lagrange multiplier rule is a consequence of augmentability and that augmentability is a consequence of the strengthened Lagrange multiplier rule. As before, we first consider the case of equality constraints and then extend our results to the case of inequality constraints.

In the preceding pages the Lagrange multiplier rule was obtained under an assumption of regularity of constraints. A problem can be regular without being augmentable, and a problem can be augmentable without being regular. Consequently augmentability and regularity are alternative but not equivalent conditions for the existence of suitable Lagrange multipliers.

In the study of augmentability it is convenient to use a theory of penalty functions. Accordingly we study the theory of penalty functions in Section 2 before we introduce the general concept of augmentability. A penalty function can be used in a computional procedure for finding the solution of a constrained minimum problem. It can also be used to obtain an extended multiplier rule which is independent of the assumptions of augmentability and regularity. This will be done in Section 7. This extended multiplier rule leads to an alternative criterion for regularity which we call *quasinormality*. Finally, in Section 10 we introduce an effective method for solving a constrained minimum problem. This method, which we call a *method of multipliers*, makes use of the concepts of augmentability and penalty functions.

The concept of augmentability has been in the folklore of variational theory for a long time. The author[†] first used it in 1946 and 1947 in the study of the problem of Bolza in the calculus of variations. Only recently, however, has its significance in the development of computational procedures been recognized.[‡]

[†]See the papers by Hestenes appearing in Vols. 60 and 61 of the *Transactions of the American Mathematical Society*.

[‡]See, for example, M. R. Hestenes, "Multiplier and Gradient Methods," *Journal of Optimization Theory and Applications*, Vol. 4 (1969), 303–320; also, M. J. D. Powell, "A method for Nonlinear Constraints in Minimization Problems," in *Optimization*, R. Fletcher (ed.), Academic Press, New York, 1969, pp. 283–298.

2. PENALTY FUNCTIONS

Normally a solution of a constrained minimum problem can be obtained as a limit of solutions of suitably chosen unconstrained minimum problems. This can be done in a number of ways. The procedure we shall use can be described briefly as follows. We first construct a nonnegative function $G(x)$ such that the points satisfying our constraints are given by the solutions of $G(x)=0$. We then add the *penalty term* $\sigma G(x)$ to the function $F(x)$ to be minimized under the given constraints. Next we obtain the minimum point $x(\sigma)$ of the *augmented function* $H(x,\sigma)=F(x)+\sigma G(x)$. Under normal circumstances the limit $x_0=\lim_{\sigma\to\infty}x(\sigma)$ exists and is the minimum point F subject to the given constraints. In most instances we restrict the points x considered to lie in a bounded closed set N. We illustrate this procedure by the following simple examples.

EXAMPLE 2.1

The point $(x_0,y_0)=(0,0)$ affords a minimum to the function $F(x,y)=x^2-y^2-4y$ subject to the constraint $g(x,y)=y=0$. If we set

$$G(x,y)=\tfrac{1}{2}[g(x,y)]^2=\tfrac{1}{2}y^2$$

and add the *penalty term* σG to F, we obtain an augmented function

$$H(x,y;\sigma)=F(x,y)+\sigma G(x,y)=x^2-4y+\left(\frac{\sigma-2}{2}\right)y^2.$$

For each $\sigma>2$ the point $[x(\sigma),y(\sigma)]=[0,4/(\sigma-2)]$ is the minimum point of H. As σ becomes infinite, the minimum point $[0,4/(\sigma-2)]$ of H converges to the minimum point $(0,0)$ of F subject to $g=0$.

Observe that, if we replace F by $F(x,y)=x^2-y^2-4y-y^3/3$, then $H=F+\sigma G$ fails to have a minimum in the xy-plane. However, if we restrict the points (x,y) to lie in a disk N of radius r about the origin, the minimum point $[x(\sigma),y(\sigma)]$ of $H(x,y;\sigma)$ on N will converge to $(x_0,y_0)=(0,0)$ as σ becomes infinite. If $\sigma>2+8/r+2r/3$, we have

$$x(\sigma)=0,\qquad y(\sigma)=\frac{8}{\sigma-2+\sqrt{\sigma^2-4\sigma-12}}$$

as the minimum point of H in N. Clearly $\lim_{\sigma\to\infty}y(\sigma)=0$.

EXAMPLE 2.2

The point $(0,0)$ minimizes the function $F(x,y)=x^2-y-y^3$ subject to the constraint $g(x,y)=y\leqslant 0$. Let

$$g^+(x,y)=\max[0,g(x,y)]=\max(0,y),\qquad G(x,y)=\tfrac{1}{2}[g^+(x,y)]^2.$$

Then the constraint $G(x,y)=0$ is equivalent to the constraint $g(x,y) \leqslant 0$. Form the augmented function

$$H(x,y;\sigma)=F(x,y)+\sigma G(x,y)=x^2-y-y^3+\frac{\sigma}{2}[\max(0,y)]^2.$$

This function fails to have a minimum in the xy-plane. However, on a closed disk N of radius r about the origin, H has a minimum point $[x(\sigma),y(\sigma)]$. Clearly $x(\sigma)=0$. If $\sigma>3r+1/r$, the point $[0,y(\sigma)]$ will be interior to N and

$$y(\sigma)=\frac{2}{\sigma+\sqrt{\sigma^2-12}}.$$

Again the point $[x(\sigma),y(\sigma)]$ converges to the minimum point $(0,0)$ of F subject to $g \leqslant 0$.

A somewhat degenerate problem is given by

EXAMPLE 2.3

The origin $(x_0,y_0,z_0)=(0,0,0)$ minimizes the function $F(x,y,z)=x+y+z^2$ subject to the constraints

$$g(x,y,z)=x+y^2 \leqslant 0, \qquad h(x,y,z)=-x \leqslant 0.$$

These constraints tell us in an unnatural manner that $x=0$, $y=0$. In this sense our problem is in a degenerate form. Proceeding as in Example 2.2, we construct the auxiliary function

$$G(x,y,z)=\tfrac{1}{2}\left\{\left[\max(0,x+y^2)\right]^2+[\max(0,-x)]^2\right\}$$

so as to obtain an equivalent constraint $G=0$. For large values of σ the minimum point $[x(\sigma),y(\sigma),z(\sigma)]$ of $H=F+\sigma G$ lies in the set of points having $x<0, y<0$, and $\sigma(x+y^2)=v>0$. Using this fact, we find that

$$x(\sigma)=-\frac{1+v}{\sigma}, \qquad y(\sigma)=-\frac{1}{v}, \qquad z(\sigma)=0,$$

where v solves the equation $2v^3-v^2=\sigma$. If σ is very large, $(\sigma/2)^{1/3}$ is an excellent estimate of v. Hence

$$\lim_{\sigma\to\infty} v(\sigma)=+\infty, \qquad \lim_{\sigma\to\infty} x(\sigma)=0, \qquad \lim_{\sigma\to\infty} y(\sigma)=0.$$

As σ becomes infinite, the minimum point of H accordingly converges to the minimum point of F subject to the constraints $g \leqslant 0$, $h \leqslant 0$.

The results given above lead us to the study of the problem of minimizing a function $F(x)$ on a compact set N subject to a constraint of the form $G(x) = 0$. The functions F and G are assumed to be continuous on N. We assume that $G(x) \geq 0$ on N and that the set S of points x in N having $G(x) = 0$ is not empty. By Theorem 2.3 of Chapter 1, these assumptions imply that there is a point x_0 in N which minimizes F on S. We assume that x_0 is unique.

The following lemma will be useful.

LEMMA 2.1

Let $\{\sigma_q\}$ be a sequence of numbers and $\{x_q\}$ be a sequence of points in N such that

$$\lim_{q \to \infty} \sigma_q = \infty, \qquad \limsup_{q \to \infty} [F(x_q) + \sigma_q G(x_q)] \leq F(x_0). \qquad (2.1)$$

Then

$$\lim_{q \to \infty} x_q = x_0.$$

In as much as $G(x) \geq 0$, relation (2.1) tells us that

$$\limsup_{q \to \infty} F(x_q) \leq F(x_0), \qquad \lim_{q \to \infty} G(x_q) = 0.$$

It follows that any limit $\bar{x}$ of a convergent subsequence of $\{x_q\}$ must have $F(\bar{x}) \leq F(x_0)$, $G(\bar{x}) = 0$. Moreover $\bar{x}$ is in N by virtue of the compactness of N. Since x_0 is an unique minimum point of F on N subject to $G = 0$, we have $\bar{x} = x_0$. Consequently every convergent subsequence of $\{x_q\}$ converges to x_0. Since $\{x_q\}$ is bounded, this is possible only if $x_0 = \lim_{q \to \infty} x_q$, as was to be proved.

The following result is basic.

THEOREM 2.1

Let $x(\sigma)$ be a minimum point of the augmented function

$$H(x, \sigma) = F(x) + \sigma G(x) \qquad (2.2)$$

on N. Then

$$\lim_{\sigma \to \infty} x(\sigma) = x_0, \qquad \lim_{\sigma \to \infty} \sigma G[x(\sigma)] = 0, \qquad (2.3)$$

where x_0 *is the minimum point of* F *on* S. *If* $0 \leqslant \sigma < \bar{\sigma}$, *we have*

$$H[x(\sigma),\sigma] \leqslant H[x(\bar{\sigma}),\bar{\sigma}] \leqslant F(x_0), \qquad (2.4a)$$

$$F[x(\sigma)] \leqslant F[x(\bar{\sigma})] \leqslant F(x_0), \qquad G[x(\sigma)] \geqslant G[x(\bar{\sigma})] \geqslant 0. \qquad (2.4b)$$

Since $G(x_0) = 0$ and $x(\sigma)$ minimizes $H(x,\sigma)$, we have the inequalities

$$H[x(\sigma),\sigma] = F[x(\sigma)] + \sigma G[x(\sigma)] \leqslant H(x_0,\sigma) = F(x_0),$$
$$(2.5)$$
$$F[x(\sigma)] \leqslant F(x_0).$$

Suppose that $\sigma < \bar{\sigma}$. Temporarily setting $\bar{x} = x(\bar{\sigma})$ and $x = x(\sigma)$, we have the inequalities

$$0 \leqslant H(\bar{x},\sigma) - H(x,\sigma) = F(\bar{x}) - F(x) + \sigma[G(\bar{x}) - G(x)],$$
$$0 \leqslant H(x,\bar{\sigma}) - H(\bar{x},\bar{\sigma}) = F(x) - F(\bar{x}) + \bar{\sigma}[G(x) - G(\bar{x})].$$

Adding these inequalities, we find that

$$0 \leqslant (\bar{\sigma} - \sigma)[G(x) - G(\bar{x})]$$

and hence that $G(x) \geqslant G(\bar{x})$. Using this fact in the first of these inequalities, we see that $F(x) \leqslant F(\bar{x})$. Hence (2.4) holds when $\sigma < \bar{\sigma}$.

Consider a sequence $\{\sigma_q\}$ tending to $+\infty$, and set $x_q = x(\sigma_q)$. By virtue of (2.5) relation (2.1) holds for the sequences $\{\sigma_q\}$ and $\{x_q\}$. By Lemma 2.1 we have

$$\lim_{q \to \infty} x_q = \lim_{q \to \infty} x(\sigma_q) = x_0.$$

From this fact it follows that $\lim_{\sigma \to \infty} x(\sigma) = x_0$. This completes the proof of Theorem 2.1.

COROLLARY 1

If there is a number σ_0 *such that one of the conditions* $F[x(\sigma_0)] = F(x_0)$, $G[x(\sigma_0)] = 0$ *is satisfied, then* $x(\sigma) = x_0$ ($\sigma \geqslant \sigma_0$), *that is, for each* $\sigma \geqslant \sigma_0$ *the point* x_0 *minimizes* $H(x,\sigma)$ *on* N.

If $F[x(\sigma_0)] = F(x_0)$, then $G[x(\sigma_0)] = 0$, by (2.5). If $G[x(\sigma_0)] = 0$, then $G[x(\sigma)] = 0$ ($\sigma \geqslant \sigma_0$), by (2.4b). Inasmuch as $F[x(\sigma)] \leqslant F(x_0)$ and $G[x(\sigma)] = 0$ ($\sigma \geqslant \sigma_0$), we have $x(\sigma) = x_0$ ($\sigma \geqslant \sigma_0$) by virtue of the uniqueness of x_0 as a minimum point of F on N subject to $G = 0$.

COROLLARY 2

If x_0 *affords a local minimum to* F *on* N, *then there is a number* σ_0 *such that* x_0 *affords a strict minimum to* H(x, σ) *whenever* $\sigma \geqslant \sigma_0$.

Let N_0 be a neighborhood of x_0 such that the relation $F(x) \geqslant F(x_0)$ holds on N_0. Since $\lim_{\sigma \to \infty} x(\sigma) = x_0$, there is a number σ_0 such that $x(\sigma_0)$ is in N_0. We then have $F[x(\sigma_0)] \geqslant F(x_0)$, as well as $F[x(\sigma_0)] \leqslant F(x_0)$. Consequently $F[x(\sigma_0)] = F(x_0)$. In view of Corollary 1, we have $x(\sigma) = x_0$ if $\sigma \geqslant \sigma_0$. It follows that x_0 affords a minimum to $H(x, \sigma)$ whenever $\sigma \geqslant \sigma_0$, as was to be proved.

As an immediate consequence of Theorem 2.1 we have

THEOREM 2.2

Let f, $g_1, \ldots, g_m$ *be continuous functions on a compact set* N. *Suppose that a point* x_0 *in* N *affords a strict minimum to* f *on* N *subject to the constraints*

$$g_\alpha(x) = 0 \qquad (\alpha = 1, \ldots, m). \tag{2.6}$$

Then $\lim_{\sigma \to \infty} x(\sigma) = x_0$, *where* x($\sigma$) *is the minimum point of the augmented function* H(x, σ) *defined by the formulas*

$$H(x, \sigma) = f(x) + \sigma G(x), \qquad G(x) = \tfrac{1}{2}\left[g_1(x)^2 + \cdots + g_m(x)^2 \right]. \tag{2.7}$$

In addition,

$$H[x(\sigma), \sigma] \leqslant H[x(\bar{\sigma}), \bar{\sigma}] \leqslant f(x_0) \qquad (\sigma < \bar{\sigma}), \tag{2.8a}$$

$$f[x(\sigma)] \leqslant f[x(\bar{\sigma})] \leqslant f(x_0), \qquad G[x(\sigma)] \geqslant G[x(\bar{\sigma})] \geqslant 0 \qquad (\sigma < \bar{\sigma}). \tag{2.8b}$$

In view of Corollary 2 of Theorem 2.1 we have this

COROLLARY

If in addition x_0 *affords a local minimum* f *on* N *then there is a number* σ_0 *such that* x_0 *affords a strict minimum on* N *to the augmented function* H(x, σ) *whenever* $\sigma \geqslant \sigma_0$.

We have the following extension of Theorem 2.2 involving the alternative augmented function

$$H(x, \mu, \sigma) = f(x) + \sum_{\alpha=1}^{m} \mu_\alpha g_\alpha(x) + \sigma G(x), \qquad G(x) = \frac{1}{2} \sum_{\alpha=1}^{m} [g_\alpha(x)]^2. \tag{2.9}$$

THEOREM 2.3

Suppose that the hypotheses of Theorem 2.2 hold. Let $x(\mu,\sigma)$ *be the minimum on* N *of the function* $H(x,\mu,\sigma)$ *defined by formula (2.9). If* M *is a bounded set of multipliers* $\mu=(\mu_1,\dots,\mu_m)$, *then*

$$\lim_{\sigma\to\infty} x(\mu,\sigma)=x_0, \qquad \lim_{\sigma\to\infty}\sigma G[x(\mu,\sigma)]=0 \qquad (2.10)$$

uniformly for all μ *in* M.

In the proof we express the inequality

$$H[x(\mu,\sigma),\mu,\sigma]\leqslant H(x_0,\mu,\sigma)=f(x_0)$$

in the form

$$f[x(\mu,\sigma)]+\sum_{\alpha=1}^{m}\mu_\alpha g_\alpha[x(\mu,\sigma)]+\sigma G[x(\mu,\sigma)]\leqslant f(x_0). \qquad (2.11)$$

Restricting μ to the bounded set M, we conclude from this inequality that

$$\lim_{\sigma\to\infty} G[x(\mu,\sigma)]=\lim_{\sigma\to\infty}\frac{1}{2}\sum_{\alpha=1}^{m}\{g_\alpha[x(\mu,\sigma)]\}^2=0.$$

Hence

$$\lim_{\sigma\to\infty} g_\alpha[x(\mu,\sigma)]=0 \qquad (\alpha=1,\dots,m). \qquad (2.12)$$

Consider now a neighborhood N_0 of x_0. There exists a positive number σ_0 such that if $\sigma\geqslant\sigma_0$ then $x(\mu,\sigma)$ is in N_0 for all μ in M. Otherwise there exists for every integer q a number $\sigma_q\geqslant q$ and a multiplier μ_q in M such that $x_q=x(\mu_q,\sigma_q)$ is not in N_0. By (2.12) we have $\lim_{q\to\infty}g_\alpha(x_q)=0$, and by (2.11)

$$\limsup_{q\to\infty}[f(x_q)+\sigma_q G(x_q)]\leqslant f(x_0).$$

In view of Lemma 2.1 we have $\lim_{q\to\infty}x_q=x_0$, contrary to our choice of x_q as a point exterior to N_0. From this contradiction we conclude that $x(\mu,\sigma)$ is in N_0 whenever μ is in M and $\sigma\geqslant\sigma_0$. Since N_0 is arbitrary, we have $\lim_{\sigma\to\infty}x(\mu,\sigma)=x_0$ uniformly for all μ in M. Combining this result with (2.11), we obtain the second limit in (2.10).

Theorem 2.1 has an interesting application to the theory of quadratic forms. To this end recall that a cone $\mathcal{C}$ can be viewed as a collection of vectors x with the property that if x is in $\mathcal{C}$ so also is ax for all scalars $a\geqslant 0$. Observe that $x=0$ is in $\mathcal{C}$.

THEOREM 2.4

Let $\mathcal{C}$ be a closed cone and let $P(x)$ and $Q(x)$ be two quadratic forms with the property that $P(x) > 0$ for all $x \neq 0$ in $\mathcal{C}$ such that $Q(x) = 0$. Suppose that $Q(x) \geqslant 0$ on $\mathcal{C}$. There is a positive constant σ_0 such that if $\sigma \geqslant \sigma_0$ then $P(x) + \sigma Q(x)$ is positive for all $x \neq 0$ in $\mathcal{C}$.

Let N be the set of all vectors in $\mathcal{C}$ having $|x| \leqslant 1$. Clearly N is compact. Let $x(\sigma)$ be a minimum point of $H(x, \sigma) = P(x) + \sigma Q(x)$ on N. Then $H[x(\sigma), \sigma] \leqslant H(0, \sigma) = 0$. If $x(\sigma) \neq 0$ and $b = |x(\sigma)|$, then $x(\sigma)/b$ is a unit vector in N, and

$$H[x(\sigma), \sigma] \leqslant H\left[\frac{x(\sigma)}{b}, \sigma\right] = \frac{H[x(\sigma), \sigma]}{b^2} \leqslant 0, \quad b \leqslant 1.$$

It follows that if $H[x(\sigma), \sigma] < 0$ we have $b = 1$. If $H[x(\sigma), \sigma] = 0$ and $b < 1$, we can replace $x(\sigma)$ by $x(\sigma)/b$. Hence either $x(\sigma)$ is a unit vector, or else $x(\sigma) = 0$. By Theorem 2.1 with $F(x) = P(x)$ and $G(x) = Q(x)$ we have $\lim_{\sigma \to \infty} x(\sigma) = 0$. Since $|x(\sigma)| = 1$ unless $x(\sigma) = 0$, this is possible only if $x(\sigma) = 0$ for large values of σ. There is accordingly a constant σ_0 such that $x(\sigma) = 0$ $(\sigma \geqslant \sigma_0)$, and hence such that $H(x, \sigma) > 0$ for all $x \neq 0$ in N. For any $x \neq 0$ in $\mathcal{C}$ the point $x/|x|$ is in N and

$$H(x, \sigma) = |x|^2 H\left(\frac{x}{|x|}, \sigma\right) > 0.$$

This proves Theorem 2.4.

EXERCISES

In Exercises 1 to 5 the hypotheses of Theorem 2.3 hold. We assume further that $f, g_1, \ldots, g_m$ are of class C' on N and that x_0 is an interior point of N. Let N_0 be a neighborhood of x_0 interior to N, and let $x(\mu, \sigma)$ minimize $H(x, \mu, \sigma)$ on N. *Hint*: See the results given in Section 9.

1. Show that there is a constant σ_0 such that, if $\sigma \geqslant \sigma_0$ and $\mu \in M$, then $x(\mu, \sigma)$ is in N_0.

2. Show that, if $\sigma \geqslant \sigma_0$ and $\mu \in M$, the point $x = x(\mu, \sigma)$ satisfies the multiplier rule $\nabla f + \lambda^* \nabla g = 0$ with $\lambda = \mu + \sigma g[x(\mu, \sigma)]$. Here λ, μ, g are column vectors, ∇f is a row vector, and ∇g is an $(m \times n)$-dimensional matrix, whose rows are the gradients of $g_1, \ldots, g_m$.

3. Suppose that x_0 is a normal point relative to the constraints $g(x) = 0$; that is, suppose that $\nabla g(x)$ has rank m on N_0. Let $\Gamma(x)$ be the transpose of the pseudoinverse of $\nabla g(x)$ (see Section 6, Chapter 3). Show that $\Gamma(x)$ is continuous on N_0. Set $\Lambda(x) = -\Gamma(x)\nabla f(x)$, where ∇f is now a column vector. Show that, if $\sigma \geqslant \sigma_0$ and $\mu \in M$, then

$$\Lambda[x(\mu, \sigma)] = \mu + \sigma g[x(\mu, \sigma)].$$

4. Use the result given in Exercise 3 to show that under the hypotheses of normality at x_0 we have

$$\lim_{\sigma \to \infty} \{ \mu + \sigma g[x(\mu,\sigma)]\} = \lambda_0$$

uniformly for all μ in M, where λ_0 is the Lagrange multiplier with which x_0 satisfies the multiplier rule $\nabla f + \lambda^* \nabla g = 0$.

5. Suppose that x_0 is a normal point of the constraints $g(x) = 0$. Let $x(\sigma)$ be the minimum point of $H(x,\sigma) = f(x) + (\sigma/2) g(x)^* g(x)$ on N. Show that, if x_0 is an interior point of N, the limit $\lambda = \lim_{\sigma \to \infty} \sigma g[x(\sigma)]$ exists and is a Lagrange multiplier of f relative to g at x_0. *Hint*: Use the result given in Exercise 4 with $\mu = 0$.

6. In the xy-plane the origin $(0,0)$ affords a strict minimum to $f(x,y) = x^2 - y^2 - 4y$ subject to $g(x,y) = y = 0$. If $\sigma > 2$, the point $[0, 4 - \mu/(\sigma-2)]$ affords a strict minimum to

$$H = f + \mu g + \frac{\sigma}{2} g^2 = x^2 + \frac{\sigma - 2}{2} y^2 + (\mu - 4) y$$

Verify the result given in Exercise 4 for this case.

7. Apply the result given in Exercise 4 to the problem in the xy-plane of minimizing $f(x,y) = x^2 - y^2 - 4y$ subject to $g(x,y) = y = 0$. Show that, if we replace $g(x,y) = y$ by $g(x,y) = y^2$, the conclusion given in Exercise 4 is invalid. Is the conclusion valid if $f(x,y) = x^2 - y^4 - 4y^2$ and $g(x,y) = y^2$?

8. In xy-space let P and Q be the quadratic forms

$$P(x,y) = x^2 + 3xy + y^2, \qquad Q(x,y) = (x-y)^2.$$

Determine σ so that $P + \sigma Q$ is a positive quadratic form.

9. The quadratic form $P(x,y) = 2x^2 + xy$ has the property that $P(x,y) > 0$ for all $(x,y) \neq (0,0)$ having $Q(x,y) = xy + y^2 = 0$. Show that $P + Q$ is positive. In this case the hypotheses of Theorem 2.4 are not satisfied. Extend this result to arbitrary two-dimensional quadratic forms P and Q.

10. Let

$$P(x) = \sum_{i,j=1}^{n} a_{ij} x^i x^j \qquad \text{and} \qquad Q(x) = |x|^2.$$

Assume that $a_{ij} = a_{ji}$. Show that, if σ is greater than the largest eigenvalue of the matrix $A = (a_{ij})$, then $P + \sigma Q$ is positive. What can be said if σ is greater than the largest nonpositive eigenvalue of A?

11. Apply Theorem 2.4 to the case in which $P(x,y) = xy - 2y^2$, $Q(x,y) = y^2$, and $\mathcal{C}$ is the cone of vectors (x,y) having $x \geqslant 0$, $y \geqslant x$.

12. Establish Theorem 2.4 by the argument used to prove Lemma 6.1 of Chapter 2.

13. Let A be a symmetric $(n \times n)$-dimensional matrix, and let D be an $(m \times n)$-dimensional matrix. Show that, if $P(x) = x^*Ax > 0$ for all $x \neq 0$ having $Dx = 0$, there is a constant σ such that the matrix $A + \sigma D^*D$ is positive definite. *Hint*: Set $Q(x) = x^*D^*Dx$, and apply Theorem 2.4.

3. REMOVAL OF CONSTRAINTS

We continue the study of the problem of minimizing a function $F(x)$ subject to the constraint $G(x) = 0$, where $G(x)$ is a nonnegative function. Suppose that x_0 is a solution to our problem. Then x_0 also minimizes the augmented function $H(x) = F(x) + \sigma G(x)$ subject to the constraint $G(x) = 0$. In favorable cases the constant σ can be chosen so that the function $H(x)$ has at least a local unconstrained minimum at x_0 relative to all points x near x_0. In this event we say that the constraint $G(x) = 0$ can be removed by adding $\sigma G(x)$ to $F(x)$. This is a simple type of augmentability. The purpose of this section is to find criteria on F and G which will permit us to remove the constraint $G(x) = 0$ in this manner.

EXAMPLE 3.1

The result given in Theorem 2.4 is a simple example of this type of augmentability. As a further example in the xy-plane consider the function $F(x,y) = x^2 + xy + y^3$, which has a minimum at the origin subject to the constraint $G(x,y) = y^2 = 0$. In this event the augmented function $H(x,y) = F(x,y) + G(x,y) = x^2 + xy + y^2 + y^3$ has a local minimum at the origin. However, if we choose $G(x,y) = y^4$, the origin still minimizes F subject of $G = 0$, but fails to afford an unrestricted local minimum to $H = F + \sigma G = x^2 + xy + y^3 + \sigma y^4$, no matter how σ is chosen.

The theorem upon which the removal of constraints is based is the following one, established in Section 3 of Chapter 1. In this theorem we assume that $H(x)$ is twice differentiable at x_0.

THEOREM 3.1

If x_0 *affords a local minimum to* H(x), *then*

$$\nabla H(x_0) = 0, \qquad H''(x_0, h) \geqslant 0 \qquad \textit{for all } h \neq 0. \tag{3.1}$$

Conversely, if

$$\nabla H(x_0) = 0, \qquad H''(x_0, h) > 0 \qquad \textit{for all } h \neq 0 \tag{3.2}$$

then there is a neighborhood N_0 *of* x_0 *and a constant* $\tau > 0$ *such that the inequality*

$$H(x) \geqslant H(x_0) + \tau|x - x_0|^2 \tag{3.3}$$

holds for all x *in* N_0.

This theorem was established in Chapter 1 under the assumptions that $H(x)$ was of class C'' on a neighborhood of x_0. However, in the proof we used only the fact that $H(x)$ is twice differentiable at x_0 in the sense that the Taylor formula

$$H(x_0 + h) = H(x_0) + H'(x_0, h) + \tfrac{1}{2}H''(x_0, h) + R(x_0, h)$$

holds at x_0 with

$$\lim_{h \to 0} \frac{R(x_0, h)}{|h|^2} = 0.$$

Returning to the problem of minimizing F subject to the constraint $G(x) = 0$, we assume that the functions F and G are twice differentiable at a point x_0 at which $G(x_0) = 0$. Since $G(x) \geqslant 0$, by hypotheses, the point x_0 minimizes $G(x)$. Consequently, by Theorem 3.1

$$\nabla G(x_0) = 0, \qquad G''(x_0, h) \geqslant 0 \qquad \text{for all } h \neq 0. \tag{3.4}$$

In general, there is a vector $h \neq 0$ such that $G''(x_0, h) = 0$, but we do not insist that this is the case.

Suppose that there is a constant σ such that x_0 affords a local minimum to a function H of the form

$$H(x) = F(x) + \sigma G(x).$$

Again by Theorem 3.1 we have

$$\nabla H(x_0) = \nabla F(x_0) + \sigma \nabla G(x_0) = \nabla F(x_0) = 0,$$

$$H''(x_0, h) = F''(x_0, h) + \sigma G''(x_0, h) \geqslant 0 \qquad \text{for all } h \neq 0.$$

The last condition implies that $F''(x_0, h) \geqslant 0$ whenever $G''(x_0, h) = 0$. This establishes the following result.

THEOREM 3.2

Suppose that there is a constant σ *such that* x_0 *affords a local minimum to*

$$H(x) = F(x) + \sigma G(x).$$

Then x_0 *affords a local minimum to* F *subject to* $G(x) = 0$. *Moreover*

$$\nabla F(x_0) = 0, \qquad F''(x_0, h) \geqslant 0 \qquad \text{whenever } h \neq 0 \text{ and } G''(x_0, h) = 0. \quad (3.5)$$

As a converse of this result we have

THEOREM 3.3

Suppose that

$$\nabla F(x_0) = 0, \qquad F''(x_0, h) > 0 \qquad \text{whenever } h \neq 0 \text{ and } G''(x_0, h) = 0. \quad (3.6)$$

Then there exist positive constants σ_0, τ *and a neighborhood* N_0 *of* x_0 *such that, if we set*

$$H(x) = F(x) + \sigma G(x) \qquad (\sigma \geqslant \sigma_0),$$

then the inequality

$$H(x) \geqslant H(x_0) + \tau |x - x_0|^2 = F(x_0) + \tau |x - x_0|^2 \quad (3.7)$$

holds for all x *in* N_0. *Moreover the inequality*

$$F(x) \geqslant F(x_0) + \tau |x - x_0|^2 \quad (3.8)$$

holds for all x *in* N_0 *having* $G(x) = 0$.

To prove this result, observe that, by (3.6), the quadratic forms $P(h) = F''(x_0, h)$ and $Q(h) = G''(x_0, h)$ satisfy the hypothesis of Theorem 2.4. It follows from Theorem 2.4 that there is a constant σ_0 such that

$$F''(x_0, h) + \sigma_0 G''(x_0, h) > 0 \qquad \text{for all } h \neq 0.$$

Consequently the function $H(x) = F(x) + \sigma_0 G(x)$ has the property that

$$\nabla H(x_0) = \nabla F(x_0) + \sigma_0 \nabla G(x_0) = 0,$$

$$H''(x_0, h) = F''(x_0, h) + \sigma_0 G''(x_0, h) > 0 \qquad (h \neq 0).$$

It follows from Theorem 3.1 that there are a positive constant τ and a neighborhood N_0 of x_0 such that (3.7) holds for all x in N_0. Since $G(x) \geqslant 0$, this inequaltiy is also valid if we replace σ_0 by any larger number σ. Inequality (3.7) reduces to (3.8) when $G(x) = 0$. This proves Theorem 3.3.

The result just obtained is a local result. If x_0 affords a strict minimum to F subject to $G = 0$ on a compact set N, a global result of the following nature can be obtained. We assume, of course, that F and G are continuous on N and are twice differentiable at x_0.

THEOREM 3.4

Suppose that x_0 *affords a strict minimum to* F *on a compact set* N *subject to the constraint* $G(x) = 0$. *Suppose further that*

$$\nabla F(x_0) = 0, \qquad F''(x_0, h) > 0 \qquad whenever\ h \neq 0\ and\ G''(x_0, h) = 0.$$

Then there are positive constants σ_0 *and* τ *such that the inequality*

$$H(x) \geqslant H(x_0) + \tau|x - x_0|^2 = F(x_0) + \tau|x - x_0|^2 \tag{3.9}$$

holds on N, *where* $H = F + \sigma G$ *and* $\sigma \geqslant \sigma_0$. *In particular,*

$$F(x) \geqslant F(x_0) + \tau|x - x_0|^2 \tag{3.10}$$

for all x *in* N *having* $G(x) = 0$.

We need only to treat the case $\sigma = \sigma_0$. By Theorem 3.3 there are positive constants σ_0 and τ and a neighborhood N_0 of x_0 such that inequality (3.9) holds on N_0 with $H = F + \sigma_0 G$. Since x_0 affords a strict minimum to F on N subject to $G = 0$, there is a constant τ_0 such that

$$\frac{F(x) - F(x_0)}{|x - x_0|^2} \geqslant \tau_0$$

for all x in $N - N_0$ having $G(x) = 0$. Setting $\tau_1 = \frac{1}{2}\min(\tau, \tau_0)$, we see that the point x_0 affords a local minimum to the function

$$\hat{F}(x) = H(x) - \tau_1|x - x_0|^2$$

and a strict minimum to $\hat{F}$ on N subject to $G = 0$. It follows from Corollary 2 to Theorem 2.1 that there is a constant σ_1 such that x_0 affords a strict minimum on N to

$$\hat{F}(x) + \sigma_1 G(x) = F(x) + (\sigma_0 + \sigma_1)G(x) - \tau_1|x - x_0|^2.$$

Hence (3.9) holds with τ replaced by τ_1 and $\sigma \geqslant \sigma_0 + \sigma_1$. Calling $\sigma_0 + \sigma_1$ a new σ_0 and τ_1 a new τ, we obtain the result stated in Theorem 3.4.

4. AUGMENTABILITY AND THE LAGRANGE MULTIPLIER RULE

We are now in a position to give an alternative derivation of the Lagrange multiplier rule discussed in Chapter 3. To this end we consider the problem of minimizing a function $f(x)$ subject to the constraints

$$g_\alpha(x) = 0 \qquad (\alpha = 1, \ldots, m). \tag{4.1}$$

We assume that the functions $f, g_1, \ldots, g_m$ are of class C'' in a neighborhood of a point x_0 satisfying these constraints. We seek conditions under which there exist multipliers $\lambda_1, \ldots, \lambda_m$ and a constant σ such that x_0 affords an unconstrained local minimum to an augmented function of the form

$$H(x) = f(x) + \sum_{\alpha=1}^{m} \lambda_\alpha g_\alpha(x) + \frac{\sigma}{2} \sum_{\alpha=1}^{m} g_\alpha(x)^2. \tag{4.2}$$

Observe that $H(x) = f(x)$ when constraints (4.1) are satisfied. Consequently, if x_0 minimizes $H(x)$, then x_0 minimizes $f(x)$ subject to constraints (4.1). If a function H of this type exists, we shall say that our problem is *augmentable* at x_0. If indeed our problem is augmentable at x_0, the replacement of f by H can be viewed as a procedure which permits us to remove constraints (4.1).

We illustrate this phenomenon by

EXAMPLE 4.1

Continuing with Example 2.1, in which the point $(x_0, y_0) = (0, 0)$ minimizes

$$f(x,y) = x^2 - y^2 - 4y \qquad \text{subject to } g(x,y) = y = 0,$$

we observe that the function

$$H(x,y; \sigma) = f + \lambda g + \frac{\sigma}{2} g^2 = x^2 + \left(\frac{\sigma-2}{2}\right) y^2 + (\lambda - 4) y$$

has a strict minimum at $(0,0)$ if $\lambda = 4$ and $\sigma > 2$. The same is true if we choose $\lambda = 4 + 2y$ and $\sigma \geqslant 0$. Observe that $\lambda = 4$ is the Lagrange multiplier for our problem. If we replace f by $f(x,y) = x^2 - y^2 - 4y - y^3/3$ and restrict y by the condition $|y| \leqslant r \ (r > 0)$, the function

$$H(x,y; \lambda, \sigma) = x^2 + \frac{\sigma-2}{2} y^2 + (\lambda - 4) y - \frac{y^3}{3}$$

will have a strict minimum at $(0,0)$ if $\lambda=4$ and $\sigma\geqslant 2+r$ or if $\lambda=4+2y$ and $\sigma\geqslant 4$. Observe that, if $\lambda=4$ and $\sigma=4+2y^2$, the restriction on y can be dropped. Finally, if we set $g(x,y)=y^2$ and $f(x,y)=x^2-y^2-4y$, then $H=x^2-4y+(\lambda-1)y^2+(\sigma/2)y^4$ fails to have a minimum at $(0,0)$ for any λ and σ, even though the origin minimizes f subject to $g=0$. However, if $g=y^2$ and $f+x^2-y^4-4y^2$, the corresponding function H with $\lambda=4$ and $\sigma>2$ is minimized at the origin.

EXAMPLE 4.2

It is clear that the function $f(x,y)=x^2+2x+y^4$ has a strict local minimum at the point $(x_0,y_0)=(0,0)$ subject to the constraint $g(x,y)=xy-x=0$. Since $\nabla g\neq0$ at $(0,0)$, the problem is normal at $(0,0)$. However, this problem is not augmentable, for consider a function

$$H=f+\lambda g+\frac{\sigma}{2}g^2=x^2\left[1+\frac{\sigma}{2}(y-1)^2\right]+(2-\lambda)x+\lambda xy+y^4.$$

If $\nabla H=0$ at $(0,0)$, we must have $\lambda=2$. Hence H must be of the form $H=x^2[1+(\sigma/2)(y-1)^2]+2xy+y^4$. We can suppose that $\sigma\geqslant0$. If $y^2<1/(1+2\sigma)$ and $x=-[y/(1+2\sigma)]$, we see that

$$H(x,y)\leqslant y^2\left(y^2-\frac{1}{1+2\sigma}\right)<0=H(0,0).$$

It follows that our problem is not augmentable at $(0,0)$. However, it is augmentable if we replace the constraint $xy-x=0$ by the equivalent local constraint $x=0$.

We now return to the general problem, and suppose that there is a function $H(x)$ of form (4.2) having a local minimum at a point x_0 satisfying constraints (4.1). Setting

$$F=f+\lambda_1g_1+\cdots+\lambda_mg_m,\qquad G=\tfrac{1}{2}(g_1^2+\cdots+g_m^2),$$

we see that H is of the type

$$H(x)=F(x)+\sigma G(x)$$

discussed in Section 3. We have

$$\nabla G(x_0)=0,\qquad G''(x_0,h)=\sum_{\alpha=1}^m[g_\alpha'(x_0,h)]^2.$$

Since x_0 minimizes $H(x)$, it follows from Theorem 3.2 that

$$\nabla F(x_0)=0, \qquad F''(x_0,h) \geqslant 0 \qquad \text{whenever } G''(x_0,h)= \sum_{\alpha=1}^{m} [\, g'_\alpha(x_0,h)]^2 = 0$$

or, equivalently,

$$\nabla F(x_0)=0, \qquad F''(x_0,h) \geqslant 0 \qquad \text{whenever } g'_\alpha(x_0,h)=0 \qquad (\alpha=1,\dots,m).$$

$$(4.3)$$

This establishes the following consequence of augmentability.

THEOREM 4.1

If x_0 affords a local minimum to a function H of the form

$$H(x)=f(x)+ \sum_{\alpha=1}^{m} \lambda_\alpha g_\alpha(x) + \frac{\sigma}{2} \sum_{\alpha=1}^{m} [g_\alpha(x)]^2,$$

then the function $F=f+\lambda_1 g_1 + \cdots +\lambda_m g_m$ must be a Lagrange function in the sense that the Lagrange multiplier rule (4.3) holds. In addition x_0 affords a local minimum to $f(x)$ subject to the constraints $g_\alpha(x)=0$ ($\alpha=1,\dots,m$).

The *Lagrange multiplier rule* (4.3) was established in Theorem 2.2, Chapter 3, under the alternative hypothesis that the gradients $\nabla g_1(x_0),\dots,$ $\nabla g_m(x_0)$ are linearly independent. As in Section 3, Chapter 3, we strengthen the multiplier rule (4.3) by excluding the equality in (4.3) when $h \neq 0$. The *strengthened Lagrange multiplier rule* then takes the form

$$\nabla F(x_0)=0, \qquad \text{where } F=f+\lambda_1 g_1 + \cdots +\lambda_m g_m, \qquad (4.4a)$$

$$F''(x_0,h)>0 \qquad \text{if } h \neq 0 \quad \text{and} \quad g'_\alpha(x_0,h)=0 \quad (\alpha=1,\dots,m). \qquad (4.4b)$$

Recalling that

$$G''(x_0,h)= \sum_{\alpha=1}^{m} [\, g'_\alpha(x_0,h)]^2,$$

we see that $g'_\alpha(x_0,h)=0$ ($\alpha=1,\dots,m$) if and only if $G''(x_0,h)=0$. It follows that relation (4.4b) can be put into the form

$$F''(x_0,h)>0 \qquad \text{if } h \neq 0 \quad \text{and} \quad G''(x_0,h)=0.$$

Consequently the hypotheses given in Theorem 3.3 are satisfied. Applying Theorem 3.3 to the case here considered, we obtain the following converse of Theorem 4.1. Here and elsewhere it is understood that x_0 satisfies constraints (4.1).

THEOREM 4.2

If the strengthened Lagrange multiplier rule (4.4) *holds at* x_0 *with multipliers* $\lambda_1, \ldots, \lambda_m$, *then there exist positive numbers* σ_0 *and* τ *and a neighborhood* N_0 *of* x_0 *such that inequality*

$$H(x) \geqslant H(x_0) + \tau |x - x_0|^2 = f(x_0) + \tau |x - x_0|^2 \tag{4.5}$$

holds for all x *in* N_0, *where*

$$H(x) = f(x) + \sum_{\alpha=1}^{m} \lambda_\alpha g_\alpha(x) + \frac{\sigma}{2} \sum_{\alpha=1}^{m} [g_\alpha(x)]^2 \qquad (\sigma \geqslant \sigma_0). \tag{4.6}$$

In particular, if a point x *in* N_0 *satisfies the constraints* $g_\alpha(x) = 0$ $(\alpha = 1, \ldots, m)$, *then*

$$f(x) \geqslant f(x_0) + \tau |x - x_0|^2. \tag{4.7}$$

We have the following extension of our last result.

THEOREM 4.3

Theorem 4.2 *remains valid if we replace the function* $H(x)$ *defined by* (4.6) *by the more general function*

$$H(x) = f(x) + \sum_{\alpha=1}^{m} \mu_\alpha(x) g_\alpha(x) + \frac{\sigma}{2} \sum_{\alpha=1}^{m} [g_\alpha(x)]^2 \qquad (\sigma \geqslant \sigma_0), \tag{4.8}$$

where $\mu_1(x), \ldots, \mu_m(x)$ *are functions of class* C' *on* N *having*

$$\mu_\alpha(x_0) = \lambda_\alpha \qquad (\alpha = 1, \ldots, m). \tag{4.9}$$

In this event H is of the form

$$H(x) = \hat{F}(x) + \sigma G(x),$$

where

$$\hat{F}(x) = F(x) + K(x), \qquad K(x) = \sum_{\alpha=1}^{m} [\mu_\alpha(x) - \lambda_\alpha] g_\alpha(x),$$

$$F(x) = f(x) + \sum_{\alpha=1}^{m} \lambda_\alpha g_\alpha(x).$$

By virtue of the next lemma, $K(x)$ is twice differentiable at x_0. Moreover, by (4.9),

$$\nabla K(x_0) = 0, \qquad K''(x_0, h) = 2 \sum_{\alpha=1}^{m} \mu_\alpha'(x_0, h) g_\alpha'(x_0, h).$$

Hence $K''(x_0, h) = 0,$ $\hat{F}''(x_0, h) = F''(x_0, h)$ whenever

$$G''(x_0, h) = \sum_{\alpha=1}^{m} [g_\alpha'(x_0, h)]^2 = 0.$$

It follows from (4.4) that

$$\nabla \hat{F}(x_0) = 0, \qquad \hat{F}''(x_0, h) > 0 \qquad \text{whenever } h \neq 0 \quad \text{and} \quad G''(x_0, h) = 0.$$

Applying Theorem 3.3 to $H = \hat{F} + \sigma G$, we obtain Theorem 4.3.

The fact that the function $K(x)$ described above is twice differentiable at x_0 follows from

LEMMA 4.1

Let u(x) *and* v(x) *be functions having* u(x₀) = v(x₀) = 0. *If* u *and* v *are differentiable at* x₀, *then the product* w(x) = u(x)v(x) *is twice differentiable at* x₀. *Moreover*

$$w''(x_0, h) = 2u'(x_0, h)v'(x_0, h). \tag{4.10}$$

Clearly $w(x_0) = 0$ and $\nabla w(x_0) = u(x_0)\nabla v(x_0) + \nabla u(x_0)v(x_0) = 0$. Since u and v are differentiable at x_0, we have

$$u(x_0 + h) = u'(x_0, h) + r(h), \qquad v(x_0 + h) = v'(x_0, h) + s(h),$$

where

$$\lim_{h \to 0} \frac{r(h)}{|h|} = 0, \qquad \lim_{h \to 0} \frac{s(h)}{|h|} = 0.$$

Hence

$$w(x_0+h)=u'(x_0,h)v'(x_0,h)+R(h)$$

with

$$\frac{R(h)}{|h|^2}=u'\left(x_0,\frac{h}{|h|}\right)\frac{s(h)}{|h|}+\frac{r(h)}{|h|}v'\left(x_0,\frac{h}{|h|}\right)+\frac{r(h)}{|h|}\frac{s(h)}{|h|}.$$

Clearly

$$\lim_{h\to0}\frac{R(h)}{|h|^2}=0.$$

Consequently w is twice differentiable at x_0, and (4.10) holds.

For each α the functions $u(x)=\mu_\alpha(x)-\lambda_\alpha$ and $v(x)=g_\alpha(x)$ satisfy the hypotheses of this lemma. Hence $K(x)=\sum_{\alpha=1}^m[\mu_\alpha(x)-\lambda_\alpha]g_\alpha(x)$ is twice differentiable at x_0, and $K''(x_0,h)=2\sum_{\alpha=1}^m\mu_\alpha'(x_0,h)g_\alpha'(x_0,h)$, as stated in the proof of Theorem 3.3.

The results given above are local in character. A global result is obtained when x_0 affords a strict minimum to f subject to constraints (4.1) on a compact set N. We assume that the functions $f,g_1,\ldots,g_m$ are of class C'' in N.

THEOREM 4.4

If in addition to the hypotheses made in Theorem 4.3 we assume that x_0 affords a strict minimum to $f(x)$ on N subject to $g_\alpha(x)=0$ ($\alpha=1,\ldots,m$), then the constants σ_0 and τ described in Theorem 4.3 can be chosen so that the inequality

$$H(x)\geq H(x_0)+\tau|x-x_0|^2=f(x_0)+\tau|x-x_0|^2$$

holds for all x in N, where H is defined by formula (4.8).

A natural choice of the functions $\mu_1(x),\ldots,\mu_m(x)$ appearing in Theorems 4.3 and 4.4 is $\mu_\alpha(x)=\lambda_\alpha$ ($\alpha=1,\ldots,m$). Another natural choice is given in

THEOREM 4.5

Suppose that the gradients $\nabla g_1(x),\ldots,\nabla g_m(x)$ are linearly independent on N; then the solutions $\mu_1(x),\ldots,\mu_m(x)$ of the minimum problem

$$\min_\mu|\nabla f(x)+\mu_1\nabla g_1(x)+\cdots+\mu_m\nabla g_m(x)|$$

are of class C′ *on* N. *Moreover* $\lambda_\alpha = \mu_\alpha(x_0)$ $(\alpha = 1, \ldots, m)$ *are the multipliers with which* x_0 *satisfies the multiplier rule*

$$\nabla f(x) + \lambda_1 \nabla g_1(x_0) + \cdots + \lambda_m \nabla_m(x_0) = 0.$$

This result was established in Chapter 3, Section 6.

EXERCISES

1. Show that the function $f(x,y) = x^2 y + x^6$ has a strict minimum at $(x_0, y_0) = (0, 0)$ subject to the constraint $g(x,y) = y = 0$. Show that this problem is not augmentable at $(0,0)$. What can be said if f is replaced by $f(x,y) = x^2 + xy$?

2. Verify that Theorems 4.1 to 4.4 are valid if the functions $f, g_1, \ldots, g_m$ are continuous on N and are twice differentiable at x_0.

3. Suppose that the hypotheses of Theorem 4.4 hold. Suppose further that x_0 is an interior point of N and a normal point relative to $g_\alpha(x) = 0$ $(\alpha = 1, \ldots, m)$. Let $x(\mu, \sigma)$ be the minimum point of $H(x, \mu, \sigma)$. Show that there are a constant σ_0 and $\tau > 0$ such that, if $\sigma \geqslant \sigma_0$ and $\mu \in M$, the inequality

$$H(x, \mu, \sigma) \geqslant H[x(\mu, \sigma), \mu, \sigma] + \tau |x - x(\mu, \sigma)|^2$$

   holds for all x in N. (See Section 9.)

4. Suppose that the hypotheses of Theorem 4.4 hold with N an open set instead of a closed set. Show that there is a function $\sigma(x)$ of class C^∞ such that the function

$$H(x) = f(x) + \sum_{\alpha=1}^{m} \left\{ \mu_\alpha(x) g_\alpha(x) + \frac{\sigma(x)}{2.} [g_\alpha(x)]^2 \right\}$$

   has a strict minimum on N at x_0. *Hint*: Use the fact that N is the union of compact sets $N_1, N_2, N_3, \ldots$ having N_q interior to N_{q+1}. Choose $\sigma_0 = \sigma_q$ effective as in Theorem 4.4 on N_q, and select $\sigma(x) \geqslant \sigma_q$ on $N_q - N_{q-1}$.

5. Apply the results given in this section to a selected list of problems in the examples and exercises of Section 2, Chapter 3.

5. MINIMA SUBJECT TO SIMPLE INEQUALITY CONSTRAINTS

In the preceding pages we based our theory on the minimization of a function $H(x)$ at an interior point x_0 of the domain considered. This led us to the Lagrange multiplier rule relative to equality constraints. We shall now consider the case in which the minimum point is on the boundary of our domain of minimization. Our boundary will be of a simple type. To describe this situation, it will be convenient to consider our functions to be defined on an open set in an $(n+p)$-dimensional space of points (x,y) $=(x^1,\ldots,x^n, y^1,\ldots,y^p)$. We seek to minimize a function $H(x,y)$ subject to constraints of the form

$$y^\alpha \leqslant 0 \qquad (\alpha = 1,\ldots,p).\tag{5.1}$$

The results obtained can be used to derive the Lagrange multiplier rule when inequality constraints are encountered.

We suppose that we are given a point (x_0,y_0) satisfying constraints (5.1). We shall tacitly assume that at least one of the components $y_0^1,\ldots,y_0^p$ is zero. However, the results obtained are valid if they are all negative. From a theoretical point of view we could assume that all these components are zero, since a negative y-component could be considered to be an x-component. However, to facilitate applications it will be conveneint to admit the case in which some of the y-components of (x_0,y_0) are negative. Accordingly we say that an index α is *active* at (x_0,y_0) if $y_0^\alpha = 0$ and *inactive* if $y_0^\alpha < 0$.

We shall assume that the function $H(x,y)$ is continuous near (x_0,y_0) and is twice differentiable at (x_0,y_0). The first and second differentials of H at (x_0,y_0) will be denoted respectively by

$$H'(x_0,y_0; h,k), \qquad H''(x_0,y_0; h,k),$$

where $(h,k)=(h^1,\ldots,h^n; k^1,\ldots,k^p)$. The variations of constraints (5.1) at (x_0,y_0) are accordingly

$$k^\alpha \leqslant 0 \qquad \text{whenever } y_0^\alpha = 0.\tag{5.2}$$

Observe that k^α is arbitrary when $y_0^\alpha < 0$. The vectors (h,k) satisfying constraints (5.2) form a convex cone $\mathcal{C}_0$. If (h,k) is in $\mathcal{C}_0$, then for a small positive value δ the points

$$x = x_0 + th, \qquad y = y_0 + tk \qquad (0 \leqslant t \leqslant \delta)$$

satisfy constraints (5.1). The subcone $\mathcal{C}$ of $\mathcal{C}_0$, defined by the relations

$$k^\alpha \leqslant 0 \text{ if } y_0^\alpha = 0, \qquad k^\alpha = 0 \text{ if } \frac{\partial H}{\partial y^\alpha}(x_0,y_0) < 0$$

plays a significant role in the second-order conditions described in

THEOREM 5.1

If the point (x_0, y_0) *affords a local minimum to* $H(x, y)$ *subject to the constraints* $y^\alpha \leqslant 0$ $(\alpha = 1, \ldots, p)$, *then*

$$\frac{\partial H}{\partial x^i}(x_0, y_0) = 0, \qquad \frac{\partial H}{\partial y^\alpha}(x_0, y_0) \leqslant 0 \qquad \text{with equality if } y_0{}^\alpha < 0. \quad (5.3a)$$

Moreover

$$H''(x_0, y_0; h, k) \geqslant 0, \qquad \text{all } (h, k) \neq (0, 0) \text{ in } \mathcal{C}, \quad (5.3b)$$

where $\mathcal{C}$ *is the cone of vectors* (h, k) *having*

$$k^\alpha \leqslant 0 \quad \text{if } y_0{}^\alpha = 0, \qquad k^\alpha = 0 \quad \text{if } \frac{\partial H}{\partial y^\alpha}(x_0, y_0) < 0. \quad (5.4)$$

Conversely, if conditions (5.3) *hold with the equality excluded in* (5.3b), *then there are a neighborhood* $\hat{N}_0$ *of* (x_0, y_0) *and a constant* $\tau > 0$ *such that the inequality*

$$H(x, y) \geqslant H(x_0, y_0) + \tau[|x - x_0|^2 + |y - y_0|^2] \quad (5.5)$$

holds for all (x, y) *in* $\hat{N}_0$ *having* $y^\alpha \leqslant 0$ $(\alpha = 1, \ldots, p)$.

Suppose first that (x_0, y_0) affords a local minimum to $H(x, y)$ subject to constraints (5.1). Then obviously (5.3a) holds, as can be seen by appropriately varying each component separately. Let (h, k) be a vector in the cone $\mathcal{C}$ defined by constraints (5.4). Then the function

$$w(t) = H(x_0 + th, y_0 + tk) \qquad (0 \leqslant t \leqslant \delta)$$

has a local minimum at $t = 0$. Moreover, by (5.3a) and (5.4),

$$w'(0) = H'(x_0, y_0; h, k) = 0.$$

Consequently

$$w''(0) = H''(x_0, y_0; h, k) \geqslant 0.$$

This establishes the second-order condition (5.3b).

To prove the last conclusion in the theorem, suppose that it is false.

Then for each integer q there is a point (x_q, y_q) such that

$$y_q^\alpha \leqslant 0 \quad (\alpha = 1, \ldots, p), \qquad t_q = \left[|x_q - x_0|^2 + |y_q - y_0|^2 \right]^{1/2} < \frac{1}{q}, \quad (5.6a)$$

$$H(x_q, y_q) - H(x_0, y_0) < \frac{t_q^2}{q}. \tag{5.6b}$$

Clearly $(x_q, y_q) \neq (x_0, y_0)$. Hence $t_q > 0$. Replace our original sequence by a subsequence, again denoted by $\{(x_q, y_q)\}$, such that the unit vectors (h_q, k_q) defined by the relations

$$h_q = \frac{x_q - x_0}{t_q}, \qquad k_q = \frac{y_q - y_0}{t_q} \tag{5.7}$$

converge to a vector (h, k). Clearly (h, k) is a unit vector. Moreover relations (5.6) are unaltered by this replacement. Renumber the indices $1, \ldots, p$ so that equations (5.3a) become

$$\frac{\partial H}{\partial x^i}(x_0, y_0) = 0 \quad (i = 1, \ldots, n), \qquad \frac{\partial H}{\partial y^\alpha}(x_0, y_0) < 0 \quad (\alpha = 1, \ldots, r),$$

$$\frac{\partial H}{\partial y^\beta}(x_0, y_0) = 0 \quad (\beta = r + 1, \ldots, p). \tag{5.8}$$

Observe that $k_q^\alpha = y_q^\alpha / t_q \leqslant 0$ if $y_0^\alpha = 0$. Hence by (5.8) we have

$$H'(x_0, y_0; h_q, k_q) = \sum_{\alpha = 1}^{r} \frac{\partial H}{\partial y^\alpha}(x_0, y_0) k_q^\alpha \geqslant 0. \tag{5.9}$$

Inasmuch as $x_q = x_0 + t_q h_q$, $y_q = y_0 + t_q k_q$, it follows by Taylor's formula that inequality (5.6b) can be put into the form

$$t_q H'(x_0, y_0; h_q, k_q) + \frac{t_q^2}{2} H''(x_0, y_0; h_q, k_q) + R_q < \frac{t_q^2}{q},$$

where

$$\lim_{q \to \infty} \frac{R_q}{t_q^2} = 0. \tag{5.10}$$

Rewriting this inequality in the form

$$\frac{H'(x_0,y_0;\, h_q,k_q)}{t_q} + \tfrac{1}{2}H''(x_0,y_0;\, h_q,k_q) + \frac{R_q}{t_q^2} < \frac{1}{q},$$

we see, by (5.10), that

$$\limsup_{q\to\infty} \frac{H'(x_0,y_0;\, h_q,k_q)}{t_q} + \tfrac{1}{2}H''(x_0,y_0;\, h,k) \leqslant 0. \tag{5.11}$$

By (5.9) the first term is nonnegative. Since $\lim_{q\to\infty} t_q = 0$, it follows that

$$\lim_{q\to\infty} H'(x_0,y_0;\, h_q,k_q) = H'(x_0,y_0;\, h,k) = \sum_{\alpha=1}^{r} \frac{\partial H}{\partial y^\alpha}(x_0,y_0)k^\alpha = 0,$$

$$\lim_{q\to\infty} H''(x_0,y_0,h_q,k_q) = H''(x_0,y_0;\, h,k) \leqslant 0.$$

Inasmuch as $(\partial H/\partial y^\alpha)(x_0,y_0) < 0$ and $k^\alpha \leqslant 0$ $(\alpha=1,\ldots,r)$, the first of these relations implies that $k^\alpha = 0$ $(\alpha=1,\ldots,r)$. The vector (h,k) is therefore a unit vector in the cone $\mathcal{C}$ defined by (5.4). The second relation contradicts our assumption that $H''(x_0,y_0;\, h,k) > 0$ for a vector (h,k) of this kind. In view of this contradiction our theorem is established.

EXAMPLE 5.1

In the two-dimensional case observe that the point $(0,0)$ affords a strict minimum to the function $H(x,y) = x^2 - y - y^3$ subject to the constraint $y \leqslant 0$. Here $H_x(0,0) = 0$, $H_y(0,0) = -1$, and $H''(0,0;\, h,k) = 2h^2$. The cone $\mathcal{C}$ defined by (5.4) is the line $k=0$. Consequently conditions (5.3) hold with the equality excluded in (5.3b). If, on the other hand, $H(x,y) = x^2 - y^3$, then again the origin affords a strict minimum to H subject to $y \leqslant 0$. We have $H_x = H_y = 0$ at $(0,0)$. Again $H''(0,0;\, h,k) = 2h^2$. However, in this case the cone $\mathcal{C}$ defined by (5.4) consists of all vectors (h,k). Accordingly the equality holds in (5.3b) if $h=0$ and k is arbitrary.

The result obtained in Theorem 5.1 plays an important role in the study of the problem of minimizing a function $F(x,y)$ subject to constraints of the type

$$G(x,y) = 0, \qquad y^\alpha \leqslant 0 \qquad (\alpha=1,\ldots,p), \tag{5.12}$$

where $G(x,y) \geqslant 0$ on the domain considered. We seek conditions which imply that a solution (x_0, y_0) of this problem also affords a local minimum to an augmented function of the form

$$H(x,y) = F(x,y) + \sigma G(x,y)$$

subject to the constraints $y^\alpha \leqslant 0$ ($\alpha = 1, \ldots, p$). In other words, we seek to remove the constraint $G = 0$ in (5.12) by the addition of the penalty term σG to F. To carry out our analysis, we assume that F and G are continuous near (x_0, y_0) and are twice differentiable at (x_0, y_0). Since (x_0, y_0) minimizes $G(x,y)$, we have

$$\frac{\partial G}{\partial x^i}(x_0, y_0) = 0, \qquad \frac{\partial G}{\partial y^\alpha}(x_0, y_0) = 0 \qquad (i = 1, \ldots, n;\ \alpha = 1, \ldots, p), \quad (5.13a)$$

$$G''(x_0, y_0;\ h, k) \geqslant 0 \qquad \text{for all } (h, k). \tag{5.13b}$$

With these preliminaries we can establish

THEOREM 5.2

Suppose that a point (x_0, y_0) satisfying constraints (5.12) affords a local minimum to an augmented function of the type

$$H(x, y) = F(x, y) + \sigma G(x, y)$$

subject to the constraints $y^\alpha \leqslant 0$ ($\alpha = 1, \ldots, p$). Then (x_0, y_0) affords a local minimum to $F(x, y)$ subject to the constraints

$$G(x, y) = 0, \qquad y^\alpha \leqslant 0 \qquad (\alpha = 1, \ldots, p).$$

Moreover at the point (x_0, y_0) we have

$$\frac{\partial F}{\partial x^i} = 0, \qquad \frac{\partial F}{\partial y^\alpha} \leqslant 0 \ \ \text{if } y_0^\alpha = 0, \qquad \frac{\partial F}{\partial y^\alpha} = 0 \ \ \text{if } y_0^\alpha < 0. \tag{5.14}$$

In addition

$$F''(x_0, y_0;\ h, k) \geqslant 0 \quad \text{for all } (h, k) \neq (0, 0) \text{ in } \mathcal{C} \text{ having } G''(x_0, y_0;\ h, k) = 0,$$
$$\tag{5.15}$$

where $\mathcal{C}$ is the cone of vectors (h, k) defined by the relations

$$k^\alpha \leqslant 0 \quad \text{if } y_0^\alpha = 0, \qquad k^\alpha = 0 \quad \text{if } \frac{\partial F}{\partial y^\alpha}(x_0, y_0) < 0. \tag{5.16}$$

This result is a simple consequence of Theorem 5.1. The first conclusion is immediate. By virtue of (5.13a) relations (5.14) for F are equivalent to relations (5.3a) for $H = F + \sigma G$. It follows that conditions (5.4) and (5.16) define the same cone $\mathcal{C}$ of vectors (h, k). Inasmuch as

$$H''(x_0, y_0; h, k) = F''(x_0, y_0; h, k) + \sigma G''(x_0, y_0; h, k),$$

inequality (5.15) is a consequence of inequality (5.3b). This proves Theorem 5.2.

Suppose now that a point (x_0, y_0) satisfies constraints (5.12) and the first-order conditions (5.14). Suppose further that the second-order condition (5.15) holds with the equality excluded. Then the quadratic forms $P(h, k) = F''(x_0, y_0; h, k)$ and $Q(h, k) = G''(x_0, y_0; h, k)$ satisfy the hypotheses of Theorem 2.4 on the cone $\mathcal{C}$ defined by (5.16). There is accordingly a constant σ_0 such that

$$F''(x_0, y_0; h, k) + \sigma_0 G''(x_0, y_0; h, k) > 0 \qquad \text{for all } (h, k) \neq (0, 0) \text{ in } \mathcal{C}.$$

It follows that the function $H = F + \sigma_0 G$ satisfies conditions (5.3) with the equality excluded in (5.3b). As a consequence of the last conclusion of Theorem 5.1, we have the following converse of Theorem 5.2 for $\sigma = \sigma_0$ and hence for $\sigma \geqslant \sigma_0$.

THEOREM 5.3

Suppose that conditions (5.14) hold at a point (x_0, y_0) satisfying the given constraints (5.12). If the second-order condition (5.15) holds with the equality excluded, then there are positive constants σ_0 and τ and a neighborhood $\hat{N}_0$ of (x_0, y_0) such that the inequality

$$H(x, y) \geqslant H(x_0, y_0) + \tau \left[|x - x_0|^2 + |y - y_0|^2 \right] \tag{5.17}$$

holds for all (x, y) in $\hat{N}_0$ having $y^\alpha \leqslant 0$ $(\alpha = 1, \ldots, p)$, where

$$H(x, y) = F(x, y) + \sigma G(x, y) \qquad (\sigma \geqslant \sigma_0). \tag{5.18}$$

In particular, if a point (x, y) in $\hat{N}_0$ satisfies constraints (5.12), then

$$F(x, y) \geqslant F(x_0, y_0) + \tau \left[|x - x_0|^2 + |y - y_0|^2 \right]. \tag{5.19}$$

Combining this result with Corollary 2 to Theorem 3.1, we have this

COROLLARY

Suppose that the hypotheses of Theorem 5.3 *hold. Suppose in addition that* (x_0, y_0) *affords a strict minimum to* F *on a compact set* $\hat{N}$ *subject to constraints* (5.12). *Then* σ_0 *and* τ *can be chosen so that* (5.17) *holds for all* (x, y) *in* $\hat{N}$ *having* $y^\alpha \leqslant 0$ $(\alpha = 1, \ldots, p)$.

The following example shows that a point (x_0, y_0) need not minimize a function of the form $H(x, y) = F(x, y) + \sigma G(x, y)$ $(\sigma > 0)$ even if conditions (5.14) and (5.15) are satisfied and the point (x_0, y_0) affords a strict local minimum to $F(x, y)$ subject to the constraints $G(x, y) = 0$, $y^\alpha \leqslant 0$ ($\alpha = 1, \ldots, p$). In this example we shall use the symbol $(\delta x, \delta y)$ in place of (h, k) for the variations of (x, y). Symbolism of this type is frequently used in variational theory.

EXAMPLE 5.2

Let N be the set of points in xyz-space having $|x| < 1$ and $|y| < 1$. It is easily verified that the point $(x_0, y_0, z_0) = (0, 0, 0)$ affords a strict minimum to $F(x, y, z) = x^2 + 2xy + y^4 - 2z$ on N subject to the constraints $z \leqslant 0$ and $G(x, y, z) = \frac{1}{2}(xy - x - z)^2 = 0$. At $(0, 0, 0)$ we have $F_x = F_y = 0$ and $F_z = -2 < 0$. Consequently condition (5.14) holds. Since $F_z = -2 < 0$, the cone $\mathcal{C}$ defined by (5.16) consists of all vectors $(\delta x, \delta y, \delta z)$ having $\delta z = 0$. The constraint $G''(0, 0, 0; \delta x, \delta y, \delta z) = (-\delta x - \delta z)^2 = 0$ tells us that $\delta x = -\delta z = 0$. It follows that $F''(0, 0, 0; \delta x, \delta y, \delta z) = 2(\delta x)^2 + 4(\delta x)(\delta y) = 0$. Consequently condition (5.15) holds also. Choose $z \leqslant 0$, and express the function $H = F + \sigma G$ in the form

$$H(x, y, z) = x^2 \left[1 + \frac{\sigma}{2}(y - 1)^2 \right] + 2xy + y^4 - \left[2 + \sigma x(y - 1) \right] z + \frac{\sigma}{2} z^2.$$

Observe that, if $|y| < 1$, as we have assumed, then

$$H(x, y, 0) \leqslant x^2(1 + 2\sigma) + 2xy + y^4.$$

Hence, if

$$0 < y^2 < \frac{1}{1 + 2\sigma}, \qquad x = \frac{-y}{1 + 2\sigma}, \qquad z = 0,$$

we have

$$H(x, y, z) \leqslant y^2 \left(y^2 - \frac{1}{1 + 2\sigma} \right) < 0.$$

Consequently for every $\sigma > 0$ the point $(0,0,0)$ fails to minimize $H(x,y,z)$ subject to the constraint $z \leqslant 0$.

EXERCISE

1. Apply Theorem 5.1 to each of the following cases with $(x_0, y_0) = (0,0)$ and with $y \leqslant 0$ as the constraint for the given function:
   (a) $x^2 - y^2$,   (b) $x^2 + y^2$,   (c) $x^2 + y^3$.

6. AUGMENTABILITY IN THE CASE OF INEQUALITY CONSTRAINTS

We are now in a position to study the problem of minimizing a function $f(x)$ subject to constraints of the form

$$g_\alpha(x) \leqslant 0 \quad (\alpha = 1, \ldots, p), \qquad g_\beta(x) = 0 \quad (\beta = p + 1, \ldots, m). \quad (6.1)$$

The cases $p = 0$ and $p = m$ have the obvious interpretations. The case $p = 0$ was studied in Chapter 3 and again in Section 4 of this chapter. Let x_0 be a point satisfying these constraints. We assume that the functions $f, g_1, \ldots, g_m$ are continuous near x_0 and are twice differentiable at x_0.

As in the case of equality constraints, we have a Lagrange multiplier rule associated with out problem. If a point x_0 is a solution to our problem, then under certain additional assumptions the Lagrange multiplier rule must hold at x_0. Conversely, if a strengthened form of this multiplier rule holds at x_0, then x_0 affords a strict local minimum to f subject to these constraints.

The *Lagrange multiplier rule* for our problem will be said to hold at x_0 if (i) the point x_0 satisfies constraints (6.1), and (ii) there exist multipliers $\lambda_1, \ldots, \lambda_m$ such that

$$\lambda_\alpha \geqslant 0 \quad (\alpha = 1, \ldots, p), \qquad \lambda_\alpha = 0 \quad \text{if } g_\alpha(x_0) < 0, \quad (6.2a)$$

$$\nabla F(x_0) = 0, \qquad \text{where } F = f + \lambda_1 g_1 + \cdots + \lambda_m g_m, \quad (6.2b)$$

$$F''(x_0, h) \geqslant 0 \qquad \text{for all } h \neq 0 \text{ in } \mathcal{C}, \quad (6.2c)$$

where $\mathcal{C}$ is the set of all vectors h having

$$g_\alpha'(x_0, h) \leqslant 0 \qquad \text{if } g_\alpha(x_0) = 0 \quad \text{and} \quad \alpha \leqslant p, \quad (6.3a)$$

$$g_\alpha'(x_0, h) = 0 \quad \text{if } \lambda_\alpha > 0 \quad \text{and} \quad \alpha \leqslant p, \quad g_\beta'(x_0, h) = 0 \quad (\beta = p + 1, \ldots, m).$$
$$(6.3b)$$

Observe that, if α is an index such that $g_\alpha(x_0) < 0$, the condition $g_\alpha(x) \leqslant 0$ holds on a neighborhood of x_0. Consequently such a constraint plays no role in local considerations about x_0. This is reflected in the fact that $\lambda_\alpha = 0$ for an index of this type. Moreover these indices are omitted in constraints (6.3).

If the equality is excluded in (6.2c), we obtain the *strengthened Lagrange multiplier rule* for our problem at x_0.

Proceeding as in Section 4, we seek to simplify our problem by removing constraints. To this end we introduce slack variables $y^1,\ldots,y^p$ and write constraints (6.1) in the form

$$y^\alpha \leqslant 0, \qquad g^\alpha(x) - y^\alpha = 0, \qquad g_\beta(x) = 0 \qquad (\alpha = 1,\ldots,p;\ \beta = p+1,\ldots,m). \tag{6.4}$$

We introduce the augmented function

$$H(x,y) = f(x) + \sum_{\alpha=1}^{p} \lambda_\alpha [\, g_\alpha(x) - y^\alpha\,] + \sum_{\beta=p+1}^{m} \lambda_\beta g_\beta(x) + \sigma G(x,y), \tag{6.5a}$$

where

$$G(x,y) = \frac{1}{2} \left\{ \sum_{\alpha=1}^{p} [\, g_\alpha(x) - y^\alpha\,]^2 + \sum_{\beta=p+1}^{m} [\, g_\beta(x)\,]^2 \right\}. \tag{6.5b}$$

Set

$$y_0^\alpha = g_\alpha(x_0) \qquad (\alpha = 1,\ldots,p). \tag{6.6}$$

Observe that $H(x,y) = f(x)$ whenever (6.4) holds. *Consequently* (x_0,y_0) *minimizes* H *subject to constraints* (6.4) *if and only if* x_0 *is a solution to our original problem.* We shall say that our *problem is augmentable* at x_0 if the multipliers $\lambda_1,\ldots,\lambda_m$ and constant σ in H can be chosen so that (x_0,y_0) affords a minimum to $H(x,y)$ subject to the simpler constraints $y^\alpha \leqslant 0$. We shall show that there is a close connection between the Lagrange multiplier rule and augmentability. But first let us consider the following examples.

EXAMPLE 6.1

In the xy-plane the point $(0,0)$ affords a local minimum to $f(x,y) = -x^2 + 4y + xy$ subject to the constraint $g(x,y) = x^2 - y \leqslant 0$. In this case the gradient of $F = f + \lambda g = (\lambda - 1)x^2 + (4 - \lambda)y + xy$ vanishes at $(0,0)$ only if $\lambda = 4$. Consequently $\lambda = 4$ is the appropriate Lagrange multiplier. Observe that $F=3x^2+xy$ fails to have an unconstrained local minimum at $(0,0)$. However, if $\sigma \geqslant 2$, the augmented function

$$H(x,y,z)=f+\lambda(g-z)+\frac{\sigma}{2}(g-z)^2=3x^2+xy-4z+\frac{\sigma}{2}(x^2-y-z)^2$$

has a minimum at $(0,0,0)$ subject to the constraint $z \leqslant 0$ whenever $|x| \leqslant 1$ and $|y| \leqslant 1$, as is readily verified. In particular, if we set $z=0$ we see that $(x,y)=(0,0)$ minimizes the function

$$H(x,y,0)=f+\lambda g+\frac{\sigma}{2}g^2=3x^2+xy+\frac{\sigma}{2}(x^2-y)^2$$

on the unit square $|x| \leqslant 1$, $|y| \leqslant 1$. If we choose $z=x^2-y$ when $x^2-y<0$ and $z=0$ when $x^2-y \geqslant 0$, then $x^2-y-z=\max(0,x^2-y)$. Hence $(x,y)=(0,0)$ affords a strict minimum to the function

$$\hat{H}(x,y)=-x^2+4y+xy+4\max(0,x^2-y)+\frac{\sigma}{2}\left[\max(0,x^2-y)\right]^2$$

for $\sigma \geqslant 2$ on the unit square $|x| \leqslant 1$, $|y| \leqslant 1$.

EXAMPLE 6.2

The origin $(x,y,z)=(0,0,0)$ affords a minimum to $f(x,y,z)=2x-y+z^2$ subject to the constraints $x+y^2 \leqslant 0$, $-x \leqslant 0$. Setting

$$F(x,y,z)=2x-y+z^2+\lambda(x+y^2)+\mu(-x),$$

we see that at $(0,0,0)$ $F_x=2+\lambda-\mu$, $F_y=-1$, $F_z=0$. For no values of λ,μ do we have $F_x=F_y=F_z=0$ at $(0,0,0)$. The Lagrange multiplier rule therefore fails to hold even though the origin affords a global strict minimum to our problem. This follows because the conditions $x+y^2 \leqslant 0$, $-x \leqslant 0$ constitute an unnatural way of stating that $x=y=0$. If we replace the original constraints by the constraints $x=0$, $y=0$ or by the four constraints $x \leqslant 0$, $-x \leqslant 0$, $y \leqslant 0$, $y \leqslant 0$, the Lagrange multiplier rule holds at $(0,0,0)$ and our problem is augmentable.

We shall see presently that the Lagrange multiplier rule (6.2) is a consequence of augmentability. Moreover we shall show that the strengthened Lagrange multiplier rule implies augmentability. The following example shows that a point x_0 can afford a strict minimum for our original problem and that the multiplier rule (6.2) can hold at x_0 without having augmentability of our problem at x_0. This problem has the additional feature that we have complete normality at x_0 in the sense that the gradients $\nabla g_\gamma(x_0)$ $(\gamma = \gamma_1,\ldots,\gamma_r)$ are linearly independent, where $\gamma_1,\ldots,\gamma_r$ are indices such that $g_\gamma(x_0)=0$. It was shown in Chapter 4 that complete normality of a solution x_0 to our original problems implies the multiplier rule (6.2). Consequently complete normality (and other constraint qualification conditions) and augmentability are alternative conditions which yield the Lagrange multiplier rule.

EXAMPLE 6.3

Let N be the interior of the unit square $|x|<1$, $|y|<1$. The point $(x_0,y_0)=(0,0)$ affords a strict minimum to $f(x,y)=x^2+2x+y^4$ on N subject to the constraint $g(x,y)=xy-x\leqslant 0$. Observe that $\nabla g(0,0)\neq 0$. The Lagrangian $F=f+\lambda g$ with $\lambda=2$ takes the form $F(x,y)=x^2+2xy+y^4$. We have $F_x=F_y=0$ at $(0,0)$ and $F''(0,0; h,k)=2h^2+4hk$. Since $\lambda=2>0$, the vector (h,k) is subject to the equality constraint $g'(0,0; h,k)=-h=0$. Hence $F''(0,0; h,k)=0$. Consequently the second-order condition (6.2b) holds. However, our problem is not augmentable. To this end consider the functions $\hat{F}=F+\lambda(g-z)$ and $G=\frac{1}{2}(g-z)^2$. We have, with $\lambda=2$,

$$\hat{F}(x,y,z)=x^2+2xy+y^4-2z, \qquad G(x,y,z)=\frac{1}{2}(xy-x-z)^2.$$

The point $(0,0,0)$ affords a strict minimum to $\hat{F}$ subject to the constraints $z\leqslant 0$, $G(x,y,z)=0$ if we restrict (x,y) to be in the unit square N. If our problem were augmentable, then for some $\sigma>0$ the origin $(0,0,0)$ would afford a local minimum to H subject to the constraint $z\leqslant 0$, contrary to the result obtained in Example 5.2. Consequently the problem here given is not augmentable at the point $(x_0,y_0)=(0,0)$.

As a first result we have

THEOREM 6.1

If the problem of minimizing f subject to constraints (6.1) is augmentable at x_0, the Lagrange multiplier rule holds at x_0.

According to our hypotheses there is a function H of form (6.5) which has a local minimum at (x_0,y_0) subject to the constraints $y^\alpha\leqslant 0$. Here y_0 is given by (6.6). Observe that the function H is of the form

$$H(x,y)=\hat{F}(x,y)+\sigma G(x,y),$$

where G is given by (6.4b) and

$$\hat{F}(x,y)=F(x)-\sum_{\alpha=1}^{p}\lambda_\alpha y^\alpha, \qquad F(x)=f(x)+\sum_{\gamma=1}^{m}\lambda_\gamma g_\gamma(x). \qquad (6.7)$$

By Theorem 5.2 we have at (x_0, y_0)

$$\frac{\partial \hat{F}}{\partial x^i} = \frac{\partial F}{\partial x^i} = 0, \qquad \frac{\partial \hat{F}}{\partial y^\alpha} = -\lambda_\alpha \leqslant 0 \quad \text{if } y_0^\alpha = 0,$$

$$\frac{\partial \hat{F}}{\partial y^\alpha} = -\lambda_\alpha = 0 \quad \text{if } y_0^\alpha < 0, \tag{6.8a}$$

$$\hat{F}''(x_0, y_0; h, k) = F''(x_0, h) \geqslant 0 \quad \text{if } (h, k) \text{ is in } \hat{\mathcal{C}}$$

$$and \qquad G''(x_0, y_0; h, k) = 0, \tag{6.8b}$$

where $\hat{\mathcal{C}}$ is the set of vectors (h, k) such that

$$k^\alpha \leqslant 0 \quad \text{if } y_0^\alpha = 0, \qquad k^\alpha = 0 \quad \text{if } \frac{\partial \hat{F}}{\partial y^\alpha} = -\lambda_\alpha < 0. \tag{6.9}$$

Our theorem will be established by showing that conditions (6.8) are equivalent to conditions (6.2). Conditions (6.8a) hold if and only if $\nabla F(x_0) = 0$ and $\lambda_\alpha \geqslant 0$ $(\alpha = 1, \ldots, p)$, with $\lambda_\alpha = 0$ if $g_\alpha(x_0) < 0$. Hence (6.8a) is equivalent to conditions (6.2a) and (6.2b). The condition

$$G''(x_0, y_0; h, k) = \sum_{\alpha=1}^{p} [g_\alpha'(x_0, h) - k^\alpha]^2 + \sum_{\beta=p+1}^{m} g_\beta'(x_0, h)^2 = 0$$

holds if and only if

$$k^\alpha = g_\alpha'(x_0, h) \quad (\alpha = 1, \ldots, p), \qquad g_\beta'(x_0, h) = 0 \quad (\beta = p+1, \ldots, m). \tag{6.10}$$

Consequently, if (6.9) and (6.10) hold, we have

$$g_\alpha'(x_0, h) \leqslant 0 \quad \text{if } g_\alpha(x_0) = 0, \qquad g_\alpha'(x_0, h) = 0 \quad \text{if } \lambda_\alpha > 0, \qquad g_\beta'(x_0, h) = 0.$$

These are conditions (6.3) defining the cone $\mathcal{C}$ in condition (6.2c). Conversely, if h is in $\mathcal{C}$, then by reversing our steps we see that, if we set $k^\alpha = g_\alpha'(x_0, h)$, the vector (h, k) is in $\hat{\mathcal{C}}$ and has $G''(x_0, y_0; h, k) = 0$. This fact establishes the equivalence of conditions (6.2c) and (6.8b), and the proof of Theorem 6.1 is complete.

It is clear from the arguments just given that the strengthened Lagrange multiplier rule at x_0 is equivalent to condition (6.8) at (x_0, y_0), strengthened so as to exclude the equality in (6.8b) when $(h, k) \neq (0, 0)$. When this fact is used, it follows from Theorem 5.3 that there are a neighborhood $\hat{N}_0$ of (x_0, y_0) and positive constants σ_0 and τ such that, if $\sigma \geqslant \sigma_0$,

$$H(x, y) \geqslant H(x_0, y_0) + 2\tau [|x - x_0|^2 + |y - y_0|^2] \tag{6.11}$$

whenever (x,y) is in $\hat{N}_0$ and $y^\alpha \leqslant 0$ $(\alpha = 1,\ldots,p)$. We shall show that there is a neighborhood N_0 of x_0 in x-space such that, if σ_0 is suitably increased, then, when $\sigma \geqslant \sigma_0$, we have

$$H(x,y) \geqslant H(x_0,y_0) + \tau|x - x_0|^2 = f(x_0) + \tau|x - x_0|^2 \qquad (6.12)$$

for all (x,y) with x in N_0 and $y^\alpha \leqslant 0$ $(\alpha = 1,\ldots,p)$. To this end choose a closed ball $\overline{N}_0$ about x_0 of radius r and a constant δ such that the set $\hat{N}$ of points (x,y) having x in $\overline{N}_0$ and $|g_\alpha(x) - y^\alpha| \leqslant (2\delta)^{1/2}$ $(\alpha = 1,\ldots,p)$ is a subset of $\hat{N}_0$. Let M be the minimum of $F(x)$ on $\overline{N}_0$. Increase the constant σ_0 chosen above so that

$$M + \sigma_0 \delta \geqslant f(x_0) + \tau r^2. \qquad (6.13)$$

Consider now a point (x,y) having x in $\overline{N}_0$ and $y^\alpha \leqslant 0$ $(\alpha = 1,\ldots,p)$. If (x,y) is in $\hat{N}$, then (x,y) is in $\hat{N}_0$. In this event (6.11) and hence (6.12) hold. If (x,y) is not in $\hat{N}$, then $G(x,y) \geqslant \delta$, $y^\alpha \leqslant 0$, and

$$H(x,y) = F(x) - \sum_{\alpha=1}^{p} \lambda_\alpha y^\alpha + \sigma G(x,y) \geqslant M + \sigma_0 \delta \geqslant f(x_0) + \tau r^2.$$

Since $|x - x_0| \leqslant r$, inequality (6.12) holds in this case also. This proves

THEOREM 6.2

Suppose that the strengthened Lagrange multiplier rule holds at x_0 *with multipliers* $\lambda_1,\ldots,\lambda_m$. *Set* $y_0^\alpha = g_\alpha(x_0)$ $(\alpha = 1,\ldots,p)$. *There exist positive constants* σ_0 *and* τ *and a neighborhood* N_0 *of* x_0 *in* x-space *such that, if* $\sigma \geqslant \sigma_0$ *and* $H(x,y)$ *is defined by* (6.5), *then the inequality*

$$H(x,y) \geqslant H(x_0,y_0) + \tau|x - x_0|^2 = f(x_0) + \tau|x - x_0|^2 \qquad (6.14)$$

holds for all (x,y) *having* x *in* N_0 *and* $y^\alpha \leqslant 0$ $(\alpha = 1,\ldots,p)$.

One can eliminate the constraints $y^\alpha \leqslant 0$ $(\alpha = 1,\ldots,p)$ by the substitution $y^\alpha = -(z^\alpha)^2$, where $z^1,\ldots,z^p$ are new slack variables.

Recall that, if a point (x,y) satisfies constraints (6.4), the $H(x,y) = f(x)$ and the point x satisfies the original constraints

$$g_\alpha(x) \leqslant 0 \quad (\alpha = 1,\ldots,p), \qquad g_\beta(x) = 0 \quad (\beta = p+1,\ldots,m). \qquad (6.15)$$

As a consequence of this fact we obtain from Theorem 6.2 the following sufficiency theorem for our original problem. This result was obtained by other means in Theorem 7.4, Chapter 4.

THEOREM 6.3

If the strengthened Lagrange multiplier rule holds at x_0, *then there are a constant* $\tau > 0$ *and a neighborhood* N_0 *of* x_0 *such that the inequality*

$$f(x) \geqslant f(x_0) + \tau |x - x_0|^2 \tag{6.16}$$

holds for all x *in* N_0 *satisfying constraints* (6.15). *Suppose in addition that* $f, g_1, \ldots, g_m$ *are continuous on a compact set* N *and that* x_0 *affords a strict minimum to* f *on* N *subject to constraints* (6.15). *Then* τ *can be modified so that inequality* (6.16) *holds on* N *subject to constraints* (6.15).

The last conclusion in the theorem follows from the first by a simple continuity argument. In a similar manner the result given in Theorem 6.2 can be extended by replacing N_0 by a larger compact set N on which $f, g_1, \ldots, g_m$ are continuous if x_0 affords a strict minimum to f on N subject to constraints (6.15). This result follows from the corollary to Theorem 5.3. Its verification will be left to the reader. To eliminate a boundedness condition on $y^1, \ldots, y^p$, we can employ the device used in the proof of Theorem 6.2.

A further consequence of Theorem 6.2 is obtained by selecting $y^\alpha = 0$ whenever $g_\alpha(x) > 0$ and $y^\alpha = g_\alpha(x)$ otherwise. When this selection has been made, we have

$$g_\alpha(x) - y^\alpha = \max[0, g_\alpha(x)] \qquad (\alpha = 1, \ldots, p). \tag{6.17}$$

The corresponding value of $H(x, y)$ is

$$\hat{H}(x) = f(x) + \sum_{\alpha=1}^{m} \lambda_\gamma \hat{g}_\gamma(x) + \frac{\sigma}{2} \sum_{\gamma=1}^{m} [\hat{g}_\gamma(x)]^2, \tag{6.18}$$

where

$$\hat{g}_\alpha(x) = \max[0, g_\alpha(x)] \quad (\alpha = 1, \ldots, p),$$

$$\hat{g}_\beta(x) = g_\beta(x) \quad (\beta = p+1, \ldots, m). \tag{6.19}$$

Observe that constraints (6.15) are equivalent to the equality constraints

$$\hat{g}_\gamma(x) = 0 \qquad (\gamma = 1, \ldots, m). \tag{6.20}$$

In view of Theorem 6.2 we have

THEOREM 6.4

Suppose that the strengthened multiplier rule holds at x_0 *with multipliers* $\lambda_1, \ldots, \lambda_m$. *Then there are a neighborhood* N_0 *of* x_0 *and positive constants* σ_0 *and* τ *such that for* $\sigma \geqslant \sigma_0$ *and* $\hat{H}(x)$ *defined by (6.18) we have*

$$\hat{H}(x) \geqslant \hat{H}_0(x) + \tau|x - x_0|^2 = f(x_0) + \tau|x - x_0|^2 \qquad (6.21)$$

for all x *in* N_0. *If in addition* x_0 *affords a strict minimum to* f *on a compact set* N *subject to the constraints* $g_\gamma(x) = 0$ $(\gamma = 1, \ldots, m)$, *then* σ_0 *and* τ *can be chosen so that (6.21) holds on* N.

In the last conclusion we assume, of course, that the functions $f, g_1, \ldots, g_m$ are continuous on N.

Consider the function $H(x,y)$ defined by formula (6.4) with $\sigma > 0$ and $\lambda_\alpha \geqslant 0$ $(\alpha = 1, \ldots, p)$. Let

$$\tilde{H}(x) = \min H(x,y) \text{ on the set } y^\alpha \leqslant 0. \qquad (6.22)$$

Inasmuch as

$$\frac{\partial H}{\partial y^\alpha} = -\lambda_\alpha - \sigma[g_\alpha(x) - y^\alpha],$$

this minimum is attained when

$$y^\alpha = \frac{\lambda_\alpha}{\sigma} + g_\alpha(x) \quad \text{if} \quad \frac{\lambda_\alpha}{\sigma} + g_\alpha(x) \leqslant 0, \qquad y^\alpha = 0 \quad \text{otherwise.}$$

For these values of y^α we have

$$g_\alpha(x) - y^\alpha = \max\left[-\frac{\lambda_\alpha}{\sigma}, g_\alpha(x)\right].$$

Consequently

$$\tilde{H}(x) = f(x) + \sum_{\gamma=1}^{m} \lambda_\alpha \tilde{g}_\alpha(x) + \frac{\sigma}{2} \sum_{\gamma=1}^{m} [\tilde{g}_\gamma(x)]^2 \qquad (6.23)$$

where

$$\tilde{g}_\alpha(x) = \max\left[-\frac{\lambda_\alpha}{\sigma}, g_\alpha(x)\right] \quad (\alpha = 1, \ldots, p),$$

$$\tilde{g}_\beta(x) = g_\beta(x) \quad (\beta = p+1, \ldots, m).$$

From this result we see that, *if the strengthened Lagrange multiplier rule holds with multipliers* $\lambda_1,\ldots,\lambda_m$, *there is a constant* σ_0 *such that if* $\sigma \geqslant \sigma_0$ *then* x_0 *affords a strict local minimum to the function* $\tilde{H}(x)$, *defined by formula* (6.23).

EXERCISES

1. Show by an example that a minimum problem with linear constraints need not be augmentable. *Hint:* Consider $f = x^2(x+y) = \min$ subject to $g(x,y) = -x-y \leqslant 0$.

2. Suppose that the strengthened Lagrange multiplier rule (6.2) holds at x_0 and that all indices are active at x_0. Show that there is a constant σ such that x_0 affords an unconstrained local minimum to the function

$$f(x) + \sum_{\alpha=1}^{m} \left\{ \lambda_\alpha g_\alpha(x) + \frac{\sigma}{2}[g_\alpha(x)]^2 \right\}.$$

Hint: Use (6.14) with $y = y_0 = 0$.

7. AN EXTENDED LAGRANGE MULTIPLIER RULE

We continue with the study of the problem of minimizing a function $f(x)$ subject to constraints of the type

$$g_\alpha(x) \leqslant 0 \quad (\alpha = 1,\ldots,p), \qquad g_\beta(x) = 0 \quad (\beta = p+1,\ldots,m). \qquad (7.1)$$

We assume that x_0 is a solution of this problem and that the functions $f, g_1,\ldots,g_m$ are of class C' on the domain under consideration. It is our purpose in this section to establish a first-order Lagrange multiplier rule without the assumptions of regularity or of augmentability used heretofore. In this multiplier rule we introduce an auxiliary nonnegative multiplier λ_0 associated with the objective function f. The precise form of the modified multiplier rule is given in

THEOREM 7.1: EXTENDED LAGRANGE MULTIPLIER RULE[†]

If x_0 *affords a minimum to* f *relative to constraints* (7.1), *there exist multipliers* $\lambda_0,\lambda_1,\ldots,\lambda_m$ *such that*

$$\lambda_0,\lambda_1,\ldots,\lambda_m \text{ are not all zero,} \qquad (7.2a)$$

$$\lambda_0,\lambda_1,\ldots,\lambda_p \text{ are nonnegative,} \qquad (7.2b)$$

[†]Cf. E. J. McShane, "The Lagrange Multiplier Rule," *American Mathematical Monthly*, Vol. 80 (1974), 922–925.

If $\lambda_1,\ldots,\lambda_m$ are not all zero, then in

every neighborhood of x_0 there is a point x   (7.2c)

such that $\lambda_\gamma g_\gamma(x) > 0$ whenever $\lambda_\gamma \neq 0$,

$$\lambda_0 \nabla f(x_0) + \lambda_1 \nabla g_1(x_0) + \cdots + \lambda_m \nabla g_m(x_0) = 0. \tag{7.2d}$$

This multiplier rule differs from the one given previously in two respects. In the earlier versions we required that $\lambda_0 = 1$. Here we allow the value $\lambda_0 = 0$. It should be observed that, if $\lambda_0 > 0$, the set of multipliers obtained by dividing each multiplier by λ_0 is a new set having $\lambda_0 = 1$. From these remarks it follows that we can always normalize the multipliers so that $\lambda_0 = 0$ or $\lambda_0 = 1$. Of course, we could use any other normalization, such as $\lambda_0^2 + \lambda_1^2 + \cdots + \lambda_m^2 = 1$, if we wished to do so.

EXAMPLE 7.1

In the xy-plane the origin minimizes $f(x,y) = y$ subject to the constraint $g(x,y) = x^2 - y^3 \leqslant 0$. We have $\lambda_0 f_y + \lambda_1 g_y = \lambda_0$ at the origin. In this case condition (7.2d) holds at the origin only if $\lambda_0 = 0$.

The second new feature in the multiplier rule (7.2) is condition (7.2c). If $1 \leqslant \alpha \leqslant p$, it implies that $\lambda_\alpha = 0$ if the constraint $g_\alpha(x) \leqslant 0$ is not violated in every neighborhood of x_0. In other words, if $g_\alpha(x) \leqslant 0$ on some neighborhood of x_0, then $\lambda_\alpha = 0$. In particular, $\lambda_\alpha = 0$ if $g_\alpha(x_0) < 0$. We also have $\lambda_\alpha = 0$ if $g_\alpha(x)$ is expressible in the form $g_\alpha(x) = -h_\alpha(x)^2$. For any index γ we have $\lambda_\gamma = 0$ if $g_\gamma(x) \equiv 0$ on some neighborhood of x_0. In addition, condition (7.2c) states that, if $\lambda_{\gamma_1},\ldots,\lambda_{\gamma_r}$ are all different from zero, then in every neighborhood of x_0 the constraints indexed by $\gamma_1,\ldots,\gamma_r$ are violated simultaneously at a point x in such a way that the values $g_{\gamma_1}(x),\ldots,g_{\gamma_r}(x)$ have respectively the same signs as the multipliers $\lambda_{\gamma_1},\ldots,\lambda_{\gamma_r}$. Observe that, if $\lambda_1 > 0$ and $\lambda_2 > 0$, we cannot have the situation $g_2(x) = -g_1(x)$, since $g_1(x)$ and $g_2(x)$ must be positive simultaneously at some point x. However, the case $g_2(x) = g_1(x)$ is not excluded.

EXAMPLE 7.2

In the xy-plane the origin minimizes the function $x^2 - y^2 - 2y$ subject to the constraints $-x^2 \leqslant 0$, $y = 0$. It has $\lambda_0 = 1$, $\lambda_1 = 0$, $\lambda_2 = 2$ as Lagrange multipliers in condition (7.2). If we replace the constraints by the equivalent constraints $-x^2 \leqslant 0$, $y \leqslant 0$, $-y \leqslant 0$, then (7.2) holds with the multipliers $\lambda_0 = 1$, $\lambda_1 = 0$, $\lambda_2 = 2$, $\lambda_3 = 0$.

This example illustrates another property of the multiplier rule (7.2), namely, that *a point x_0 satisfies the multiplier rule relative to constraints (7.1)*

*if and only if it satisfies the multiplier rule relative to the equivalent
constraints*

$$g_\alpha(x) \leqslant 0 \quad (\alpha = 1,\ldots,m), \qquad g_{m-p+\beta}(x) = -g_\beta(x) \leqslant 0 \quad (\beta = p+1,\ldots,m).$$

$$(7.3)$$

This property is not enjoyed by the multiplier rule obtained from (7.2) by
replacing condition (7.2c) by the condition that $\lambda_\alpha = 0$ whenever $g_\alpha(x_0) < 0$.
Suppose that x_0 satisfies condition (7.2) relative to constraints (7.1) with a
set of multipliers $\lambda_0, \lambda_1, \ldots, \lambda_m$. Set $\mu_\rho = \lambda_\rho$ $(\rho = 0, \ldots, p)$. If $\lambda_\beta > 0$, set $\mu_\beta = \lambda_\beta$,
$\mu_{m-p+\beta} = 0$. Otherwise set $\mu_\beta = 0$, $\lambda_{m-p+\beta} = -\lambda_\beta$. Then x_0 satisfies the
multiplier rule (7.2) relative to (7.3) with the set of nonnegative multipliers
$\mu_0, \ldots, \mu_m$. It is necessary only to check the corresponding condition (7.2c).
In doing so, we observe that, if $\lambda_\beta g_\beta(x) > 0$, then for $\lambda_\beta > 0$ we have
$\mu_\beta g_\beta(x) = \lambda_\beta g_\beta(x) > 0$, $\mu_{m-p+\beta} = 0$, and for $\lambda_\beta < 0$ we have $\mu_\beta = 0$,
$\mu_{m-p+\beta} g_{m-p+\beta}(x) = \lambda_\beta g_\beta(x) > 0$. Conversely, if x_0 satisfies the multiplier
rule (7.2) relative to constraints (7.3) with a set of multipliers
$\mu_0, \mu_1, \ldots, \mu_{2m-p}$, these multipliers are nonnegative. For $\beta = p+1, \ldots, m$, the
functions $g_\beta(x)$ and $g_{m-p+\beta}(x) = -g_\beta(x)$ cannot be positive simultaneously. Hence at least one of the multipliers μ_β, $\mu_{m-p+\beta}$ must be zero.
Using this fact, we can easily verify that x_0 satisfies the multiplier rule
relative to (7.1) with the multipliers $\lambda_0 = \mu_0$, $\lambda_\alpha = \mu_\alpha$, $\lambda_\beta = \mu_\beta - \mu_{m-p+\beta}$.

In view of this result in dealing with Theorem 7.1 we can assume
without loss of generality that $p = m$, that is, that all constraints are
inequality constraints. However, to facilitate applications we prefer to
retain form (7.1) in the statement of our results.

In the preceding pages we showed that, under the hypothesis of regularity or of augmentability, a solution x_0 to our minimum problem has
associated with it a set of multipliers $\lambda_1, \ldots, \lambda_m$ such that

$$\lambda_\alpha \geqslant 0 \quad (\alpha = 1,\ldots,p) \quad \text{with } \lambda_\alpha = 0 \text{ if } g_\alpha(x_0) < 0, \qquad (7.4a)$$

$$\nabla f(x_0) + \lambda_1 \nabla g_1(x_0) + \cdots + \lambda_m \nabla g_m(x_0) = 0. \qquad (7.4b)$$

Obviously, if (7.2) holds with $\lambda_0 = 1$, then (7.4) holds. We shall show that, *if
(7.4) holds at x_0 with a set of multipliers $\lambda_1, \ldots, \lambda_m$, then these multipliers can
be chosen so that (7.2) holds at x_0 with the multipliers $\lambda_0 = 1, \lambda_1, \ldots, \lambda_m$.* It is
necessary only to select the multipliers in (7.4) so that the number of
nonzero multipliers is as small as possible. If these multipliers are all zero,
(7.2) holds with $\lambda_0 = 1$. Otherwise, we can suppose that only inequality
constraints occur. In addition we can assume that the constraints have
been indexed so that $\lambda_1, \ldots, \lambda_r$ are positive and the remaining multipliers

are zero. Then the gradients $\nabla g_1(x_0), \ldots, \nabla g_r(x_0)$ are linearly independent; otherwise, there would exist multipliers $\mu_1, \ldots, \mu_r$, not all zero, such that

$$\mu_1 \nabla g_1(x_0) + \cdots + \mu_r \nabla g_r(x_0) = 0.$$

The multipliers $\hat{\lambda}_\rho = \lambda_\rho + s\mu_\rho$ $(\rho = 1, \ldots, r)$, $\hat{\lambda}_\sigma = \lambda_\sigma$ $(\sigma \geqslant r)$ would satisfy (7.4b), and we could select s so that $\hat{\lambda}_\rho \geqslant 0$ for $\rho = 1, \ldots, r$ and so that $\hat{\lambda}_\rho = 0$ for some index $\rho \leqslant r$. The new set $\hat{\lambda}_1, \ldots, \hat{\lambda}_m$ would have at most $r - 1$ nonzero elements, contrary to our choice of $\lambda_1, \ldots, \lambda_m$ as a set with the fewest number of nonzero multipliers. It follows that the gradients $\nabla g_1(x_0), \ldots, \nabla g_r(x_0)$ are linearly independent. We can therefore choose vectors $h_1, \ldots, h_r$ such that $g'_\rho(x_0, h_\gamma) = \delta_{\rho\gamma}$ $(\rho, \gamma = 1, \ldots, r)$, where $\delta_{\rho\rho} = 1, \delta_{\rho\gamma} = 0$ $(\rho \neq \gamma)$. Setting $h = h_1 + \cdots + h_r$, we have $g'_\rho(x_0, h) = 1$ $(\rho = 1, \ldots, r)$. Since $g_\rho(x_0) = 0$, it follows that there is a constant δ such that $g_\rho(x_0 + th) > 0$ on $0 < t \leqslant \delta$ for $\rho = 1, \ldots, r$. Condition (7.2c) therefore holds for this special set of multipliers, as was to be proved.

We come now to the proof of Theorem 7.1. In this proof we can assume without loss of generality that x_0 affords a strict local minimum to f subject to constraints (7.1). This follows because we can replace $f(x)$ by $f(x) + |x - x_0|^4$ without altering relations (7.2). Under this assumption there is a closed ball N about x_0 such that $f(x) > f(x_0)$ for all $x \neq x_0$ in N satisfying constraints (7.1). Set

$$\hat{g}_\alpha(x) = \max[0, g_\alpha(x)] \quad (\alpha \leqslant p), \qquad \hat{g}_\beta(x) = g_\beta(x) \quad (\beta > p), \quad (7.5a)$$

$$G(x) = \tfrac{1}{2} \left[\hat{g}_1(x)^2 + \cdots + \hat{g}_m(x)^2 \right]. \tag{7.5b}$$

Observe that constraints (7.1) are equivalent to the single constraint $G(x) = 0$. Observe further that the function $G(x)$ is of class C' on N and has

$$\nabla G(x) = \hat{g}_1(x) \nabla g_1(x) + \cdots + \hat{g}_m(x) \nabla g_m(x) \tag{7.6}$$

as its gradient. Let $x(\sigma)$ be the minimum point on N of the augmented function

$$H(x, \sigma) = f(x) + \sigma G(x).$$

By Theorem 2.1 we have $\lim_{\sigma \to \infty} x(\sigma) = x_0$. There is accordingly a constant $\sigma_0 > 0$ such that $x(\sigma)$ is interior to N whenever $\sigma \geqslant \sigma_0$. Hence when $\sigma \geqslant \sigma_0$ we have $\nabla H[x(\sigma), \sigma] = 0$, that is

$$\nabla f[x(\sigma)] + \sigma \hat{g}_1[x(\sigma)] \nabla g_1[x(\sigma)] + \cdots + \sigma \hat{g}_m[x(\sigma)] \nabla g_m[x(\sigma)] = 0.$$

Dividing each term in this expression by the square root of the sum of the squares of the coefficients of the gradients, we obtain the equation

$$\mu_0(\sigma)\nabla f[x(\sigma)] + \mu_1(\sigma)\nabla g_1[x(\sigma)] + \cdots + \mu_m(\sigma)\nabla g_m[x(\sigma)] = 0, \quad (7.7)$$

where

$$\mu_0(\sigma) = \frac{1}{d(\sigma)}, \quad \mu_\gamma(\sigma) = \frac{\sigma}{d(\sigma)}\hat{g}_\gamma[x(\sigma)] \quad (\gamma = 1,\ldots,m), \quad (7.8a)$$

$$d(\sigma) = \left[1 + \sigma^2 \sum_{\gamma=1}^{m} \hat{g}_\gamma[x(\sigma)]^2\right]^{1/2} = \{1 + 2\sigma^2 G[x(\sigma)]\}^{1/2}. \quad (7.8b)$$

By construction we have

$$\mu_0(\sigma)^2 + \mu_1(\sigma)^2 + \cdots + \mu_m(\sigma)^2 = 1. \quad (7.9)$$

Consider a sequence $\{\sigma_q\}$ such that $\lim_{q\to\infty}\sigma_q = \infty$. In view of (7.9) the sequences of multipliers $\{\mu_\rho(\sigma_q)\}$ are bounded and hence have convergent subsequences. We can therefore assume that the original sequence $\{\sigma_q\}$ was chosen so that the limits

$$\lim_{q\to\infty}\mu_\rho(\sigma_q) = \lambda_\rho \quad (\rho = 0,1,\ldots,m)$$

exist. We also have $\lim_{q\to\infty}x(\sigma_q) = x_0$. Setting $d_q = d(\sigma_q)$, $x_q = x(\sigma_q)$, we have, by (7.8),

$$\lim_{q\to\infty}\frac{1}{d_q} = \lambda_0, \quad \lim_{q\to\infty}\frac{\sigma_q}{d_q}\hat{g}_\gamma(x_q) = \lambda_\gamma \quad (\gamma = 1,\ldots,m), \quad (7.10)$$

in addition to the relation $\lim_{q\to\infty}x_q = x_0$. Using (7.9) and (7.7), we see that

$$\lambda_0^2 + \lambda_1^2 + \cdots + \lambda_m^2 = 1,$$

$$\lambda_0\nabla f(x_0) + \lambda_1\nabla g_1(x_0) + \cdots + \lambda_m\nabla g_m(x_0) = 0.$$

It is clear that the multipliers $\lambda_0, \lambda_1,\ldots,\lambda_m$ are not all zero. Since $d_q > 0$, we have $\lambda_0 \geq 0$. Inasmuch as $\hat{g}_\alpha(x_q) \geq 0$ ($\alpha \leq p$), we have $\lambda_\alpha \geq 0$ ($\alpha = 1,\ldots,p$). By (7.10) there is a number q_0 such that, if $q \geq q_0$ and $\lambda_\alpha \neq 0$, then $\hat{g}_\alpha(x_q) = g_\alpha(x_q)$ is not zero and has the same sign as λ_α. Hence (7.2c) holds. It follows that the multiplier rule (7.2) is satisfied, as was to be proved.

COROLLARY 1.

Suppose that

$$\liminf_{\sigma \to \infty} \sigma^2 G[x(\sigma)] < \infty. \tag{7.11}$$

There exists a sequence $\{\sigma_q\}$ tending to infinity such that the multiplier rule (7.2) holds with the multipliers

$$\lambda_0 = 1, \qquad \lambda_\gamma = \lim_{q \to \infty} \sigma_q \hat{g}_\gamma(x_q) \qquad (\gamma = 1, \dots, m), \tag{7.12}$$

where $x_q = x(\sigma_q)$. In this event

$$\lim_{q \to \infty} 2\sigma_q^2 G(x_q) = \lambda_1^2 + \cdots + \lambda_m^2. \tag{7.13}$$

If (7.11) holds, the sequence $\{\sigma_q\}$ described in the proof of Theorem 7.1 can be chosen so that

$$\lim_{q \to \infty} d_q = \lim_{q \to \infty} \left[1 + 2\sigma_q^2 G(x_q) \right] < \infty.$$

Then the multipliers in (7.2) given by limits (7.10) have $\lambda_0 > 0$. Dividing these multipliers by λ_0, we obtain a new set of multipliers of form (7.12). Relation (7.13) follows from (7.12) and formula (7.5b) for $G(x)$.

COROLLARY 2.

Suppose that

$$\liminf_{\sigma \to \infty} \sigma |x(\sigma) - x_0| < \infty. \tag{7.14}$$

Then (7.11) holds. Moreover there exist a sequence $\{\sigma_q\}$ of positive numbers, a vector h, and a subset Γ of indices $1, \dots, m$ such that, if $x_q = x(\sigma_q)$, then

$$\lim_{q \to \infty} \sigma_q = \infty, \qquad \lim_{q \to \infty} \sigma_q(x_q - x_0) = h, \tag{7.15a}$$

$$\hat{g}_\gamma(x_q) = g_\gamma(x_q) \quad (\gamma \text{ in } \Gamma), \qquad \hat{g}_\gamma(x_q) = 0 \quad \text{otherwise.} \tag{7.15b}$$

In this event multipliers (7.12) take the form

$$\lambda_0 = 1, \qquad \lambda_\gamma = g_\gamma'(x_0, h) \quad (\gamma \text{ in } \Gamma), \qquad \lambda_\gamma = 0 \quad \text{otherwise.} \tag{7.16}$$

To verify this result, we can suppose that $g_\gamma(x_0) = 0$ ($\gamma = 1, \dots, m$). Select

K so that $|\nabla g_\gamma(x)| \leqslant K$ on N. Then if x is in N we have

$$|\hat{g}_\gamma(x)| \leqslant |g_\gamma(x) - g_\gamma(x_0)| \leqslant K|x - x_0|.$$

Consequently, by (7.4b),

$$G(x) \leqslant nK^2|x - x_0|^2$$

for all x in N. Combining this result with (7.14), we see that condition (7.11) is satisfied. By virtue of (7.14) we can select a sequence $\{\sigma_q\}$ such that (7.15a) holds for some vector h. Obviously this sequence can be modified so that (7.15b) holds also. If γ is in Γ, we have

$$\lim_{q\to\infty} \sigma_q \hat{g}_\gamma(x_q) = \lim_{q\to\sigma} \sigma_q[\, g_\gamma(x_q) - g_\gamma(x_0)] = g_\gamma'(x_0, h).$$

Combining this result with (7.12), we obtain formulas (7.16) for the multipliers $\lambda_0, \lambda_1, \ldots, \lambda_m$:

EXAMPLE 7.3

In the one-dimensional case the point $x = 0$ affords a strict minimum to $f(x) = x^2 - 8x$ subject to the constraint $g(x) = x \leqslant 0$. The augmented function $H(x,\sigma) = f(x) + \sigma G(x)$ with $G(x) = \frac{1}{2}[\max(0, x)]^2$ has a minimum at $x(\sigma) = 8/(2 + \sigma)$. We have

$$\lim_{\sigma\to\infty} \sigma x(\sigma) = 8, \qquad \lim_{\sigma\to\infty} \sigma^2 G[x(\sigma)] = \lim_{\sigma\to\infty} \frac{32\sigma^2}{(2+\sigma)^2} = 32,$$

$$\lambda = \lim_{\sigma\to\infty} \sigma g[x(\sigma)] = 8.$$

Hence (7.2) holds at $x = 0$ with $\lambda_0 = 1$ and $\lambda = 8$. Suppose now that we replace x by x^3. Then $x = 0$ affords a strict minimum to $f(x) = x^6 - 8x^3$ subject to the constraint $g(x) = x^3 \leqslant 0$ and $G(x) = \frac{1}{2}[\max(0, x^3)]^2$. In this case the augmented function $H(x,\sigma) = f(x) + \sigma G(x)$ has a minimum at $x(\sigma) = 2(2 + \sigma)^{-1/3}$. We have

$$\lim_{\sigma\to\infty} \sigma^2 G[x(\sigma)] = 32 \qquad and \qquad \lambda = \lim_{\sigma\to\infty} \sigma g[x(\sigma)] = 8.$$

Again $\lambda_0 = 1$, $\lambda = 8$ are the multipliers described in Corollary 1. However, $\lim_{\sigma\to\infty} \sigma x(\sigma) = \infty$, so that condition (7.14) fails to hold.

EXAMPLE 7.4

Observe that in xyz-space the origin $(x_0, y_0, z_0) = (0,0,0)$ affords a strict minimum to the function $f(x,y,z) = ax + by + z^2$ subject to the constraints

$$g_1(x,y,z) = x + y^2 \leqslant 0, \qquad g_2(x,y,z) = -x \leqslant 0. \qquad (7.17)$$

The corresponding tangential constraints are

$$g_1'(0,0,0; \delta x, \delta y, \delta z) = \delta x \leqslant 0, \qquad g_2'(0,0,0; \delta x, \delta y, \delta z) = -\delta x \leqslant 0.$$

They imply that $\delta x = 0$. The vector $(\delta x, \delta y, \delta z) = (0,1,0)$ satisfies these tangential constraints but is not a tangent at $(0,0,0)$ to the set S of points $(0,0,z)$ defined by constraints (7.17). Hence the usual constraint qualification conditions are not satisfied. Set $H = f + \sigma G$, where

$$G(x,y,z) = \tfrac{1}{2}\left\{ \left[\max(0, x+y^2) \right]^2 + \left[\max(0, -x) \right]^2 \right\}.$$

Consider first the case $b = 0$. Then the minimum point of H is $x(\sigma) = -a/\sigma$, $y(\sigma) = 0$, $z(\sigma) = 0$. Moreover

$$\sigma^2 G[x(\sigma), y(\sigma), z(\sigma)] = \frac{a^2}{2}.$$

By Corollary 1 the multiplier rule (7.2) holds with $\lambda_0 = 1$. If $a > 0$, we have $\lambda_1 = 0$, $\lambda_2 = a$. If $a \leqslant 0$, we have $\lambda_1 = a$, $\lambda_2 = 0$. If $b \neq 0$, at the minimum point $[x(\sigma), y(\sigma), z(\sigma)]$ of H we have the relations

$$x < 0, \qquad x + y^2 > 0, \qquad 2y(a + \sigma x) = b, \qquad a + \sigma x + \sigma(x + y^2) = 0,$$

$$2\sigma^2 G(x,y,z) = \frac{b^2}{4y^2} + \left(\frac{-b}{2y} + a \right)^2.$$

Since $\lim_{\sigma \to \infty} y(\sigma) = 0$, we have

$$\lim_{\sigma \to \infty} \sigma^2 G[x(\sigma), y(\sigma), z(\sigma)] = +\infty.$$

Consequently we must have $\lambda_0 = 0$ when $b \neq 0$.

8. QUASINORMALITY

It is clear that the multipliers $\lambda_0, \lambda_1, \ldots, \lambda_m$ described in Theorem 7.1 can be chosen so that $\lambda_0 = 1$ if conditions (7.2) cannot hold when $\lambda_0 = 0$, that is, if the following condition holds at x_0: There exists no set of multipliers $\lambda_1, \ldots, \lambda_m$ such that

$$\lambda_1, \ldots, \lambda_m \text{ are not all zero,} \tag{8.1a}$$

$$\lambda_\alpha \geqslant 0 \quad (\alpha = 1, \ldots, p), \qquad \sum_{\gamma=1}^{m} \lambda_\gamma \nabla g_\gamma(x_0) = 0, \tag{8.1b}$$

$$\begin{gathered} \text{In every neighborhood of } x_0 \text{ there is a point } x \text{ such} \\ \text{that } \lambda_\gamma g_\gamma(x) > 0 \text{ for all } \gamma \text{ having } \lambda_\gamma \neq 0. \end{gathered} \tag{8.1c}$$

We shall say that a point x_0 in the set S defined by the constraints

$$g_\alpha(x) \leqslant 0, \qquad g_\beta(x) = 0 \qquad (\alpha = 1, \ldots, p; \beta = p+1, \ldots, m) \tag{8.2}$$

is a *quasinormal point* of S if there is no set of multipliers $\lambda_1, \ldots, \lambda_m$ satisfying conditions (8.1). It is our purpose in this section to show that quasinormality implies regularity. The concept, of regularity was discussed in Sections 7 and 10 in Chapter 4. It is the condition that every solution h of the tangential constraints

$$g'_\alpha(x_0, h) \leqslant 0 \quad (1 \leqslant \alpha \leqslant p; g_\alpha(x_0) = 0), \qquad g'_\beta(x_0, h) = 0 \quad (\beta > p)$$

at x_0 is a tangent vector of S at x_0. Inasmuch as a constraint $g_\alpha(x) \leqslant 0$ for which $g_\alpha(x_0) < 0$ plays no role in the conditions of quasinormality and of regularity, we can suppose that $g_\alpha(x_0) = 0$ ($\gamma = 1, \ldots, m$). Then the tangential constraints for S at x_0 take the form

$$g'_\alpha(x_0, h) \leqslant 0, \qquad g'_\beta(x_0, h) = 0 \qquad (\alpha = 1, \ldots, p; \beta = p+1, \ldots, m). \tag{8.3}$$

We continue with the assumption that the functions $g_1, \ldots, g_m$ are of class C'.

It should be noted that in view of (8.1c) the condition of quasinormality is not wholly a point condition. A simpler condition, that is, a point condition, is the condition of normality defined at the end of Section 10 in Chapter 4. The point x_0 is a *normal point* of S if the following condition holds:

$$\begin{gathered} \text{If } \sum_{\gamma=1}^{m} \lambda_\gamma \nabla g_\gamma(x_0) = 0, \quad \lambda_\alpha \geqslant 0 \quad [\alpha \leqslant p \text{ with } \lambda_\alpha = 0 \text{ if } g_\alpha(x_0) < 0], \\ \text{then} \quad \lambda_\gamma = 0 \quad (\gamma = 1, \ldots, m). \end{gathered} \tag{8.4}$$

Observe that in this definition we admit inactive constraints at x_0. When inactive constraints have been deleted, as we have assumed, the criterion for normality takes a simpler form:

$$\text{If } \sum_{\gamma=1}^{m} \lambda_\gamma \nabla g_\gamma(x_0)=0, \lambda_\alpha \geqslant 0 \quad (\alpha \leqslant p), \text{ then } \lambda_\gamma=0 \quad (\gamma=1,\ldots,m). \quad (8.5)$$

It is clear that a *normal point* of S is a *quasinormal point* of S. Consequently we will have shown that normality implies regularity once we have shown that quasinormality implies regularity.

The following lemma indicates the naturalness of the concept of quasinormality.

LEMMA 8.1

Suppose that the functions $g_1,\ldots,g_p$ *are concave and the functions* $g_{p+1},\ldots,g_m$ *are linear; then a point* x_0 *in S is a quasinormal point of S.*

Again we can assume that $g_\gamma(x_0)=0$ $(\gamma=1,\ldots,m)$. In view of our concavity and linearity assumptions we have

$$g_\alpha(x) \leqslant g'_\alpha(x_0,x-x_0) \ (\alpha \leqslant p), \quad g_\beta(x)=g'_\beta(x_0,x-x_0) \ (\beta>p). \quad (8.6)$$

The inequality involving g follows from inequality (5.7) in Chapter 1 with $f(x)=-g_\alpha(x)$. The relation involving g_β is an identity. Let $\lambda_1,\ldots,\lambda_m$ be multipliers satisfying conditions (8.1b) and (8.1c). Using (8.1b) and (8.6), we see that

$$\sum_{\gamma=1}^{m} \lambda_\gamma g_\gamma(x) \leqslant \sum_{\gamma=1}^{m} \lambda_\gamma g'_\gamma(x_0,x-x_0)=0. \quad (8.7)$$

By (8.1c) we can select a point x near x_0 such that, if $\lambda_\gamma \neq 0$, then $\lambda_\gamma g_\gamma(x)>0$. It follows from (8.7) that we must have $\lambda_\gamma=0$ $(\gamma=1,\ldots,m)$. Consequently x_0 is a quasinormal point of S, as was to be proved.

An important property of quasinormality is given in

LEMMA 8.2

If a point x_0 *in S is quasinormal relative to constraints (8.2), it is quasinormal relative to the equivalent constraints*

$$g_\gamma(x) \leqslant 0 \quad (\gamma=1,\ldots,m), \qquad -g_\beta(x) \leqslant 0 \quad (\beta=p+1,\ldots,m). \quad (8.8)$$

Inasmuch as we cannot have $g_\beta(x) > 0$ and $-g_\beta(x) > 0$ simultaneously, it is readily verified that condition (8.1c) is preserved when constraints (8.2) are replaced by the equivalent constraints (8.8). In the proof we use the fact that all the multipliers are nonnegative when the constraints are of form (8.8).

Let $\mathcal{H}$ be the class of vectors h satisfying the tangential constraints (8.3), and let r be the number of indices $\alpha \leqslant p$ for which there is a vector h in $\mathcal{H}$ such that $g'_\alpha(x_0, h) < 0$. As in Section 10, Chapter 4, we can suppose that our constraints have been renumbered so that $g'_\sigma(x_0, h) = 0$ $(\sigma = r+1, \ldots, m)$ for every vector h in $\mathcal{H}$. Let T be the set of points satisfying the reduced set of constraints

$$g_\tau(x) \leqslant 0 \quad (\tau = r+1, \ldots, p), \qquad g_\beta(x) = 0 \quad (\beta = p+1, \ldots, m). \quad (8.9)$$

As was seen in Section 10, Chapter 4, the tangential constraints for (8.9) take the form

$$g'_\sigma(x_0, h) = 0 \qquad (\sigma = r+1, \ldots, m). \quad (8.10)$$

We have

LEMMA 8.3

A point is a quasinormal point of S *if and only if it is a quasinormal point of* T. *A point is a normal point of* S *if and only if it is a normal point of* T.

To prove this result, let $\lambda_1, \ldots, \lambda_m$ be a set of multipliers such that

$$\sum_{\gamma=1}^{m} \lambda_\gamma \nabla g_\gamma(x_0) = 0, \qquad \lambda_\alpha \geqslant 0 \quad (\alpha = 1, \ldots, p). \quad (8.11)$$

For every vector h in $\mathcal{H}$ we have $g'_\sigma(x_0, h) = 0$ $(\sigma = r+1, \ldots, m)$, and hence, because $g'_\gamma(x_0, h) = \langle \nabla g_\gamma(x_0), h \rangle$,

$$0 = \sum_{\gamma=1}^{m} \lambda_\gamma g'_\gamma(x_0, h) = \sum_{\rho=1}^{r} \lambda_\rho g'_\rho(x_0, h).$$

Since each term in the last sum is nonpositive, we have $\lambda_\rho g'_\rho(x_0, h) = 0$ $(\rho = 1, \ldots, r)$. Inasmuch as there exists for each $\rho \leqslant r$ a vector h in $\mathcal{H}$ such that $g'_\rho(x_0, h) < 0$, it follows that $\lambda_\rho = 0$ $(\rho = 1, \ldots, r)$. The conditions for normality and quasinormality therefore depend only on constraints (8.9). This proves the lemma.

We come now to the main result to be established in this section.

THEOREM 8.1

If x_0 is a quasinormal point of S, *it is a regular point of* S.

In the proof we can assume, by Lemma 8.2, that the set S is defined by inequality constraints

$$g_\alpha(x) \leqslant 0 \qquad (\alpha = 1, \ldots, p). \qquad (8.12)$$

We can assume that $x_0 = 0$ and that $g_\alpha(0) = 0$ ($\alpha = 1, \ldots, p$). By Lemma 10.1, Chapter 4, the point x_0 is a regular point of S if and only if it is a regular point of the set T appearing in Lemma 8.3. Hence we can assume that $S = T$. Then the tangential constraints take the simpler form

$$g'_\alpha(0, h) = 0 \qquad (\alpha = 1, \ldots, p). \qquad (8.13)$$

Consequently every solution h of these equations is orthogonal to the gradients $\nabla g_1(0), \ldots, \nabla g_p(0)$.

Having made these simplifications, we proceed as follows. Let N be a closed ball about $x_0 = 0$, and let $h \neq 0$ be a solution of tangential constraints (8.13) Choose a constant $\epsilon > 0$ such that the point $x = 2\epsilon h$ is interior to N. We shall show that there is a curve $x(t)$ ($0 \leqslant t \leqslant \epsilon$) in $S \cap N$ such that $x(0) = x_0 = 0$, $\dot{x}(0) = h$. This signifies that h is a tangent vector to S at x_0, as is to be proved. To establish the existence of such a curve, we select for each t on $0 \leqslant t \leqslant \epsilon$ a point $x(t, \sigma)$ in N which minimizes the function

$$H(x, t, \sigma) = |x - th|^2 + t\sigma \sum_{\alpha=1}^{p} [\hat{g}_\alpha(x)]^2 \qquad (8.14)$$

on N, where, as before, $\hat{g}_\alpha(x) = \max [0, g_\alpha(x)]$. Inasmuch as

$$|x(t, \sigma) - th|^2 \leqslant H[x(t, \sigma), t, \sigma] \leqslant H(0, t, \sigma) = |th|^2 \leqslant \epsilon^2 |h|^2, \qquad (8.15)$$

it follows that $|x(t, \sigma)| \leqslant 2\epsilon |h|$. By virtue of our choice of ϵ the point $x(t, \sigma)$ is interior to N. Consequently at $x(t, \sigma)$ we have

$$\tfrac{1}{2} \nabla H = x - th + \sigma t \sum_{\alpha=1}^{p} \hat{g}_\alpha(x) \nabla g_\alpha(x) = 0.$$

For $t > 0$ this can be put into the form

$$\mu_0(t, \sigma)[x(t, \sigma) - th] + t \sum_{\alpha=1}^{p} \mu_\alpha(t, \sigma) \nabla g[x(t, \sigma)] = 0, \qquad (8.16)$$

where

$$\mu_0(t,\sigma) = \frac{1}{d(t,\sigma)}, \qquad \mu_\alpha(t,\sigma) = \frac{\sigma \hat{g}_\alpha[x(t,\sigma)]}{d(t,\sigma)} \qquad (8.17a)$$

$$d(t,\sigma) = \left\{ 1 + \sigma^2 \sum_{\alpha=1}^{p} \hat{g}_\alpha[x(t,\sigma)]^2 \right\}^{1/2}. \qquad (8.17b)$$

By construction we have

$$\mu_0(t,\sigma)^2 + \cdots + \mu_p(t,\sigma)^2 = 1, \qquad \mu_\alpha(t,\sigma) \geqslant 0 \qquad (\alpha=1,\ldots,p). \quad (8.18)$$

For each $t > 0$, select a sequence $\{\sigma_q\}$ having $\lim_{q \to \infty} \sigma_q = \infty$ such that the following limits exist:

$$\lim_{q \to \infty} x(t,\sigma_q) = x(t), \qquad \lim_{q \to \infty} \mu_\rho(t,\sigma_q) = \mu_\rho(t) \qquad (\rho=0,1,\ldots,p).$$

In view of (8.14) and (8.15) we have

$$|x(t) - th| \leqslant t|h|, \qquad \hat{g}_\alpha[x(t)] = 0. \qquad (8.19)$$

Consequently $x(t)$ is in S. By the use of (8.16), (8.17), and (8.18) we see that, for each $t > 0$ on $0 < t \leqslant \epsilon$,

$$\mu_0(t)^2 + \cdots + \mu_p(t)^2 = 1, \qquad \mu_\rho(t) \geqslant 0 \qquad (\rho=0,1,\ldots,p). \quad (8.20a)$$

$$\mu_0(t)\left[\frac{x(t)}{t} - h \right] + \sum_{\alpha=1}^{p} \mu_\alpha(t) \nabla g_\alpha[x(t)] = 0, \qquad (8.20b)$$

in every neighborhood $x(t)$ there is a point x such that, if $\mu_\alpha(t) > 0$, then $\hat{g}_\alpha(x) = g_\alpha(x) > 0$. $\qquad (8.20c)$

By (8.19) we have

$$\lim_{t \to 0} x(t) = x_0 = 0 \quad \text{and} \quad \left| \frac{x(t)}{t} \right| \leqslant 2|h|.$$

It remains to show that $\lim_{t \to 0} x(t)/t = h$. To this end we select a sequence of positive numbers $\{t_q\}$ converging to zero such that for $x_q = x(t_q)$ we have $\lim_{q \to \infty} x_q/t_q = h_0$. It is sufficient to show that $h_0 = h$. Since x_q is in S, the vector h_0 is tangent to S at x_0 and hence is orthogonal to the gradients

$\nabla g_1(0), \ldots, \nabla g_p(0)$. In view of (8.20a) we can replace the sequence $\{t_q\}$ by a subsequence, again denoted by $\{t_q\}$, such that the limits

$$\lim_{q \to \infty} \mu_\rho(t_q) = \lambda_\rho \qquad (\rho = 0, 1, \ldots, p)$$

exist. By virtue of (8.20) we have

$$\lambda_0^2 + \lambda_1^2 + \cdots + \lambda_p^2 = 1, \qquad \lambda_\rho \geqslant 0 \qquad (\rho = 0, 1, \ldots, p), \qquad (8.21\text{a})$$

$$\lambda_0(h_0 - h) + \sum_{\alpha=1}^{p} \lambda_\alpha \nabla g_\alpha(0) = 0, \qquad (8.21\text{b})$$

in every neighborhood of $x_0 = 0$ there is a point x such that, if $\lambda_\alpha > 0$ $(\alpha > 0)$, then $g_\alpha(x) > 0$.   (8.21c)

If $\lambda_0 = 0$, then $\lambda_1, \ldots, \lambda_p$ are not all zero, by (8.21a). In this event conditions (8.21b) and (8.21c) would violate the quasinormality of $x_0 = 0$. Hence $\lambda_0 > 0$. Equation (8.21b) then tells us that $h = h_0 + k$, where k is a vector orthogonal to h and to h_0. This is possible only if $k = 0$. Hence $h_0 = h$ and $\dot{x}(0) = h$, as was to be proved.

It should be noted that we have not asserted that the function $x(t)$ is a continuous function of t on $0 \leqslant t \leqslant \epsilon$. It is, however, continuous at $t = 0$.

9. EXTENSIONS OF EARLIER RESULTS

We return to the problem considered in Section 4, namely, that of minimizing a function $f(x)$ subject to a set of equality constraints

$$g_\alpha(x) = 0 \qquad (\alpha = 1, \ldots, m < n). \qquad (9.1)$$

We assume that this problem has a unique solution x_0 on a compact set N and that x_0 is an interior point of N. It is assumed that the functions f, $g_1, \ldots, g_m$ are of class C'' on N and that the matrix

$$g_x(x) = \left(\frac{\partial g_\alpha(x)}{\partial x^j} \right) \quad (\alpha = 1, \ldots, m; j = 1, \ldots, n) \qquad (9.2)$$

has rank m at x_0. Then there exists a unique set of Lagrange multipliers $\lambda_1, \ldots, \lambda_m$ such that

$$\nabla F(x_0) = 0, \qquad \text{where } F = f + \lambda_1 g_1 + \cdots + \lambda_m g_m. \qquad (9.3)$$

As in Section 4, we introduce the augmented function

$$H(x,\mu,\sigma)=f(x)+\sum_{\alpha=1}^{m}\left\{\mu_\alpha g_\alpha(x)+\frac{\sigma}{2}\left[g_\alpha(x)\right]^2\right\}. \qquad (9.4)$$

When it is convenient to do so, we use the vector notations $\mu=(\mu_1,\ldots,\mu_m)$ and $\lambda=(\lambda_1,\ldots,\lambda_m)$. A first property of the minimum point $x(\mu,\sigma)$ of $H(x,\mu,\sigma)$ is given in

LEMMA 9.1

Let M *be a bounded set of multipliers* $\mu=(\mu_1,\ldots,\mu_m)$. *If* $x(\mu,\sigma)$ *is the minimum point of* $H(x,\mu,\sigma)$ *on* N, *then*

$$\lim_{\sigma\to\infty}x(\mu,\sigma)=x_0, \qquad \lim_{\sigma\to\infty}\left\{\mu_\alpha+\sigma g_\alpha[x(\mu,\sigma)]\right\}=\lambda_\alpha \qquad (9.5)$$

uniformly for all μ *in* M.

The first relation was established in Theorem 2.4. Let N_0 be a neighborhood of x_0 interior to N on which matrix (9.2) has rank m. Select σ_0 such that, if $\sigma\geqslant\sigma_0$ and μ is in M, then $x(\mu,\sigma)$ is in N_0. Since $x(\mu,\sigma)$ minimizes $H(x,\mu,\sigma)$ on N, we have at $x=x(\mu,\sigma)$ the relations

$$\nabla H(x,\mu,\sigma)=\nabla f(x)+\sum_{\alpha=1}^{m}\left\{\left[\mu_\alpha+\sigma g_\alpha(x)\right]\nabla g_\alpha(x)\right\}=0$$

In view of the result given in Section 6, Chapter 3, the multipliers $\Lambda_1,\ldots,\Lambda_m$ which minimize the length

$$\left|\nabla f(x)+\sum_{\alpha=1}^{m}\Lambda_\alpha\nabla g_\alpha(x)\right|$$

with x in N_0 are given by the formula

$$\Lambda_\alpha(x)=-\sum_{i=1}^{n}\Gamma_{\alpha i}(x)\frac{\partial f(x)}{\partial x^i},$$

where $\Gamma(x)=(\Gamma_{\alpha i}(x))$ is the transpose of the pseudoinverse of matrix (9.2). Inasmuch as $\nabla H(x,\mu,\sigma)=0$ at $x=x(\mu,\sigma)$ it follows that

$$\mu_\alpha+\sigma g_\alpha[x(\mu,\sigma)]=\Lambda_\alpha[x(\mu,\sigma)] \qquad (\alpha=1,\ldots,m). \qquad (9.6)$$

Since $\Lambda_\alpha(x)$ is continuous on N_0 and $\Lambda_\alpha(x_0) = \lambda_\alpha$, we have

$$\lim_{\sigma \to \infty} \{ \mu_\alpha + \sigma g_\alpha[x(\mu, \sigma)] \} = \lambda_\alpha \quad (\alpha = 1, \ldots, m)$$

uniformly for all μ in M, as was to be proved.

A somewhat different result is given in

LEMMA 9.2

If $\{ \mu_q \}$ *is a bounded sequence of multipliers and* $\{ \sigma_q \}$ *is a bounded sequence of positive numbers with the property that* $\lim_{q \to \infty} x_q = x_0$, *where* $x_q = x(\mu_q, \sigma_q)$, *then* $\lim_{q \to \infty} \mu_q = \lambda$, *where* $\lambda = (\lambda_1, \ldots, \lambda_m)$ *are the Lagrange multipliers associated with* x_0.

If q is so large that matrix (9.2) has rank m at $x_q = x(\mu_q, \sigma_q)$, equation (9.6) holds with $\mu = \mu_q$ and $\sigma = \sigma_q$. Consequently, using vector notations, we have, since $g(x_0) = 0$ and $\{ \sigma_q \}$ is bounded,

$$\lim_{q \to \infty} \mu_q = \lim_{q \to \infty} \left[\mu_q + \sigma_q g(x_q) \right] = \lim_{q \to \infty} \Lambda(x_q) = \lambda,$$

as was to be proved.

We are now in a position to establish the following extension of Theorem 4.4. As in Theorem 4.4, we assume that, in addition to (9.3), the second-order condition

$$F''(x_0, h) > 0 \quad \text{for all } h \ne 0 \text{ having } g_\alpha'(x_0, h) = 0 \quad (\alpha = 1, \ldots, m) \quad (9.7)$$

holds. Conditions (9.3) and (9.7) together constitute the strengthened Lagrange multiplier rule at x_0.

THEOREM 9.1

Let M *be a bounded set of multipliers* μ. *Under the assumptions made above, there exist constant* σ_0 *and* $\tau > 0$ *such that, if* $\sigma \ge \sigma_0$ *and* μ *is in* M, *then the inequality*

$$H(x, \mu, \sigma) - H[x(\mu, \sigma), \mu, \sigma] \ge \tau |x - x(\mu, \sigma)|^2 \quad (9.8)$$

holds for all x *in* N.

Suppose that the conclusion in the theorem is false. Then for every integer q there exist a number $\sigma_q > q$, a multiplier μ_q in M, and a point $\bar{x}_q$ in N such that, if we set $x_q = x(\mu_q, \sigma_q)$, then

$$H\left(\bar{x}_q, \mu_q, \sigma_q\right) - H\left(x_q, \mu_q, \sigma_q\right) < \frac{1}{q} |\bar{x}_q - x_q|^2. \quad (9.9)$$

By Lemma 9.1 we have

$$\lim_{q\to\infty} x_q = x_0, \qquad \lim_{q\to\infty} \lambda_{q\alpha} = \lambda_\alpha \qquad (\alpha = 1,\dots,m), \qquad (9.10a)$$

where

$$\lambda_{q\alpha} = \mu_{q\alpha} + \sigma_q g_\alpha(x_q) \qquad (\alpha = 1,\dots,m). \qquad (9.10b)$$

Inasmuch as $H(x_q,\mu_q,\sigma_q) \leqslant H(x_0,\mu_q,\sigma_q) = f(x_0)$, we have, by (9.9),

$$\limsup_{q\to\infty} H(\bar{x}_q,\mu_q,\sigma_q) \leqslant f(x_0).$$

It follows from Lemma 2.1 that $\lim_{q\to\infty}\bar{x}_q = x_0$. In view of (9.9) we have $\bar{x}_q \neq x_q$. Let h_q be the unit vector defined by the relations

$$h_q = \frac{\bar{x}_q - x_q}{t_q}, \qquad t_q = |\bar{x}_q - x_q|. \qquad (9.11)$$

The sequence $\{h_q\}$ has a convergent subsequence. Accordingly we can suppose that our original sequences have been chosen so that the sequence $\{h_q\}$ converges to a vector h. Clearly h is a unit vector. It is easily verified that

$$\lim_{q\to\infty} \frac{g_\alpha(\bar{x}_q) - g_\alpha(x_q)}{t_q} = g'_\alpha(x_0,h). \qquad (9.12)$$

Observe further that, if we set

$$F_q(x) = f(x) + \sum_{\alpha=1}^{m} \lambda_{q\alpha} g_\alpha(x),$$

where $\lambda_{q\alpha}$ is defined by (9.10b), we have

$$\nabla H(x_q,\mu_q,\sigma_q) = \nabla F_q(x_q) = \nabla f(x_q) + \sum_{\alpha=1}^{m} \lambda_{q\alpha} \nabla g_\alpha(x_q) = 0$$

whenever x_q is interior to N. Using this fact, together with (9.10a), we find that

$$\lim_{q\to\infty} \frac{F_q(\bar{x}_q) - F_q(x_q)}{t_q^2} = \tfrac{1}{2} F''(x_0,h), \qquad (9.13)$$

where F is the Lagrangian appearing in equations (9.3). We write inequality (9.9) in the form

$$\frac{F_q(\bar{x}_q) - F_q(x_q)}{t_q^2} + \sigma_q \sum_{\alpha=1}^{m} \left[\frac{g(\bar{x}_q) - g(x_q)}{t_q} \right]^2 < \frac{1}{q}. \qquad (9.14)$$

Inasmuch as $\sigma_q \geqslant q$, it follows from (9.12), (9.13), and (9.14) that

$$F''(x_0, h) \leqslant 0, \qquad g'_\alpha(x_0, h) = 0 \qquad (\alpha = 1, \dots, m).$$

Since $h \neq 0$, this contradicts condition (9.7), thus proving Theorem 9.1.

COROLLARY

If $\bar{\mu}$ is in M, $\xi > 0$, *and* $\bar{x} = x(\bar{\mu}, \sigma_0 + \xi)$, *then the multipliers* $\mu_\alpha = \bar{\mu}_\alpha + \xi g_\alpha(\bar{x})$ $(\alpha = 1 \cdots m)$ *satisfy the inequality*

$$|\bar{\mu} - \lambda|^2 \geqslant |\mu - \lambda|^2 + 4\tau \xi |\bar{x} - x_0|^2, \qquad (9.15)$$

where $\lambda = (\lambda_1 \cdots \lambda_m)$ *are the Lagrange multipliers at* x_0.

In view of (9.8) we have the inequalities

$$H(\bar{x}, \lambda, \sigma_0) \geqslant H(x_0, \lambda, \sigma_0) + \tau |\bar{x} - x|^2 = f(x_0) + \tau |\bar{x} - x_0|^2,$$

$$f(x_0) = H(x_0, \bar{\mu}, \sigma_0 + \xi) > H(\bar{x}, \bar{\mu}, \sigma_0 + \xi) + \tau |\bar{x} - x_0|^2.$$

Adding these inequalities, we find that

$$-\sum_{\alpha=1}^{m} \left\{ (\bar{\mu}_\alpha - \lambda_\alpha) g_\alpha(\bar{x}) + \frac{\xi}{2} [g_\alpha(\bar{x})]^2 \right\} \geqslant 2\tau |\bar{x} - x_0|^2.$$

Combining this result with the relation

$$|\mu - \lambda|^2 = |\bar{\mu} - \lambda + \xi g(\bar{x})|^2 = |\bar{\mu} - \lambda|^2 + \xi \sum_{\alpha=1}^{m} \left[2(\bar{\mu}_\alpha - \lambda_\alpha) g_\alpha(\bar{x}) + \xi g_\alpha(\bar{x})^2 \right],$$

we obtain the desired inequality (9.15).

10. A METHOD OF MULTIPLIERS

We continue with the problem of minimizing a function $f(x)$ subject to the equality constraints

$$g_\alpha(x) = 0 \qquad (\alpha = 1, \ldots, m < n). \tag{10.1}$$

As in Section 9, we assume that our problem has a unique solution x_0 on a compact set N, that x_0 is an interior point of N, and that constraints (10.1) are normal at x_0 in the sense that the gradients $\nabla g_1(x_0), \ldots, \nabla g_m(x_0)$ are linearly independent. We assume also that the strengthened Lagrange multiplier rule holds at x_0. Then there exist unique multipliers $\lambda_1, \ldots, \lambda_m$ such that

$$\nabla F(x_0) = 0, \qquad \text{where } F = f + \lambda_1 g_1 + \cdots + \lambda_m g_m, \tag{10.2a}$$

$$F''(x_0, h) \geq 0 \quad \text{for all } h \neq 0 \text{ having } g'_\alpha(x_0, h) = 0 \quad (\alpha = 1, \ldots, m). \tag{10.2b}$$

As before, it will be convenient to use vector notations and component notations interchangeably. For example, $g(x)$ denotes the column vector with components $g_1(x), \ldots, g_m(x)$, μ is a vector with components $\mu_1, \ldots, \mu_m$, and λ is the set of multipliers $\lambda_1, \ldots, \lambda_m$.

In Section 2 it was shown that, if $\{\sigma_q\}$ is a sequence of positive numbers tending to ∞, then x_0 is the limit of the sequence of minimum points x_q on N of the augmented function

$$f(x) + \frac{\sigma_q}{2} \left[g_1(x)^2 + \cdots + g_m(x)^2 \right].$$

As a consequence of Lemma 9.1 we have

$$\lambda = \lim_{q \to \infty} \sigma_q g(x_q).$$

This computational procedure for finding the minimum point x_0 of $f(x)$ subject to the constraints $g(x) = 0$ is known as a *Method of penalty functions*. It is an effective method when the multipliers (or sensitivity constants) $\lambda_1, \ldots, \lambda_m$ are small. However, experience has shown that numerical difficulties arise when some of these multipliers are large. The purpose of this section is to give an alternative algorithm which has better convergence properties than the method of penalty functions. It is based on the properties of the augmented function

$$H(x, \mu, \sigma) = f(x) + \sum_{\alpha=1}^{m} \left[\mu_\alpha g_\alpha(x) + \frac{\sigma}{2} g_\alpha(x)^2 \right] \tag{10.3}$$

described in Section 9.

THEOREM 10.1

Select a sequence of positive numbers $\xi_0, \xi_1, \xi_2, \ldots$ *having* $\xi_q \geqslant \xi_0 > 0$. *Given a multiplier* μ_0, *there exists a constant* σ_0 *such that, if for* $q = 1, 2, 3, \ldots$ *we select* x_q *and* μ_q *successively by the conditions that*

$$x_q \text{ minimizes } H(x, \mu_{q-1}, \sigma_0 + \xi_{q-1}) \text{ on N}, \qquad (10.4a)$$

$$\mu_q = \mu_{q-1} + \xi_{q-1} g(x_q), \qquad (10.4b)$$

then $\{x_q\}$ *converges to* x_0 *and* $\{\mu_q\}$ *converges to the Lagrange multiplier* λ *associated with* x_0. *In fact, there are an integer* q_0 *and positive numbers* η, K, L *such that if* $q \geqslant q_0$ *then*

$$|g(x_{q+1})| \leqslant \frac{|g(x_q)|}{1 + \eta \xi_q}, \qquad (10.5a)$$

$$|x_q - x_0| \leqslant K|g(x_q)|, \qquad |\mu_q - \lambda| \leqslant L|g(x_q)|. \qquad (10.5b)$$

Before establishing this result, it will be instructive to apply algorithm (10.4) to the special case given in

EXAMPLE 10.1

Consider the problem of minimizing the function

$$f(x) = \tfrac{1}{2}x^* A x - \lambda_0 b^* x + c \qquad (A^* = A, b \neq 0)$$

subject to the constraint $g(x) = b^* x = 0$. Its Lagrangian is

$$F(x) = f(x) + \lambda g(x) = \tfrac{1}{2}x^* A x + (\lambda - \lambda_0)b^* x + c.$$

The strengthened Lagrange multiplier rule (10.2) holds at $x = 0$ if $\lambda = \lambda_0$ and $F''(0, h) = h^* A h > 0$ whenever $h \neq 0$ and $g'(0, h) = b^* h = 0$. When this condition holds, as we shall assume, the point $x = 0$ is the solution to our problem. The augmented function (10.3) takes the form

$$H(x, \mu, \sigma) = \tfrac{1}{2}x^*(A + \sigma b b^*)x + (\mu - \lambda_0)b^* x + c.$$

We select σ_0 so that the matrix $A_0 = A + \sigma_0 b b^*$ is positive definite. The constant σ_0 so chosen has the property described in Theorem 10.1. To see that this is the case, select a multiplier μ and a constant $\xi > 0$. Let $\bar{x}$ minimize

$$H(x, \mu, \sigma_0 + \xi) = \tfrac{1}{2}x^* A_0 x + (\mu - \lambda_0)b^* x + c + \frac{\xi}{2}x^* b b^* x.$$

Then $\nabla H = 0$ at $\bar{x}$, so that

$$A_0 \bar{x} = (\lambda_0 - \bar{\mu})b, \qquad \bar{\mu} = \mu + \xi g(\bar{x}),$$

$$\bar{x} = (\lambda_0 - \bar{\mu})A_0^{-1}b, \qquad g(\bar{x}) = (\lambda_0 - \bar{\mu})\eta, \qquad \eta = b^* A_0^{-1}b,$$

$$\mu - \lambda_0 = \bar{\mu} - \lambda_0 - \xi g(\bar{x}) = (\bar{\mu} - \lambda_0)(1 + \eta\xi).$$

Consequently we have

$$\bar{x} = \frac{\lambda_0 - \mu}{1 + \eta\xi} A_0^{-1}b, \qquad \bar{\mu} - \lambda_0 = \frac{\mu - \lambda_0}{1 + \eta\xi}, \qquad g(\bar{x}) = \frac{\eta(\lambda_0 - \mu)}{1 + \eta\xi}.$$

From these relations it is seen that algorithm (10.4) takes the form

$$x_{q+1} = \frac{x_q}{1 + \eta\xi_q}, \qquad \mu_{q+1} - \lambda_0 = \frac{\mu_q - \lambda_0}{1 + \eta\xi_q}, \qquad g(x_{q+1}) = \frac{g(x_q)}{1 + \eta\xi_q}.$$

If $\xi_q = \xi > 0$ for all values of q, we have

$$x_q = \frac{(\lambda_0 - \mu_0)A_0^{-1}b}{(1 + \eta\xi)^q}, \qquad \mu_q - \lambda_0 = \frac{\mu_0 - \lambda_0}{(1 + \eta\xi)^q}, \qquad g(x_q) = \frac{(\lambda_0 - \mu_0)\eta}{(1 + \eta\xi)^q}.$$

In this event $x_q \to 0$, $\mu_q \to \lambda_0$, $g(x_q) \to 0$ linearly with constant $1/(1 + \eta\xi)$.

We now turn to the proof of Theorem 10.1. To this end select a closed ball N_0 about x_0 interior to N on which the gradients $\nabla g_1(x), \ldots, \nabla g_m(x)$ are linearly independent. This is possible by virtue of our hypotheses that they are linearly independent at x_0. After selecting an initial multiplier μ_0, select a closed ball M about $\mu = \lambda$ which contains μ_0. Let $x(\mu, \sigma)$ be the minimum point of $H(x, \mu, \sigma)$ on N. By Lemma 9.1 $\lim_{\sigma \to \infty} x(\mu, \sigma) = x_0$ uniformly for all μ in M. Accordingly we can select σ_0 so that, if $\sigma \geqslant \sigma_0$ and μ is in M, then $x(\mu, \sigma)$ is in N_0. By virtue of Theorem 9.1 the constant σ_0 and a constant $\tau > 0$ can be chosen so that the inequality

$$H(x, \mu, \sigma) - H[x(\mu, \sigma), \mu, \sigma] \geqslant \tau |x - x(\mu, \sigma)|^2 \tag{10.6}$$

holds for all x in N whenever $\sigma \geqslant \sigma_0$ and μ is in M. The constant σ_0 chosen in this manner has the property described in Theorem 10.1.

Starting with μ_0, let $\{x_q\}$ and $\{\mu_q\}$ be the sequences generated by algorithm (10.4). By virtue of the corollary to Theorem 9.1 we have the inequality

$$|\mu_{q-1} - \lambda|^2 \geqslant |\mu_q - \lambda|^2 + 4\tau\xi_{q-1}|x_q - x_0|^2 \tag{10.7}$$

whenever μ_{q-1} is in M. Since μ_0 is in M, it follows from this inequality that μ_q is in M for all values of q. Moreover, by summation, we find from (10.7) that

$$|\mu_0 - \lambda|^2 \geqslant 4\tau \sum_{q=1}^{\infty} \xi_{q-1} |x_q - x_0|^2.$$

Since $\xi_q \geqslant \xi_0 > 0$, the sequence $\{x_q\}$ converges to x_0. There is accordingly an integer q_0 such that, if $q \geqslant q_0$, then x_q is interior to N_0. Suppose that $q \geqslant q_0$. Since x_q minimizes $H(x, \mu_{q-1}, \sigma_0 + \xi_{q-1})$, we have

$$H_x(x_q, \mu_{q-1}, \sigma_0 + \xi_{q-1}) = \nabla f(x_q)$$

$$+ \sum_{\alpha} \left\{ \mu_{\alpha, q-1} + \left[\sigma_0 + \xi_{q-1} g_\alpha(x_q) \right] \right\} \nabla g_\alpha(x_q) = 0.$$

Since $\mu_q = \mu_{q-1} + \xi_{q-1} g(x_q)$, it is seen, as in the proof of Lemma 9.1, that

$$\mu_q + \sigma_0 g(x_q) = \Lambda(x_q),$$

where $\Lambda(x)$ is the multiplier appearing in equation (9.6). We have accordingly

$$\lim_{q \to \infty} \mu_q = \lim_{q \to \infty} \left[\mu_q + \sigma_0 g(x_q) \right] = \lim_{q \to \infty} \Lambda(x_q) = \Lambda(x_0) = \lambda,$$

as stated in Theorem 10.1.

It remains to establish a rate of convergence. To this end observe that, by (10.6), the Hessian matrix $H_{xx} - 2\tau I$ of $H(x, \lambda, \sigma_0) - \tau|x - x_0|^2$ is nonnegative at $x = x_0$. By continuity there are a closed ball N_1 about x_0 and a closed ball M_1 about λ such that, if x is in N_1 and μ is in M_1, the inequality

$$h^* H_{xx}(x, \mu, \sigma_0) h \geqslant \tau|h|^2 \tag{10.8}$$

holds for all vectors h. We can select N_1 in N_0 and M_1 in M. By virtue of this inequality it follows from Taylor's Theorem that, if $\bar{x}$ is a point in N_1 and $\bar{\mu}$ is a multiplier in M_1 such that $H_x(\bar{x}, \bar{\mu}, \sigma_0) = 0$, the inequality

$$H(x, \bar{\mu}, \sigma_0) - H(\bar{x}, \bar{\mu}, \sigma_0) \geqslant \frac{\tau}{2}|x - \bar{x}|^2 \tag{10.9}$$

holds for all x in N_1.

Inasmuch as $x_q \to x_0$ and $\mu_q \to \lambda$, we can find an integer q_0 such that, if $q \geqslant q_0$, then x_q is in N_1 and μ_q is in M_1. Since

$$H_x(x_q, \mu_{q-1}, \sigma_0 + \xi_{q-1}) = H_x(x_q, \mu_q, \sigma_0) = 0,$$

it follows from (10.9) that

$$H(x_{q+1},\mu_q,\sigma_0) - H(x_q,\mu_q,\sigma_0) > \frac{\tau}{2}|x_{q+1}-x_q|^2,$$

$$H(x_q,\mu_{q+1},\sigma_0) - H(x_{q+1},\mu_{q+1},\sigma_0) > \frac{\tau}{2}|x_{q+1}-x_q|^2.$$

Adding these inequalities and using the relation

$$\mu_{q+1} = \mu_q + \xi_q g(x_{q+1}), \tag{10.10}$$

we find that

$$\xi_q \sum_{\alpha=1}^{m} \left[g_\alpha(x_q) g_\alpha(x_{q+1}) - g_\alpha(x_{q+1})^2 \right] \geq \tau|x_{q+1}-x_q|^2.$$

Consequently, if $q > q_0$,

$$\xi_q \left[|g(x_{q+1})| |g(x_q)| - |g(x_{q+1})|^2 \right] \geq \tau|x_{q+1}-x_q|^2. \tag{10.11}$$

This implies that $|g(x_q)| > |g(x_{q+1})|$ $(q \geq q_0)$.

As a further consequence of inequality (10.8) the determinant $|H_{xx}(x,\mu,\sigma_0)|$ is different from zero whenever x is in N_1 and μ is in M_1. In fact, because of linear independence of the gradients $\nabla g_1(x), \ldots, \nabla g_m(x)$ on N_1, the augmented determinant

$$\begin{vmatrix} H_{xx}(x,\mu,\sigma_0) & g_x(x)^* \\ g_x(x) & 0 \end{vmatrix} \tag{10.12}$$

is different from zero for these values of x and μ. Here $g_x(x)^*$ is the matrix whose column vectors are the gradients $\nabla g_1(x), \ldots, \nabla g_m(x)$. By the implicit function theorem the equations

$$H_x(x,\mu,\sigma_0) = 0, \qquad g(x) = y \tag{10.13}$$

have unique solutions $x = x(y)$, $\mu = \mu(y)$ of class C' on a spherical neighborhood Y_1 of $y = 0$ such that $x(y)$ is in N_1, $\mu(y)$ is in M_1, and $x(0) = x_0$, $\mu(0) = \lambda$. Let K, L, and L_1 be constants such that

$$|x(y) - x(\bar{y})| \leq K|y - \bar{y}|, \qquad |\mu(y) - \mu(\bar{y})| \leq L|y - \bar{y}|, \tag{10.14a}$$

$$|g(x) - g(\bar{x})| \leq L_1|x - \bar{x}|, \tag{10.14b}$$

where y, $\bar{y}$ are in Y_1 and $x, \bar{x}$ are in N_1. Increase q_0 if necessary so that $y_q = g(x_q)$ is in Y_1 whenever $q \geqslant q_0$. We then have the relations

$$y_q = g(x_q), \qquad x_q = x(y_q), \qquad \mu_q = \mu(y_q) \qquad (q \geqslant q_0). \qquad (10.15)$$

Moreover by (10.14)

$$|\mu_{q+1} - \mu_q| \leqslant L|y_{q+1} - y_q| \leqslant L_0|x_{q+1} - x_q|, \qquad L_0 = LL_1. \qquad (10.16)$$

Combining these results with (10.10) and (10.11), we find that for $q > q_0$

$$\xi_q^2|y_{q+1}|^2 = |\mu_{q+1} - \mu_q|^2 \leqslant L_0^2|x_{q+1} - x_q|^2 \leqslant \frac{\xi_q}{\eta}|y_{q+1}|\big[|y_q| - |y_{q+1}|\big],$$

where $\eta = \tau/L_0$. Consequently

$$(1 + \eta\xi_q)|y_{q+1}| \leqslant |y_q|.$$

Hence (10.5a) holds. Inequalities (10.5b) follow from relations (10.14) and (10.15). This completes the proof of Theorem 10.1.

Algorithm (10.4) and its analogue for infinite dimensional problems were studied by R. Rupp in his dissertation and in subsequent papers. Variants of this algorithm have been used by several authors, including D. Bertsekas, A. Miele, and R. Rockafellar.[†] In numerical computations one normally modifies the algorithm (10.4) so that x_q is a suitable estimate of the minimum point rather than the minimum point itself. In addition it may be desirable to modify the updating formula (10.4b) for the multipliers. We shall not discuss these modifications in this book.

[†]References to the works of these and other authors can be found in the following articles:

D. Bertsekas, "Combined Primal-Dual and Penalty Function Methods," *SIAM Journal on Control*, Vol. 13 (1975), 521–545.

A. Miele, P. Mosely, A. Levy, and G. Coggins, "On the Methods of Multipliers for Mathematical Programming," *Journal of Optimization Theory and Applications*, Vol. 10 (1972), 1-33.

R. Rockafellar, "The Multiplier Method of Hestenes and Powell Applied to Convex Programming," *Journal of Optimization Theory and Applications*, Vol. 12 (1973), 555–562.

R. Rupp, "A Nonlinear Optimal Control Minimization Technique," *Transactions of the American Mathematical Society*, Vol. 178 (1973), 357-381. See also, "On the Combination of the Multiplier Method of Hestenes and Powell with Newton's Method," *Journal of Optimization Theory and Applications*, Vol. 14 (1975), 167–188.

6

IMAGES AND LAGRANGE MULTIPLIERS

1. INTRODUCTION

We continue with the study of the problem introduced in Chapter 4. We suppose that we are given a point x_0 in a set X that minimizes a function $f(x)$ on the subset S of X defined by constraints of the form

$$g_\alpha(x) \leqslant 0 \quad (\alpha = 1,\ldots,p), \qquad g_\beta(x) = 0 \quad (\beta = p+1,\ldots,m). \qquad (1.1)$$

In the preceding pages X was a set in an n-dimensional Euclidean space. Moreover, certain continuity and differentiability properties were imposed on the functions $f, g_1, \ldots, g_m$. In the present chapter we make no assumptions with regard to X initially; the set X can lie in any space whatever. When we are concerned with convexity, we assume that X is a convex set in a real linear space. Since no topology is introduced on X, we cannot impose continuity conditions on the functions $f, g_1, \ldots, g_m$. Of course in our applications, we impose conditions on the set X and on the functions $f, g_1, \ldots, g_m$ in order to obtain the desired form of the Lagrange multiplier rule. Because of the generality of this approach, the principal results obtained are applicable to variational problems and optimal control problems, as well as to finite dimensional problems. However, we shall not be concerned with these applications except for certain elementary examples which are easily understood. Although the dimensionality of X plays no significant role in our theory, we suggest that initially the reader consider X to be a set in a Euclidean space. Most of our examples will be finite dimensional in character.

The technique to be used in this chapter is based on the observation that the set X is mapped onto a set W in an $(m+1)$-dimensional Euclidean space of points $w = (u, v^1, \ldots, v^m)$ by the transformation

$$u = f(x) - f(x_0), \qquad v^\gamma = g_\gamma(x) \qquad (\gamma = 1, \ldots, m), \qquad (1.2)$$

where x_0 minimizes f on S. We center our attention on the image W of X and on the image $w_0 = (u_0, v_0)$ of x_0 under this transformation. The fact that x_0 minimizes f on X subject to constraints (1.1) imposes conditions on the image set W which can be used to determine Lagrange multipliers. For example, if W is convex, a supporting m-plane of W at w_0 determines a set of Lagrange multipliers for our problem. If W is not convex, Lagrange multipliers are determined by a supporting m-plane of the tangent cone of W at w_0 or by a supporting m-plane of a suitably chosen convex subcone of the tangent cone. Examples illustrating this approach will be given in Section 2. These examples are simple and can be solved by inspection. The theory of cones and their duals plays a significant role in our considerations. It is therefore recommended that the reader become familiar with the theory of cones presented in Section 3 of Chapter 4 before attempting to master the material in this chapter.

In dealing with convex functions, we modify the procedure described above and define the set W to be the set of points $w = (u, v)$ for which there are a point x in X and a number $\rho \geqslant 0$ such that

$$u \geqslant \rho[f(x) - f(x_0)], \qquad v^\gamma \geqslant \rho g_\gamma(x) \qquad (\gamma = 1, \ldots, m). \qquad (1.3)$$

This simplifies our procedure and enables us to obtain Lagrange multipliers without specific reference to tangent spaces. The convex case is discussed in Sections 3 and 4. Applications to infinite dimensional problems are given in Section 5.

When no convexity assumptions are made, we use transformation (1.2) and study the nature of the tangent cone of W at w_0. In Section 6 we consider the case in which there are no equality constraints. This case is simpler because no implicit function theorems are needed. To treat problems involving equality constraints, we introduce in Section 9 the concept of a derived cone in the tangent cone of W at w_0. A derived cone determines a set of Lagrange multipliers, at least in a generalized sense. Applications to specific problems are made by constructing a suitable derived cone of W at w_0. In general, the derived cone used does not coincide with the tangent cone of W at w_0. In the convex case the tangent cone of W at w_0 is a derived cone. In the case of inequality constraints, Lagrange multipliers exist for every convex cone in the tangent cone of W at w_0 even if it is not a derived cone.

The proof that every derived cone determines a set of Lagrange multipliers is given in Section 10. Since we admit equality constraints, the proof is obtained with the help of a general implicit function theorem. The usual implicit function theorem is not applicable without additional assumptions. Even when the usual implicit function theorem can be used, it is not applicable directly but can be employed only after an application of theorems on the extensibility of functions.

The reader who has mastered the material in this chapter is well prepared for the study of very general control problems by the techniques developed by the author in his book on variational theory and optimal control theory.[†]

2. ILLUSTRATIVE EXAMPLES

The techniques to be used in this chapter can be illustrated by considering simple two- and three-dimensional examples.

EXAMPLE 2.1

Consider the problem of finding the point (x_0, y_0) in the unit disk

$$x^2 + y^2 \leqslant 1$$

which is nearest to the point $(5, 0)$. The solution is obviously the point $(1, 0)$. Analytically we seek to minimize the function

$$f(x, y) = (x - 5)^2 + y^2$$

subject to the inequality constraint

$$g(x, y) = x^2 + y^2 - 1 \leqslant 0.$$

To apply the Lagrange multiplier rule described in Chapter 4, we set

$$F(x, y) = f(x, y) + \lambda g(x, y)$$

so that

$$F(x, y) = (x - 5)^2 + y^2 + \lambda(x^2 + y^2 - 1).$$

[†]M. R. Hestenes, *Calculus of Variations and Optimal Control Theory*, John Wiley and Sons, New York, 1966. See also E. J. McShane, "On Multipliers for Lagrange Problems," *American Journal of Mathematics*, Vol. LXI (1939), 809–819.

Then

$$F_x = 2(x-5) + 2\lambda x, \qquad F_y = 2y + 2\lambda y.$$

Setting each of these equal to zero and using the relation

$$g(x,y) = x^2 + y^2 - 1 = 0,$$

we obtain as solution $x_0 = 1$, $y_0 = 0$, and $\lambda = 4$. There is one other solution, namely, $x_1 = -1$, $y_1 = 0$, $\lambda = -6$, which determines the point (x_1, y_1) in the disk whose distance from $(5,0)$ is a maximum.

We shall now determine the multiplier rule by a geometric argument. To this end we let W be the set of all points $w = (u,v)$ defined by the transformation

$$u = f(x,y) - f(x_0, y_0), \qquad v = g(x,y). \tag{2.1}$$

In our case

$$u = (x-5)^2 + y^2 - 16, \qquad v = x^2 + y^2 - 1.$$

Let W_0 be the set of points w in W having $v \leqslant 0$. These points are images of the points (x,y) satisfying the constraint $g(x,y) \leqslant 0$. Choosing the u-axis to be the vertical axis, we find that the sets W and W_0 have the form shown in Figure 2.1. This figure is schematic and is not drawn to scale. We choose the u-axis to be the vertical axis so that the lowest point w_0 in W_0 is the image of our solution (x_0, y_0). The set W is defined by the inequality

$$(v - u)^2 \leqslant 20(u + 4v),$$

as can be verified by substitution. Clearly W is convex. The tangent to W at the origin $w_0 = (0,0)$ is

$$u + 4v = 0.$$

This line is a line of support of W. Every point $w = (u,v)$ in W satisfies the inequality

$$u + 4v \geqslant 0.$$

Using formula (2.1), we find that

$$f(x,y) + 4g(x,y) \geqslant f(x_0, y_0) = f(x_0, y_0) + 4g(x_0, y_0).$$

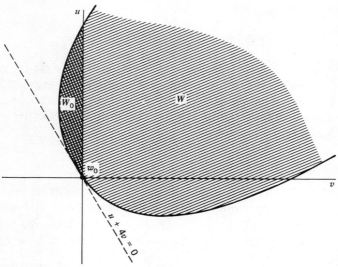

Figure 2.1

The function $F = f + 4g$ takes the form

$$F = 5(x-1)^2 + y^2.$$

This function is the Lagrange function for our problem. At the point $(1,0)$ we have

$$F_x = 0, \qquad F_y = 0,$$

as required by the Lagrange multiplier rule.

Because of the fact that the functions f and g are convex, we can obtain the result described above by the following alternative proceedure. Let $\hat{W}$ be the set of points $(\hat{u}, \hat{v})$ such that there exist a point (x,y) and a constant $\rho \geqslant 0$ such that

$$\hat{u} \geqslant \rho[f(x,y) - f(x_0, y_0)], \qquad \hat{v} \geqslant \rho g(x,y).$$

In this case

$$\hat{u} \geqslant \rho(x^2 + y^2 - 10x + 9), \qquad \hat{v} \geqslant \rho(x^2 + y^2 - 1).$$

These inequalities imply the relation

$$\hat{u} + 4\hat{v} \geqslant 5\rho\left[(x-1)^2 + y^2\right] \geqslant 0.$$

If (u,v) is in W, the ray $\hat{u} = \rho u$, $\hat{v} = \rho v$ ($\rho \geqslant 0$) is in $\hat{W}$. The closure of the set of points on these rays forms the tangent space for W at $(0,0)$. The line $u + 4v = 0$ is the boundary of $\hat{W}$. In view of this result we can use $\hat{W}$ to determine the Lagrange multiplier rule. This method is effective whenever the functions f and g are convex.

EXAMPLE 2.2

Consider the problem of finding the largest box that can be inserted in a sphere of radius r, and assume that the center of the box coincides with the center of the sphere. For simplicity choose $r = \sqrt{3}$. Then the problem is equivalent to that of maximizing the product xyz subject to the constraint

$$g(x,y,z) = x^2 + y^2 + z^2 - 3 \leqslant 0.$$

In addition we restrict x,y,z to be positive. The set of positive points (x,y,z) will be denoted by $\mathcal{D}$. Stated as a minimum problem, what we seek is to minimize the function

$$f(x,y,z) = -xyz$$

on $\mathcal{D}$ subject to the constraints $g(x,y,z) \leqslant 0$. The minimum point is the point $(x_0, y_0, z_0) = (1,1,1)$.

Proceeding as in Example 2.1, let W be the image of $\mathcal{D}$ under the transformation

$$u = f(x,y,z) - f(x_0, y_0, z_0) = 1 - xyz, \qquad v = g(x,y,z) = x^2 + y^2 + z^2 - 3.$$

Observe that $u < 1$ and $v > -3$ on $\mathcal{D}$. Moreover

$$v - \frac{2}{z}(1-u) + 3 - z^2 = (x-y)^2 \geqslant 0.$$

The left member as a function of z has a minimum when z is a solution of the equation

$$u = 1 - z^3.$$

From this result it follows that W is the set of points (u,v) defined by the relations

$$u = 1 - z^3, \qquad v \geqslant 3(z^2 - 1) \qquad (z > 0).$$

Part of the graph of W is shown in Figure 2.2. The origin $w_0 = (0, 0)$ is the

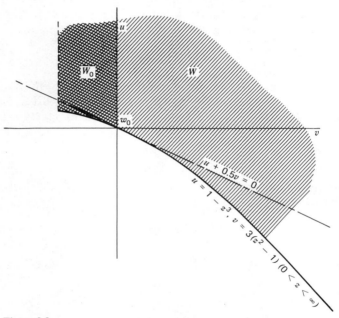

Figure 2.2

image of the minimizing point. The tangent line to the boundary of W is

$$u + 0.5v = 0.$$

This line is the line of support of the tangent space

$$u + 0.5v \geqslant 0$$

of W at w_0. The coefficient $\lambda = 0.5$ is the Lagrange multiplier λ, for if we set

$$F = f + \tfrac{1}{2} g = -xyz + \tfrac{1}{2}(x^2 + y^2 + z^2 - 3),$$

we have

$$F_x = -yz + x = 0, \qquad F_y = -zx + y = 0, \qquad F_z = -xy + z = 0$$

at the minimum point $(x_0, y_0, z_0) = (1, 1, 1)$. Observe that in this case the point $(1, 1, 1)$ does not afford a local minimum to F.

The procedure used in Examples 2.1 and 2.2 to obtain the Lagrange multiplier rule can be summarized as follows. Let x_0 minimize a function $f(x)$ on an open set $\mathcal{D}$ subject to the constraint $g(x) \leqslant 0$. Suppose that $g(x_0) = 0$. Let W be the image of $\mathcal{D}$ under the transformation

$$u = f(x) - f(x_0), \qquad v = g(x). \tag{2.2}$$

The minimum point x_0 is transformed into the origin $w_0 = (0, 0)$. Let W_0 be the set of points $w = (u, v)$ in W having $v \leqslant 0$. Then $u \geqslant 0$ for every point $w = (u, v)$ in W_0. It follows that no point $w = (u, v)$ in W satisfies the relations

$$u < 0, \qquad v \leqslant 0. \tag{2.3}$$

The point $(0, 0)$ is therefore a boundary point of W, as indicated schematically in Figure 2.3. The tangent to the boundary W at w_0 is of the form

$$\lambda u + \mu v = 0.$$

Since no point (u, v) in W satisfies relations (2.3), it follows that λ and μ

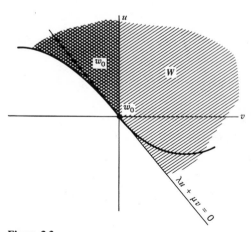

Figure 2.3

have the same sign. Consequently we can select λ and μ so that $\lambda \geqslant 0, \mu \geqslant 0$. The function

$$F = \lambda f + \mu g$$

has the property that $\nabla F(x_0) = 0$ if f and g are differentiable at x_0. This rule with certain modifications will be established in the sections that follow. In the examples given above, we are able to choose $\lambda = 1$. That this is *not* always possible is shown by

EXAMPLE 2.3

The origin $(x_0, y_0) = (0,0)$ minimizes the function $f(x,y) = y$ subject to the constraint

$$g(x,y) = x^2 - y^3 \leqslant 0.$$

In this case the set W of points (u,v) having

$$u = f(x,y) - f(x_0, y_0) = y, \qquad v = g(x,y) = x^2 - y^3$$

is determined by the inequality

$$v + u^3 \geqslant 0,$$

as indicated in Figure 2.4. The tangent to the curve at $(0,0)$ is the line $v = 0$. Consequently $\lambda = 0$ and $\mu = 1$ in the tangential equation $\lambda u + \mu v = 0$. The

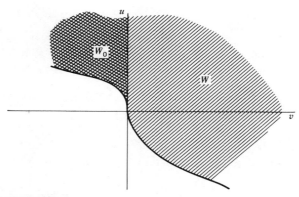

Figure 2.4

function F takes the form

$$F = \lambda f + \mu g = g = x^2 - y^3.$$

Clearly $F_x = F_y = 0$ at the solution $(0,0)$ of our problem.

In the following example the boundary of W has a corner point at the image $w_0 = (0,0)$ of the solution (x_0, y_0) of the constrained minimization problem.

EXAMPLE 2.4

The origin $(x_0, y_0) = (0,0)$ minimizes the function

$$f(x,y) = x^2 - 3xy + y^2$$

subject to the constraint

$$g(x,y) = xy \leqslant 0.$$

As before, let W be the set of points (u,v) defined by the transformation

$$u = f(x,y) - f(x_0, y_0) = x^2 - 3xy + y^2, \qquad v = g(x,y) = xy.$$

The x-axis $y = 0$ and the y-axis $x = 0$ are transformed into the positive u-axis. The line $y = mx$ $(m \neq 0)$ is transformed into the ray

$$u = (1 - 3m + m^2)x^2, \qquad v = mx^2.$$

In this event

$$u = \sigma v, \qquad \sigma = m + \frac{1}{m} - 3.$$

If $m > 0$, then $-1 \leqslant \sigma < \infty$. If $m < 0$, then $-\infty < \sigma \leqslant -5$. It follows that W is the set of points (u,v) satisfying the inequalities $u + v \geqslant 0$, $u + 5v \geqslant 0$. If $1 \leqslant \mu \leqslant 5$, then

$$u + \mu v = x^2 + (\mu - 3)xy + y^2 \geqslant 0$$

on the set W. The line $u + \mu v = 0$ is therefore a line of support of W at the origin whenever $1 \leqslant \mu \leqslant 5$, as shown in Figure 2.5. Observe that the line of support is not unique.

The following example also illustrates the complications that may arise.

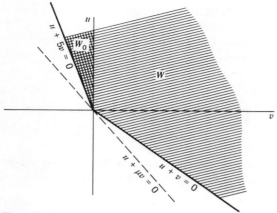

Figure 2.5

EXAMPLE 2.5

The origin $(x_0,y_0)=(0,0)$ minimizes the function $f(x,y)=x^2y$ subject to the constraint $g(x,y)=-y\leqslant 0$. In this case the sets W and W_0 determined by the transformation

$$u=x^2y, \qquad v=-y$$

take the form indicated in Figure 2.6. The points $(0,v)$ with $v\neq 0$ are not in W. The boundary of W has a singularity at $w_0=(0,0)$. The procedure given

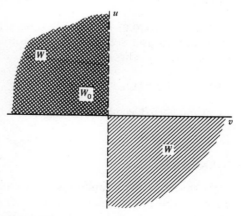

Figure 2.6

in later sections for determining the support line $\lambda u + \mu v = 0$ restricts us to the second quadrant and determines $\lambda = 1$, $\mu = 0$ as an admissible set of multipliers. Obviously the gradient of $F = \lambda f + \mu g = x^2 y$ vanishes at $(0,0)$ when $\lambda = 1$ and $\mu = 0$.

EXERCISES

In Exercises 1 to 10 determine the set W defined by the transformation

$$u = f(x,y) - f(x_0,y_0), \qquad v = g(x,y)$$

with $g(x_0,y_0) = 0$. Sketch W and the subset W_0 of W on which $v \leqslant 0$. If (x_0,y_0) minimizes $f(x,y)$ subject to $g(x,y) \leqslant 0$, determine the lines of support $\lambda u + \mu v = 0$ of W at $(0,0)$.

	$f(x,y)$	$g(x,y)$	(x_0,y_0)
1.	$y + x^2 + y^3$	$-y$	$(0,0)$
2.	$|x| - 2y$	y	$(0,0)$
3.	$x^2 + y^2$	xy	$(0,0)$
4.	$x^2 - 7xy + 4y^2$	xy	$(0,0)$
5.	xy	$x^2 - y^2$	$(0,0)$
6.	x^2	xy	$(0,0)$
7.	$y - x^2 - y^2$	$2x^2 - y$	$(0,0)$
8.	$x^2 + y^2 - 6x - 8y + 9$	$x^2 + y^2 - 1$	$\left(\frac{3}{5}, \frac{4}{5}\right)$
9.	$x^2 + y^4 - y^3 + 2y$	$x^2 - y$	$(0,0)$
10.	$x^2 + y$	$x^2 - y^3$	$(0,0)$

11. Show that the functions

$$f(x,y) = x^2 + y^2 + 6x + 5, \qquad g(x,y) = x^2 + y^2 - 2x$$

are convex and that $(x_0,y_0) = (0,0)$ minimizes f subject to $g(x,y) \leqslant 0$. Construct the set W as described in Section 1. Next construct the set $\hat{W}$ of all points (u,v) such that the inequality

$$u \geqslant \rho[f(x,y) - f(x_0,y_0)], \qquad v \geqslant \rho g(x,y)$$

has a solution (x,y) and $\rho \geqslant 0$. Geometrically, what is the relation between the sets W and $\hat{W}$?

3. CONVEX PROGRAMMING

Let $f, g_1, \ldots, g_p$ be real-valued convex functions on a convex set X. Recall that a set X is convex if the line segment $\bar{x} + t(x - \bar{x})$ $(0 \leqslant t \leqslant 1)$ is in X whenever its end points x and $\bar{x}$ are in X. Along such a line segment we have the relations

$$f[\bar{x}+t(x-\bar{x})] \leqslant (1-t)f(\bar{x})+tf(x) \qquad (0 \leqslant t \leqslant 1), \qquad (3.1a)$$

$$g_\alpha[\bar{x}+t(x-\bar{x})] \leqslant (1-t)g_\alpha(\bar{x})+tg_\alpha(x) \qquad (\alpha=1,\ldots,p), \qquad (3.1b)$$

by virtue of the convexity of f and g_α. Relations (3.1) can be put into the alternative forms

$$f[\bar{x}+t(x-\bar{x})]-f(\bar{x}) \leqslant t[f(x)-f(\bar{x})] \qquad (0 \leqslant t \leqslant 1), \qquad (3.2a)$$

$$g_\alpha[\bar{x}+t(x-\bar{x})]-g_\alpha(\bar{x}) \leqslant t[g_\alpha(x)-g_\alpha(\bar{x})] \qquad (\alpha=1,\ldots,p). \qquad (3.2b)$$

Let S be the set of all points x in X satisfying

$$g_\alpha(x) \leqslant 0 \qquad (\alpha=1,\ldots,p). \qquad (3.3)$$

We assume that the set S is not empty. By virtue of inequality (3.1b) it is seen that the line segment $\bar{x}+t(x-\bar{x})$ $(0 \leqslant t \leqslant 1)$ is in S whenever x and $\bar{x}$ are in S. The set S is accordingly convex.

We seek conditions under which a point x_0 in S affords a minimum to f on S. A problem of this type is called a *convex programming problem*. In general, convex programming problems also admit linear equality constraints of the form

$$g_\beta(x)=0 \qquad (\beta=p+1,\ldots,m).$$

This case will be discussed later. A simple convex programming problem was described in Example 2.1.

If the functions $f,g_1,\ldots,g_p$ are linear, our problem becomes a linear programming problem. Since linear functions are convex, linear programming can be considered to be a special case of convex programming.

The following lemma shows that in convex programming a local minimum is also a global minimum.

LEMMA 3.1

Let X_0 be a convex subset of X containing x_0 and having the property that for each point x in X there is a point $\hat{x}$ in X_0 of the form $\hat{x}=x_0+t(x-x_0)$ for some positive number t on $0<t<1$. Then x_0 minimizes f on S if and only if x_0 minimizes f on $S_0=S\cap X_0$.

Clearly x_0 minimizes f on S_0 if it minimizes f on the larger set S. Suppose that x_0 minimizes f on S_0 and that there is a point x in S such that $f(x)<f(x_0)$. Choose t on $0<t<1$ so that $\hat{x}=x_0+t(x-x_0)$ is in X_0. Since

S is convex, $\hat{x}$ is also in S and hence in $S_0 = S \cap X_0$. But $f(\hat{x}) < f(x_0)$, by (3.2a), with $\bar{x} = x_0$, contrary to our hypotheses. This proves Lemma 3.1.

In the study of the minimizing properties of a point x_0 in S we can disregard inactive constraints at x_0, that is, constraints $g_\alpha(x) \leqslant 0$ having $g_\alpha(x_0) < 0$. This fact is established in

LEMMA 3.2

Suppose that x_0 *minimizes* f *on* X *subject to constraints* (3.3). *Let* $\alpha_1, \ldots, \alpha_r$ *be the indices* α *such that* $g_\alpha(x_0) = 0$. *Then* x_0 *minimizes* f *on the set* S_r *of all points* x *in* X *satisfying the constraints*

$$g_\alpha(x) \leqslant 0 \qquad (\alpha = \alpha_1, \ldots, \alpha_r). \tag{3.4}$$

Suppose that there is a point x in X satisfying constraints (3.4) and having $f(x) < f(x_0)$. We shall show that there is a point $\hat{x} = x_0 + t(x - x_0)$ in S having $f(\hat{x}) < f(x_0)$. To this end we use relation (3.2) with $\bar{x} = x_0$ and $0 < t < 1$ to obtain the relations

$$f(\hat{x}) - f(x_0) \leqslant t[f(x) - f(x_0)] < 0, \tag{3.5a}$$

$$g_\alpha(\hat{x}) - g_\alpha(x_0) \leqslant t[g_\alpha(x) - g_\alpha(x_0)]. \tag{3.5b}$$

If α is one of the indices $\alpha_1, \ldots, \alpha_r$, then $g_\alpha(x_0) = 0$ and $g_\alpha(\hat{x}) \leqslant t g_\alpha(x) \leqslant 0$ for all t on $0 < t < 1$. If α is not one of the indices $\alpha_1, \ldots, \alpha_r$, we have $g_\alpha(x_0) < 0$. In view of (3.5b) we can select the positive parameter t so small that $g_\alpha(\hat{x}) < 0$ for all indices α distinct from $\alpha_1, \ldots, \alpha_r$. For this choice of t the point $\hat{x}$ is in S and has $f(\hat{x}) < f(x_0)$, by (3.5a). This contradiction establishes Lemma 3.2.

The main result in convex programming to be proved in this section is given in

THEOREM 3.1

Suppose that x_0 *minimizes* f *on the subset* S *of* X *defined by inequality constraints* (3.3). *Then there exist nonnegative multipliers* $\lambda_0, \lambda_1, \ldots, \lambda_p$, *not all zero, such that* x_0 *minimizes the function*

$$F(x) = \lambda_0 f(x) + \lambda_1 g_1(x) + \cdots + \lambda_p g_p(x)$$

on X, *and such that the minimum value of* F *on* X *is*

$$F(x_0) = \lambda_0 f(x_0). \tag{3.6}$$

If none of the functions $g_1,\ldots,g_p$ *is identically zero on* S, *the multiplier* λ_0 *is positive and the multipliers* $\lambda_0,\ldots,\lambda_p$ *can be chosen so that* $\lambda_0=1$.

The multipliers $\lambda_0,\lambda_1,\ldots,\lambda_p$ are called *Lagrange multipliers*, and the function F is termed a *Lagrangian*.

Observe that condition (3.6) is equivalent to the condition that

$$\lambda_1 g_1(x_0)+\cdots+\lambda_p g_p(x_0)=0.$$

Since each term is nonpositive, this equation holds if and only if each term is zero and hence if and only if $\lambda_\alpha=0$ whenever $g_\alpha(x_0)<0$. Consequently *condition (3.6) is equivalent to the condition that* $\lambda_\alpha=0$ *for each index* α *having* $g_\alpha(x_0)<0$.

Assuming that the first conclusion in Theorem 3.1 has been established, we can verify the second conclusion as follows. Suppose that $\lambda_0=0$. Then, since $g_\alpha(x)\leqslant 0$ $(\alpha=1,\ldots,p)$ on S, we have the relation

$$F(x)=\lambda_1 g_1(x)+\cdots+\lambda_p g_p(x)\leqslant F(x_0)=0$$

on S as well as the inequality $F(x)\geqslant F(x_0)$. It follows that

$$\lambda_1 g_1(x)+\cdots+\lambda_p g_p(x)=0$$

at each point x in S. Since no term in this sum is positive, it follows that each term is identically zero on S. In view of our assumption that none of the functions $g_1,\ldots,g_p$ vanishes identically on S, this is possible only if $\lambda_1,\ldots,\lambda_p$ are all zero. Since $\lambda_0=0$, this contradicts the fact that $\lambda_0,\lambda_1,\ldots,\lambda_p$ are not all zero. It follows that $\lambda_0>0$. Replacing λ_γ by λ_γ/λ_0 $(\gamma=0,1,\ldots,p)$, we obtain a new set of multipliers, again denoted by $\lambda_0,\lambda_1,\ldots,\lambda_p$, with the property that $\lambda_0=1$. This proves the second conclusion in the theorem under the assumption that the first has been established.

Before establishing the first conclusion in Theorem 3.1, it is of interest to observe that there are cases in which the multiplier λ_0 must be zero. This fact is illustrated by

EXAMPLE 3.1

In the three-dimensional xyz-plane the point $(x_0,y_0,z_0)=(0,0,0)$ minimizes the function

$$f(x,y,z)=2x+4y+z^2$$

subject to the constraints

$$g_1(x,y,z) = x^2 \leqslant 0, \qquad g_2(x,y,z) = y^2 \leqslant 0.$$

The set S consists of all points of the form $(0,0,z)$. If $\lambda_0, \lambda_1, \lambda_2$ are nonnegative multipliers, not all zero, the function

$$F(x,y,z) = \lambda_0(2x + 4y + z^2) + \lambda_1 x^2 + \lambda_2 y^2$$

has a minimum at $(x_0, y_0, z_0) = (0,0,0)$ if and only if $\lambda_0 = 0$. Observe that λ_1 and λ_2 are arbitrary nonnegative multipliers having $\lambda_1 + \lambda_2 > 0$.

EXAMPLE 3.2

In the xy-plane the origin affords a strict minimum to the function $f(x,y) = x + y$ subject to the constraint $g(x,y) = \max(-x, -y) \leqslant 0$. For this problem the Lagrangian F described in Theorem 3.1 can be taken in the form $F(x,y) = x + y + 2\max(-x, -y) = |x - y|$, as is readily verified. Inasmuch as $g(x,y)$ is not differentiable at the origin, the multiplier rules described in Chapters 4 and 5 are not applicable to this problem.

We turn to the proof of the first conclusion in Theorem 3.1. In view of Lemma 3.2 we can assume, without loss of generality, that all constraints are active. We then have $g_\alpha(x_0) = 0$ $(\alpha = 1,\ldots,p)$. Deleting inactive constraints does not alter the Lagrangian F described in Theorem 3.1, since multipliers corresponding to inactive constraints are chosen to be zero. After making this simplification we consider the set W of points $w = (u,v)$ $= (u, v^1, \ldots, v^p)$, for which there are a point x in X and a number $\rho \geqslant 0$ such that

$$u \geqslant \rho[f(x) - f(x_0)], \qquad v^\alpha \geqslant \rho g_\alpha(x) \qquad (\alpha = 1,\ldots,p). \tag{3.7}$$

Setting $x = x_0$, it is seen that $w_0 = (0,0)$ is in W. We shall show that there exist nonnegative multipliers $\lambda_0, \lambda_1, \ldots, \lambda_p$, not all zero, such that the inequality

$$\lambda_0 u + \lambda_1 v^1 + \cdots + \lambda_p v^p \geqslant 0 \tag{3.8}$$

holds for all points $w = (u, v^1, \ldots, v^p)$ in W. For each point x in X the point $w = (u,v)$ determined by the transformation

$$u = f(x) - f(x_0), \qquad v^\alpha = g_\alpha(x) \qquad (\alpha = 1,\ldots,p)$$

is in W. Consequently, by (3.8), the inequality

$$\lambda_0[f(x)-f(x_0)]+\lambda_1 g_1(x)+\cdots+\lambda_p g_p(x)\geqslant 0$$

holds for all x in X. Since $g_\alpha(x_0)=0$ $(\alpha=1,\ldots,p)$, we have

$$F(x)=\lambda_0 f(x)+\lambda_1 g_1(x)+\cdots+\lambda_p g_p(x)\geqslant F(x_0)=\lambda_0 f(x_0)$$

on X, as stated in Theorem 3.1.

It remains to establish inequality (3.8) on W. This will be done with the help of three lemmas, the first of which is

LEMMA 3.3

The set W *is a convex cone. It contains all points* $w=(u,v)$ *such that* $u\geqslant 0$ *and* $v^\alpha\geqslant 0$ $(\alpha=1,\ldots,p)$.

The last conclusion follows from (3.7) with $\rho=0$ and x as any point in X. If $w=(u,v)$ satisfies relation (3.7) with a point x in S and a constant $\rho\geqslant 0$, then for $t\geqslant 0$ the point $tw=(tu,tv)$ satisfies the relation

$$tu\geqslant t\rho[f(x)-f(x_0)],\qquad tv^\alpha\geqslant t\rho g_\alpha(x).$$

Hence if w is in W so also is tw for all $t\geqslant 0$. The set W is accordingly a cone. Since W is a cone, we can establish the convexity of W by showing that if w and $\bar w$ are in W so also is $w+\bar w$. To this end let $w=(u,v)$ be a point in W. Select x in X and $\rho\geqslant 0$ so that (3.7) holds. For a second point $\bar w=(\bar u,\bar v)$ in W select $\bar x$ and $\bar\rho$ so that

$$\bar u\geqslant\bar\rho[f(\bar x)-f(x_0)],\qquad \bar v^\alpha\geqslant\bar\rho g_\alpha(\bar x)\qquad(\alpha=1,\ldots,p).$$

We then have

$$u+\bar u\geqslant\rho f(x)+\bar\rho f(\bar x)-(\rho+\bar\rho)f(x_0),\qquad v^\alpha+\bar v^\alpha\geqslant\rho g_\alpha(x)+\bar\rho g_\alpha(\bar x).$$

Set $\sigma=\rho+\bar\rho$. If $\sigma=0$, then $\rho=\bar\rho=0$ and $u+\bar u\geqslant 0$, $v^\alpha+\bar v^\alpha\geqslant 0$. Consequently, $w+\bar w=(u+\bar u,v+\bar v)$ is in W. If $\sigma\neq 0$, we set $s=\rho/\sigma$ and $t=\bar\rho/\sigma$. Then $s+t=1$ and

$$u+\bar u\geqslant\sigma[sf(x)+tf(\bar x)-f(x_0)],\qquad v^\alpha+\bar v^\alpha\geqslant\sigma[sg_\alpha(x)+tg_\alpha(\bar x)].$$

In view of the convexity of f and g_α we have

$$u+\bar u\geqslant\sigma[f(sx+t\bar x)-f(x_0)],\qquad v^\alpha+\bar v^\alpha\geqslant\sigma g_\alpha(sx+t\bar x).$$

Since X is convex, the point $sx + t\bar{x}$ is in X. Consequently $w + \bar{w} = (u + \bar{u}, v + \bar{v})$ is in W. The set W is accordingly a convex cone, as was to be proved.

LEMMA 3.4

There is no point $w = (u, v)$ *in* W *having* $u < 0$, $v^\alpha \leqslant 0$ $(\alpha = 1, \ldots, p)$. *The closure* $\overline{W}$ *of* W *contains no point* $w = (u, v)$ *having* $u < 0$, $v^\alpha < 0$ $(\alpha = 1, \ldots, p)$.

Suppose that there is a point $w = (u, v)$ in W having $u < 0$, $v^\alpha \leqslant 0$ $(\alpha = 1, \ldots, p)$. Then there are a point x in X and a number $\rho \geqslant 0$ such that

$$0 > u \geqslant \rho[f(x) - f(x_0)], \qquad 0 \geqslant v^\alpha \geqslant \rho g_\alpha(x).$$

These inequalities imply that $\rho > 0$ and that

$$f(x) < f(x_0), \qquad g_\alpha(x) \leqslant 0,$$

contrary to our assumption that x_0 minimizes f on S.

If the closure $\overline{W}$ of W contains a point w whose components are negative, the set W has this property also, contrary to our first conclusion. This proves the lemma.

We are now in a position to complete the proof of Theorem 3.1 by showing that an inequality of form (3.8) holds on W. This will be done in

LEMMA 3.5

There exist nonnegative multipliers $\lambda_0, \lambda_1, \ldots, \lambda_p$, *not all zero, such that the inequality*

$$\lambda_0 u + \lambda_1 v^1 + \cdots + \lambda_p v^p \geqslant 0 \tag{3.8}$$

holds for all points $w = (u, v^1, \ldots, v^p)$ *in* W. *These multipliers can be chosen so that* $\lambda_0 = 1$ *if and only if the point* $(-1, 0, \ldots, 0)$ *is not in the closure* $\overline{W}$ *of* W.

In view of Lemma 3.4 the convex cone W is not the whole space. Consequently there is a point in $\hat{w} \neq 0$ in the dual cone W^* of W. The inner product $\langle \hat{w}, w \rangle$ of $\hat{w}$ with a vector w in W accordingly is nonpositive, that is,

$$\langle \hat{w}, w \rangle \leqslant 0$$

for all w in W. The vector $\lambda = -\hat{w} = (\lambda_0, \lambda_1, \ldots, \lambda_p)$ therefore has the property that

$$\langle \lambda, w \rangle = \lambda_0 u + \lambda_1 v^1 + \cdots + \lambda_p v^p = -\langle \hat{w}, w \rangle \geqslant 0 \tag{3.9}$$

for all w in W. In view of the fact that the vectors

$$e_0 = (1,0,\ldots,0), \qquad e_1 = (0,1,0,\ldots,0),\ldots,e_p = (0,\ldots,0,1) \qquad (3.10)$$

are in W, by Lemma 3.3, we have

$$\langle \lambda, e_\beta \rangle = \lambda_\beta \geqslant 0 \qquad (\beta = 0,1,\ldots,p).$$

This proves the first conclusion in the lemma.

By continuity inequality (3.9) holds for all w in the closure $\overline{W}$ of W. If $w = -e_0$ is in $\overline{W}$, we have $\langle \lambda, -e_0 \rangle = -\lambda_0 \geqslant 0$ and hence $\lambda_0 = 0$. On the other hand, if $-e_0$ is not in $\overline{W}$, it is the sum

$$-e_0 = \hat{w} + w$$

of orthogonal vectors w in $\overline{W}$ and $\hat{w} = (\hat{u}, \hat{v})$ in the dual cone W^* of W, as was seen in Theorem 3.1 in Chapter 4. Since $-e_0$ is not in $\overline{W}$, we have $\hat{w} \neq 0$. Inasmuch as w is orthogonal to $\hat{w}$, we have

$$-\hat{u} = \langle \hat{w}, -e_0 \rangle = \langle \hat{w}, \hat{w} + w \rangle = |\hat{w}|^2 > 0.$$

If we use this vector $\hat{w}$ to determine the multiplier $\lambda = -\hat{w}$, we have $\lambda_0 = -\hat{u} > 0$. Replacing λ_β by λ_β/λ_0, we obtain a new set with $\lambda_0 = 1$. This completes the proof of Lemma 3.5.

If X is a linear space and the functions $f, g_1, \ldots, g_p$ are linear, the multipliers $\lambda_0, \ldots, \lambda_p$ can be chosen so that $\lambda_0 = 1$. Moreover $F(x) = F(x_0)$ on X. To see this, we can suppose that the minimum point x_0 of f on S is the point $x_0 = 0$ and that all constraints are active at x_0. We can also replace $f(x)$ by $f(x) - f(x_0)$. Then the functions $f, g_1, \ldots, g_p$ are linear forms. We have $\rho f(x) = f(\rho x)$, $\rho g_\alpha(x) = g_\alpha(\rho x)$ for all numbers ρ. The set W of points $w = (u,v)$ defined by (3.7) is therefore determined by the simpler inequalities

$$u \geqslant f(x), \qquad v^\alpha \geqslant g_\alpha(x) \qquad (\alpha = 1,\ldots,p), \qquad (3.11)$$

where x is in X. The image W_1 of X under the transformation $u = f(x)$, $v^\alpha = g_\alpha(x)$ $(\alpha = 1,\ldots,p)$ is a linear manifold. It follows from (3.11) that every point w in W is expressible in the form

$$w = w_1 + a_0 e_0 + \cdots + a_p e_p,$$

where w_1 is in $W_1, a_0, \ldots, a_p$ are nonnegative numbers, and $e_0, \ldots, e_p$ are vectors (3.10). Since W_1 is a linear space of dimension $k \leqslant p$, it is generated by k vectors $w_1, \ldots, w_k$. The cone W is therefore generated by the finite set of vectors $w_1, \ldots, w_k, -w_1, \ldots, -w_k, e_0, \ldots, e_p$. According to Theorem 3.3, Chapter 4, the cone W is closed. As was seen in Lemma 3.4, the vector $-e_0 = (-1, 0, \ldots, 0)$ is not in the closed cone W. Using Lemma 3.5 and Theorem 3.1, we find that there exist multipliers $\lambda_0, \ldots, \lambda_p$ with $\lambda_0 = 1$ such that $x_0 = 0$ minimizes the function $F = f + \lambda_1 g_1 + \cdots + \lambda_p g_p$ on X. Since $F(-x) = -F(x) \geqslant F(0) = 0$, we have $F(x) \equiv 0$ on X. This proves

THEOREM 3.2

Suppose that $f, g_1, \ldots, g_p$ *are linear functions on a linear space* X. *If a point* x_0 *in* S *minimizes* f *on the set* S *of all points in* X *satisfying the constraints*

$$g_\alpha(x) \leqslant 0 \qquad (\alpha = 1, \ldots, p)$$

then there exist nonnegative multipliers $\lambda_1, \ldots, \lambda_p$, *with* $\lambda_\alpha = 0$ *if* $g_\alpha(x_0) < 0$, *such that the equality*

$$F(x) = F(x_0)$$

holds for all points x *in* X, *where*

$$F = f + \lambda_1 g_1 + \cdots + \lambda_p g_p.$$

We return to the more general case in which the functions $f, g_1, \ldots, g_p$ are assumed to be convex on a convex set X, and consider a function of the form

$$F(x, \mu) = f(x) + \mu_1 g_1(x) + \cdots + \mu_p g_p(x). \tag{3.12}$$

Let M be the set of multipliers $\mu = (\mu_1, \ldots, \mu_p)$ whose components are nonnegative. We assume that x_0 is a point in the convex set X which has associated with it a set of multipliers $\lambda = (\lambda_1, \ldots, \lambda_p)$ in M such that the inequality

$$F(x, \lambda) \geqslant F(x_0, \lambda)$$

holds for all x in X. We suppose further that $g_\alpha(x_0) = 0$ $(\alpha = 1, \ldots, p)$. Then, as was seen above, the point x_0 minimizes f on the set S of all points x in X satisfying the constraints

$$g_\alpha(x) \leqslant 0 \qquad (\alpha = 1, \ldots, p).$$

Moreover, since $g_\alpha(x_0) = 0$, we have the trivial relation

$$F(x_0, \lambda) = \max_{\mu \in M} F(x_0, \mu) = f(x_0).$$

Given μ in M, we have

$$\inf_{x \in X} F(x, \mu) \leqslant \inf_{x \in S} F(x, \mu) \leqslant F(x_0, \mu) = F(x_0, \lambda) = \min_{x \in X} F(x, \lambda).$$

Consequently

$$\max_{\mu \in M} \inf_{x \in X} F(x, \mu) = \max_{\mu \in M} \inf_{x \in S} F(x, \mu) = F(x_0, \lambda) = f(x_0). \qquad (3.13)$$

Similarly

$$\sup_{\mu \in M} F(x, \mu) \geqslant F(x, \lambda) \geqslant F(x_0, \lambda) = \max_{\mu \in M} F(x_0, \mu).$$

Note that $\sup_{\mu \in M} F(x, \mu) = \infty$ unless x is in S. Consequently

$$\min_{x \in X} \sup_{\mu \in M} F(x, \mu) = \min_{x \in S} \sup_{\mu \in M} F(x, \mu) = F(x_0, \lambda). \qquad (3.14)$$

These results are summarized in

THEOREM 3.3

Under the hypotheses made in the last paragraph we have

$$f(x_0) = F(x_0, \lambda) = \max_{\mu \in M} \inf_{x \in X} F(x, \mu) = \min_{x \in X} \sup_{\mu \in M} F(x, \mu). \qquad (3.15)$$

These relations also hold when X is replaced by S.

If X is a compact convex set and $f, g_1, \ldots, g_p$ are continuous on X, then

$$\inf_{x \in S} F(x, \mu) = \min_{x \in S} F(x, \mu), \qquad \sup_{x \in S} F(x, \mu) = \max_{x \in S} F(x, \mu).$$

In this case relations (3.15) with X replaced by S can be written in the form

$$f(x_0) = F(x_0, \lambda) = \max_{\mu \in M} \min_{x \in S} F(x, \mu) = \min_{x \in S} \max_{\mu \in M} F(x, \mu). \qquad (3.16)$$

EXERCISES

1. Let S be the points in the xy-plane defined by the relations

    $$x^2+y^2-2x \leqslant 0, \qquad x^2+y^2-1 \leqslant 0.$$

    Let (a,b) be a point not in S. Find the point (x_0,y_0) in S nearest to (a,b), first by geometrical considerations and next by the use of the function

    $$F= \alpha[(x-a)^2+(y-b)^2]+\beta(x^2+y^2-2x)+\gamma(x^2+y^2-1),$$

    where α, β, γ are the multipliers $\lambda_0, \lambda_1, \lambda_2$ appearing in Theorem 3.1. The function F must be expressible in the form

    $$F=\rho[(x-x_0)^2+(y-y_0)^2-\sigma],$$

    where $\rho > 0$. Why? Consider the surface

    $$u=(x-a)^2+(y-b)^2, \qquad v=x^2+y^2-2x, \qquad w=x^2+y^2-1$$

    in uvw-space. Show that the vector (α, β, γ) is a normal to this surface at the point (u_0, v_0, w_0) corresponding to (x_0,y_0). The solution (x_0,y_0) is one of the points

    $$\left(\frac{1}{2}, \pm \frac{\sqrt{3}}{2}\right), \quad \left(\frac{a}{\xi}, \frac{b}{\xi}\right), \quad \left(1+\frac{a-1}{\eta}, \frac{b}{\eta}\right),$$

    where $\xi= \sqrt{a^2+b^2}$, $\eta=\sqrt{(a-1)^2+b^2}$.

2. Show that the condition in Theorem 3.1, that none of the functions $g_1,\ldots,g_p$ is identically zero on the set S defined by the inequalities $g_\alpha(x) \leqslant 0$, is equivalent to the condition that there exists a point x in S such that $g_\alpha(x)<0$ $(\alpha=1,\ldots,p)$.

3. Show that Theorem 3.2 remains valid if X is a convex set and x_0 is an inner point of X in the sense described in the next section. Only minor modifications in the proof are needed to show that in this case the set W is a closed convex cone.

4. In the xy-plane let X be the set of points (x,y) having $x \geqslant 0$. Let $f(0,y)=y^2$, $f(x,y)=y-1$ $(x>0)$. Show that f is convex on X. Show that f has a minimum at $(0,0)$ subject to the constraint $g(x,y)=x \leqslant 0$. Show that the relation $F(x,y)$ $=\lambda_0 f(x,y)+\lambda g(x,y) \geqslant 0$ holds on X with $\lambda_0 \geqslant 0$, $\lambda \geqslant 0$, $\lambda_0+\lambda>0$ only if $\lambda_0=0$.

5. Let X be the set of points (x,y) having $x \geqslant 0$ and having $y \geqslant 0$ whenever $x=0$. The function $f(x,y)=y$ has a minimum on X at $(0,0)$ subject to the constraint $g(x,y)=x \leqslant 0$. Show that the function $F=\lambda_0 f+\lambda g$ described in Theorem 3.1 has $\lambda_0=0$. Why cannot Theorem 3.2 be applied?

6. Suppose that x_0 minimizes f on the set S defined by constraints (3.3). Let

$\beta_1, \ldots, \beta_r$ be the indices which are active for every minimum point of f on S. Show that x_0 minimizes f relative to the constraints $g_\beta(x) \leqslant 0$ ($\beta = \beta_1, \ldots, \beta_r$). Show that, if $\lambda_0, \lambda_1, \ldots, \lambda_m$ are multipliers related to x_0 as described in Theorem 3.1, then $\lambda_\alpha = 0$ for all $\alpha > 0$ not in the set $\beta_1, \ldots, \beta_r$. Show that Theorem 3.1 holds with the same set of multipliers for every minimum point of f on S.

7. What is the connection between the results given in Theorem 3.1 and those obtained in Exercise 6, Section 7, Chapter 4?

8. Show that the function $|x+y+2| + 2\max(-x, -y)$ is a Lagrangian for the problem of minimizing $|x+y+2|$ subject to the constraint $\max(-x, -y) \leqslant 0$.

4. CONVEX PROGRAMMING WITH LINEAR CONSTRAINTS

We continue the study of convex programming problems on a convex set X. To develop the theory further, it will be convenient to assume that the solution to our problem is an inner point of the convex set X. A point x_0 will be said to be an *inner point* of a convex set X if for every x in X there is a number $\epsilon > 0$ such that the point $x_0 + t(x - x_0)$ is in X whenever $-\epsilon \leqslant t \leqslant 1$. In other words, at an inner point x_0 of X a line segment in X having x_0 as an end point can be extended in X so that x_0 is no longer an end point. If X is a linear space, all of its points are inner points.

With this definition in mind we can establish

THEOREM 4.1

Let f *be a convex function on a convex set* X. *Let* S *be the set of all points* x *in* X *satisfying a set of linear constraints*

$$g_\beta(x) = 0 \qquad (\beta = 1, \ldots, m). \tag{4.1}$$

Suppose there is an inner point x_0 *of* X *in* S *that affords a minimum to* f *on* S. *Then there exists a set of constant multipliers* $\lambda_1, \ldots, \lambda_m$ *such that* x_0 *minimizes the function*

$$F = f + \lambda_1 g_1 + \cdots + \lambda_m g_m$$

on X.

In the proof we can assume without loss of generality that $x_0 = 0$. Then the linear functions g_β are homogeneous in x and hence are linear forms of x. We can assume further that these linear forms are linearly independent on X. With these simplifications we proceed as follows. Let W be the set of points $w = (u, v) = (u, v^1, \ldots, v^m)$ such that there is a point x in X and a number $\rho \geqslant 0$ satisfying the relations

$$u \geqslant \rho[f(x) - f(x_0)], \qquad v^\beta = \rho g_\beta(x). \tag{4.2}$$

Since f is convex and $g_\beta(x)$ are linear, it follows readily that the set W is a convex cone. Setting $\rho = 0$ in (4.2), we see that the point $e_0 = (1, 0, \ldots, 0)$ is in W. The point $-e_0 = (-1, 0, \ldots, 0)$, however, is not in W, for otherwise there would exist a point x in X and a constant $\rho \geqslant 0$ such that

$$-1 \geqslant \rho[f(x) - f(x_0)], \qquad 0 = \rho g_\beta(x).$$

This implies that $\rho > 0$ and hence that $g_\beta(x) = 0$ and $f(x) < f(x_0)$. Since this contradicts our assumption that $f(x) \geqslant f(x_0)$ on S, it follows that $-e_0$ is not in W. The dual W^* of W therefore contains a nonnull vector $w^* = (-\lambda_0, -\lambda_1, \ldots, -\lambda_m)$. We have

$$-\langle w^*, w \rangle = \lambda_0 u + \lambda_1 v^1 + \cdots + \lambda_m v^m \geqslant 0 \qquad (4.3)$$

for all vectors $w = (u, v)$ in W. Setting $w = e_0$, we see that $\lambda_0 \geqslant 0$. Given a point x in X, the point $w = (u, v)$ with

$$u = f(x) - f(x_0), \qquad v^\beta = g_\beta(x)$$

is in W. In view of (4.3) we have

$$\lambda_0[f(x) - f(x_0)] + \lambda_1 g_1(x) + \cdots + \lambda_m g(x) \geqslant 0 \qquad (4.4)$$

on X. If $\lambda_0 = 0$, we would have $\sum_\beta \lambda_\beta g_\beta(x) \geqslant 0$ on X. Since $x_0 = 0$ is an inner point of X there is for each point x in X a point $-\epsilon x$ $(\epsilon > 0)$ in X. Hence we also have

$$0 \leqslant \sum_\beta \lambda_\beta g_\beta(-\epsilon x) = -\epsilon \sum_\beta \lambda_\beta g_\beta(x).$$

This implies that $\sum_\beta \lambda_\beta g_\beta(x) = 0$ on X, which is impossible since $g_1, \ldots, g_m$ are linearly independent on X. Consequently $\lambda_0 > 0$. Replacing λ_β by $\lambda_\beta / \lambda_0$ in (4.4), we see that

$$F(x) = f(x) + \sum_\beta \lambda_\beta g_\beta(x) \geqslant f(x_0) = F(x_0),$$

as was to be proved.

The results given in Theorems 3.1 and 4.1 can be used to obtain

THEOREM 4.2

Let $f, g_1, \ldots, g_p$ be convex functions on a convex set X. Let $g_{p+1}, \ldots, g_m$ be linear (affine) functions on X. Suppose that an inner point x_0 of X satisfies the *constraints*

$$g_\alpha(x) \le 0 \quad (\alpha = 1,\ldots,p), \qquad g_\beta(x) = 0 \quad (\beta = p+1,\ldots,m) \qquad (4.5)$$

and affords a minimum to f *on X subject to these constraints. Then there exist constant multipliers* $\lambda_0 \ge 0, \lambda_1,\ldots,\lambda_m$, *not all zero, such that*

$$\lambda_\alpha \ge 0 \quad (1 \le \alpha \le p) \quad \text{with } \lambda_\alpha = 0 \text{ if } g_\alpha(x_0) < 0 \qquad (4.6)$$

and such that x_0 *affords a minimum on* X *to the function*

$$F = \lambda_0 f + \lambda_1 g_1 + \cdots + \lambda_m g_m.$$

If none of the functions $g_1,\ldots,g_p$ *is identically zero on the set* S *defined by constraints* (4.5), *then the multipliers can be chosen so that* $\lambda_0 = 1$.

Let $\hat{X}$ be the set of points x in X such that

$$g_\beta(x) = 0 \quad (\beta = p+1,\ldots,m). \qquad (4.7)$$

Since these constraints are linear, the set $\hat{X}$ is convex. By virtue of Theorem 3.1 there exist nonnegative multipliers $\lambda_0, \lambda_1,\ldots,\lambda_p$, not all zero, such that if we set

$$\hat{F} = \lambda_0 f + \lambda_1 g_1 + \cdots + \lambda_p g_p$$

we have

$$\hat{F}(x) \ge \hat{F}(x_0) = \lambda_0 f(x_0)$$

on $\hat{X}$. Since $\lambda_1 g_1(x_0) + \cdots + \lambda_p g_p(x_0) = 0$, we have $\lambda_\alpha = 0$ when $g_\alpha(x_0) < 0$. Consequently (4.6) holds. In addition, if none of the functions $g_1,\ldots,g_p$ is identically zero on S, we can choose these multipliers such that $\lambda_0 = 1$, by Theorem 3.1.

Since x_0 is an inner point of X which minimizes $\hat{F}$ subject to the linear constraints (4.7), these exist, by Theorem 4.1, multipliers $\lambda_{p+1},\ldots,\lambda_m$ such that x_0 minimizes

$$F = \hat{F} + \lambda_{p+1} g_{p+1} + \cdots + \lambda_m g_m.$$

This proves Theorem 4.2.

If the functions $g_1,\ldots,g_m$ appearing in Theorem 4.2 are linear, the multipliers $\lambda_0, \lambda_1,\ldots,\lambda_m$ described in Theorem 4.2 can be chosen so that $\lambda_0 = 1$. If f is linear, this result can be found in Exercise 3, Section 3.

However, we assume only that f is convex, and this case appears to be somewhat more difficult. As a first step in the proof we establish

LEMMA 4.1

Let x_0 be an inner point of a convex set X, and suppose that x_0 belongs to the subset S of all points x in X satisfying the set of linear constraints

$$g_\alpha(x) \leqslant 0 \qquad (\alpha = 1,\dots,r). \tag{4.8}$$

Suppose that each of the functions $g_\alpha(x)$ is identically zero on S. Then there exist positive multipliers $\mu_1,\dots,\mu_r$ such that

$$\mu_1 g(x_1) + \cdots + \mu_r g_r(x) = 0 \tag{4.9}$$

on X.

In the proof of this result we can assume that $x_0 = 0$. Since $g_\alpha(x_0) = 0$, the linear functions g_α are linear forms on X. For x in X, set $g_\alpha(ax) = ag_\alpha(x)$ $(a \geqslant 0)$. Then g is defined on the cone of vectors ax with x in X and $a \geqslant 0$. Since $x_0 = 0$ is an inner point of X, this cone is a linear space, and we can accordingly assume that X is a linear space. When these extensions are made, the lemma is an immediate consequence of Theorem 3.5, Chapter 4.

LEMMA 4.2

Suppose that the hypotheses in Lemma 4.1 hold. Suppose further that x_0 minimizes f on X subject to the constraints

$$g_\alpha(x) \leqslant 0 \qquad (\alpha = 1,\dots,r). \tag{4.10}$$

Then there exist positive numbers $\lambda_1,\dots,\lambda_r$ such that x_0 minimizes the function $F = f + \lambda_1 g_1 + \cdots + \lambda_r g_r$ on X.

By virtue of our hypotheses inequality (4.10) is equivalent to the equality relations

$$g_\alpha(x) = 0 \qquad (\alpha = 1,\dots,r). \tag{4.11}$$

By virtue of Theorem 4.1 there exist multipliers $\hat{\lambda}_1,\dots,\hat{\lambda}_r$ such that x_0 affords a minimum to

$$\hat{F} = f + \hat{\lambda}_1 g_1 + \cdots + \hat{\lambda}_r g_r \tag{4.12}$$

on X. Select a positive constant c such that $\lambda_\alpha = \hat{\lambda}_\alpha + c\mu_\alpha > 0$ $(\alpha = 1,\dots,r)$, where $\mu_1,\ldots,\mu_r$ are chosen as described in Lemma 4.1. We have accordingly the relations

$$F(x)=f(x)+\sum_\alpha \lambda_\alpha g_\alpha(x)=\hat F(x)+c\sum_\alpha \mu_\alpha g_\alpha(x)$$

$$=\hat F(x)\geq \hat F(x_0)=f(x_0)=F(x_0)$$

for every x in X. This proves the lemma.

We are now in a position to prove

THEOREM 4.3

Suppose that an inner point x_0 *of a convex set* X *minimizes a convex function* f *on* X *subject to a set of linear constraints*

$$g_\alpha(x)\leq 0 \qquad (\alpha=1,\ldots,p). \tag{4.13}$$

Then there exist nonnegative multipliers $\lambda_1,\ldots,\lambda_p$, *with* $\lambda_\alpha=0$ *if* $g_\alpha(x_0)<0$, *such that* x_0 *affords a minimum on* X *to the function*

$$F=f+\lambda_1 g_1+\cdots+\lambda_p g_p.$$

Let S be the set of points x in X satisfying the linear constraints (4.13). If none of the functions $g_1,\ldots,g_p$ is identically zero on S, the theorem follows from Theorem 3.1. Suppose that some of these functions, say $g_1,\ldots,g_r$, vanish on S while the remaining functions $g_{r+1},\ldots,g_p$ are not identically zero on S. Let $\hat X$ be the points in X satisfying the constraints

$$g_\beta(x)\leq 0 \qquad (\beta=1,\ldots,r). \tag{4.14}$$

Then S is the set of points in $\hat X$ satisfying the constraints

$$g_\gamma(x)\leq 0 \qquad (\gamma=r+1,\ldots,p). \tag{4.15}$$

By Theorem 3.1 with $\hat X$ playing the role of X we find that there exist nonnegative multipliers $\lambda_{r+1},\ldots,\lambda_p$ [with $\lambda_\gamma=0$ if $g_\gamma(x_0)<0$], such that x_0 minimizes the function

$$\hat f=f+\lambda_{r+1}g_{r+1}+\cdots+\lambda_p g_p$$

on $\hat X$. It follows that if we replace f by $\hat f$ we can delete constraints (4.15). If the functions $g_1,\ldots,g_r$ are not identically zero on the new set S defined by relations (4.14), we repeat this procedure and diminish the number of constraints. Two situations can arise: we can eliminate all constraints, in which case the theorem is established; or else we obtain a set of constraints

(4.14) with the property that $g_1, \ldots, g_r$ vanish identically on the subset of X defined by (4.14). In this situation we apply Lemma 4.2 to obtain the theorem. This proves Theorem 4.3.

As a final result we have

THEOREM 4.4

Suppose that an inner point x_0 *of a convex set* X *minimizes a convex function* f *subject to a set of linear constraints*

$$g_\alpha(x) \leqslant 0 \quad (\alpha = 1, \ldots, p), \qquad g_\beta(x) = 0 \quad (\beta = p+1, \ldots, m). \qquad (4.16)$$

Then there is a set of multipliers $\lambda_1, \ldots, \lambda_m$ *such that*

$$\lambda_\alpha \geqslant 0 \qquad [\alpha = 1, \ldots, p \; \text{with} \; \lambda_\alpha = 0 \; \text{if} \; g_\alpha(x_0) < 0]$$

and such that x_0 *affords a minimum to* $F = f + \lambda_1 g_1 + \cdots + \lambda_m g_m$ *on* X.

This result follows readily from Theorem 4.3 by replacing constraints (4.16) by the constraints

$$g_\alpha(x) \leqslant 0, \qquad g_\beta(x) \leqslant 0, \qquad -g_\beta(x) \leqslant 0 \qquad (\alpha = 1, \ldots, p; \; \beta = p+1, \ldots, m).$$

The details of the proof will be left to the reader.

EXAMPLE 4.1

We consider the following discrete optimal control problem.[†] In this problem we have $k+1$ n-dimensional vectors $x_1, \ldots, x_{k+1}$, called *states*, and k m-dimensional vectors $u_1, \ldots, u_k$, called *controls*. They are connected by the relations

$$x_{i+1} - x_i = Ax_i + Bu_i \qquad (i = 1, \ldots, k), \qquad (4.17)$$

where A and B are matrices of the appropriate dimensions. The integer k is fixed. An augmented vector $x = (x_1, \ldots, x_{k+1})$ will be called a *trajectory* if it is defined by the "motion" (4.17) with a set of controls $u = (u_1, \ldots, u_k)$. We seek a control set u_0 which transfers a given initial point $x_1 = a$ to a given terminal point $x_{k+1} = b$ via a trajectory x_0 so as to minimize the function

$$f(u) = \tfrac{1}{2} \left[|u_1|^2 + \cdots + |u_k|^2 \right]. \qquad (4.18)$$

[†]For a discussion of discrete optimal control problems, see, for example, M. Canon, C. Cullum, Jr., and E. Polak, *Theory of Optimal Control and Mathematical Programming*, McGraw-Hill Book Co., New York, 1970.

This is a convex programming problem in the variables x and u. According to Theorem 4.1, this problem has an optimal solution (x_0, u_0) if and only if a set of Lagrange multipliers $p_1, \ldots, p_k, q, r$ can be chosen so that (x_0, u_0) minimizes the Lagrangian

$$F(x,u) = f(u) + \sum_{i=1}^{k} p_i^* (x_{i+1} - x_i - Ax_i - Bu_i) + q^*(b - x_{k+1}) + r^*(x_1 - a).$$

At the minimum point the gradient of F with respect to x and u must vanish. This yields the relations

$$p_1 + A^* p_1 = r, \qquad p_{i-1} - p_i = A^* p_i,$$
$$p_k = q, \qquad u_i = B^* p_i \qquad (i = 1, \ldots, k) \tag{4.19a}$$

in addition to the original constraints

$$x_1 = a, \qquad x_{i+1} - x_i = Ax_i + Bu_i \quad (i = 1, \ldots, k), \qquad x_{k+1} = b. \tag{4.19b}$$

Because of the convexity of F in x and u, a minimum point (x_0, u_0) of F exists if and only if equations (4.19) can be satisfied. To find the solution of (4.19), if it exists, we introduce the matrices

$$C_1 = B, \qquad C_{i+1} = (I+A)C_i = (I+A)^i B \qquad (i = 1, \ldots, k-1) \tag{4.20}$$

and observe that equations (4.19b) can be put into the form

$$x_{i+1} = (I+A)^i a + C_i u_1 + \cdots + C_1 u_i \qquad (i = 1, \ldots, k-1), \tag{4.21a}$$
$$b = (I+A)^k a + C_k u_1 + \cdots + C_1 u_k. \tag{4.21b}$$

Similarly, by (4.19a), we have

$$p_i = (I+A^*) p_{i+1} = (I+A^*)^{k-i} q, \qquad u_i = C_{k-i+1}^* q. \tag{4.22}$$

Using these values of u_i in equations (4.21), we obtain the formulas

$$x_{i+1} = (I+A)^i a + (C_i C_k^* + \cdots + C_1 C_{k-i+1}^*) q, \qquad u_i = C_{k-i+1}^* q \tag{4.23}$$

for the optimal solution, provided q has been chosen so that

$$b - (I+A)^k a = Dq, \qquad D = C_k C_k^* + \cdots + C_1 C_1^*. \tag{4.24}$$

This choice of q can always be made if the matrix D is nonsingular. If D is singular, there are vectors a and b for which equation (4.24) has no solution for q. When equation (4.24) has no solution for q, an optimal solution (x_0, u_0) fails to exist. In fact, there is no trajectory $x = (x_1, \ldots, x_{k+1})$ whatever which transfers $x_1 = a$ to $x_{k+1} = b$. In optimal control theory the condition that equations (4.19b) have at least one solution (x, u) for every choice of a and b is called *complete controllability*. It is equivalent that equation (4.21b) can be solved for $u_1, \ldots, u_k$ for each choice of a and b. This can occur if and only if the $(n \times km)$-dimensional matrix $C = (C_k \ C_{k-1} \cdots C_1)$ has rank n, that is, if and only if the matrix $D = CC^*$ is nonsingular. Consequently, the condition $\det D \neq 0$ is the condition of complete controllability. On the other hand, equations (4.19b) are solvable for x and u for arbitrary choices of a and b if and only if the matrix of the coefficients of x and u has full rank, that is, if and only if constraints (4.19b) on x and u are normal in the sense defined in Section 6, Chapter 3. It follows that the concepts of controllability and normality are the same for problems of this type.

Normally control problems have additional constraints of the form $g(x, u) \leqslant 0$ or $g(x, u) = 0$, but we shall not pursue this situation further.

EXERCISES

1. Show that the multipliers described in Theorem 4.2 can be chosen so that $\lambda_0 = 1$ if the functions $g_1, \ldots, g_p$, which are identically zero on S, are linear on X.

2. Apply Theorem 4.3 to the problem in the xy-plane of minimizing the function $|x| - y$ subject to the constraint $y \leqslant 0$. Why cannot Theorem 2.1, Chapter 4 be applied?

3. Apply Theorem 4.2 to the problem of minimizing the function $2y + y^2$ subject to the constraints $|x| - y \leqslant 0$, $x + y = 0$. Are the multipliers unique?

4. Apply Theorem 4.3 to the problem of minimizing the function $\max(x, y)$, subject to the constraints $3 - 2x - y \leqslant 0$, $x - 2y + 1 \leqslant 0$.

5. Establish the converse of Lemma 4.1.

6. Solve the optimal control problem described in Example 4 for the following cases:
   (a) $m = n = 1, a = 1, b = 0, A = B = 1, k = 4$; recompute with $a = 0, b = 1$.
   (b) $m = 1, n = 2, a = \begin{pmatrix} 0 \\ 0 \end{pmatrix}, b = \begin{pmatrix} 1 \\ 0 \end{pmatrix}, A = \begin{pmatrix} 0 & 1 \\ -1 & 0 \end{pmatrix}, B = \begin{pmatrix} 1 \\ 1 \end{pmatrix}, k = 4$.
   (c) Replace A in (b) by $A = \begin{pmatrix} 0 & 1 \\ 1 & 0 \end{pmatrix}$. Does a solution exist? What can be said if $b = \begin{pmatrix} 1 \\ 1 \end{pmatrix}$?

7. Show that the condition of complete controllability described in Example 4.1 is equivalent to the condition that the matrix $(B \ AB \cdots A^{k-1}B)$ has rank n.

Show that, if $k \geqslant n$, this matrix has rank n if and only if the matrix $(B\ AB\ \cdots\ A^{n-1}B)$ has rank n.

8. Show that, if in Example 4.1 we delete the constraint $x_{k+1} = b$, then $u_0 = 0$ is the optimal control.

9. Discuss the optimal control problem obtained from the one given in Example 4.1 by replacing $f(u)$ by

$$f(x,u) = \tfrac{1}{2}\big[|x_1|^2 + \cdots + |x_{k+1}|^2 + |u_1|^2 + \cdots + |u_k|^2\big].$$

10. Discuss the case in which equation (4.17) are replaced by the system

$$x_{i+1} - x_i = A_i x_i + B_i u_i \qquad (i = 1, \ldots, k).$$

5. FURTHER EXAMPLES

The results in Sections 3 and 4 are applicable to infinite dimensional problems. A simple application is given in

EXAMPLE 5.1

Let $\mathscr{E}$ be all piecewise continuous functions

$$u: \qquad u(x) \qquad (0 \leqslant x \leqslant b).$$

The class $\mathscr{E}$ is a linear space. We seek to minimize the integral

$$I(u) = \int_0^b \sqrt{1 + u(x)^2}\ dx$$

subject to the constraint

$$J(u) = c - \int_0^b u(x)\,dx = 0,$$

where c is a constant.

Inasmuch as $\sqrt{1 + u^2}$ is a convex function of u (see Exercise 11, Section 5, Chapter 1), it follows that $I(u)$ is a convex function of the function u, that is,

$$(1-\theta)I(u) + \theta I(v) = \int_0^1 \Big[(1-\theta)\sqrt{1+u(x)^2} + \theta\sqrt{1+v(x)^2}\,\Big]dx$$

$$\geqslant \int_0^1 \sqrt{1 + [(1-\theta)u(x) + \theta v(x)]^2}\ = I[(1-\theta)u + \theta v],$$

for all θ on $0 \leqslant \theta \leqslant 1$. Since

$$\int_0^b u(x)\,dx$$

is a linear form in u, Theorem 4.1 is applicable with u playing the role of x. It follows that if u_0 is a solution to our problem there exists a multiplier λ such that u_0 minimizes the integral

$$F(u) = I(u) + \lambda K(u) = \lambda c + \int_0^b \left[\sqrt{1 + u(x)^2} - \lambda u(x) \right] dx.$$

Since there are no constraints on u, it follows that for each x the value $u_0(x)$ must minimize the integrand

$$f(u) = \sqrt{1 + u^2} - \lambda u.$$

Hence $u_0(x)$ must satisfy the equation

$$f'(u) = \frac{u}{\sqrt{1 + u^2}} - \lambda = 0.$$

Consequently $u_0(x) = \alpha = $ constant. Since

$$\int_0^b u_0(x)\,dx = \alpha b = c,$$

we find that $\alpha = c/b$ and that

$$\lambda = \frac{c/b}{\sqrt{1 + c^2/b^2}} = \frac{c}{\sqrt{b^2 + c^2}}.$$

Our solution $u_0(x) = c/b$ therefore minimizes the integral

$$F(u) = \int_0^b \left[\sqrt{1 + u(x)^2} - \frac{cu(x)}{\sqrt{b^2 + c^2}} \right] dx.$$

The problem we have solved is equivalent to that of finding the shortest arc

$$y : \quad y(x) \quad (0 \leqslant x \leqslant b)$$

joining the point $(0,0)$ to the point (b,c). The length of y is given by the integral

$$\int_0^b \sqrt{1+y'(x)^2}\ dx.$$

Moreover

$$\int_0^b y'(x)\,dx = y(b) - y(0) = c - 0 = c.$$

The solution is the line segment

$$y_0(x) = \frac{cx}{b} \qquad (0 \leqslant x \leqslant b).$$

If we set $u(x) = y'(x)$, this problem takes the form given earlier with $u_0(x) = y_0'(x) = c/b$ as its solution.

EXAMPLE 5.2

Let X be the class of piecewise continuous functions

$$x: \qquad x(t) \qquad (-\infty < t < \infty)$$

such that $x(t) > 0$ and the following integrals are finite:

$$\int_{-\infty}^{\infty} tx(t)\,dt, \quad \int_{-\infty}^{\infty} t^2 x(t)\,dt.$$

The set X is a convex set of functions x. Moreover the function

$$f(x) = \int_{-\infty}^{\infty} x(t) \log x(t)\,dt$$

is convex. This follows because $\varphi(x) = x \log x$ is convex in x for $x > 0$ in view of the relation $\varphi''(x) = (1/x) > 0$. We seek a function

$$x_0: \qquad x_0(t) \qquad (-\infty < t < \infty)$$

which minimizes $f(x)$ subject to the constraints

$$g_1(x) = \int_{-\infty}^{\infty} x(t)\,dt - 1 = 0,$$

$$g_2(x) = \int_{-\infty}^{\infty} t^2 x(t)\,dt - \sigma^2 = 0, \qquad (5.1)$$

where $\sigma > 0$. In this case Theorem 4.1 is applicable with $m = 2$. Accordingly the minimizing function x_0 must minimize the function

$$F(x) = f(x) + \lambda g_1(x) + \mu g_2(x) = \int_{-\infty}^{\infty} G[t, x(t)]\, dt,$$

where

$$G(t, x) = x \log x + \lambda x + \mu t^2 x.$$

Clearly x_0 minimizes $F(x)$ if and only if

$$G(t, x) \geqslant G[t, x_0(t)]$$

for each t on $-\infty < t < \infty$. Consequently

$$G_x = \log x + 1 + \lambda + \mu t^2 = 0$$

when $x = x_0(t)$. The function $x_0(t)$ is therefore of the form

$$x_0(t) = A e^{-\mu t^2}.$$

Since $x_0(t)$ must satisfy relations (5.1), the constants A and μ are determined by the relations

$$A \int_{-\infty}^{\infty} e^{-\mu t^2}\, dt = 1, \qquad A \int_{-\infty}^{\infty} t^2 e^{-\mu t^2}\, dt = \sigma^2.$$

These equations yield $\mu = 1/2\sigma^2$, $A = 1/\sigma\sqrt{2\pi}$. The function

$$x_0(t) = \frac{1}{\sigma\sqrt{2\pi}} e^{-t^2/2\sigma^2}$$

is therefore the solution to our problem.

EXERCISES

1. For the class X of piecewise continuous functions x: $x(t)$ $(0 \leqslant t \leqslant 1)$ determine the function x_0: $x_0(t)$ $(0 \leqslant t \leqslant 1)$ such that

$$I(x) = \int_0^1 x(t)\, dt = \min, \qquad J(x) = \int_0^1 x(t)^2\, dt - 9 \leqslant 0.$$

2. As in Exercise 1 determine x_0 in X such that

$$I(x) = \int_0^1 [2x(t) - x(t)^2]\, dt = \min, \qquad J(x) = \int_0^1 6t|x(t)|\, dt - 1 \leqslant 0.$$

3. Let $y: y(t)$ $(0 \leqslant t \leqslant 1)$ be a piecewise continuous function. Find the function x_0 in X (see Exercise 1) such that

$$\langle x, y \rangle = \int_0^1 x(t) y(t)\, dt = \max, \qquad J(x) = \int_0^1 |x(t)|^p\, dt \leqslant 1,$$

where p is chosen so that $1 < p < \infty$. What is the maximum value of $\langle x, y \rangle$?

4. For the class X_1 of piecewise continuous functions $x: x(t)$ $(0 \leqslant t \leqslant 1)$ having $|x(t)| \leqslant 1$, determine x_0 such that

$$I(x) = \int_0^1 (2 - 5t) x(t)\, dt = \min, \qquad J(x) = \int_0^1 4tx(t)\, dt - 1 = 0.$$

5. Let X be the class of integrable functions $x: x(t)$ $(0 \leqslant t \leqslant 1)$ such that the function $J(x)$ defined in Exercise 3 has a finite value. Let $L(x)$ be a linear form on X such that $|L(x)| \leqslant [J(x)]^{1/p}$ on X. It is known that the problem $J(x) = \min$ for all x in X having $L(x) = 1$ has a solution $x_0: x_0(t)$ $(0 \leqslant t \leqslant 1)$. Show, by Theorem 4.1, that there is a multiplier λ such that x_0 minimizes $F(x) = J(x) - p\lambda L(x)$ on X. Set $y(t) = |x_0(t)|^{p-1} \operatorname{signum} [x_0(t)]$. Show that

$$\left(\frac{d}{ds} \right) F(x_0 + sx) \Big|^{s=0} = \int_0^1 py(t) x(t)\, dt - p\lambda L(x) = 0$$

for all x in X. Show that $J(x_0) = \lambda = \int_0^1 |y(t)|^q\, dt$, where $q = p/(p-1)$.

6. MINIMA RELATIVE TO GENERAL INEQUALITY CONSTRAINTS

The method used in Section 5 for the convex case can be modified so as to be applicable to the nonconvex case. The modified procedure is an extension of the method illustrated in Section 2.

The problem we shall consider is that of minimizing a function f on a set X subject to the inequality constraints

$$g_\alpha(x) \leqslant 0 \qquad (\alpha = 1, \ldots, p). \tag{6.1}$$

The set of points x in X satisfying these constraints will be denoted by S. We assume that we are given a minimum point x_0 of f on S. Let W be the image of X under the transformation

$$w^0 = f(x), \qquad w^\alpha = g_\alpha(x) \qquad (\alpha = 1, \ldots, p). \tag{6.2}$$

Let w_0 be the image of x_0. Let $\mathcal{K}_0$ be the tangent cone (tangent space) of W at w_0. It consists of all vectors k for which there exists a sequence $\{w_q\}$ converging to w_0 in the direction k. Accordingly a vector k is in $\mathcal{K}_0$ if there are a sequence $\{w_q\}$ of points in W and a sequence $\{t_q\}$ of positive numbers such that

$$t_q \to 0, \qquad \frac{w_q - w_0}{t_q} \to k. \tag{6.3}$$

It should be noted that the vector k in $\mathcal{K}_0$ can be interpreted as a (generalized) derivative of the functions $f, g_1, \ldots, g_p$ at x_0, even if these functions are not differentiable in the usual sense. This follows because the second relation in (6.3) can be put into the form

$$\lim_{q \to \infty} \frac{f(x_q) - f(x_0)}{t_q} = k^0, \qquad \lim_{q \to \infty} \frac{g_\alpha(x_q) - g_\alpha(x_0)}{t_q} = k^\alpha \qquad (\alpha = 1, \ldots, p),$$

$$\tag{6.4}$$

where x_q is a point in X such that

$$w_q{}^0 = f(x_q), \qquad w_q{}^\alpha = g_\alpha(x_q).$$

The main purpose of this section is to establish the following generalized Lagrange multiplier rule.

THEOREM 6.1

Let $\mathcal{K}$ be a convex cone contained in the tangent cone $\mathcal{K}_0$ of W at w_0. Under the assumption that x_0 minimizes f *on X subject to constraints (6.1), there exist multipliers $\lambda_0 \geqslant 0, \lambda_1, \ldots, \lambda_p$, not all zero, such that*

$$\lambda_\alpha \geqslant 0 \qquad [1 \leqslant \alpha \leqslant p \ with \ \lambda_\alpha = 0 \ if \ g_\alpha(x_0) < 0] \tag{6.5}$$

and such that

$$L(k) = \lambda_\rho k^\rho = \lambda_0 k^0 + \cdots + \lambda_p k^p \geqslant 0 \tag{6.6}$$

for all vectors k *in* $\mathcal{K}$.

Observe that in (6.6) we have indicated that the repeated index ρ is to be summed over its range. Throughout the rest of this chapter we shall use the convention that a repeated index in a term is to be summed over its range unless otherwise specified or implied.

Before establishing Theorem 6.1 let us show how this theorem can be used to obtain the following variant of the Lagrange multiplier rule. This variant was established in Section 7, Chapter 5, under somewhat stronger hypotheses. As in convex programming, we introduce an auxiliary non-negative multiplier λ_0. As was seen in Example 2.3, this multiplier could be zero.

THEOREM 6.2

Let x_0 be an interior point of a set X in $\mathcal{E}^n$. Suppose that the functions f and g are differentiable at x_0. If x_0 minimizes f on the set S of points x in X satisfying the constraints

$$g_\alpha(x) \leqslant 0 \qquad (\alpha = 1,\dots,p),$$

then there exist nonnegative multipliers $\lambda_0,\lambda_1,\dots,\lambda_p$, not all zero, such that $\lambda_\alpha = 0$ if $g_\alpha(x_0) < 0$ and such that $\nabla F(x_0) = 0$, where

$$F = \lambda_0 f + \lambda_1 g_1 + \cdots + \lambda_p g_p. \tag{6.7}$$

If x_0 is a normal point of S, then $\lambda_0 > 0$ and the multipliers can be chosen so that $\lambda_0 = 1$.

To show that Theorem 6.2 is a consequence of Theorem 6.1, let $\mathcal{K}$ be the class of all vectors $k = (k^0,\dots,k^p)$ defined by the linear transformation

$$k^0 = f'(x_0, h), \qquad k^\alpha = g'_\alpha(x_0, h) \qquad (\alpha = 1,\dots,p), \tag{6.8}$$

where, as before, $f'(x_0, h)$ and $g'_\alpha(x_0, h)$ are the differentials of f and g_α at x_0. In view of the relations

$$\lim_{t \to 0} \frac{f(x_0 + th) - f(x_0)}{t} = f'(x_0, h), \qquad \lim_{t \to 0} \frac{g_\alpha(x_0 + th) - g_\alpha(x_0)}{t} = g'_\alpha(x_0, h),$$

it follows that a vector k in $\mathcal{K}$ is a tangent vector to W at w_0 and hence is in $\mathcal{K}_0$. Choosing $\lambda_0,\dots,\lambda_p$ as described in Theorem 6.1, we see from (6.6), (6.8), and (6.7) that

$$L(k) = \lambda_0 f'(x_0, h) + \lambda_\alpha g'_\alpha(x_0, h) = F'(x_0, h) \geqslant 0$$

for every vector h, where, according to our convention, α is to be summed from 1 to p. This is possible only if $\nabla F(x_0) = 0$, as was to be proved.

Suppose next that $\lambda_0 = 0$. Then $\lambda_1,\dots,\lambda_p$ are not all zero, $\lambda_\alpha = 0$ if

$g_\alpha(x_0)<0$, and $\nabla F(x_0)=\lambda_\alpha \nabla g_\alpha(x_0)=0$. This violates the condition for normality of x_0 given in Section 10, Chapter 4. Consequently, if x_0 is a normal point of S, we have $\lambda_0>0$. Dividing each multiplier by λ_0, we obtain a new set of multipliers having $\lambda_0=1$. This completes the proof that Theorem 6.2 is a consequence of Theorem 6.1.

We turn now to the proof of Theorem 6.1. To this end let $\mathcal{K}^-$ be the cone whose nonnull elements satisfy the relations

$$k^0<0, \qquad k^\alpha<0 \qquad [1\leqslant \alpha \leqslant p \text{ if } g_\alpha(x_0)=0].$$

We make no restriction on k^α when $g_\alpha(x_0)<0$, that is, when α is an inactive index at x_0.

LEMMA 6.1

No vector $k\neq0$ *in* $\mathcal{K}^-$ *belongs to* $\mathcal{K}_0$.

Suppose there is a vector $k\neq0$ in $\mathcal{K}^-$ that belong to $\mathcal{K}_0$. Let $\{w_q\}$ be a sequence in W converging to w_0 in the direction k. Select a sequence $\{t_q\}$ of positive numbers such that

$$t_q\to0, \qquad \frac{w_q-w_0}{t_q}\to k.$$

Let x_q be a point in X such that

$$w_q{}^0=f(x_q), \qquad w_q{}^\alpha=g_\alpha(x_q).$$

We then have

$$\frac{f(x_q)-f(x_0)}{t_q}\to k^0, \qquad \frac{g_\alpha(x_q)-g_\alpha(x_0)}{t_q}\to k^\alpha.$$

Since $k^0<0$ and $k^\alpha<0$ whenever $g_\alpha(x_0)=0$, it follows from these relations that there is an integer q_0 such that for $q\geqslant q_0$ we have

$$f(x_q)<f(x_0), \qquad g_\alpha(x_q)<0 \qquad \text{if } g_\alpha(x_0)=0.$$

In addition we can increase q_0 if necessary so that

$$g_\alpha(x_q)<0 \qquad \text{if } g_\alpha(x_0)<0$$

whenever $q\geqslant q_0$. These inequalities imply that when $q\geqslant q_0$ the point x_q is a point in S having $f(x_q)<f(x_0)$, contrary to our assumption that x_0 minimizes f on S. This proves Lemma 6.1.

LEMMA 6.2

Let $\mathcal{K}$ be a convex cone in $\mathcal{K}_0$ and let $\mathcal{K}^+ = \mathcal{K} - \mathcal{K}^-$. Then $\mathcal{K}^+$ is a convex cone whose closure contains no vector $k \neq 0$ in $\mathcal{K}^-$.

Since $\mathcal{K}^-$ is obviously convex, so also are the cones $-\mathcal{K}^-$ and $\mathcal{K}^+$ $= \mathcal{K} - \mathcal{K}^-$. Suppose first that the cones $\mathcal{K}^+$ and $\mathcal{K}^-$ have a nonnull vector $\hat{k}$ in common. Since $\hat{k}$ is in $\mathcal{K}^+$, it is expressible in the form $\hat{k} = k - k^-$, where k is in $\mathcal{K}$ and k^- is in $\mathcal{K}^-$. The vector $k = \hat{k} + k^-$ is therefore in $\mathcal{K}^-$ as well as in $\mathcal{K}$. Since $\hat{k} \neq 0$, so also is k. This situation, however, is impossible, by Lemma 6.1.

Suppose next there is a vector $k \neq 0$ in $\mathcal{K}^-$ that belongs to the closure of $\mathcal{K}^+$. Then k is a limit of a sequence $\{k_q\}$ of vectors in $\mathcal{K}^+$. In particular,

$$k_q^{\,0} \to k^0 < 0, \qquad k_q^{\,\alpha} \to k^\alpha < 0 \qquad \text{if } g_\alpha(x_0) = 0.$$

This implies that k_q is in $\mathcal{K}^-$ for large values of q, which we have shown to be impossible. Hence there is no $k \neq 0$ in the closure of $\mathcal{K}^+$ that belongs to $\mathcal{K}^-$.

We are now in a position to complete the proof of Theorem 6.1. Let $\mathcal{K}$ be a convex cone in $\mathcal{K}_0$, and let $\mathcal{K}^+ = \mathcal{K} - \mathcal{K}^-$. In view of Lemma 6.2 the dual cone of $\mathcal{K}^+$ contains a vector $\hat{k} \neq 0$. Set

$$\lambda_\rho = -\hat{k}^\rho \qquad (\rho = 0, 1, \dots, p).$$

Then

$$L(k) = \lambda_\rho k^\rho = -\hat{k}^\rho k^\rho \geqslant 0$$

for every vector k in $\mathcal{K}^+$ and hence in the closure $\overline{\mathcal{K}^+}$ of $\mathcal{K}^+$. Observe that the closure of $-\mathcal{K}^-$ is in $\overline{\mathcal{K}^+}$. It follows that the vectors e_β having $e_\beta^{\,\beta} = 1$, $e_\beta^{\,\rho} = 0$ $(\rho \neq \beta)$ are in $\overline{\mathcal{K}^+}$. Consequently

$$L(e_\beta) = \lambda_\beta \geqslant 0 \qquad (\beta = 0, 1, \dots, p).$$

On the other hand, if $g_\alpha(x_0) < 0$, then $-e_\alpha$ is also in $\overline{\mathcal{K}^+}$. This implies that

$$L(-e_\alpha) = -\lambda_\alpha \geqslant 0 \qquad \text{if } g_\alpha(x_0) < 0.$$

Hence $\lambda_\alpha = 0$ if $g_\alpha(x_0) < 0$. This completes the proof of Theorem 6.1.

We have the following analogue of Theorem 4.1.

THEOREM 6.3

Suppose that the image W *of* X *under the transformation*

$$w^0 = f(x), \qquad w^\alpha = g_\alpha(x) \qquad (\alpha = 1, \ldots, p) \tag{6.9}$$

is convex. If x_0 *minimizes* f *on the subset* S *of* X *defined by the constraints*

$$g_\alpha(x) \leqslant 0 \qquad (\alpha = 1, \ldots, p)$$

then there exist nonnegative multipliers $\lambda_0, \lambda_1, \ldots, \lambda_p$, *not all zero, such that* $\lambda_\alpha = 0$ *if* $g_\alpha(x_0) < 0$ *and such that* x_0 *minimizes the function*

$$F = \lambda_0 f + \lambda_1 g_1 + \cdots + \lambda_p g_p. \tag{6.10}$$

Moreover $F(x_0) = \lambda_0 f(x_0)$. *If none of the functions* $g_1, \ldots, g_p$ *is identically zero on* S, *then* $\lambda_0 > 0$ *and the multipliers* $\lambda_0, \ldots, \lambda_p$ *can be chosen so that* $\lambda_0 = 1$.

Since W is convex, so also is the tangent cone $\mathcal{K}_0$ of W at the image w_0 of x_0. By Theorem 6.1 with $\mathcal{K} = \mathcal{K}_0$ there exist nonnegative multipliers $\lambda_0, \lambda_1, \ldots, \lambda_p$, not all zero, such that

$$L(k) = \lambda_\rho k^\rho \geqslant 0$$

for all k in $\mathcal{K}_0$. Moreover $\lambda_\alpha = 0$ if $g_\alpha(x_0) < 0$. Since W is convex, the vector $k = w - w_0$ is in k_0 for each w in W. By virtue of (6.9) a vector $k = w - w_0$ has the form

$$k^0 = f(x) - f(x_0), \qquad k^\alpha = g_\alpha(x) - g_\alpha(x_0).$$

It follows that

$$\lambda_0[f(x) - f(x_0)] + \lambda_\alpha[g_\alpha(x) - g_\alpha(x_0)] \geqslant 0$$

for all x in S, that is, $F(x) \geqslant F(x_0)$ on X, where F is defined by (6.10). Since $\lambda_\alpha = 0$ whenever $g_\alpha(x) < 0$, it follows that $\lambda_\alpha g_\alpha(x_0) = 0$ and hence that $F(x_0) = \lambda_0 f(x_0)$. If $\lambda_0 = 0$, then $\lambda_\alpha g_\alpha(x) \geqslant \lambda_\alpha g_\alpha(x_0) = 0$. In this event $\lambda_\alpha g_\alpha(x)$ $= 0$ on S. If no $g_\alpha(x)$ is identically zero on S, this implies that $\lambda_\alpha = 0$ $(\alpha = 1, \ldots, p)$. This is impossible, however, since the multipliers $\lambda_0, \ldots, \lambda_p$ are not all zero. Consequently $\lambda_0 > 0$ in this case. Replacing λ_ρ by λ_ρ / λ_0, we obtain a new set, again denoted by $\lambda_0, \ldots, \lambda_p$, such that $\lambda_0 = 1$. This proves Theorem 6.3.

The following example shows that Theorem 6.3 is not a corollary of Theorem 3.1.

EXAMPLE 6.1

In the xy-plane the origin $(x_0,y_0)=(0,0)$ minimizes the function

$$f(x,y)=x^2-3xy+y^2$$

subject to the constraint

$$g(x,y)=xy\leqslant 0.$$

As was seen in Example 2.4, the set W of points (u,v) defined by

$$u=x^2-3xy+y^2, \qquad v=xy$$

is a convex cone. In this case $\mathcal{K}_0$ coincides with W. The function

$$F=f+\mu g=x^2+(\mu-3)xy+y^2 \qquad (1<\mu<5)$$

has a proper minimum at the origin. The functions f and g are not convex. Consequently Theorem 3.1 is not applicable.

EXERCISES

1. How does Theorem 6.2 differ from Theorem 7.1, Chapter 5?

2. Suppose that $g_2=-g_1$ and that $g_1(x_0)=0$. Show that the multipliers $\lambda_0=0,\lambda_1=\lambda_2=1,\lambda_\alpha=0\ (\alpha>2)$ have the properties described in Theorem 6.2.

3. Why cannot Theorem 6.2 be used to obtain a satisfactory multiplier rule for the case of equality constraints by replacing each equality constraint by a pair of inequality constraints?

4. Show that Theorem 3.1 is a consequence of Theorem 6.1.

5. Apply Theorem 6.3 to the two-dimensional problem in which we minimize $f(x,y)=(x^2+y^2)^{1/2}+2y$ subject to the constraint $g(x,y)=x^2-y\leqslant 0$. Is the Lagrangian F unique? Is Theorem 3.1 applicable? Is Theorem 6.2 applicable? *Hint*: Use polar coordinates.

6. Let X be an open set in $\mathcal{E}^n$, and let S be the set of points x in X satisfying constraints (6.1). Suppose that the functions $f,g_1,\dots,g_p$ are continuous at a point x_0 in S. Let W be the image of X and w_0 be the image of x_0 under transformation (6.2). Suppose that there exist nonnegative multipliers $\lambda_0=1,\lambda_1,\dots,\lambda_p$, not all zero, such that $\lambda_\alpha=0$ if $g_\alpha(x_0)<0$ and such that $\lambda_\rho k^\rho>0$ for all tangent vectors $k\neq 0$ of W at w_0. Show that x_0 affords a local minimum to f on S and to $F=f+\lambda_\alpha g_\alpha$ on X.

7. Show that, if the vector $-e_0=(-1,0,\dots,0)$ is not in the closure of the cone $\mathcal{K}^+$ described in Lemma 6.2, the multipliers $\lambda_0,\dots,\lambda_p$ appearing in Theorem 6.1 can be chosen so that $\lambda_0>0$. *Hint*: Recall that $-e_0$ is the sum of orthogonal vectors k and $\hat{k}$, where k is in the closure of $\mathcal{K}^+$ and $\hat{k}$ is in its dual cone. Show that $\hat{k}^0>0$. Use $\hat{k}$ in the paragraph preceding Theorem 6.3.

7. APPLICATIONS TO QUADRATIC FORMS

The results of Section 6 can be used to obtain a generalization of the result for quadratic forms given in Section 6, Chapter 2. In the earlier chapter we sought conditions which ensured the existence of a multiplier μ such that the linear combination

$$P(x) + \mu Q(x)$$

of two quadratic forms P and Q is positive on a Euclidean space $\mathscr{E}$. In the present section we first admit an infinite dimensional space $\mathscr{E}$ and later restrict it to be finite dimensional.

Recall that a quadratic function $Q(x)$ on a real linear space $\mathscr{E}$ is a function that has associated with is a bilinear form $Q(x,y)$ such that

$$Q(x) = Q(x,x), \qquad Q(x,y) = Q(y,x),$$

$$Q(x, ay + bz) = aQ(x,y) + bQ(x,z)$$

for all x,y,z in $\mathscr{E}$ and all real numbers a and b. We have the identity

$$Q(ax + by) = a^2 Q(x) + 2abQ(x,y) + b^2 Q(y).$$

The theorem we shall prove is

THEOREM 7.1

Let P *and* Q *be quadratic forms such that* $P(x) > 0$ *for all* $x \neq 0$ *in* $\mathscr{E}$ *having* $Q(x) \leqslant 0$. *There exist nonnegative multipliers* λ *and* μ, *not both zero, such that*

$$\lambda P(x) + \mu Q(x) \geqslant 0 \tag{7.1}$$

for all x *in* $\mathscr{E}$.

This theorem states that, if the point $x = 0$ affords a strict minimum to P subject to the constraint $Q(x) \leqslant 0$, there exist nonnegative multipliers λ and μ, not both zero, such that $x = 0$ affords a minimum to $F = \lambda P + \mu Q$.

Theorem 7.1 follows from Theorem 6.1 and

LEMMA 7.1

The image W *of* $\mathscr{E}$ *under the transformation*

$$u = P(x), \qquad v = Q(x) \tag{7.2}$$

is a convex cone.

Assuming for the moment that this lemma has been established, we can prove Theorem 7.1 as follows. Since W is a convex cone, its closure coincides with the tangent space $\mathcal{K}_0$ of W at $w_0 = (0,0)$. Selecting $\mathcal{K} = W$ in Theorem 6.1, we find that there exist nonnegative multipliers λ, μ, not both zero, such that

$$\lambda u + \mu v \geq 0$$

for every point $w = (u,v)$ in W. Since the points in W are of form (7.2), we see that $\lambda P(x) + \mu Q(x) \geq 0$ on $\mathcal{E}$, as was to be proved.

To prove Lemma 7.1, observe that the identities

$$P(\alpha x) = \alpha^2 P(x), \qquad Q(\alpha x) = \alpha^2 Q(x)$$

imply that $(\alpha^2 u, \alpha^2 v)$ is in W whenever (u,v) is in W. It follows that W is a cone.

To prove that W is convex, select two vectors $w = (u', v')$ and $w'' = (u'', v'')$ in W. If they are linearly dependent, $aw' + bw''$ is in W for all $a \geq 0$, $b \geq 0$, since W is a cone. Suppose therefore that they are linearly independent. Select x and y in $\mathcal{E}$ such that

$$u' = P(x), \qquad v' = Q(x), \qquad u'' = P(y), \qquad v'' = Q(y).$$

Since w' and w'' are linearly independent, we can select ρ and σ such that

$$P(x,y) = \rho u' + \sigma u'', \qquad Q(x,y) = \rho v' + \sigma v''.$$

Then

$$P(\alpha x + \beta y) = \alpha^2 P(x) + 2\alpha\beta P(x,y) + \beta^2 P(y) = au' + bu'',$$

$$Q(\alpha x + \beta y) = \alpha^2 Q(x) + 2\alpha\beta Q(x,y) + \beta^2 Q(y) = av' + bv'',$$

where

$$a = \alpha^2 + 2\rho\alpha\beta, \qquad b = \beta^2 + 2\sigma\alpha\beta. \tag{7.3}$$

The convexity of W will be established if we show that for every pair of positive numbers a and b equation (7.3) possesses a real solution α and β, for then the point $aw' + bw''$ will be the image of $\alpha x + \beta y$ under transformation (7.2). To see that equation (7.3) has at least one solution (α, β), set $\beta = m\alpha$. Then (7.3) takes the form

$$a = \alpha^2 (1 + 2\rho m), \qquad b = \alpha^2 (m^2 + \sigma m).$$

These equations require that

$$a(m^2 + 2\sigma m) = b(1 + 2\rho m).$$

Since a and b are positive, this equation has a solution m such that $\rho m \geq 0$. The numbers

$$\alpha = (1 + 2\rho m)^{1/2}, \qquad \beta = m\alpha$$

satisfy equations (7.3), and Lemma 7.1 is established.

As a corollary of this result we have the following modification of Theorem 7.1.

THEOREM 7.2

If there exists a pair of numbers u *and* v *such that the equations*

$$u = P(x), \qquad v = Q(x)$$

have no solution x *in* $\mathcal{E}$, *that is, if the image* W *of* $\mathcal{E}$ *under transformation (7.2) is not the* uv-*plane, then there exist multipliers* λ, μ, *not both zero, such that*

$$\lambda P(x) + \mu Q(x) \geq 0$$

for all x *in* $\mathcal{E}$.

In this event it is sufficient to choose λ, μ so that $(-\lambda, -\mu)$ is in the dual cone of W. Here we use the fact that, if W is not the uv-plane, neither is its closure $\overline{W}$.

LEMMA 7.2

Suppose that dim $\mathcal{E} > 2$ *and that there exist vectors* x *and* y *such that*

$$P(x) > 0, \qquad Q(x) = 0, \qquad P(y) < 0, \qquad Q(y) = 0.$$

Then there is a point $x_0 \neq 0$ *in* $\mathcal{E}$ *such that* $P(x_0) = Q(x_0) = 0$.

In the proof we can assume that $P(x) = -P(y) = 1$. If $Q(x,y) = 0$, then

$$Q(\alpha x + y) = \alpha^2 Q(x) + 2\alpha Q(x,y) + Q(y) = 0$$

for all values of α. In this case we can select α so that

$$P(\alpha x + y) = \alpha^2 + 2\alpha P(x,y) - 1 = 0.$$

The vector $x_0 = \alpha x + y$ then has $P(x_0) = Q(x_0) = 0$, as desired. Suppose next that $b = Q(x,y) \neq 0$. Replacing Q by Q/b, we obtain the relation $Q(x,y) = 1$. Since dim $\mathcal{E} > 2$, there is a vector $z \neq 0$ in $\mathcal{E}$ such that

$$Q(x,z) = Q(y,z) = 0.$$

Having chosen z in this manner, we see that the equations

$$P(z + \alpha x + \beta y) = 0, \qquad Q(z + \alpha x + \beta y) = 0$$

in α and β are of the form

$$\alpha^2 + 2B\alpha\beta - \beta^2 + 2D\alpha + 2E\beta + F = 0, \qquad 2\alpha\beta + f = 0. \tag{7.4}$$

If $f \neq 0$, then, by multiplying the first of these equations by $4\alpha^2$, we see that these equations are equivalent to a system of the form

$$4\alpha^4 + a\alpha^3 + b\alpha^2 + c\alpha - f^2 = 0, \qquad 2\alpha\beta + f = 0,$$

which has a real solution (α, β). If $f = 0$, equations (7.4) have a real solution (α, β) with $\alpha = 0$ if $F \geq 0$ and with $\beta = 0$ if $F < 0$, as is readily verified. Selecting a real solution (α, β) of equations (7.4), we find that the point $x_0 = z + \alpha x + \beta y$ has the desired property $P(x_0) = Q(x_0) = 0$. This proves Lemma 7.2.

COROLLARY

If dim $\mathcal{E} > 2$ *and the image* W *of* $\mathcal{E}$ *under* (7.2) *is the* uv-*plane, then there is a point* $x_0 \neq 0$ *in* $\mathcal{E}$ *such that* $P(x_0) = Q(x_0) = 0$.

Combining this result with Theorem 7.2, we obtain

THEOREM 7.3

If dim $\mathcal{E} > 2$ *and there is no point* $x \neq 0$ *such that* $P(x) = Q(x) = 0$, *then there exist multipliers* λ, μ, *not both zero, such that the inequality*

$$\lambda P(x) + \mu Q(x) \geq 0$$

holds on $\mathcal{E}$.

As a further result we have

THEOREM 7.4

Suppose that $P(x) = Q(x) = 0$ *only in case* $x = 0$ *and that the image* W *of* $\mathcal{E}$ *under the transformation* $u = P(x)$, $v = Q(x)$ *is closed. In addition, if* dim $\mathcal{E}$

$=2$, *suppose further that* W *is not the* uv-*plane. Then there exist multipliers* λ, μ *such that*

$$\lambda P(x) + \mu Q(x) > 0$$

for all $x \neq 0$ *in* $\mathcal{E}$.

In view of the corollary to Lemma 7.2 the convex cone W is not the uv-plane. Suppose that W is the half plane

$$\lambda u + \mu u \geqslant 0 \qquad [(\lambda, \mu) \neq (0,0)].$$

Observe that the relations

$$-\mu P(x) + \lambda Q(x) = 0, \qquad \lambda P(x) + \mu Q(x) = 0$$

hold if and only if $P(x) = Q(x) = 0$ and hence if and only if $x = 0$. By replacing P and Q by $-\mu P + \lambda Q$ and $\lambda P + \mu Q$, respectively, we see that we may assume that W is the half plane $v \geqslant 0$. Since W is closed, there exist points x and y in $\mathcal{E}$ such that

$$P(x) = 1, \qquad Q(x) = 0, \qquad P(y) = -1, \qquad Q(y) = 0.$$

Since $Q(x) \geqslant 0$ on $\mathcal{E}$, we have

$$Q(\alpha x + y) = 2\alpha Q(x,y) \geqslant 0$$

for all α. Hence $Q(x,y) = 0$. As was seen in the proof of Lemma 7.2, the number α can be chosen so that the nonnull vector $z = \alpha x + y$ has the property that $P(z) = Q(z) = 0$. This contradicts our hypotheses. It follows that W is not a half plane. There is accordingly a vector $(-\lambda, -\mu)$ in the dual cone of W such that

$$-\lambda u - \mu v < 0$$

for all points $(u, v) \neq (0, 0)$ in W. The multipliers λ, μ so obtained have the property that

$$\lambda P(x) + \mu Q(x) > 0$$

for all $x \neq 0$ in $\mathcal{E}$. This proves Theorem 7.4.

LEMMA 7.3

If dim $\mathcal{E} < \infty$ *and there is no point* $x \neq 0$ *such that* $P(x) = Q(x) = 0$, *then the image* W *of* $\mathcal{E}$ *under* (7.2) *is closed.*

Suppose that W is not closed. Then there is a limit point $w_0 = (u_0, v_0)$ of W that is not in W. Select a sequence of points $w_q = (u_q, v_q)$ $(q = 1, 2, 3, \ldots)$ in W converging to w_0. Choose x_q in $\mathcal{E}$ such that

$$u_q = P(x_q), \qquad v_q = Q(x_q).$$

Then

$$\lim_{q \to \infty} P(x_q) = u_0, \qquad \lim_{q \to \infty} Q(x_q) = v_0.$$

We have $\lim_{q \to \infty} |x_q| = \infty$, where $|x|$ is the Euclidean norm of x. Otherwise a subsequence of $\{x_q\}$ would converge to a point x_0 having $P(x_0) = u_0$, $Q(x_0) = v_0$, which is impossible since (u_0, v_0) is not in W. Replace $\{x_q\}$ by a subsequence, again denoted by $\{x_q\}$, such that the unit vectors $y_q = x_q / |x_q|$ $(q = 1, 2, 3, \ldots)$ converge to a vector y_0. Clearly $|y_0| = 1$, so that $y_0 \neq 0$. Moreover

$$P(y_0) = \lim_{q \to \infty} P(y_q) = \lim_{q \to \infty} \frac{P(x_q)}{|x_q|^2} = 0, \qquad Q(y_0) = \lim_{q \to \infty} \frac{Q(x_q)}{|x_q|^2} = 0.$$

This too is impossible. Consequently W is closed, and Lemma 7.3 is established.

Combining this lemma with Theorem 7.4, we find that, if $\dim \mathcal{E} < \infty$ and $P(x) > 0$ whenever $x \neq 0$ and $Q(x) = 0$, there are multipliers λ, μ such that

$$\lambda P(x) + \mu Q(x) > 0 \qquad (x \neq 0).$$

If there is a point $x \neq 0$ such that $Q(x) = 0$, then $\lambda P(x) > 0$ and $P(x) > 0$. In this event $\lambda > 0$, and we may replace λ, μ by $1, \mu / \lambda$, that is, we can select λ, μ so that $\lambda = 1$. If $Q(x) \neq 0$ for all $x \neq 0$, we can suppose that $Q(x) > 0$ if $x \neq 0$. In this event we can select $\lambda = 0$ and $\mu = 1$. These multipliers are in the interior to the dual cone of W. Consequently there is a set of effective multipliers with $\lambda > 0$. Again we can select λ, μ so that $\lambda = 1$. This yields the following modification of Theorem 7.1.

THEOREM 7.5

Suppose that $\dim \mathcal{E} < \infty$. *If* $P(x) > 0$ *whenever* $x \neq 0$ *and* $Q(x) = 0$, *then there exists a multiplier* μ *such that* $P + \mu Q$ *is positive in* $\mathcal{E}$.

This theorem was established in Section 6, Chapter 2, by other means. A similar result, which is valid in the infinite dimensional case, is given in

THEOREM 7.6

If there is no sequence $\{x_q\}$ of vectors in $\mathscr{E}$ such that $\lim_{q\to\infty} P(x_q) = -1$ and $\lim_{q\to\infty} Q(x_q) = 0$, then there is a multiplier μ such that $P + \mu Q$ is nonnegative on $\mathscr{E}$.

In this event the vector $w_0 = (-1, 0)$ is not in the closure $\overline{W}$ of the convex cone W. Choose orthogonal vectors w in $\overline{W}$ and $w^* = (-\lambda, -\mu)$ in the dual cone W^* of W so that $w_0 = w + w^*$. Clearly $w^* \neq 0$. The inner product of w^* and $w_0 = w + w^*$ yields the relation $\lambda = \lambda^2 + \mu^2 > 0$. Since w^* is in W^* we have, as before, the inequality $\lambda P(x) + \mu Q(x) \geqslant 0$ on $\mathscr{E}$, from which the theorem follows after a division by λ.

EXERCISES

1. Let $\mathscr{E}$ be the class of all sequences $x = (x_1, x_2, x_3, \dots)$ having $\sum_{n=1}^{\infty} x_n^2 < \infty$. Let P and Q be the quadratic forms

$$P(x) = \sum_{n=1}^{\infty} x_{2n-1}^2, \qquad Q(x) = \sum_{n=1}^{\infty} (2x_{2n-1}x_{2n} + c_n x_{2n}^2),$$

where $c_n > c_{n+1} > 0$. Set $c = \lim_{n\to\infty} c_n$. Then

$$P(x) + \mu Q(x) = \sum_{n=1}^{\infty} \left[(x_{2n-1} + \mu x_{2n})^2 + \mu(c_n - \mu)x_{2n}^2 \right] \geqslant 0$$

if $0 \leqslant \mu \leqslant c$. Show that $P(x) = Q(x) = 0$ only if $x = 0$. Show that, if $c = 0$, then $P + \mu Q > 0$ is impossible. Show that, if $c > 0$, then $P + \mu Q > 0$ if and only if $0 < \mu < c$.

2. With $\mathscr{E}$ as in Exercise 1 let

$$P(x) = \sum_{n=1}^{\infty} (x_{2n-1}^2 + 2x_{2n-1}x_{2n}), \qquad Q(x) = \sum_{n=1}^{\infty} \left[2x_{2n-1}x_{2n} + \left(4 + \frac{1}{n}\right)x_{2n}^2 \right].$$

Show that $P + Q > 0$ and that $P + \mu Q$ is indefinite if $\mu \neq 1$.

3. In the finite dimensional case, let $P(x) = x^*Ax$, $Q(x) = x^*Bx$, where A and B are symmetric matrices. Suppose that $P(x) > 0$ if $Q(x) = 0$ and $x \neq 0$. Show that there is a nonsingular matrix X such that X^*AX and X^*BX are diagonal matrices.

4. Let $P, Q_1, \dots, Q_m$ be quadratic forms on $\mathscr{E}^n$. Suppose that every nontrivial linear combination $\lambda_1 Q_1 + \cdots + \lambda_m Q_m$ is indefinite. Suppose further that $P(x) > 0$ whenever $x \neq 0$ and $Q_\alpha(x) = 0$ $(\alpha = 1, \dots, m)$. Show that there are multipliers $\lambda_1, \dots, \lambda_m$ such that $P + \lambda_1 Q_1 + \cdots + \lambda_m Q_m$ is positive definite. See M. R. Hestenes and E. J. McShane, "A Theorem on Quadratic Forms with Applica-

tions in the Calculus of Variations," *Transactions of the American Mathematical Society*, Vol. 47 (1940), 501–512. M. R. Hestenes, "Pairs of Quadratic Forms," *Linear Algebra and its Applications*, Vol. 1 (1968), 397–407. See also the papers "On the Mapping of Quadratic Forms"; "On the Mapping of n Quadratic Forms"; "On Linear Combinations of Quadratic Forms" by L. L. Dines *Bulletin of the American Mathematical Society*, Vol. 47 (1941), 494–498; Vol. 48 (1942), 467–471; Vol. 49 (1943), 388–393.

8. IMPLICIT FUNCTION THEOREMS

To extend the results given in the preceding sections, we shall employ a general implicit function theorem that is a consequence of the following fixed point theorem.

THEOREM 8.1

A continuous mapping of the ball

$$|x| \leqslant r \tag{8.1}$$

into itself has a fixed point. Analytically, let $F_i(x)$ $(i=1,\ldots,n)$ *be* n *continuous functions on the set* (8.1) *such that*

$$|F(x)| = [F_i(x)F_i(x)]^{1/2} \leqslant r$$

on this set. Then there is a point x_0 *such that*

$$|x_0| \leqslant r \quad and \quad x_0{}^i = F_i(x_0).$$

The proof of this result will be omitted.[†] This theorem is one form of the Brouwer fixed point theorem.

THEOREM 8.2

Let $G_\alpha(x,t)$ $(\alpha=1,\ldots,m)$ *be continuous real-valued functions on the domain*

$$|x| \leqslant r, \quad 0 \leqslant t \leqslant \delta.$$

Suppose that at $t=0$

$$G_\alpha(x,0) = a_{\alpha i}x^i \quad (\alpha=1,\ldots,m; \ i=1,\ldots,n), \tag{8.2}$$

[†]For the proof see, for example, L. M. Graves, *Theory of Functions of Real Variables*, McGraw-Hill Book Co., New York, 1946, p. 149.

where the matrix $(a_{\alpha i})$ *of constants has rank* m. *Let*

$$N(t) = \max |G(x,t) - G(x,0)| \quad on \quad |x| \leqslant r. \tag{8.3}$$

There exist a constant M *and a function*

$$x(t) \qquad (0 \leqslant t \leqslant \delta'; \; \delta' \leqslant \delta)$$

such that $x(0) = 0$ *and*

$$|x(t)| \leqslant MN(t) \leqslant r, \qquad G_\alpha[x(t), t] = 0 \qquad (0 \leqslant t \leqslant \delta'). \tag{8.4}$$

Moreover

$$\lim_{t \to 0^+} x(t) = x(0) = 0.$$

It should be noted that we draw no conclusion concerning the continuity of $x(t)$ when $t > 0$.

To prove this result, select constants $a_{\beta j}$ ($\beta = m+1, \ldots, n$; $j = 1, \ldots, m$) such that the matrix $A = (a_{ij})$ is nonsingular. Select M so that

$$|A^{-1}x| \leqslant M|x|,$$

and set

$$G_\beta(x,t) = a_{\beta j}x^j \qquad (\beta = m+1, \ldots, n).$$

The functions $G_1, \ldots, G_n$ then satisfy the hypotheses in the theorem. Moreover, since $G_\beta(x,t) = G_\beta(x,0)$ ($\beta > m$), the value of $N(t)$ is unaltered. Since $N(t)$ is continuous on $0 \leqslant t \leqslant \delta$ and $N(0) = 0$, we can select a constant $\delta' > 0$ so that

$$r(t) = MN(t) \leqslant r \qquad (0 \leqslant t \leqslant \delta' \leqslant \delta).$$

The function

$$F(x,t) = x - A^{-1}G(x,t) = A^{-1}[G(x,0) - G(x,t)]$$

satisfies the inequality

$$|F(x,t)| \leqslant MN(t) = r(t) \leqslant r$$

on the set

$$|x| \leqslant r \qquad (0 \leqslant t \leqslant \delta')$$

and hence also on the smaller set

$$|x| \leqslant r(t) \qquad (0 \leqslant t \leqslant \delta').$$

By Theorem 8.1 with r replaced by $r(t)$, it follows that for each t on $0 \leqslant t \leqslant \delta'$ there is a point $x(t)$ such that

$$|x(t)| \leqslant r(t) = MN(t),$$

$$x(t) = F[x(t), t] = x(t) - A^{-1}G[x(t), t].$$

We have accordingly

$$A^{-1}G[x(t), t] = 0, \qquad G[x(t), t] = 0.$$

Consequently (8.4) holds. Since $N(t)$ is continuous and $N(0) = 0$, we have $x(0) = 0$ and $\lim_{t \to 0^+} x(t) = 0$, as was to be proved.

Theorem 8.2 has the following extension.

THEOREM 8.3

Let $G_\alpha(x, t, b)$ $(\alpha = 1, \ldots, m)$ *be continuous real-valued functions of the point* $(x, t, b) = (x^1, \ldots, x^n, t, b^1, \ldots, b^p)$ *on the domain*

$$|x| \leqslant r, \qquad 0 \leqslant t \leqslant \delta, \qquad |b| \leqslant \epsilon.$$

Suppose that

$$G_\alpha(x, 0, b) = a_{\alpha j} x^j \qquad (\alpha = 1, \ldots, m; j = 1, \ldots, n)$$

where $(a_{\alpha j})$ *is a constant matrix of rank* m. *Let*

$$N(t) = \max |G(x, t, b) - G(x, 0, b)| \quad on \quad |x| \leqslant r, |b| \leqslant \epsilon.$$

There is a constant M > 0, *a constant* $\delta' > 0$ *with* $\delta' \leqslant \delta$, *and a function*

$$x(t, b) \qquad (0 \leqslant t \leqslant \delta', |b| \leqslant \epsilon)$$

such that

$$\lim_{t \to \infty} x(t, b) = x(0, b) = 0 \text{ uniformly on } |b| \leqslant \epsilon,$$

$$|x(t, b)| \leqslant MN(t) \leqslant r, \qquad G_\alpha[x(t, b), t, b] = 0$$

$$(\alpha = 1, \ldots, n) \text{ on } 0 \leqslant t \leqslant \delta', |b| \leqslant \epsilon.$$

The proof is like that of Theorem 7.2 with $G_\alpha(x, t)$ replaced by $G_\alpha(x, t, b)$. The verification of this result will be left as an exercise.

9. DERIVED CONES AND DERIVED SETS

In Section 6 we considered the problem of minimizing a function f on a set X subject to inequality constraints of the form

$$g_\alpha(x) \leqslant 0 \qquad (\alpha = 1,\dots,p).$$

We observed that the transformation

$$w^0 = f(x), \qquad w^\alpha = g_\alpha(x) \qquad (\alpha = 1,\dots,p)$$

mapped X into a set W in a Euclidean space $\mathcal{E}^{p+1}$. The solution x_0 of our problem is mapped into a point w_0. A generalized Lagrange multiplier rule was determined by each convex cone $\mathcal{K}$ of tangent vectors of W at w_0.

In Section 10 we shall be concerned with the case in which we have a point x_0 which minimizes a function f on a set X subject to an enlarged set of constraints

$$g_\alpha(x) \leqslant 0 \quad (\alpha = 1,\dots,p), \qquad g_\beta(x) = 0 \quad (\beta+1,\dots,m).$$

Proceeding as before, we map X into a set W in $\mathcal{E}^{m+1}$ by the transformation

$$w^0 = f(x), \qquad w^\gamma = g_\gamma(x) \qquad (\gamma = 1,\dots,m).$$

We denote the image of x_0 by w_0. The introduction of the equality constraints leads to a more delicate analysis involving implicit function theorems. For this reason we shall use convex cones of tangent vectors having an additional property which we shall describe presently. These special types of cones will be called *derived cones*; a set of vectors that generates a derived cone will be termed *a derived set*. The adjective "derived" is used to emphasize that a vector in a derived cone can be interpreted as a vector of derivatives of the functions $f, g_1,\dots,g_m$ used to define the set W.

To introduce these concepts, we consider first the case in which the set W is a convex set in $\mathcal{E}^{m+1}$. Let w_0 be a point in W. As was seen in Lemma 4.3, Chapter 4, the tangent space $\mathcal{K}_0$ of W at w_0 is a convex cone. It is the closure of the class $\hat{\mathcal{K}}$ of inner tangent vectors of W at w_0. The class $\hat{\mathcal{K}}$ is generated by the class $\mathcal{K}$ of vectors of the form $k = w - w_0$, where w is in W. Normally the class $\mathcal{K}$ is not a cone. However, it has the following property. Let $k_1,\dots,k_N$ be a finite set of vectors in $\mathcal{K}$, not necessarily distinct. There is a constant $\delta > 0$ such that the truncated cone

$$w(\epsilon_1,\dots,\epsilon_N) = w_0 + k_j\epsilon_j \qquad (0 \leqslant \epsilon_j \leqslant \delta) \tag{9.1}$$

is in W. To see that this is the case, choose w_j in W so that

$$k_j = w_j - w_0 \qquad (j = 1, \ldots, N).$$

Then

$$w(\epsilon) = w_0 + (w_j - w_0)\epsilon_j = (1 - \epsilon_1 - \cdots - \epsilon_N)w_0 + w_j\epsilon_j.$$

If $\delta \leqslant 1/N$, then $\epsilon_1 + \cdots + \epsilon_N \leqslant 1$ whenever $0 \leqslant \epsilon_j \leqslant \delta$. It follows from the convexity of W that the point $w(\epsilon)$ is in W whenever $\delta \leqslant 1/N$.

For an arbitrary set W and a point w_0 in W, a set of tangent vectors $k_1, \ldots, k_N$ of W at w_0 fails to have the property that the truncated cone (9.1) is in W for a small constant δ. However, it may be in W if we modify $w(\epsilon)$ so that it is of the form

$$w(\epsilon) = w_0 + k_j\epsilon_j + r(\epsilon) \qquad (0 \leqslant \epsilon_j \leqslant \delta; j = 1, \ldots, N), \qquad (9.2a)$$

where

$$\lim_{\epsilon \to 0} \frac{r(\epsilon)}{|\epsilon|} = 0. \qquad (9.2b)$$

Here we may select $|\epsilon| = \epsilon_1 + \cdots + \epsilon_N$. If a set of vectors $k_1, \ldots, k_N$ has the property that there is a surface $w(\epsilon)$ of form (9.2) in W, then $k_1, \ldots, k_N$ is said to define a *differential cone for* $\mathbf{W}$ *at* w_0. This cone consists of all vectors of the form

$$k = k_j\alpha_j \qquad (\alpha_j \geqslant 0; j = 1, \ldots, N). \qquad (9.3)$$

Each vector k of this type is a tangent vector of W at w_0, for by setting $\epsilon_j = t\alpha_j$ the curve

$$v(t) = w(t\alpha) = w_0 + kt + r(t\alpha) \qquad (0 \leqslant t \leqslant \sigma)$$

will be in W if σ is small. Moreover if $\alpha \neq 0$ we have

$$\lim_{t \to 0^+} \frac{r(t\alpha)}{t} = 0$$

by virtue of (9.2b). Hence $\dot{v}(0) = k$ and k is a tangent vector of W at w_0, as was to be proved.

We are now in a position to define derived sets and derived cones. A class $\mathcal{K}$ of vectors will be called a *derived set for* $\mathbf{W}$ *at* w_0 if every finite set of vectors $k_1, \ldots, k_N$ in $\mathcal{K}$ defines a differential cone for W at w_0. A derived set that is a convex cone will be called a *derived cone*. If $\mathcal{K}$ is a derived set, the class $\hat{\mathcal{K}}$ generated by $\mathcal{K}$ is a convex cone in the tangent space $\mathcal{K}_0$ of W at w_0. It is also a derived cone for W at w_0, as stated in

LEMMA 9.1

If $\mathcal{K}$ is a derived set for W *at* w$_0$, *the cone $\hat{\mathcal{K}}$ generated by $\mathcal{K}$ is a derived cone for* W *at* w$_0$.

It is clear that $\hat{\mathcal{K}}$ is a convex cone. We shall show that it is also a derived set. To this end let $\hat{k}_1, \ldots, \hat{k}_M$ be a set of vectors in $\hat{\mathcal{K}}$. Since $\hat{\mathcal{K}}$ is generated by $\mathcal{K}$, there exist vectors $k_1, \ldots, k_N$ in $\mathcal{K}$ such that

$$\hat{k}_i = k_j a_{ji} \qquad (a_{ji} \geqslant 0; j = 1, \ldots, N; i = 1, \ldots, M).$$

Since $\mathcal{K}$ is a derived set for W at w_0, we can select a surface $w(\epsilon)$ of form (9.2) in W. If $\hat{\delta}$ is a sufficiently small positive number, the numbers

$$\epsilon_j = a_{ji} \hat{\epsilon}_i \qquad (0 \leqslant \hat{\epsilon}_i \leqslant \hat{\delta})$$

will satisfy the inequality $0 \leqslant \epsilon_j \leqslant \delta$. Using the matrix notation $\epsilon = A\hat{\epsilon}$, we see that

$$\hat{w}(\hat{\epsilon}) \equiv w(A\hat{\epsilon}) = w_0 + k_j a_{ji} \hat{\epsilon}_i + r(A\hat{\epsilon})$$

takes the form

$$\hat{w}(\hat{\epsilon}) = w_0 + \hat{k}_i \hat{\epsilon}_i + r(A\hat{\epsilon}) \qquad (0 \leqslant \hat{\epsilon}_i \leqslant \hat{\delta}), \qquad (9.4)$$

where

$$\lim_{\hat{\epsilon} \to 0} \frac{r(A\hat{\epsilon})}{|\hat{\epsilon}|} = 0.$$

Since by construction surface (9.4) is in W, it follows that $\hat{\mathcal{K}}$ is a derived set for W at w_0, as was to be proved.

The following lemma will be useful in applications.

LEMMA 9.2

If

$$w(\epsilon_1, \ldots, \epsilon_N) \qquad (0 \leqslant \epsilon \leqslant \delta; j = 1, \ldots, N) \qquad (9.5)$$

is a surface of class C′ *in* W *such that* w(0)=w$_0$, *then the vectors*

$$k_j = \frac{\partial w(0)}{\partial \epsilon_j} \qquad (j=1,\ldots,N) \qquad (9.6)$$

define a differential cone for W *at* w$_0$.

This follows from the fact that by Taylor's theorem surface (9.5) is of form (9.2) with $k_1,\ldots,k_N$ given by (9.6).

As remarked above, we shall be interested mainly in sets W that are determined by a set of functions $g_0=f,g_1,\ldots,g_m$ on a set X via the transformation

$$w^\rho = g_\rho(x) \qquad (\rho=0,1,\ldots,m).$$

In vector notation this transformation takes the form

$$w = g(x).$$

Let $w_0=g(x_0)$ be the image of a point x_0 in X. It will be convenient to express the concepts given above in terms of the vector function g. A tangent vector k of W at x_0 is the limit

$$\lim_{q\to\infty} \frac{w_q - w_0}{t_q} = k,$$

where w_q is in W, t_q is positive, and $\lim_{q\to\infty} t_q=0$. Selecting x_q in X so that $w_q = g(x_q)$, we have

$$\lim_{q\to\infty} \frac{g(x_q)-g(x_0)}{t_q} = k. \qquad (9.7)$$

Accordingly k can be interpreted as a directional derivative of $g(x)$ at x_0. In this context the tangent cone $\mathcal{K}_0$ of W at w_0 is the class of directional derivatives of $g(x)$ at x_0. Similarly, if $w(t)$ $(0\leqslant t\leqslant\delta)$ is an arc in W having $w(0)=w$ and $\dot{w}(0)=k$, then

$$\lim_{t=0^+} \frac{g[x(t)]-g(x_0)}{t} = k, \qquad (9.8)$$

where $x(t)$ is chosen so that $w(t)=g[x(t)]$. Observe that we cannot speak of the convergence of a sequence $\{x_q\}$ or of the continuity of $x(t)$, since no topology has been introduced on X.

The concept of a differential cone can be expressed in the following alternative form. A set of vectors $k_1, \ldots, k_N$ defines a *differential cone for* g(x) *at* x_0 if there exists a family

$$x(\epsilon) = x(\epsilon_1, \ldots, \epsilon_N) \qquad (0 \leqslant \epsilon_j \leqslant \delta; j = 1, \ldots, N)$$

in X such that $x(0) = x_0$, and such that the function $g[x(\epsilon)]$ is continuous and the remainder $r(\epsilon)$ in the formula

$$g[x(\epsilon)] = g(x_0) + k_j \epsilon_j + r(\epsilon) \qquad (0 \leqslant \epsilon_j \leqslant \delta) \tag{9.9a}$$

satisfies the relation

$$\lim_{\epsilon \to 0} \frac{r(\epsilon)}{|\epsilon|} = 0. \tag{9.9b}$$

A set $\mathcal{K}$ of vectors in $\mathcal{E}^{m+1}$ forms a *derived set for* g(x) *at* x_0 if every finite set $k_1, \ldots, k_N$ of vectors in $\mathcal{K}$ defines a differential cone for $g(x)$ at x_0. A convex cone that is a derived set for $g(x)$ at x_0 is said to be a *derived cone for* g(x) *at* x_0.

In these definitions the functions $g_0 = f, g_1, \ldots, g_m$ are real-valued functions on an arbitrary set X. The set X need not be in a Euclidean space. We shall give two examples. The first is a standard situation in Euclidean space, and the second is concerned with an infinite dimensional space of arcs.

EXAMPLE 9.1

Let $g_0 = f, g_1, \ldots, g_m$ be functions of class C' in an open set X in a Euclidean space $\mathcal{E}^n$. Let x_0 be a point in X. The class $\mathcal{K}$ of all vectors k of the form

$$k = g'(x_0, h) \tag{9.10}$$

is a linear space forming a derived cone for $g(x)$ ar x_0. Here $g'(x, h)$ is the usual differential

$$g_\rho'(x, h) = \frac{\partial g_\rho(x)}{\partial x^j} h^j.$$

To see that this is the case, let $k_1, \ldots, k_N$ be vectors in $\mathcal{K}$ and select vectors $h_1, \ldots, h_N$ in $\mathcal{E}^n$ so that

$$k_j = g'(x_0, h_j) \qquad (j = 1, \ldots, N).$$

Using the Taylor expansion

$$g(x) = g(x_0) + g'(x, x - x_0) + r_1(x_0, x - x_0),$$

we find that for $x(\epsilon) = x_0 + h_j \epsilon_j$ we have

$$g[x(\epsilon)] = g(x_0) + g'(x_0, h_j \epsilon_j) + r_1(x_0, h_j \epsilon_j).$$

Since

$$g'(x_0, h_j \epsilon_j) = g'(x_0, h_j) \epsilon_j = k_j \epsilon_j,$$

we see that $g[x(\epsilon)]$ is expressible in form (9.9a). Relation (9.9b) follows from the property

$$\lim_{x \to x_0} \frac{r_1(x_0, x - x_0)}{|x - x_0|} = 0$$

of the remainder term r_1 in Taylor's formula.

It should not be concluded that every tangent vector k of W at w_0 is necessarily of the form $k = g'(x_0, h)$. For example, if g is of class C'' on x_0 and h is a vector satisfying the relation

$$g'(x_0, h) = 0,$$

the arc $x(t) = x_0 + t^{1/2} h$ ($0 \leqslant t \leqslant \delta$) emanates from x_0 and has

$$\lim_{t \to 0^+} \frac{g[x(t)] - g(x_0)}{t} = \tfrac{1}{2} g''(x_0, h).$$

Consequently $g''(x_0, h)$ is in $\mathcal{K}_0$ whenever $g'(x_0, h) = 0$. Here $g''(x_0, h)$ is the second differential of $g(x)$ at x_0. Recall that we do not require the differentiability of $x(t)$ at $t = 0$.

Let $\mathcal{K}$ be the class of all vectors k of form (9.10), and let $\tilde{k}$ be a nonnull vector of the form

$$\tilde{k} = \tfrac{1}{2} g''(x_0, \tilde{h}),$$

where $g'(x_0, \tilde{h}) = 0$. Then the set $\mathcal{K}_1$ of all vectors of the form $k + \alpha \tilde{k}$, where k is in $\mathcal{K}$ and $\alpha \geqslant 0$, is also a derived cone for $g(x)$ at x_0. The proof of this fact will be left to the reader.

A simple infinite dimensional case is given in

EXAMPLE 9.2

Let X be the class of all piecewise continuous arcs

$$x: \quad x^i(t) \quad (a \leqslant t \leqslant b; i=1,\ldots,n)$$

lying in a region $\mathcal{R}$ in $\mathcal{E}^n$. Let

$$g_i(x) = \int_a^b x^i(t)\, dt \quad (i=1,\ldots,n).$$

Let

$$x_0: \quad x_0^i(t) \quad (a \leqslant t \leqslant b)$$

be a particular arc in X. Given a point $(\bar{t},\bar{x})$ in $\mathcal{R}$ with $a \leqslant \bar{t} < b$, construct the arc

$$x(\epsilon): \quad x^i(t,\epsilon) = \bar{x}^i \quad (\bar{t} \leqslant t \leqslant \bar{t}+\epsilon), \quad x^i(t,\epsilon) = x_0^i(t) \quad \text{otherwise}$$

for each ϵ on an interval $0 < \epsilon \leqslant \delta \leqslant b - \bar{t}$. For $\epsilon = 0$, set $x^i(t,\epsilon) = x_0^i(t)$ $(a \leqslant t \leqslant b)$. If δ is small, then for ϵ on the interval $0 \leqslant \epsilon \leqslant \delta$ the arc

$$x(\epsilon): \quad x^i(t,\epsilon) \quad (a \leqslant t \leqslant b)$$

is in X and has $x(0) = x_0$. Moreover

$$g_i[x(\epsilon)] = g_i(x_0) + \int_{\bar{t}}^{\bar{t}+\epsilon} \left[\bar{x}^i - x_0^i(t) \right] dt.$$

In vector notation this becomes

$$g[x(\epsilon)] = g(x_0) + \int_{\bar{t}}^{\bar{t}+\epsilon} \left[\bar{x} - x_0(t) \right] dt.$$

The limit

$$k = \lim_{\epsilon \to 0^+} \frac{g[x(\epsilon)] - g(x_0)}{\epsilon} = \bar{x} - x_0(\bar{t}+0)$$

is accordingly a directional derivative of $g(x)$ at x_0. In a similar manner it is seen that $k = \bar{x} - x_0(\bar{t}-0)$ is a directional derivative of $g(x)$ at x_0.

Using the same arguments, we can show that in the more general case in which $g(x)$ is of the form

$$g(x) = c + \int_a^b G[t, x(t)]\, dt,$$

where G is continuous, the quantity $k = G(\bar{t}, \bar{x}) - G[\bar{t}, x_0(\bar{t} \pm 0)]$ is a directional derivative of $g(x)$ at x_0 for each $\bar{t}$ on $a \leqslant t \leqslant b$ and for each $\bar{x}$ under consideration.

This example serves to illustrate the generality of the concept of directional derivatives given here. Derivatives of this type play an important role in variational theory and optimal control theory. In exceptional cases it may be desirable to use a more general type of derived sets and cones than those defined above.[†]

10. MINIMA RELATIVE TO EQUALITY AND INEQUALITY CONSTRAINTS

We are now in a position to consider more fully the problem of minimizing a function f on a set X subject to constraints of the form

$$g_\alpha(x) \leqslant 0 \quad (\alpha = 1, \ldots, p); \qquad g_\beta(x) = 0 \quad (\beta = p+1, \ldots, m). \quad (10.1)$$

As before, we denote by S the set of points x in X satisfying constraints (10.1). We assume that we are given a point x_0 in S that minimizes f on S. We have, associated with x_0, the class $\mathcal{K}_0$ of directional derivatives k of $g_0 = f, g_1, \ldots, g_m$ in the sense described in Section 9. We also have, associated with x_0, a cone $\mathcal{K}^-$ in $\mathcal{E}^{m+1}$ whose nonnull elements k satisfy the relations

$$k^0 < 0, \qquad k^\alpha < 0 \quad [1 \leqslant \alpha \leqslant p, g_\alpha(x_0) = 0], \qquad k^\beta = 0 \quad (\beta = p+1, \ldots, m).$$

$$(10.2)$$

Observe that k^α is arbitrary if $g_\alpha(x_0) < 0$. The cone $\mathcal{K}^-$ is convex. Intuitively, there is no vector $k \neq 0$ in $\mathcal{K}^-$ that is in $\mathcal{K}_0$. This intuitive result, which we cannot establish without further hypothesis, is suggested by

[†]See A. Gittleman, "A General Multiplier Rule," *Journal of Optimization and Applications*, Vol. 7 (1971), 29–38.

Hestenes first used the concept of derived sets in his paper "On Variational Theory and Optimal Control Theory," *Journal SIAM Control*, Vol. 3 (1965), 23–48. An equivalent concept was introduced by M. D. Cannon, C. D. Cullum, Jr., and E. Polak in their paper "Constrained Minimization Problems in Finite Dimensional Spaces," *Journal SIAM Control*, Vol. 4 (1966), 528–547.

LEMMA 10.1

Given a vector $k \neq 0$ *in* $\mathcal{K}^-$, *there is no arc* $x(t)$ $(0 \leqslant t \leqslant \delta)$ *in* X *such that* $x(0) = x_0$, *and such that with* $g_0 = f$ *we have*

$$\lim_{t \to 0^+} \frac{g_\rho[x(t)] - g_\rho(x_0)}{t} = k^\rho \qquad (\rho = 0, \ldots, m) \tag{10.3}$$

$$g_\beta[x(t)] = 0 \qquad (0 \leqslant t \leqslant \delta; \ \beta = p+1, \ldots, m). \tag{10.4}$$

Observe that no assumption is made with regard to the continuity of $g_\rho[x(t)]$ or of $x(t)$. The function $g_\rho[x(t)]$, however, is continuous at $t = 0$ by virtue of relation (10.3). Observe further that, since $k^\beta = 0$ ($\beta = p+1, \ldots, m$) for a vector in $\mathcal{K}^-$, condition (10.3) for $\rho > p$ is consistent with condition (10.4).

To prove this result, suppose that such an arc exists for a vector $k \neq 0$ in $\mathcal{K}^-$. Then we can select $\delta' > 0$ so small that for each index ρ having $k^\rho < 0$ we have

$$g_\rho[x(t)] - g_\rho(x_0) < 0 \qquad (0 \leqslant t \leqslant \delta'; \ k^\rho < 0).$$

In particular, by (10.2), this holds when $\rho = 0$ and when ρ is an active index for x_0. Hence on $0 < t \leqslant \delta'$ we have

$$f[x(t)] < f(x_0), \qquad g_\alpha[x(t)] < 0 \quad \text{if } g_\alpha(x_0) = 0 \text{ and } \alpha \leqslant p.$$

If α is an inactive index for x_0, then $g_\alpha(x_0) < 0$. Since

$$\lim_{t \to 0^+} g_\alpha[x(t)] = g_\alpha(x_0) < 0,$$

we can diminish δ' so that

$$g_\alpha[x(t)] < 0 \qquad (0 \leqslant t \leqslant \delta')$$

for these indices also. It follows that for t on the interval $0 < t \leqslant \delta'$ we have

$$f[x(t)] < f(x_0), \qquad g_\alpha[x(t)] < 0 \quad (\alpha = 1, \ldots, p),$$

$$g_\beta[x(t)] = 0 \quad (\beta = p+1, \ldots, m),$$

contrary to our assumption that x_0 minimizes f on X subject to constraints (10.1). This proves Lemma 10.1.

We shall show next that no vector $k \neq 0$ in $\mathcal{K}^-$ can be interior to a derived cone $\mathcal{K}$. In fact, it cannot be interior to the larger cone $\mathcal{K}^+ = \mathcal{K} - \mathcal{K}^-$. This result is given in the following lemma. In this lemma and elsewhere the vectors $e_0, e_1, \ldots, e_m$ are the basis vectors for $\mathcal{E}^{m+1}$, that is,

$e_j^{\,j}=1$ and $e_j^{\,\rho}=0$ $(\rho\neq j)$. We continue to use the notation $g_0=f$. Then g is a vector whose components are $g_0,g_1,\dots,g_m$.

LEMMA 10.2

Let $\mathcal{K}$ be a derived cone for $g(x)$ *at* x_0. *Set* $N=m-p$. *Given a vector* $k\neq0$ *in* $\mathcal{K}^-$, *there is no constant* $\sigma>0$ *such that the vectors*

$$k+e_{p+1}\epsilon_1+\cdots+e_m\epsilon_N \qquad (-\sigma\leqslant\epsilon_j\leqslant\sigma;\,j=1,\dots,N) \qquad (10.5)$$

are in the cone $\mathcal{K}^+=\mathcal{K}-\mathcal{K}^-$. *In particular, no vector* $k\neq0$ *in* $\mathcal{K}^-$ *is interior to* $\mathcal{K}^+$.

Suppose that such a constant $\sigma>0$ exists for a vector $\bar{k}\neq0$ in $\mathcal{K}^-$. Then the vectors

$$(N+1)\bar{k}_j=\bar{k}+e_{p+j}\sigma \qquad (j=1,\dots,N),$$

$$(N+1)\bar{k}_0=\bar{k}-(e_{p+1}+\cdots+e_n)\sigma,$$

are in $\mathcal{K}^+=\mathcal{K}-\mathcal{K}^-$. Moreover

$$\bar{k}=\bar{k}_0+\cdots+\bar{k}_N.$$

Since $\mathcal{K}^+=\mathcal{K}-\mathcal{K}^-$ is a cone, the vector $\bar{k}_j$ is also in $\mathcal{K}^+$. It is therefore expressible in the form $\bar{k}_j=k_j-\tilde{k}_j$, where k_j is in $\mathcal{K}$ and $\tilde{k}_j$ is in $\mathcal{K}^-$. The vectors

$$k_j=\bar{k}_j+\tilde{k}_j \qquad (j=0,1,\dots,N)$$

are in $\mathcal{K}$, and their sum

$$k=k_0+\cdots+k_N=\bar{k}+\tilde{k}_0+\cdots+\tilde{k}_N \qquad (10.6)$$

is a nonnull vector in $\mathcal{K}^-$. Moreover the matrix

$$\left(k_j^{\,\beta}\right)=\begin{bmatrix} -\sigma & \sigma & 0 & 0 & \cdots & 0 \\ -\sigma & 0 & \sigma & 0 & \cdots & 0 \\ \vdots & \vdots & \vdots & \vdots & \vdots & 0 \\ -\sigma & 0 & \cdots & 0 & & \sigma \end{bmatrix} \qquad \begin{array}{l}(\beta=p+1,\dots,N),\\ (j=0,1,\dots,N)\end{array} \qquad (10.7)$$

has rank N.

We now use the fact that $\mathcal{K}$ is a derived set. Accordingly there exists a function

$$x(\epsilon) = x(\epsilon_0, \epsilon_1, \ldots, \epsilon_N) \qquad (0 \leqslant \epsilon_j \leqslant \delta)$$

in X such that $x(0) = x_0$ and such that $g[x(\epsilon)]$, with $g_0 = f$, is continuous and is expressible in the form

$$w(\epsilon) = g[x(\epsilon)] = g(x_0) + k_j \epsilon_j + r(\epsilon) \qquad (0 \leqslant \epsilon_j \leqslant \delta; j = 0, 1, \ldots, N), \quad (10.8)$$

where

$$\lim_{\epsilon \to 0} \frac{r(\epsilon)}{|\epsilon|} = 0. \tag{10.9}$$

Choose h to be the point $(1, 1, \ldots, 1)$ in the set $\mathcal{E}^{N+1}$ of points $z = (z^0, \ldots, z^N)$. Then, by (10.6),

$$k = k_j h^j. \tag{10.10}$$

Given a point z such that $|z| \leqslant 1$, select $\delta' > 0$ so that

$$\epsilon_j = th^j + tz^j \leqslant \delta$$

whenever $0 \leqslant t \leqslant \delta'$. Set

$$F_\rho(z, t) = \frac{1}{t} \{ g_\rho[x(th + tz)] - g_\rho(x_0) \} - k^\rho, \tag{10.11}$$

$$F_\rho(z, 0) = k_j^\rho z^j, \tag{10.12}$$

where $|z| \leqslant 1$. Observe that, by (10.8) and (10.10), we have

$$F_\rho(z, t) = k_j^\rho z^j + \frac{r(th + tz)}{t} \qquad (0 < t \leqslant \delta'). \tag{10.13}$$

Consequently

$$\lim_{t \to 0^+} F_\rho(z, t) = 0 \qquad \text{uniformly on } |z| \leqslant 1.$$

Since matrix (10.7) has rank N, the functions $G_\gamma(z, t) = F_{p+\gamma}(z, t)$ $(\gamma = 1, \ldots, N)$ satisfy the hypotheses of Theorem 8.2. There is accordingly a function

$$z(t) \qquad (0 \leqslant t \leqslant \delta'')$$

such that

$$G_\gamma[z(t),t] = F_{p+\gamma}[z(t),t] = 0, \qquad \lim_{t \to 0^+} z(t) = z(0) = 0. \qquad (10.14)$$

In view of (10.13) we have

$$\lim_{t \to 0^+} F_\rho[z(t),t] = 0 \qquad (\rho = 0,1,\ldots,m). \qquad (10.15)$$

Setting

$$x(t) = x[th + tz(t)] \qquad (0 \leqslant t \leqslant \delta''),$$

we find that

$$F_\rho[z(t),t] = \frac{g_\rho[x(t)] - g_\rho(x_0)}{t} - k^\rho \qquad (\rho = 0, 1,\ldots,m). \qquad (10.16)$$

Consequently, by (10.15), we have

$$\lim_{t \to 0^+} \frac{g_\rho[x(t)] - g_\rho(x_0)}{t} = k^\rho.$$

In view of (10.14) we also have, with $\beta = p + \gamma$,

$$G_\gamma[z(t),t] = \frac{g_\beta[x(t)]}{t} = 0.$$

Therefore $g_\beta[x(t)] = 0$. This contradicts the result given in Lemma 10.1, thus proving the first conclusion in Lemma 10.2. The second conclusion is a simple consequence of the first.

We are now in a position to prove the following generalized multiplier rule.

THEOREM 10.1

Suppose that x_0 minimizes f *on the subset* S *of* X *defined by the constraints*

$$g_\alpha(x) \leqslant 0 \quad (\alpha = 1,\ldots,p), \qquad g_\beta(x) = 0 \quad (\beta = p+1,\ldots,m).$$

Let $\mathcal{K}$ be a derived set for $f, g_1, \ldots, g_m$ *at* x_0. *There exists a set of multipliers* $\lambda_0 \geqslant 0, \lambda_1, \ldots, \lambda_m$, *not all zero, such that*

$$\lambda_\alpha \geqslant 0 \qquad [\alpha = 1, \ldots, p \text{ with } \lambda_\alpha = 0 \text{ if } g_\alpha(x_0) < 0] \qquad (10.17a)$$

and such that

$$L(k) = \lambda_\rho k^\rho \geqslant 0 \qquad\qquad\qquad\qquad (10.17b)$$

for every vector k *in* $\mathcal{K}$.

To prove this result, let $\hat{\mathcal{K}}$ be the convex cone generated by $\mathcal{K}$. Then $\hat{\mathcal{K}}$ is a derived cone for $f, g_1, \ldots, g_m$ at x_0. Let $\mathcal{K}^+ = \hat{\mathcal{K}} - \mathcal{K}^-$. Suppose that the closure $\overline{\mathcal{K}}^+$ of $\mathcal{K}^+$ coincides with $\mathcal{E}^{m+1}$. Since $\mathcal{K}^+$ and $\overline{\mathcal{K}}^+$ have the same interior, by Lemma 3.6 Chapter 4, it follows that $\mathcal{K}^+ = \overline{\mathcal{K}}^+ = \mathcal{E}^{m+1}$. Consequently every vector $k \neq 0$ in $\mathcal{K}^-$ is an interior point of $\mathcal{K}^+$. This is impossible, however, by virtue of Lemma 10.2. It follows that $\overline{\mathcal{K}}^+$ does not coincide with $\mathcal{E}^{m+1}$. There is accordingly a nonnull vector $\lambda = (\lambda_0, \lambda_1, \ldots, \lambda_m)$ such that $-\lambda$ is in the dual of $\overline{\mathcal{K}}^+$. Consequently

$$\langle -\lambda, k \rangle \leqslant 0$$

for all k in $\overline{\mathcal{K}}^+$ or, equivalently,

$$L(k) = \langle \lambda, k \rangle = \lambda_0 k^0 + \lambda_1 k^1 + \cdots + \lambda_m k^m \geqslant 0$$

for all k in $\overline{\mathcal{K}}^+$. Since the cones $\mathcal{K}$, $\hat{\mathcal{K}}$, and $-\mathcal{K}^-$ are subsets of $\mathcal{K}^+$, we have

$$L(k) \geqslant 0 \qquad \text{on } \mathcal{K}, \text{ on } \hat{\mathcal{K}}, \text{ and on } -\mathcal{K}^-,$$

as well as on their closures. Since $L(k) \geqslant 0$ on $-\mathcal{K}^-$, we have

$$L(k) \leqslant 0 \qquad \text{on } \mathcal{K}^- \text{ and on its closure.}$$

As before, we denote by e_j the vector in $\mathcal{E}^{m+1}$ such that $e_j^j = 1$ and $e_j^\rho = 0$ $(\rho \neq j)$. For j in the range $0 \leqslant j \leqslant p$, the vector $-e_j$ is in the closure of $\mathcal{K}^-$ and e_j is in the closure of $-\mathcal{K}^-$. Hence

$$L(e_j) = \lambda_j \geqslant 0 \qquad (0 \leqslant j \leqslant p).$$

If j is an inactive index for x_0, that is, if $g_j(x_0) < 0$, then e_j is in the closure of $\mathcal{K}^-$ and $L(e_j) = \lambda_j \leqslant 0$. Consequently $\lambda_j = 0$ whenever $g_j(x_0) < 0$. This completes the proof of Theorem 10.1.

COROLLARY

If the vector $-e_0 = (-1, 0, \ldots, 0)$ is in the closure $\overline{\mathcal{K}^+}$ of $\mathcal{K}^+ = \hat{\mathcal{K}} - \mathcal{K}^-$, then the multipliers $\lambda_0, \lambda_1, \ldots, \lambda_m$ described in Theorem 10.1 have $\lambda_0 = 0$. If $-e_0$ is not in $\overline{\mathcal{K}^+}$, these multipliers can be chosen so that $\lambda_0 > 0$. If the closures of $\hat{\mathcal{K}}$ and $\mathcal{K}^-$ have a vector k in common such that $k^0 < 0$, then $-e_0$ is in $\overline{\mathcal{K}^+}$.

Suppose first that $-e_0$ is in $\overline{\mathcal{K}^+}$. Then the linear form $L(k)$ in (10.17) has the property that

$$L(-e_0) = -\lambda_0 \geqslant 0.$$

Since $\lambda_0 \geqslant 0$, this implies that $\lambda_0 = 0$.

Suppose next that $-e_0$ is not in $\overline{\mathcal{K}^+}$. Then by Theorem 3.1, Chapter 4, $-e_0$ is expressible as the sum

$$-e_0 = k + (-\lambda)$$

of orthogonal vectors k in $\overline{\mathcal{K}^+}$ and $-\lambda$ in the dual of $\overline{\mathcal{K}^+}$. We have

$$\lambda_0 = \langle \lambda, e_0 \rangle = \langle \lambda, \lambda - k \rangle = \langle \lambda, \lambda \rangle = |\lambda|^2 > 0.$$

The multipliers $\lambda_0 > 0, \lambda_1, \ldots, \lambda_m$ determined in this manner have the properties described in Theorem 10.1.

Suppose finally that there is a vector k having $k^0 < 0$ which is common to the closures of $\hat{\mathcal{K}}$ and $\mathcal{K}^-$. We can suppose that $k^0 = -2$. Then the vector $k_1 = k + e_0$ is in $\overline{\mathcal{K}^-}$ and $-e_0 = k - k_1$ is in $\overline{\mathcal{K}^+}$, as was to be proved.

Observe that, if we set

$$F = \lambda_0 g_0 + \lambda_1 g_1 + \cdots + \lambda_m g_m$$

with $g_0 = f$, then

$$\lim_{q \to \infty} \frac{F(x_q) - F(x_0)}{t_q} = L(k) = \lambda_\rho k^\rho$$

whenever the relations

$$\lim_{q \to \infty} \frac{g(x_q) - g(x_0)}{t_q} = k$$

hold. It follows that $L(k)$ can be considered to be a directional derivative of F determined by k. With this interpretation Theorem 10.1 can be restated as follows.

THEOREM 10.2

Let $\mathcal{K}$ *be a derived set for* f, $g_1, \ldots, g_m$ *at* x_0. *Suppose that* x_0 *minimizes* f *on* X *subject to the constraints*

$$g_\alpha(x) \leqslant 0 \quad (\alpha = 1, \ldots, p), \qquad g_\beta(x) = 0 \quad (\beta = p+1, \ldots, m).$$

Then there exist multipliers $\lambda_0 \geqslant 0, \lambda_1, \ldots, \lambda_m$, *not all zero, and a function*

$$F = \lambda_0 f + \lambda_1 g_1 + \cdots + \lambda_m g_m$$

such that $\lambda_\alpha \geqslant 0$ $(1 \leqslant \alpha \leqslant p)$ *with* $\lambda_\alpha = 0$ *if* $g_\alpha(x_0) < 0$, *and such that the directional derivatives*

$$L(k) = \lambda_\rho k^\rho$$

of F *determined by* $\mathcal{K}$ *are nonnegative.*

We now turn to the case in which X is an open set in $\mathcal{E}^n$ and the functions $g_0 = f, g_1, \ldots, g_m$ are differentiable at x_0. In this event the set $\mathcal{K}$ of vectors k of the form

$$k = g'(x_0, h) \tag{10.18}$$

for h in $\mathcal{E}^n$ forms a linear subspace of $\mathcal{E}^{m+1}$ and is a derived cone for $g(x)$ at x_0. Using this derived set in Theorem 10.1 or 10.2, we see that upon setting $F = \lambda_\rho g_\rho$ we have

$$L(k) = \lambda_\rho k^\rho = \lambda_\rho g'_\rho(x_0, h) = F'(x_0, h) \geqslant 0$$

for all vectors h. It follows that the gradient $\nabla F(x_0) = 0$. This yields

THEOREM 10.3

Suppose that x_0 *is a point in an open set* X *in* $\mathcal{E}^n$ *which minimizes* f *on* X *subject to the constraints*

$$g_\alpha(x) \leqslant 0 \quad (\alpha = 1, \ldots, p), \qquad g_\beta(x) = 0 \quad (\beta = p+1, \ldots, m)$$

Suppose that f, $g_1, \ldots, g_m$ *are differentiable at* x_0. *Then there exist multipliers* $\lambda_0 \geqslant 0, \lambda_1, \ldots, \lambda_m$, *not all zero, such that*

$$\lambda_\alpha \geqslant 0 \qquad [1 \leqslant \alpha \leqslant p \text{ with } \lambda_\alpha = 0 \text{ if } g_\alpha(x_0) < 0]$$

and such that the gradient of

$$F = \lambda_0 f + \lambda_1 g_1 + \cdots + \lambda_m g_m$$

at x_0 *is zero.*

In the next theorem we assume that f and $g_1,\ldots,g_m$ are twice differentiable at x_0. We have the following extension of Theorem 10.3.

THEOREM 10.4†

Suppose that the hypotheses of Theorem 10.3 *are satisfied. Given a solution* $h \neq 0$ *of the equations*

$$g'_\alpha(x_0, h) = 0 \qquad [\alpha = 1,\ldots,m; g_\alpha(x_0) = 0], \qquad (10.19)$$

there exists a Lagrange function F *of the type described in Theorem* 10.3 *such that*

$$F''(x_0, h) \geqslant 0.$$

In the proof we can assume that all indices $\alpha = 1,\ldots,m$ are active at x_0. This follows because if α is inactive we can replace X by a neighborhood of x_0 on which $g_\alpha(x) < 0$. When this has been done, we can delete the inactive constraints.

Suppose now that all indices are active at x_0 and that $h_0 \neq 0$ satisfies relations (10.19). Let $g_0 = f$, and

$$k_0 = \tfrac{1}{2} g''(x_0, h_0). \qquad (10.20)$$

Let $\mathcal{K}$ be the class of all vectors k of form (10.18), where h is arbitrary. Let $\mathcal{K}_1$ be the set of vectors of the form $k + \alpha k_0$, where k is in $\mathcal{K}$ and $\alpha \geqslant 0$. We shall show that $\mathcal{K}_1$ is a derived set for $g(x)$ at x_0. To this end, let $k_1,\ldots,k_N$ be N vectors in $\mathcal{K}_1$. If they are in $\mathcal{K}$, they define a differential cone. If they are not in $\mathcal{K}$, then

$$k_j = \bar{k}_j + \alpha_j k_0 \qquad (\alpha_j \geqslant 0; j = 1,\ldots,N),$$

where $\bar{k}_j$ is in $\mathcal{K}$. It follows from this relation that it is sufficient to show that the vectors $k_0, \bar{k}_1,\ldots,\bar{k}_N$ define a differential cone. To this end choose

†Cf. M. J. Cox, "On Necessary Conditions for Relative Minima," *American Journal of Mathematics*, Vol. LXVI (1944), 170-198.

$\bar{h}_j$ such that

$$\bar{k}_j = g'\left(x_0, \bar{h}_j\right).$$

Let

$$x(\epsilon) = x_0 + h_0 \epsilon_0^{1/2} + \bar{h}_1 \epsilon_1 + \cdots + \bar{h}_N \epsilon_N. \qquad (10.21)$$

Since g is twice differentiable at x_0, we have

$$g(x) = g(x_0) + g'(x_0, x - x_0) + \tfrac{1}{2} g''(x_0, x - x_0) + r_2(x_0, x - x_0),$$

where

$$\lim_{x \to x_0} \frac{r_2(x_0, x - x_0)}{|x - x_0|^2} = 0. \qquad (10.22)$$

Consequently, by (10.19), (10.20), and (10.21),

$$g[x(\epsilon)] = g(x_0) + \bar{k}_j \epsilon_j + k_0 \epsilon_0 + r(\epsilon),$$

where

$$r(\epsilon) = \tfrac{1}{2} p(\epsilon) + r_2[x_0, x(\epsilon) - x_0],$$
$$p(\epsilon) = g''[x_0, x(\epsilon) - x_0] - g''(x_0, h_0)\epsilon_0.$$

When the fact that $g''(x_0, h)$ is quadratic in h is used, it follows from (10.21) that there is a constant C such that

$$|p(\epsilon)| \leqslant C\left[\sqrt{\epsilon_0} \, (\epsilon_1 + \cdots + \epsilon_N) + \epsilon_1^2 + \cdots + \epsilon_N^2 \right].$$

Setting $|\epsilon| = \epsilon_0 + \epsilon_1 + \cdots + \epsilon_N$, we see that

$$\lim_{\epsilon \to 0^+} \frac{p(\epsilon)}{|\epsilon|} = 0.$$

Similarly since the ratio

$$\frac{|x(\epsilon) - x_0|^2}{|\epsilon|}$$

is bounded, it follows that

$$\lim_{\epsilon \to 0^+} \frac{r_2[x_0, x(\epsilon) - x_0]}{|\epsilon|} = 0.$$

Consequently

$$\lim_{\epsilon \to 0} \frac{r(\epsilon)}{|\epsilon|} = 0.$$

The vectors $k_0, \bar{k}_1, \ldots, \bar{k}_N$ therefore define a derived cone for $g(x)$ at x_0. Hence the cone $\mathcal{K}_1$ is a derived cone for $g(x)$ at x_0. By Theorem 10.1 there exist multipliers $\lambda_0 \geq 0, \lambda_1, \ldots, \lambda_m$ such that (10.17) holds for $\mathcal{K} = \mathcal{K}_1$. As was seen in the proof of Theorem 10.3, the gradient of

$$F = \lambda_0 f + \lambda_1 g_1 + \cdots + \lambda_m g_m$$

at x_0 is zero. Moreover

$$L(k_0) = \tfrac{1}{2}\lambda_\rho g_\rho''(x_0, h_0) = \tfrac{1}{2}F''(x_0, h) \geq 0.$$

This proves Theorem 10.4.

EXAMPLE 10.1

In the xy-plane the origin affords a minimum to the function $f(x,y) = (x^2 + y^2)^{1/2} + 2y + 2y^3$ subject to the constraint $g(x,y) = y + y^3 - x^2 = 0$. Since f is not differentiable at the origin, the multiplier rule given in Theorem 10.2 is not applicable. However, Theorem 10.1 is applicable. To see this, let W be the set of points $w = (u, v)$ defined by the transformation

$$u = (x^2 + y^2)^{1/2} + 2y + 2y^3, \qquad v = y + y^3 - x^2.$$

The point $w_0 = (0, 0)$ is the image of the origin in xy-space. The nature of W can be seen more clearly if we transform to polar coordinates by setting $x = r\cos\theta, y = r\sin\theta$ $(0 \leq r < \infty, -\pi \leq \theta \leq \pi)$. Then

$$u = r + 2r\sin\theta + 2r^3\sin^3\theta, \qquad v = r\sin\theta + r^3\sin^3\theta - r^2\cos^2\theta.$$

The set W is represented schematically by the shaded portion shown in Figure 10.1. As before, we take the u-axis to be the vertical axis. The derivatives of u and v with respect to r at $r = 0$ give us the vector (h, k)

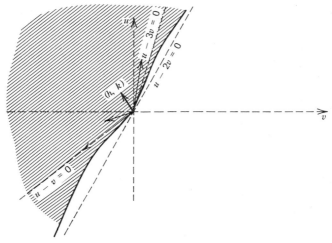

Figure 10.1

having

$$h = 1 + 2 \sin\theta, \qquad k = \sin\theta \qquad (-\pi \leqslant \theta \leqslant \pi).$$

The vectors (h, k) of this type generate the tangent cone of W at w_0. They form a derived set to which Theorem 10.1 is applicable. The multipliers $\lambda_0 \geqslant 0$, λ described in this theorem must be such that

$$\lambda_0 h + \lambda k = \lambda_0 + (2\lambda_0 + \lambda)\sin\theta \geqslant 0$$

for all values of θ. This implies that $\lambda_0 > 0$. We accordingly choose $\lambda_0 = 1$. Then λ must satisfy the inequality $-3 \leqslant \lambda \leqslant -1$. If $-3 < \lambda < -1$, the origin affords a local minimum to $F = f + \lambda g$. The ideal choice is $\lambda = -2$, for, in this case the origin affords a global minimum to F.

EXAMPLE 10.2

The results given in this section are particularly useful in the infinite dimensional case. As an illustration, consider the problem of minimizing

$$f(x) = \int_0^1 F[t, x(t)] \, dt$$

in the class of piecewise continuous real-valued functions $x : x(t)$ $(0 \leqslant t \leqslant 1)$

having $|x(t)| \leqslant 1$ and satisfying the constraint

$$g(x) = \int_0^1 G[t, x(t)] \, dt - c = 0.$$

We assume that F and G are continuous real-valued functions. Suppose that the function x_0: $x_0(t)$ $(0 \leqslant t \leqslant 1)$ is a minimizing function. As was seen in Example 9.2, for each number $\bar{x}$ having $|\bar{x}| \leqslant 1$ and for each t on $0 \leqslant t \leqslant 1$ the vector (h, k) defined by the formulas

$$h = F(t, \bar{x}) - F[t, x_0(t)], \qquad k = G(t, \bar{x}) - G[t, x_0(t)] \qquad (10.23)$$

is a directional derivative of $f(x)$, $g(x)$ at x_0. At a point of discontinuity of x_0, we interpret $x_0(t)$ to be either $x_0(t-0)$ or $x_0(t+0)$. It can be shown that the class $\mathcal{K}$ of all vectors (h, k) of this type is a derived set for f, g at x_0. Assuming that this is the case, Theorem 10.1 tells us that there are multipliers $\lambda_0 \geqslant 0$, λ such that $\lambda_0 h + \lambda k \geqslant 0$ for all (h, k) in $\mathcal{K}$. Using formulas (10.23) for h, k and setting $H = \lambda_0 F + \lambda G$, we find that

$$H(t, \bar{x}) - H[t, x_0(t)] = \lambda_0 \{ F(t, x) - F[t, x_0(t)] \}$$
$$+ \lambda \{ G(t, \bar{x}) - G[t, x_0(t)] \} \geqslant 0.$$

Consequently, for each t on $0 \leqslant t \leqslant 1$, the point $x_0(t)$ minimizes $H(t, \bar{x})$ subject to the constraint $|\bar{x}| \leqslant 1$. Under normal circumstances we have $\lambda_0 > 0$, so that we can choose $\lambda_0 = 1$.

As an illustration consider the problem

$$f(x) = \int_0^1 (2 - 5t) x(t) \, dt = \min,$$

$$g(x) = \int_0^1 4tx(t) \, dt - 1 = 0, \qquad |x(t)| \leqslant 1.$$

In this case for each t the function $H(t, \bar{x}) = [\lambda_0(2 - 5t) + 4\lambda t] \bar{x}$ subject to $|\bar{x}| \leqslant 1$ has a minimum at $x_0(t) = -\text{signum} \, [\lambda_0(2 - 5t) + 4\lambda t]$. If $x_0(t) = 1$ or $x_0(t) = -1$ on $0 \leqslant t \leqslant 1$, then $g(x_0) \neq 0$. Since $g(x_0) = 0, x_0(t)$ must change sign at some point $t = c$ on $0 < t < 1$. We have accordingly $x_0(t) = -1$ $(0 \leqslant t \leqslant c)$, $x_0(t) = 1$ $(c \leqslant t \leqslant 1)$. To determine c, we evaluate $g(x_0)$ and obtain $g(x_0) = -4c^2 + 1 = 0$. Hence $c = \frac{1}{2}$. Since $c = 2\lambda_0 / (5\lambda_0 - 4\lambda) = \frac{1}{2}$, we have $\lambda_0 = 1$, $\lambda = \frac{1}{4}$ as suitable choices of λ_0 and λ.

The proof that $\mathcal{K}$ is a derived set for f, g at x_0 can be found in Chapter

5, Section 6, in the author's book entitled *Calculus of Variations and Optimal Control Theory*, listed in the bibliography.

EXERCISES

1. Apply Theorem 10.1 or 10.2 to some of the problems described in the examples and exercises of Section 2.

2. In the xy-plane, the points $(0,0)$ and $(3,0)$ afford a global minimum to $f(x,y)=(x^2+y^2)$ $(6y+x^2-9)$ on the set S defined by the constraint $g(x,y)$ $=(x^2+y^2)$ $(3-x-y)=0$. Show that $(0,0)$ is an isolated point of S. Show that $(0,0)$ and $(3,0)$ afford a global minimum to $F=f+6g$. Under the transformation $u=f(x,y)$, $v=g(x,y)$ of $X=\mathcal{E}^2$ onto W, the points $(0,0)$ and $(3,0)$ are mapped into the same point, $w_0=(0,0)$. Consequently the derived sets of f,g at $(0,0)$ and at $(3,0)$ are the same. Find a suitable derived set. What happens to W and its derived sets at w_0 if we restrict X to be the unit disk $x^2+y^2\leqslant 1$?

3. Using the notations of Sections 9 and 10, suppose that all indices are active at x_0. Introduce the slack variables $y_0, y_1,\ldots,y_p$, and let Z be the set of points $z=(x,y_0,\ldots,y_p)$ having x in X. Set $G_0(z)=f(x)+y_0^2, G_\alpha(z)=g_\alpha(x)+y_\alpha^2$ (α $=1,\ldots,p$), $G_\beta(z)=g_\beta(x)$ ($\beta=p+1,\ldots,m$). Show that x_0 minimizes $f(x)$ on X subject to constraints (10.1) if and only if $z_0=(x_0,0)$ minimizes $G_0(z)$ on Z subject to the constraints $G_\gamma(z)=0$ ($\gamma=1,\ldots,m$). Let W^+ be the image of Z under the transformation $w=G(z)$. How is W^+ related to the set W defined by the transformation $w=g(x)$ of X, as in Section 9? How are the tangent cones of W and W^+ at $w_0=g(x_0)=G(z_0)$ related? Show that the cone $\mathcal{K}^+$ used in the proof of Theorem 10.1 is a derived cone of W^+ at w_0. Hence apply Theorem 10.1 to the transformed problem to obtain the original Theorem 10.1. Establish a similar result for the case in which inactive constraints occur.

11. FURTHER THEOREMS ON TANGENT SPACES AND DERIVED SETS

Let W be a set of points $w=(w^0,\ldots,w^m)$ in a Euclidean space $\mathcal{E}^{m+1}$. Let w_0 be a point in W. As before, we denote by $\mathcal{K}_0$ the tangent cone of W at w_0. As a first result we have

THEOREM 11.1

Suppose that W *is convex in a neighborhood of* w_0. *Given a vector* k *in* $\mathcal{K}_0$, *there is a continuous arc* w(t) $(0\leqslant t\leqslant\delta)$ *in* W *such that* w(0)=w_0 *and* $\dot{w}(0)=$k.

Since W is convex in a neighborhood of w_0, no generality is lost if we assume that W is convex. If $k=0$, the arc $w(t)=w_0+tk$ $(0\leqslant t\leqslant 1)$ has the desired property. Suppose therefore that $k\neq 0$. It is sufficient to discuss the case in which k is a unit vector. If k is an inner tangent of W at x_0, there is a line segment of the form $w(t)=w_0+tk$ $(0\leqslant t\leqslant\delta)$ in W. It remains to consider the case in which k is not an inner tangent. Select a sequence

$\{w_q\}$ of points in W converging to w_0 in the direction k. Since k is a unit vector, we have

$$t_q = |w_q - w_0| \to 0, \qquad k_q = \frac{w_q - w_0}{t_q} \to k \qquad \text{as } q \to \infty. \qquad (11.1)$$

We can suppose that $t_{q+1} < t_q$. Set

$$w_q(t) = w_q + \beta_q(t)(w_{q+1} - w_q), \qquad \beta_q = \frac{t_q - t}{t_q - t_{q+1}}. \qquad (11.2)$$

The curve $w(t)$ $(0 \leqslant t \leqslant t_1)$ having $w(0) = w_0$ and

$$w(t) = w_q(t) \qquad (t_{q+1} \leqslant t \leqslant t_q)$$

has the desired properties. Since W is convex, this curve is in W. The curve is obviously continuous. To see that $\dot{w}(0) = k$, set

$$k(t) = \frac{w(t) - w_0}{t} \qquad (0 < t \leqslant t_1).$$

On the interval $[t_{q+1}, t_q]$ we have, by (11.2),

$$k(t) = \frac{w_q(t) - w_0}{t} = a_q(t)k_q + b_q(t)k_{q+1},$$

where

$$a_q = \frac{t_q}{t}(1 - \beta_q) \geqslant 0, \qquad b_q = \frac{t_{q+1}}{t}\beta_q \geqslant 0, \qquad a_q + b_q = 1.$$

Consequently

$$k(t) - k = a_q(t)(k_q - k) + b_q(t)(k_{q+1} - k).$$

Since $k_q \to k$ as $q \to \infty$, it follows that $k(t) \to k$ as $t \to 0$, as was to be proved.

The curve $w(t)$ $(0 \leqslant t \leqslant t_1)$ normally has a discontinuous derivative when $t = t_q$. It is of interest to observe that we can modify our construction so as to obtain a curve of class C' on $0 \leqslant t \leqslant t_1$ and of class $C^{(\infty)}$ on $0 < t \leqslant t_1$. This can be done by replacing the subarc

$$w(t) \qquad \left(\bar{t}_q = \frac{t_q + t_{q+1}}{2} \leqslant t \leqslant \bar{t}_{q-1} = \frac{t_{q-1} + t_q}{2}\right)$$

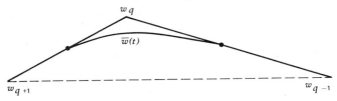

Figure 11.1

by an arc

$$\overline{w}(t) \qquad \left(\overline{t}_q \leqslant t \leqslant \overline{t}_{q-1} \right)$$

of class $C^{(\infty)}$ lying in the triangle having the points w_{q+1}, w_q, w_{q-1} as its vertices as indicated in Figure 11.1. This arc is to be chosen so that $w(t) = \overline{w}(t)$ on the intervals $\overline{t}_q \leqslant t \leqslant \overline{t}_q + \delta$ and $\overline{t}_{q-1} - \delta \leqslant t \leqslant \overline{t}_{q-1}$ for a small constant δ. The details of this construction are left to the reader.

THEOREM 11.2

If W *is convex in a neighborhood of* w_0, *the tangent space* $\mathcal{K}_0$ *of* W *at* w_0 *is a derived cone for* W *at* w_0.

Again we can assume that W is convex. Let $k_1, \ldots, k_N$ be vectors in $\mathcal{K}_0$. Select continuous arcs

$$w_j(t) = w_0 + k_j t + r_j(t) \qquad (0 \leqslant t \leqslant N\delta)$$

in W such that

$$\lim_{t \to 0^+} \frac{r_j(t)}{t} = 0.$$

Since W is convex, it contains the surface

$$w(\epsilon) = \frac{1}{N} \sum_{j=1}^{n} w_j(N\epsilon_j) = w_0 + k_j \epsilon_j + r(\epsilon) \qquad (0 \leqslant \epsilon_j \leqslant \delta),$$

where

$$r(\epsilon) = \sum_{j=1}^{n} \frac{1}{N} r_j(N\epsilon_j).$$

Since

$$\lim_{\epsilon \to 0} \frac{r(\epsilon)}{|\epsilon|} = \sum_{j=1}^{n} \lim_{\epsilon \to 0} \frac{r_j(N\epsilon_j)}{N|\epsilon|} = 0,$$

it follows that $k_1, \ldots, k_N$ defines a differential cone for W at w_0. It then follows that $\mathcal{K}_0$ is a derived set. Since it is a convex cone, it is a derived cone, as was to be proved.

THEOREM 11.3

Let $\mathcal{K}$ be a derived cone for W *at* w_0. *Suppose that $\mathcal{K}$ has an interior vector* k^*. *Then there exist positive constants ϵ and δ such that the line segment* $w_0 + tk$ $(0 \leqslant t \leqslant \delta)$ *is in* W *for every vector* k *having* $|k - k^*| \leqslant \epsilon$.

Let $h_1, \ldots, h_m$ be mutually orthogonal unit vectors orthogonal to k^*. Since k^* is an interior point of $\mathcal{K}$, we can select a constant $\alpha > 0$ such that the vectors

$$k_0 = \frac{1}{m+1} k^* - \alpha(h_1 + \cdots + h_m), \qquad k_j = \frac{1}{m+1} k^* + \alpha h_j$$

are in $\mathcal{K}$. Inasmuch as

$$k^* = k_0 + \cdots + k_m,$$

the vector k^* is interior to the subcone $\mathcal{K}_1$ of $\mathcal{K}$ generated by $k_0, k_1, \ldots, k_m$. Since $\mathcal{K}$ is a derived set, there is a continuous surface

$$w(\epsilon_0, \epsilon_1, \ldots, \epsilon_m) \qquad (0 \leqslant \epsilon_j \leqslant \delta; j = 0, 1, \ldots, m)$$

of the form

$$w(\epsilon) = w_0 + k_j \epsilon_j + r(\epsilon),$$

where

$$\lim_{\epsilon \to 0} \frac{r(\epsilon)}{|\epsilon|} = 0.$$

By an application of Theorem 12.2 in the next section with $\epsilon_0, \ldots, \epsilon_m$ playing the role of $x_1, \ldots, x_m$ and $0, 1, \ldots, m$ playing the role of $1, \ldots, m$, it is seen that there exist constants ϵ and δ such that the line segment $w_0 + tk$ $(0 \leqslant t \leqslant \delta)$ is in W whenever $|k - k^*| \leqslant \epsilon$, as was to be proved.

THEOREM 11.4

A point w_0 *in* W *is an interior point of* W *if and only if* $\mathcal{E}^{m+1}$ *is a derived set for* W *at* w_0.

This result is a consequence of Theorem 11.3. Its proof will be left as an exercise.

EXERCISES

1. Prove Theorem 11.4.
2. Carry out the details of the application of Theorem 12.2 to the proof of Theorem 11.3.
3. Construct a set W possessing a boundary point w_0 whose tangent space is the space $\mathcal{E}^{m+1}$. In this event $\mathcal{E}^{m+1}$ is not a derived cone for W at w_0.

12. AUXILIARY THEOREMS

In Chapters 3 and 4 it was affirmed that a completely normal point x_0 of the set S defined by the constraints

$$g_\rho(x) \leqslant 0 \quad (\rho = 1, \dots, p), \qquad g_\sigma(x) = 0 \quad (\sigma = p+1, \dots, m \leqslant n)$$

is a regular point of S if the functions $g_1, \dots, g_m$ are differentiable at x_0. This result is a consequence of Theorem 5.3 of Chapter 3. However, the proof of Theorem 5.3 was postponed, and it is our purpose to supply it here. We do so by establishing a slightly more general theorem which will enable us to complete the proof of Theorem 11.3. Suppose that we have a set of continuous functions $g_1, \dots, g_m$ on a convex set S_0 in $\mathcal{E}^n$. Suppose that the functions $g_\alpha(x)$ have a differential $g'_\alpha(x_0, h)$ at a point x_0 in S. Suppose further that there exist vectors $h_1, \dots, h_m$ such that

$$|g'_\alpha(x_0, h_\beta)| \neq 0 \qquad (\alpha, \beta = 1, \dots, m). \tag{12.1}$$

This is the condition of linear independence of the linear forms $g'_\alpha(x_0, h)$ in h. Suppose further that there is a continuous vector $h(b)$ of $b = (b_1, \dots, b_q)$ on $|b| \leqslant \epsilon$ such that

$$x(z, t, b) = x_0 + th_\beta z^\beta + th(b) \tag{12.2}$$

is in S_0 whenever

$$|z| \leqslant r, \qquad 0 \leqslant t \leqslant \delta, \qquad |b| \leqslant \epsilon. \tag{12.3}$$

We have the following result.

THEOREM 12.1

Under the hypotheses given above there exists for each b *on the set* $|b| \leqslant \epsilon$ *a curve*

$$x(t, b) \qquad (0 \leqslant t \leqslant \delta')$$

in S_0 *such that*

$$g_\alpha[x(t,b)] = g_\alpha(x_0) + t g'_\alpha[x_0, h(b)] \qquad (\alpha = 1, \ldots, m), \tag{12.4}$$

$$\lim_{t=0^+} x(t,b) = x(0,b) = x_0 \text{ uniformly on } |b| \leqslant \epsilon, \tag{12.5}$$

$$\dot{x}(0,b) = \lim_{t \to 0^+} \frac{x(t,b) - x_0}{t} = h(b) \text{ uniformly on } |b| \leqslant \epsilon. \tag{12.6}$$

To prove this result, set

$$k^\alpha(b) = g'_\alpha[x_0, h(b)] \qquad (\alpha = 1, \ldots, m).$$

For (z, t, b) on domain (12.3) set

$$G_\alpha(z,t,b) = \frac{1}{t} \{ g_\alpha[x(z,t,b)] - g_\alpha(x_0) \} - k^\alpha(b) \qquad (0 < t \leqslant \delta),$$

$$G_\alpha(z,0,b) = g'_\alpha(x_0, h_\beta) z^\beta \tag{12.7}$$

where $x(z,t,b)$ is given by (12.2). The function $G_\alpha(x,t,b)$ is continuous at $t = 0$ in view of the fact that $g_\alpha(x)$ has a differential $g'_\alpha(x_0, h)$ at x_0. The functions $G_\alpha(z,t,b)$ satisfy the hypotheses of Theorem 8.3 with z playing the role of x. According to Theorem 8.3, the equations

$$G_\alpha(z,t,b) = 0 \qquad (\alpha = 1, \ldots, m) \tag{12.8}$$

have solutions

$$z(t,b) \qquad (0 \leqslant t \leqslant \delta'; |b| \leqslant \epsilon)$$

such that

$$\lim_{t \to 0} z(t,b) = z(0,b) = 0 \qquad \text{uniformly on } |b| \leqslant \epsilon. \tag{12.9}$$

Setting

$$x(t,b) = x_0 + t h_\beta z^\beta(t,b) + t h(b), \tag{12.10}$$

we see that $\lim_{t \to 0^+} x(t,b) = x(0,b) = x_0$ uniformly on $|b| \leqslant \epsilon$. Setting $z = z(t,b)$ in (12.8), we see by (12.7) that

$$g_\alpha[x(t,b)] = g_\alpha(x_0) + t k^\alpha(b),$$

as stated in (12.4). Finally, when (12.10) is written in the form

$$\frac{x(t,b) - x_0}{t} = h_\beta z^\beta(t,b) + h(b),$$

it follows from (12.9) that the final relation (12.6) in Theorem 12.1 holds. This proves Theorem 12.1.

Theorem 5.3 in Chapter 3 is the special case of Theorem 12.1 in which h is independent of b.

In the next theorem we consider the case in which S_0 is the n-cube

$$0 \leqslant x^i \leqslant \epsilon_0 \qquad (i = 1, \ldots, n)$$

in $\mathcal{E}^n$. Let

$$w^\alpha = g_\alpha(x) \qquad (\alpha = 1, \ldots, m) \tag{12.11}$$

be a continuous map of S_0 onto a set W of points $w = (w^1, \ldots, w^m)$ in $\mathcal{E}^m$. The point $x_0 = 0$ is mapped into the point $w_0 = g(0)$. We assume that the functions $g_\alpha(x)$ have a differential

$$g'_\alpha(0,h) = k_j^\alpha h^j$$

at $x_0 = 0$ whose Jacobian matrix

$$(k_j^\alpha) \qquad (\alpha = 1, \ldots, m; j = 1, \ldots, n) \tag{12.12}$$

has rank m. The vectors $k_j = (k_j^1, \ldots, k_j^m)$ $(j = 1, \ldots, n)$ generate a cone $\mathcal{K}$ in $\mathcal{E}^m$. Since matrix (12.12) has rank m, this cone possesses interior points. In particular, every vector k of the form $k = k_j h^j$ with $h^j > 0$ $(j = 1, \ldots, n)$ is interior to $\mathcal{K}$. Conversely every vector k interior to $\mathcal{K}$ can be represented in this manner, for let k_0 be a vector interior to $\mathcal{K}$ and select $h_0{}^j \geqslant 0$ so that

$$k_0 = k_j h_0{}^j.$$

For $\epsilon \geqslant 0$ sufficiently small, the vector $\bar{k} = k_0 - \epsilon(k_1 + \cdots + k_n)$ is interior to $\mathcal{K}$. Choose $\bar{h}^j \geqslant 0$ so that $\bar{k} = k_j \bar{h}^j$. Then

$$k_0 = \tfrac{1}{2}\big[k_0 + \bar{k} + \epsilon(k_1 + \cdots k_n) \big] = k_j h^j,$$

where

$$h^j = \tfrac{1}{2}\big(h_0{}^j + \bar{h}^j + \epsilon \big) > 0 \qquad (j = 1, \ldots, n).$$

With these preliminaries we can prove

THEOREM 12.2

Let k_0 be a vector interior to the cone $\mathcal{K}$ generated by the vectors $k_1, \ldots, k_n$ described above. There exist positive constants ϵ and δ such that the truncated cone

$$w(t, b) = w_0 + t\big(k_0 + k_j b^j \big) \qquad (0 \leqslant t \leqslant \delta; |b| \leqslant \epsilon)$$

at $w_0 = g(0)$ is in the image W of the n-cube S_0 under mapping (12.1). The point $w(t, b)$ is interior to W if $0 < t < \delta$ and $|b| < \epsilon$.

To establish this result, recall that the interior vector k_0 of $\mathcal{K}$ is representable in the form

$$k_0 = k_j h_0{}^j$$

where $h_0{}^j > 0$ $(j = 1, \ldots, n)$. Choose $\epsilon > 0$ such that $\epsilon < h_0{}^j$. Then the vector $h(b)$ defined by the formula

$$h^j(b) = h_0{}^j + b^j \qquad (|b| \leqslant \epsilon)$$

has positive components. Since the matrix $(k_j{}^\alpha)$ has rank m, we can suppose that the submatrix $(k_\beta{}^\alpha)$ $(\alpha, \beta = 1, \ldots, m)$ is nonsingular. If c is a small positive constant, the vectors $h_1, \ldots, h_m$ defined by the relations

$$h_\beta{}^i = \delta_\beta{}^i + c \qquad \big(\delta_i{}^i = 1, \delta_\beta{}^i = 0; i \neq \beta \big)$$

will have positive components and will be such that

$$|g'_\alpha(0,h_\beta)| = |k_j{}^\alpha h_\beta{}^j| \neq 0.$$

Choose $r > 0$ so small that the vector

$$h_\beta z^\beta + h(b) \qquad (|z| \leqslant r, |b| \leqslant \epsilon)$$

has positive components, Next select $\delta > 0$ so that the point

$$x(z,t,b) = t\left[h_\beta z^\beta + h(b)\right]$$

is in S_0 whenever

$$|z| \leqslant r, \qquad 0 \leqslant t \leqslant \delta, \qquad |b| \leqslant \epsilon.$$

By virtue of Theorem 12.1 there is, for each b having $|b| \leqslant \epsilon$, a curve

$$x(t,b) \qquad (0 \leqslant t \leqslant \delta')$$

such that the corresponding curve

$$w^\alpha(t,b) = g_\alpha[x(t,b)] = w_0{}^\alpha + t\left(k_0 + k_j b^j\right)$$

is in W. This proves the first conclusion in Theorem 12.2. The second conclusion follows from the first, as is readily verified.

APPENDIX

1. INTRODUCTION

The appendix is devoted to a summary of the basic analytic, geometric, and topologic concepts that are used throughout this book. We begin with the study of Euclidean n-space and some elementary properties of vector spaces. We review the concepts of inner product and norms. We next recall the basic theorems on convergent sequences and related set theory. After introducing the concept of global and local minima, we recall the basic theorems relative to maxima and minima of functions of one variable. These theorems are the basis of analogous theorems for minimizing functions of n variables and, in fact, for minimizing functions of infinitely many variables. The appendix concludes with the concept of the class of a function and with a derivation of Taylor's theorem. The concepts of the gradient of a function and of directional derivatives are basic throughout this book.

2. EUCLIDEAN n-SPACE

Throughout this book we shall be concerned mainly with the study of real-valued functions on a set S in a Euclidean space $\mathcal{E}^n$. By a Euclidean space $\mathcal{E}^n$ is meant a space whose points are representable by n-tuples $x=(x^1,\ldots,x^n)$, $y=(y^1,\ldots,y^n),\ldots$ such that the distance between two points x and y is given by the formula

$$|x-y| = \left[\sum_{i=1}^{n} (x^i - y^i)^2 \right]^{1/2}. \tag{2.1}$$

It should be noted that under normal circumstances superscripts will be used to designate components. Thus x^i is the ith component or coordinate of x. Subscripts will serve to distinguish points. For example, x_1 is the point $(x_1{}^1,\ldots,x_1{}^n)$, and x_2 is the point $(x_2{}^1,\ldots,x_2{}^n)$. However, we shall have occasion to denote an n-tuple of real numbers $(b_1,\ldots,b_n)$ by $b=(b_1,\ldots,b_n)$. These variations in notations will be made clear in context. Also, observe that "points" are represented by "vectors."

The letters $a,b,c,\ldots$ usually denote real numbers. However, at times they may be used to designate points or vectors. Similarly the Greek letters $\alpha,\beta,\gamma,\ldots$ normally denote numbers but may denote vectors when this is expressly stated or implied.

One of the important features of Euclidean n-space is that it is an n-dimensional linear space. A *linear space* $\mathcal{E}$ is a set of elements $x,y,z,\ldots$, called *vectors*, for which the operations of addition of vectors and multiplication of vectors by *scalars* $a,b,c,\ldots$ are defined and are subject to the usual rules of vector analysis. The basic rules from which all others can be derived are given in the following set.

1. $x+y=y+x$, $x+(y+z)=(x+y)+z$.
2. There is a vector 0 such that $x+0=x$ for all x. For each x there is an element $(-x)$ such that $x+(-x)=0$.
3. $ax=xa$, $a(bx)=abx$, $(a+b)x=ax+bx$, $a(x+y)=ax+ay$, $1\cdot x=x$, $0\cdot x=0$, where 0 in the left member denotes the scalar zero.

We are interested only in the case in which the scalars are real numbers unless the contrary is expressly stated.

A *subspace* $\mathcal{B}$ (also: linear manifold) of $\mathcal{E}$ is a subset of $\mathcal{E}$ which itself constitutes a linear space with the same operations as those defined in $\mathcal{E}$, and with the same scalar field. As can be verified from the basic properties of a linear space, a subset $\mathcal{B}$ of $\mathcal{E}$ is a subspace of $\mathcal{E}$ if and only if it has the following two properties: (*a*) the sum $x+y$ of each pair of vectors in $\mathcal{B}$ is in $\mathcal{B}$, and (*b*) the product bx of a vector x in $\mathcal{B}$ by a scalar b is in $\mathcal{B}$.

A set of m vectors $x_1,\ldots,x_m$ in $\mathcal{E}$ is said to be a set of *linearly independent* vectors if a relation of the form

$$a_1 x_1 + \cdots + a_m x_m = 0$$

holds only when the scalars $a_1,\ldots,a_m$ are all zero. Vectors are *linearly dependent* if they are not linearly independent. If there are n vectors $x_1,\ldots,x_n$ forming a maximal set of linearly independent vectors in $\mathcal{E}$, then $\mathcal{E}$ is said to be *n-dimensional*. In this event every vector x in $\mathcal{E}$ is expressible uniquely in the form

$$x = a_1 x_1 + \cdots + a_n x_n,$$

and the vectors $x_1, \ldots, x_n$ are said to form a *basis* for $\mathcal{E}$. The dimension of a subspace $\mathcal{B}$ of $\mathcal{E}$ is defined similarly.

If $x_1, \ldots, x_m$ are a set of vectors chosen from $\mathcal{E}$, the set $\mathcal{B}$ consisting of all possible linear combinations

$$x = a_1 x_1 + \cdots + a_m x_m$$

is easily shown to be a linear subspace of $\mathcal{E}$. The set $\mathcal{B}$ is called the subspace *generated* or *spanned* by $x_1, \ldots, x_m$. The dimension of $\mathcal{B}$ is at most m and is equal to m if and only if $x_1, \ldots, x_m$ are linearly independent. More generally, if S is a nonempty subset of $\mathcal{E}$, the *subspace* $\mathcal{C}$ *generated* by S is the set of all linear combinations $x = a_1 x_1 + \cdots + a_q x_q$ of vectors $x_1, \ldots, x_q$ in S.

Two vectors x and y are *collinear* if one is a multiple of the other, that is, if they are linearly dependent. The zero vector is collinear with every vector y.

Euclidean space $\mathcal{E}^n$ is an example of *n*-dimensional linear space. *Vector addition* and *scalar multiplication* are defined by the formulas

$$x + y = (x^1 + y^1, \ldots, x^n + y^n), \qquad ax = (ax^1, \ldots, ax^n).$$

The vector $0 = (0, \ldots, 0)$ is the *null* or *zero vector*. The vectors

$$e_1 = (1, 0, \ldots, 0), \qquad e_2 = (0, 1, 0, \ldots, 0), \qquad \ldots, \qquad e_n = (0, 0, \ldots, 0, 1)$$

are linearly independent and form a basis for $\mathcal{E}^n$. A vector $x = (x^1, \ldots, x^n)$ in $\mathcal{E}^n$ is given by the formula

$$x = x^1 e_1 + x^2 e_2 + \cdots + x^n e_n.$$

When matrix notations are used, a vector x is normally considered to be a column vector, that is,

$$x = \begin{bmatrix} x^1 \\ \vdots \\ x^n \end{bmatrix}.$$

This is done in order to be consistent with standard matrix operations. The transpose (a row vector) of x is denoted by x^*, that is, $x^* = (x^1, \ldots, x^n)$. Using this convention, we can consider a set of vectors $x_1, \ldots, x_r$ to be the column vectors of a $(n \times r)$-dimensional matrix X. Then

$$X = \left(x_j^i \right) \qquad (i = 1, \ldots, n; j = 1, \ldots, r),$$

where i is the row index and j is the column index. The vectors $x_1,\dots,x_r$ are linearly independent if and only if X has rank r. When matrix notations are not used, we usually express x as a row vector for typographical reasons.

The *inner product* $\langle x,y\rangle$ of two vectors x and y in $\mathscr{E}^n$ is defined by the formula

$$\langle x,y\rangle = x^1 y^1 + \cdots + x^n y^n = \sum_{i=1}^n x^i y^i = x*y. \tag{2.2}$$

The basic properties of the inner product are as follows:

1. $\langle x,x\rangle \geqslant 0$ for every x; $\langle x,x\rangle = 0$ if and only if $x = 0$ (the zero vector).
2. $\langle x,y\rangle = \langle y,x\rangle$.
3. $\langle ax + by, z\rangle = a\langle x,z\rangle + b\langle z,y\rangle$; $\langle z, ax + by\rangle = a\langle z,x\rangle + b\langle z,y\rangle$.

The first two properties follow at once from definition (2.2) and the properties of the real numbers. The third property is established by the use of property 2 and the computations

$$\langle ax + by, z\rangle = \sum (ax^i + by^i) z^i = \sum ax^i z^i + \sum by^i z^i$$

$$= a\langle x,z\rangle + b\langle y,z\rangle$$

$$= a\langle z,x\rangle + b\langle z,y\rangle$$

$$= \langle z, ax + by\rangle.$$

The Euclidean *norm*, or *length*, of a vector x is defined by

$$|x| = \langle x,x\rangle^{1/2} = \left[(x^1)^2 + \cdots + (x^n)^2 \right]^{1/2}. \tag{2.3}$$

From (2.3) and the properties of the inner product there follow these basic properties:

1. $|x| \geqslant 0$ for every x; $|x| = 0$ if and only if $x = 0$.
2. $|ax| = |a||x|$ for each scalar a.
3. $|x + y| \leqslant |x| + |y|$ (triangle inequality).

First, if a,b are scalars and x,y are vectors, we have

$$|ax + by|^2 = \langle ax + by, ax + by\rangle = a\langle x, ax + by\rangle + b\langle y, ax + by\rangle$$

$$= a\left[a\langle x,x\rangle + b\langle x,y\rangle \right] + b\left[a\langle y,x\rangle + b\langle y,y\rangle \right]$$

$$= a^2 |x|^2 + 2ab\langle x,y\rangle + b^2 |y|^2.$$

Here properties 2 and 3 of the inner product play an important role. Hence

$$|ax + by|^2 = a^2|x|^2 + 2ab\langle x,y \rangle + b^2|y|^2. \tag{2.4}$$

Next, an important inequality, called the *Cauchy-Schwartz inequality*, states that

$|\langle x,y \rangle| \leqslant |x||y|$, the equality holding if and only if x, y are collinear.   (2.5)

It is evident that (2.5) holds if $y = 0$. If $y \neq 0$, we set

$$a = |y|, \qquad b = -\frac{\langle x,y \rangle}{|y|}$$

in (2.4) and find that

$$|ax + by|^2 = |y|^2|x|^2 - 2|y|\frac{\langle x,y \rangle^2}{|y|} + \frac{\langle x,y \rangle^2}{|y|^2}|y|^2$$

$$= |x|^2|y|^2 - |\langle x,y \rangle|^2.$$

Since $|ax + by| > 0$ unless $ax + by = 0$, this yields (2.5) for the case $y \neq 0$.

The triangle property of the norm is obtained if we select $a = 1$ and $b = 1$ in (2.4), for in that case, by virtue of (2.5),

$$|x + y|^2 = |x|^2 + 2\langle x,y \rangle + |y|^2$$

$$= (|x| + |y|)^2 - 2(|x||y| - \langle x,y \rangle)$$

$$\leqslant (|x| + |y|)^2.$$

If $|x| = 1$, then x is called a *unit vector*. Whenever $x \neq 0$, the vector $y = x/|x|$ is a unit vector in the direction of x.

The *distance* between points x,y in $\mathcal{E}^n$ is the length $|x - y|$ of the vector difference $x - y$. The following basic properties of distance are evident:

1. $|x - y| \geqslant 0$; $|x - y| = 0$ if and only if $x = y$.
2. $|y - x| = |x - y|$.
3. $|x - z| \leqslant |x - y| + |y - z|$.

Inequality (2.5) enables us to define the angle θ between two nonnull vectors x and y by the formula

$$\cos\theta = \frac{\langle x,y \rangle}{|x||y|}.$$

We may restrict θ to lie in the interval $0 \leqslant \theta \leqslant \pi$.

Two vectors x and y are *orthogonal* (perpendicular) if $\langle x,y \rangle = 0$. The zero vector is orthogonal to every vector. A vector z is said to be *orthogonal to a subset* $\mathcal{B}$ *of* $\mathcal{E}^n$ if it is orthogonal to each vector in $\mathcal{B}$. If z is orthogonal to the generators $y_1, \ldots, y_m$ of a subspace $\mathcal{B}$, then

$$\langle z, b_1 y_1 + \cdots + b_m y_m \rangle = b_1 \langle z, y_1 \rangle + \cdots + b_m \langle z, y_m \rangle = 0$$

for all choices of the scalars $b_1, \ldots, b_m$. Consequently z is orthogonal to a subspace $\mathcal{B}$. Observe further that, if z_1 and z_2 are orthogonal to $\mathcal{B}$, then so is $z_1 + z_2$, as well as cz_1 for every choice of the scalar c. The class $\mathcal{C}$ of all vectors which are orthogonal to $\mathcal{B}$ is a subspace called the *orthogonal complement of* $\mathcal{B}$. It is frequently denoted by $\mathcal{B}^{\perp}$.

A set of vectors $y_1, \ldots, y_m$ is said to be *orthonormal* if

$$\langle y_i, y_j \rangle = \delta_{ij} \qquad (i,j = 1, \ldots, m), \tag{2.6}$$

where $\delta_{ii} = 1$, $\delta_{ij} = 0$ $(i \neq j)$. It is readily verified that orthonormal vectors are linearly independent. A basis $y_1, \ldots, y_m$ of a subspace $\mathcal{B}$ that is orthonormal is called an *orthonormal basis for* $\mathcal{B}$. We shall see presently that every subspace has an orthonormal basis. The coordinate vectors $e_1, \ldots, e_m$ described above form an orthonormal basis for $\mathcal{E}^n$.

Let $y_1, \ldots, y_m$ be a set of orthonormal vectors, and let $\mathcal{B}$ be the subspace generated by them. Given any vector x, set

$$b_i = \langle y_i, x \rangle \qquad (i = 1, \ldots, m).$$

Let y and z be the vectors defined by the formulas

$$y = b_1 y_1 + \cdots + b_m y_m, \qquad z = x - y.$$

The vector y is in $\mathcal{B}$ and has the property that

$$\langle y_i, y \rangle = b_1 \langle y_i, y_1 \rangle + \cdots + b_m \langle y_i, y_m \rangle = b_i = \langle y_i, x \rangle$$

by virtue of (2.6). From the relations

$$\langle y_i, z \rangle = \langle y_i, x - y \rangle = \langle y_i, x \rangle - \langle y_i, y \rangle = 0$$

it is seen that z is orthogonal to each of the vectors $y_1,\dots,y_m$ and hence to $\mathcal{B}$ itself. A vector x in $\mathcal{E}^n$ is therefore expressible in the form $x = y + z$, where y is in $\mathcal{B}$ and z is orthogonal to $\mathcal{B}$. Moreover this representation is unique, for if $x = y + z = \bar{y} + \bar{z}$, where y, $\bar{y}$ are in $\mathcal{B}$ and $z, \bar{z}$, the vector $\bar{z} - z = y - \bar{y}$ would be in $\mathcal{B}$ and in $\mathcal{B}^\perp$ and hence would be orthogonal to itself. This is possible only if $\bar{z} - z = y - \bar{y} = 0$, as was to be proved. The vector y is called the *orthogonal projection* of x on $\mathcal{B}$.

The result just described can be used to prove that every subspace $\mathcal{B}$ has an orthonormal basis. We sketch a proof as follows. It is clearly true if the dimension m of $\mathcal{B}$ is one. Suppose that it is true for subspaces of dimension $< m$, where $1 < m \leqslant n$. Let $x_1,\dots,x_m$ be a basis for an m-dimensional subspace $\mathcal{B}$. The vectors $x_1,\dots,x_{m-1}$ generate an $(m-1)$-dimensional space and hence can be replaced by an orthonormal set $y_1,\dots,y_{m-1}$. Moreover x_m is expressible as the sum of a linear combination of $y_1,\dots,y_{m-1}$ and a vector $z \neq 0$ orthogonal to $y_1,\dots,y_{m-1}$. Setting $y_m = z/|z|$, we obtain an orthonormal basis $y_1,\dots,y_m$ for $\mathcal{B}$, as is readily verified.

As a further consequence of these results we can show that, if $\mathcal{B}$ is a linear subspace, $(\mathcal{B}^\perp)^\perp = \mathcal{B}$. Clearly $(\mathcal{B}^\perp)^\perp \supset \mathcal{B}$. Recall that a vector x is expressible as the sum $x = y + z$ of a vector y in $\mathcal{B}$ and z in $\mathcal{B}^\perp$. If x is in $(\mathcal{B}^\perp)^\perp$, then z is orthogonal to x as well as to y and hence is orthogonal to itself. This is possible only if $z = 0$ or, equivalently, if $x = y$. Consequently $(\mathcal{B}^\perp)^\perp = \mathcal{B}$, as was to be proved.

In the two-dimensional case we normally use the notation (x,y) in place of (x^1, x^2) to designate points or vectors. In this case we refer to our space as *xy-space*. Other symbols such as (x_1, y_1), (x_2, y_2), (a,b), $(h,k),\dots$ are used to denote points or vectors in xy-space. The quantity $xh + yk$ is the inner product of (x,y) and (h,k). The term *uv-space* signifies that points are usually designated as (u,v) in place of (x,y).

Similarly three-dimensional space is frequently called *xyz-space* or *uvw-space*. Points and vectors are then represented by triples, such as (x,y,z), (x_0, y_0, z_0), (a,b,c), $(u,v,w),\dots$. The sum $a\alpha + b\beta + c\gamma$ is the inner product of the vectors (a,b,c) and (α, β, γ). This inner product can be used to find the equation of a plane through a point with a given normal. For example, if $(a,b,c) \neq (0,0,0)$, the equation

$$a(x - x_0) + b(y - y_0) + c(z - z_0) = 0 \qquad (2.7)$$

represents a plane through the point (x_0, y_0, z_0) having (a,b,c) as its normal. The general equation of the plane is given by

$$ax + by + cz + d = 0.$$

Similarly, in the n-dimensional case the set of points $x = (x^1, \ldots, x^n)$ satisfying a linear equation of the form

$$b_1 x^1 + b_2 x^2 + \cdots + b_n x^n = c$$

with $(b_1, \ldots, b_n) \neq (0, \ldots, 0)$ defines a *hyperplane* or an $(n-1)$-*plane*. If we set $b = (b_1, \ldots, b_n)$, then, in terms of the inner product, the equation of an $(n-1)$-plane π_{n-1} takes the form

$$\langle b, x \rangle = c.$$

If x_0 is a point on π_{n-1}, then $\langle b, x_0 \rangle = c$ and the equation of π_{n-1} can be put into the alternative form

$$\langle b, x - x_0 \rangle = 0.$$

The vector b is a normal to the $(n-1)$-plane π_{n-1}.

EXERCISES

1. In general, two vectors x and y determine a parallelogram with $x+y$ and $x-y$ as diagonals, as shown in the following diagram:

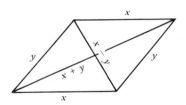

    Establish the parallelogram law

    $$|x+y|^2 + |x-y|^2 = 2|x|^2 + 2|y|^2,$$

    which states that the sum of the squares of the diagonals is equal to the sum of the squares of the sides. Show that the parallelogram is a rectangle if and only if $|x+y| = |x-y|$.

2. Show that if x and y are nonnull vectors the vectors $x+y$ and $x-y$ are orthogonal if and only if $|x| = |y|$.

3. Show that the identity

$$|x-y|^2=|x|^2+|y|^2-2\langle x,y\rangle$$

is the law of cosines, provided that $x\neq0$ and $y\neq0$.

4. Establish the relation

$$\begin{vmatrix}\langle x,x\rangle & \langle x,y\rangle \\ \langle y,x\rangle & \langle y,y\rangle\end{vmatrix}=|x|^2|y|^2\sin^2\theta,$$

where θ is the angle between x and y. This determinant is called the *Grammian of* x *and* y. Its value is the square of the area of the parallelogram having x and y as sides. For the case $n=4$, find the area of the parallelogram having $x=(1,1,1,1)$ and $y=(1,-1,1,1)$ as its sides.

5. Show that a set of vectors $x_1,\ldots,x_r$ are linearly independent if and only if the determinant

$$|\langle x_i,x_j\rangle| \qquad (i,j=1,\ldots,r)$$

is not zero. This determinant is called the *Grammian of* $x_1,\ldots,x_r$. Its value is the square of the volume of the r-dimensional parallelopiped determined by $x_1,\ldots,x_r$. Considering $x_1,\ldots,x_r$ to be the column vectors of a matrix X, show that the Grammian of $x_1,\ldots,x_r$ is the determinant of the matrix X^*X, where X^* is the transpose of X. Note that $x_1^*,\ldots,x_r^*$ are the row vectors of X^* and that $x_i^*x_j=\langle x_i,x_j\rangle$. What are the value of the Grammian, and the form of X^*X, if $x_1,\ldots,x_r$ are orthonormal?

6. Given a vector $b\neq0$ and a constant c, the set of points x satisfying the equation

$$\langle b,x\rangle=c$$

forms an $(n-1)$-plane π_{n-1}. Show that, if $x=x_0$ is a point in π_{n-1}, then

$$\langle b,x-x_0\rangle=0$$

as an alternative equation for π_{n-1}. The vector b is called a *normal* to π_{n-1}. Show that for an arbitrary point x the quantity

$$d(x)=\frac{\langle b,x-x_0\rangle}{|b|}=\frac{\langle b,x\rangle-c}{|b|}$$

is a directed distance from x to π_{n-1}. What is the significance of the sign of $d(x)$? Observe that $d(0)=-c/|b|$.

7. Given two linearly independent vectors b_1 and b_2 and two constants c_1 and c_2, the set of points x satisfying the equations

$$\langle b_1, x \rangle = c_1, \qquad \langle b_2, x \rangle = c_2$$

forms an $(n-2)$-plane π_{n-2}. Show that, if $x = x_0$ is a point in π_{n-2}, then

$$\langle b_1, x - x_0 \rangle = 0, \qquad \langle b_2, x - x_0 \rangle = 0$$

are alternative equations for π_{n-2}. Show that, if $b = \beta_1 b_1 + \beta_2 b_2$ is a nonnull linear combination of b_1 and b_2, the $(n-1)$-plane

$$\langle b, x - x_0 \rangle = 0$$

contains the $(n-2)$-plane π_{n-2}. The set of vectors b of this form is said to be normal to π_{n-2}.

8. Let x_0 be a fixed point, and let r be a positive number. The points x satisfying the equation

$$|x - x_0| = r$$

are called an $(n-1)$-*sphere* or $(n-1)$-*spherical surface* S_{n-1} having x_0 as its center and r as its radius. Show that, if x_1 is a point on S_{n-1}, the $(n-1)$-plane π_{n-1} defined by the equation

$$\langle x_1 - x_0, x - x_0 \rangle = r^2$$

is tangent to S_{n-1} at the point x_1. For the case $n = 4$ find the tangent 3-plane to the 3-spherical surface

$$(x^1 - 1)^2 + (x^2 + 1)^2 + (x^3 - 2) + (x^4 - 3)^2 = 7$$

at the point $(2, -2, 3, 1)$.

9. Given two distinct points x and y, show that

$$z = x + t(y - x) = (1 - t)x + ty \qquad (-\infty < t < \infty)$$

is a parametric representation of the line L through x and y. Show that, if t is restricted to the interval $0 \leqslant t \leqslant 1$, one obtains the line segment joining x to y. For the case $n = 4$ find a parametric equation of the line through the points $x = (1, 1, 1, 1)$ and $y = (2, -2, 2, -2)$.

10. Given a point x_0 and a vector $p \neq 0$, show that the points x determined by the equation

$$x = x_0 + \alpha p \qquad (-\infty < \alpha < \infty)$$

form a straight line π_1 through x_0 in the direction p. Show that if $|p| = 1$ then α

is the directed distance from x to x_0. Show that the $(n-1)$-plane π_{n-1} given by $\langle p, x - x_0 \rangle = 0$ cuts π_1 orthogonally at x_0. For the case $n=3$, find the equation of the line π_1 through $x_0 = (1,1,1)$ in the direction $p = (2, -3, 4)$. What is the equation of the 2-plane π_2 through x_0 orthogonal to π_1?

11.   Show that, if u and v are linearly independent vectors and x_0 is a given point, then

$$x = x_0 + \alpha u + \beta v,$$

with α, β arbitrary, represents a 2-plane π_2 through x_0 parallel to u and v. Show that the $(n-2)$-plane π_{n-2} determined by the equations

$$\langle u, x - x_0 \rangle = 0, \qquad \langle v, x - x_0 \rangle = 0$$

cuts π_2 orthogonally at the point x_0. Find the point at which π_2 intersects the $(n-2)$-plane

$$\langle u, x \rangle = c, \qquad \langle v, x \rangle = d.$$

For the case $n=5$, find the parametric equation of the 2-plane π_2 through the point $x_0 = (1,2,3,4,5)$ parallel to the vectors $u = (1, -1, 1, -1, 1)$ and $v = (1,1,1,1,0)$; also find the equation of the 3-plane π_3 perpendicular to π_2 and passing through the point x_0.

12.   Given three points x_0, x_1, and x_2, not on a line, show that the points

$$x = \alpha_0 x_0 + \alpha_1 x_1 + \alpha_2 x_2$$

determined by the numbers $\alpha_0, \alpha_1, \alpha_2$ satisfying the constraint

$$\alpha_0 + \alpha_1 + \alpha_2 = 1$$

lie in the 2-plane π_2 passing through the points x_0, x_1, and x_2. The numbers α_0, α_1, α_2 are called the *barycentric coordinates* of x relative to x_0, x_1, x_2. Show that the triangle having x_0, x_1, x_2 as its vertices is determined by nonnegative values of α_0, α_1, α_2. Show that the centroid of this triangle is given by $\alpha_0 = \alpha_1 = \alpha_2 = \frac{1}{3}$. For the case $n=6$, find the equation of the 2-plane π_2 through the points $x_0(1,1,1,1,1,1,)$, $x_1 = (1, -1, 0, 0, 1, -1)$, and $x_2 = (0, 0, 1, -1, 0, 0)$. Using barycentric coordinates, find the centroid of the triangle having x_0, x_1, and x_2 as its vertices.

13.   Let x_0 be a fixed point and $u_1, \ldots, u_k$ be linearly independent vectors. The set of points x expressible in the form

$$x = x_0 + \alpha_1 u_1 + \cdots + \alpha_k u_k$$

forms a k-plane π_k through the point x_0. Show that the k-plane π_k intersects the $(n-k)$-plane π_{n-k} given by

$$\langle u_j, x - x_0 \rangle = 0 \qquad (j = 1, \ldots, k)$$

orthogonally at the point x_0. In the case $n = 4$, find the 2-plane π_2 through the point $x_0 = (2, 3, 4, 5)$ parallel to the vectors $u_1 = (1, -1, 2, -2)$ and $u_2 = (1, 1, -5, 7)$. Determine the 2-plane orthogonal to π_2 and passing through the point x_0.

14. The $k + 1$ points $x_0, x_1, \ldots, x_k$ are said to be independent if they do not lie in a $(k - 1)$-plane. Show that they are independent if and only if the vectors

$$u_1 = x_1 - x_0, \qquad u_2 = x_2 - x_0, \ldots, \qquad u_k = x_k - x_0$$

are linearly independent. Given a set of independent points $x_0, x_1, \ldots, x_k$, the set of points x determined by the equations

$$x = \alpha_0 x_0 + \alpha_1 x_1 + \cdots + \alpha_k x_k, \qquad \alpha_0 + \alpha_1 + \cdots + \alpha_k = 1$$

lies on the k-plane π_k passing through the points $x_0, x_1, \ldots, x_k$. The numbers $\alpha_0, \alpha_1, \ldots, \alpha_k$ are the *barycentric coordinates* of the point x relative to $x_0, \ldots, x_k$. The configuration of points x defined by

$$x = \alpha_0 x_0 + \cdots + \alpha_k x_k \qquad (\alpha_0 \geqslant 0, \ldots, \alpha_k \geqslant 0; \alpha_0 + \cdots + \alpha_k = 1) \qquad (2.6)$$

is called a *k-simplex with $x_0, \ldots, x_k$ as its vertices.* Show that a 1-simplex is a line segment, a 2-simplex is a triangle, and a 3-simplex is a tetrahedron. The centroid of the k-simplex is given by the values

$$\alpha_j = \frac{1}{k + 1} \qquad (j = 0, 1, \ldots, k).$$

If $x_0, \ldots, x_k$ are dependent, the corrresponding k-simplex defined by (2.6) is said to be *degenerate*. For the case $n = 3$, find the barycentric coordinates of a point x relative to the points $x_0 = (0, 0, 0)$, $x_1 = (1, 0, 0)$, $x_2 = (0, 1, 0)$, $x_3 = (0, 0, 1)$. Also find the barycentric coordinates of a point x relative to $x_0 = (1, 1, 1)$, $x_1 = (1, 0, 0)$, $x_2 = (0, 1, 0)$, $x_3 = (0, 0, 1)$.

15. Let $u_1, \ldots, u_k$ be an orthonormal set of vectors. Given a vector w, set

$$a_i = \langle u_i, w \rangle.$$

Recall that the vector

$$v = w - (a_1 u_1 + \cdots + a_k u_k)$$

is orthogonal to $u_1, \ldots, u_k$ and hence to every vector u expressible as a linear combination

$$u = \alpha_1 u_1 + \cdots + \alpha_k u_k$$

of $u_1, \ldots, u_k$. For the case $n = 4$ show that

$$u_1 = \left(\tfrac{1}{2}, \tfrac{1}{2}, \tfrac{1}{2}, \tfrac{1}{2}\right), \qquad u_2 = \left(\tfrac{1}{2}, -\tfrac{1}{2}, \tfrac{1}{2}, -\tfrac{1}{2}\right), \qquad u_3 = \left(\tfrac{1}{2}, \tfrac{1}{2}, -\tfrac{1}{2}, -\tfrac{1}{2}\right)$$

are orthonormal. Selecting $w = (0, 0, 0, 1)$, find the vector v orthogonal to u_1, u_2, u_3 such that $w = a_1 u_1 + a_2 u_2 + a_3 u_3 + v$.

16. Let $u_1, \ldots, u_k$ be a set of k linearly independent vectors. Show that an orthogonal set of vectors $v_1, \ldots, v_k$ can be obtained by the following *Gram-Schmidt process*.
    (a) Set $v_1 = u_1$, $d_1 = |v_1|^2$.
    (b) Having obtained $v_1, \ldots, v_{i-1}, d_1, \ldots, d_{i-1}$ ($i \geq 2$), set

$$a_{ij} = \frac{\langle u_i, v_j \rangle}{d_j} \qquad (j = 1, \ldots, i-1),$$

$$v_i = u_i - \sum_{j=1}^{i-1} a_{ij} v_j, \qquad d_i = |v_i|^2.$$

Show that for each i the vector v_i is a linear combination of $u_1, \ldots, u_i$. Show that, if we set $c_i = d_i^{-1/2}$ and $w_i = c_i v_i = v_i / |v_i|$, the vectors $w_1, \ldots, w_k$ form an orthonormal set. Carry out this process for the case $n = 4$ with $u_1 = (1, 1, 1, 1)$, $u_2 = (1, 0, 0, 0)$, $u_3 = (1, -1, 1, 1)$. *Hint*: See Section 8 in Chapter 1.

17. Modify the Gram-Schmidt process given in Exercise 16 as follows.
    (a) Set $v_1 = u_1$, $c_1 = 1/|v_1|$, $w_1 = c_1 v_1$.
    (b) Having obtained $w_1, \ldots, w_{i-1}$, set

$$b_{ij} = \langle u_i, w_j \rangle, \qquad v_i = u_i - \sum_{j=1}^{i-1} b_{ij} w_j, \qquad c_i = \frac{1}{|v_i|}, \qquad w_i = c_i v_i.$$

Show that $w_1, \ldots, w_k$ are orthonormal. Carry out this process for the vectors u_1, u_2, u_3 given in Exercise 16.

18. Show that

$$\left| \sum_{i,j} a_{ij} b_{ij} \right|^2 \leq \left(\sum_{i,j} a_{ij} a_{ij} \right) \left(\sum_{i,j} b_{ij} b_{ij} \right),$$

where $\sum_{ij}$ denotes $\sum_{i=1}^m \sum_{j=1}^n$. *Hint*: Consider (a_{ij}) and (b_{ij}) to be *mn*-dimensional vectors indexed by ij, and apply (2.5).

19. Show that

$$\left| \sum_{i,j} a_{ij} x^i y^j \right|^2 \leq \left(\sum_{i,j} a_{ij} a_{ij} \right) |x|^2 |y|^2$$

where i and j are summed from 1 to n. *Hint*: Take $b_{ij} = x^i y^j$ in Exercise 18.

20. Show that

$$\left| \sum a_{ijk} x^i y^j z^k \right|^2 \leq \left(\sum a_{ijk} a_{ijk} \right) |x|^2 |y|^2 |z|^2,$$

where $\sum$ denotes $\sum_{i=1}^n \sum_{j=1}^n \sum_{k=1}^n$.

21. Let $\mathcal{E}$ be the class of real-valued continuous functions $x:x(t)$ $(a \leqslant t \leqslant b)$. Show that $\mathcal{E}$ is a linear space. Moreover, if $y:y(t)$ $(a \leqslant t \leqslant b)$ is a second function in $\mathcal{E}$, show that

$$\langle x,y \rangle = \int_a^b x(t)y(t)\,dt$$

is an inner product. Show that if $a = -\pi$ and $b = \pi$ the functions $x(t) = \sin t$ $(-\pi \leqslant t \leqslant \pi)$ and $y(t) = \cos t$ $(-\pi \leqslant t \leqslant \pi)$ are orthogonal. Construct another pair of orthogonal functions.

22. Let $\mathcal{C}$ be the class of all continuous functions $x:x(t)$ $(a \leqslant t \leqslant b)$ having a continuous derivative $\dot{x}(t)$ on $[a,b]$. Show that $\mathcal{C}$ is a linear space having

$$\langle x,y \rangle = x(a)y(a) + \int_a^b \dot{x}(t)\dot{y}(t)\,dt$$

as an inner product. Show that if $a = -\pi$ and $b = \pi$ the functions $x(t) = \sin t$ $(-\pi \leqslant t \leqslant \pi)$ and $y(t) = \cos t$ $(-\pi \leqslant t \leqslant \pi)$ are orthogonal relative to this inner product. Find another pair of orthogonal functions.

3. BASIC CONCEPTS

By the δ-*neighborhood of a point* x_0 *in* $\mathcal{E}^n$ is meant the set of points x lying in the open sphere

$$|x - x_0| < \delta,$$

about x_0 of radius δ.

Let S be a set in $\mathcal{E}^n$. A point x_0 is an *interior point* of S if S contains a δ-neighborhood of x_0. A point x_0 is an *accumulation point* or a *limit point* of S if every δ-neighborhood of x_0 contains a point $x \neq x_0$ belonging to S. A limit point of S need not be in S. A point x_0 is an *isolated point* of S if x_0 is in S but is not a limit point of S. A point x_0 is a *boundary point* of S if every δ-neighborhood of x_0 contains points in S and points not in S. Finally a point x_0 is an *exterior point* of S if it is interior to the *complement* of S (the set of points not in S).

A set S is *open* if all of its points are interior points. It is *closed* if it contains its limit points. A consequence of these definitions is that the complement of an open set is closed, and the complement of a closed set is open. A set S is *bounded* if it is contained in a sphere about the origin, that is, if there is a positive number r such that $|x| \leqslant r$ for every x in S. A bounded closed set is said to be *compact*.

In general, it is not convenient to restrict neighborhoods of a point to be δ-neighborhoods. Accordingly we define any open set containing a point x

to be a *neighborhood of x*. A neighborhood of a point accordingly need not be spherical but can be cubical as well.

By a *neighborhood of a set S* will be meant an open set N containing S. Of particular interest, by a δ-*neighborhood* of S is meant a set of points each of which lies in a δ-neighborhood of some point x in S. The δ-neighborhood of S is accordingly the union of the δ-neighborhoods of its points.

A sequence $\{x_q\}$ of points in $\mathcal{E}^n$ is said to *converge to* x_0 (to have x_0 as its *limit*) if

$$\lim_{q \to \infty} |x_q - x_0| = 0,$$

that is, if for every $\delta > 0$ there is an integer p such that x_q is in the δ-neighborhood of x_0 whenever $q > p$. Each of the symbols "$\lim_{q \to \infty} x_q = x_0$," "$\lim x_q = x_0$," "$x_q \to x_0$" signifies that x_0 is the limit of the sequence $\{x_q\}$. If $x_q \to x_0$ and $\{y_q\}$ is a subsequence of $\{x_q\}$, then $y_q \to x_0$. A sequence $\{x_q\}$ is a *Cauchy sequence* if

$$\lim_{p,q \to \infty} |x_p - x_q| = 0.$$

As is well known, a sequence $\{x_q\}$ in $\mathcal{E}^n$ converges if and only if it is a Cauchy sequence. A sequence $\{x_q\}$ is *bounded* if there is a number r such that $|xq| \leqslant r$ for every integer q. A point x_0 is an *accumulation point* of a sequence $\{x_q\}$ if it is the limit of a subsequence of $\{x_q\}$.

THEOREM 3.1

A set S is closed if and only if the limits of convergent sequences in S are in S.

The proof of this result will be left as an exercise.

THEOREM 3.2   BOLZANO-WEIERSTRASS THEOREM

Every bounded sequence $\{x_q\}$ of points in $\mathcal{E}^n$ possesses a convergent subsequence.

The proof of Theorem 3.2 can be found in the standard textbooks on analysis.

A function f is said to be *continuous on* a set S if it is continuous at each point x_0 in S. It is *continuous at a point* x_0 *in* S if

$$f(x_q) \to f(x_0) \qquad \text{whenever } x_q \in S \text{ and } x_q \to x_0 \qquad (3.1)$$

or, equivalently, if there is a positive function $\delta(\epsilon)$ defined for all $\epsilon > 0$ such that

$$x \text{ in } S \quad \text{and} \quad |x - x_0| < \delta(\epsilon) \text{ implies } |f(x) - f(x_0)| < \epsilon. \quad (3.2)$$

If x_0 is a limit point of S, this definition is equivalent to the condition that

$$\lim_{x \to x_0} f(x) = f(x_0) \text{ on } S. \quad (3.3)$$

We say that

$$\lim_{x \to x_0} f(x) = b \text{ on } S \quad (3.4)$$

if x_0 is a limit point of S and there is a positive function $\delta(\epsilon)$ defined for all $\epsilon > 0$ such that

$$x \text{ in } S \quad \text{and} \quad 0 < |x - x_0| < \delta(\epsilon) \text{ implies } |f(x) - b| < \epsilon. \quad (3.5)$$

In using limits we normally omit the phrase "on S" and write

$$\lim_{x \to x_0} f(x) = b \quad (3.6)$$

with the understanding that x is restricted to be in S as indicated in (3.5). The point x_0, however, need not be in S but must be a limit point of S.

It is assumed that the reader is familiar with the basic properties of limits and continuity.

Occasionally we shall make use of the concepts of upper and lower limits. Let x_0 be a limit point of a set S on which a function f is defined. By the *upper limit of* f *on* S *at* x_0, written as

$$\limsup_{x \to x_0} f(x) = b \text{ on } S,$$

will be meant the largest number b (including $+\infty$) for which there exists a sequence $\{x_q\}$ of points in S distinct from x_0 such that $\lim_{q \to \infty} f(x_q) = b$. The smallest number b (including $-\infty$) having this property is the *lower limit of* f *on* S *at* x_0 and is designated by

$$\liminf_{x \to x_0} f(x) = b.$$

Upper and lower limits of sequences are defined similarly.

Convex sets play an important role in optimization. A set S is said to be *convex* if for every pair of points x and y in S the line segment

$$z = (1 - t)x + ty \qquad (0 \leqslant t \leqslant 1)$$

is in S. If $x = y$, this line segment reduces to a point. It is easily verified that an open sphere

$$|x - x_0| < r$$

of radius r about a point x_0 is convex. So also is its closure. Similarly ᴈ ᴉ open interval

$$a^i < x^i - x_0{}^i < b^i \qquad (i = 1, \ldots, n)$$

about x_0 is convex. The closure of a convex set is convex. Every k-plane is convex. The intersection of convex sets is convex. We consider the null set to be convex.

If $x_0, x_1, \ldots, x_k$ are $k + 1$ points in a convex set, then so also is the point

$$x = \sum_{i=0}^{k} \alpha_i x_i, \qquad \text{where } \alpha_i \geqslant 0, \quad \sum_{i=0}^{n} \alpha_i = 1. \tag{3.7}$$

This is true for $k = 1$. Suppose that it is true for $k = m$, and let $x_0, x_1, \ldots, x_{m+1}$ be $m + 2$ points in S. Consider the sum

$$\bar{x} = \beta_0 x_0 + \cdots + \beta_{m+1} x_{m+1}, \qquad \text{where } \beta_j \geqslant 0, \quad \sum_{j=0}^{m+1} \beta_j = 1.$$

If $\beta_{m+1} = 1$, then $\beta_j = 0$ $(j \geqslant m)$ and $\bar{x} = x_{m+1}$ is in S. If $\beta_{m+1} < 1$, we have

$$\bar{x} = (1 - \beta_{m+1})(\alpha_0 x_0 + \cdots + \alpha_m x_m) + \beta_{m+1} x_{m+1}, \tag{3.8}$$

where

$$\alpha_j = \frac{\beta_j}{1 - \beta_{m+1}} \geqslant 0 \qquad (j = 0, 1, \ldots, m).$$

We have

$$\alpha_0 + \cdots + \alpha_m = \frac{\beta_0 + \cdots + \beta_m}{1 - \beta_{m+1}} = \frac{1 - \beta_{m+1}}{1 - \beta_{m+1}} = 1.$$

By the induction hypotheses the point $\alpha_0 x_0 + \cdots + \alpha_m x_m$ is in S. By (3.8) it follows that $\bar{x}$ is in S, as was to be proved.

The linear combination (3.7) of $x_0, x_1, \ldots, x_k$ in which $\alpha_0, \ldots, \alpha_k$ are restricted to be nonnegative and to have their sum equal to unity is called a *convex linear combination* of $x_0, x_1, \ldots, x_k$. We have just proved that for every integer k the convex linear combination of points $x_0, x_1, \ldots, x_k$ in a convex set of S also belongs to S. The points $x_0, x_1, \ldots, x_k$ need not be independent; in fact, they will always be dependent if $k > n$. The largest integer k for which there exist $k+1$ independent points $x_0, x_1, \ldots, x_k$ in S will be called the *dimension* of S. If $x_0, x_1, \ldots, x_k$ are $k+1$ independent points in a convex set S of dimension k, then S is a convex subset of the k-plane π_k containing $x_0, x_1, \ldots, x_k$.

By the *convex hull* of a set S will be meant the smallest convex set containing S. Its closure is called the *closed convex hull* of S.

EXERCISES

1. Prove Theorem 3.1.
2. Show that, if Theorem 3.2 holds in the one-dimensional case, it holds in the n-dimensional case.
3. Find a proof of Theorem 3.2 for the one-dimensional case.
4. Show that the union of two convex sets need not be convex.
5. Show that the interior of an ellipse in the xy-plane is convex.
6. Show that if $a > 0$ the set of points (x, y) in the xy-plane lying above the parabola $y = ax^2 + bx + c$ is a convex set.
7. Prove that the closure of a convex set is a convex set.
8. Prove that the intersection of convex sets is a convex set.
9. Let (x_0, y_0, z_0), (x_1, y_1, z_1), (x_2, y_2, z_2) be three points in xyz-space. Show that they are independent (see Exercise 14 in Section 2) if and only if the matrix

$$\begin{bmatrix} x_0 & x_1 & x_2 \\ y_0 & y_1 & y_2 \\ z_0 & z_1 & z_2 \\ 1 & 1 & 1 \end{bmatrix}$$

    has rank 3. Use this fact to show that the points $(1, 1, 1)$, $(1, -1, 1)$, $(-1, 1, 1)$ are the vertices of a triangle.

10. Let $x_0, x_1, \ldots, x_k$ be $k+1$ points. Show that they are independent if and only if the $[(n+1) \times (k+1)]$-dimensional matrix

$$\begin{pmatrix} x_j^{\,i} \\ c_j \end{pmatrix} \qquad (i = 1, \ldots, n; \, j = 0, 1, \ldots, k)$$

    with $c_j = 1 \; (j = 0, 1, \ldots, k)$ has rank $k+1$. Here j is the column index, and i is the row index for the first n rows. For the case $n=4$, show that the points $x_0=(1,1,1,1)$, $x_1=(1,-1,1,-1)$, $x_2=(1,1,-1,1)$, $x_3=-x_0$ are the vertices of a tetrahedron.

11. Let $u_1,\ldots,u_k$ be k linearly independent vectors. Given a number $\alpha\neq0$ and a point $\bar{x}$, show that the points

$$x_0=\bar{x}-\alpha(u_1+\cdots+u_k), \qquad x_j=\bar{x}+\alpha u_j \qquad (j=1,\ldots,k)$$

are the vertices of a k-simplex having $\bar{x}$ as its centroid.

12. For a given vector $b\neq0$ and a given scalar c, the set S of all points x such that $\langle b,x\rangle<c$ is called an *open half space*. Its closure $\bar{S}$ is called a *closed half space* or simply a *half space*. Show that $\bar{S}$ is defined by the inequality $\langle b,x\rangle\leqslant c$. Show that S and $\bar{S}$ are convex. Is the set defined by the inequality $\langle b,x\rangle\geqslant c$ a half space?

13. The intersection of a finite number of (closed) half spaces is called a *polytope* or a *polyhedron*. Show that a polytope is a convex set. Frequently, the term "polyhedron" is used to signify a "bounded polytope".

14. Let S be a nonempty subset of $\mathcal{E}^n$. Let T be the set of all convex linear combinations of points $x_0,x_1,\ldots,x_k$ in S (k arbitrary). Show that T is convex. Show further that T is the convex hull of S.

4. EXTREME POINTS OF FUNCTIONS

This section is devoted to the study of real-valued functions on a nonempty set S in $\mathcal{E}^n$. We begin with the concepts of the least upper bound and the greatest lower bound of a function f on S. The largest number m (with $m=-\infty$ admitted) such that $f(x)\geqslant m$ for all x in S is called the *greatest lower bound* of f on S, or the *infimum* of f on S. It is denoted by "$\inf_{x\in S}f(x)$" or by "$\inf f(x)$ on S" or simply by "$\inf f(x)$." In general, the value $\inf f(x)$ may or may not be taken on by f on S. If there is a point x_0 in S such that

$$f(x_0)=\inf f(x) \text{ on } S,$$

this is expressed by writing

$$f(x_0)=\min f(x) \text{ on } S \qquad \text{or} \qquad f(x_0)=\min_{x\in S} f(x).$$

Such a point x_0 is said to *minimize* f on S, and $f(x_0)$ is the *minimum* of f on S. The symbol "$\min f(x)$ on S" is not used unless it is known that the value $\inf f(x)$ on S is attained at some point x_0 in S.

Similarly the *least upper bound*, or the *supremum*, of f on S is the smallest number M (with $M=+\infty$ admitted) such that $f(x)\leqslant M$ for all x in S. It is denoted by "$\sup_{x\in S}f(x)$" or by "$\sup f(x)$ on S" or by "$\sup f(x)$." If there is a point x_1 in S such that

$$f(x_1) = \sup f(x) \text{ on } S,$$

then this supremum is the *maximum* of f on S, and we write

$$f(x_1) = \max f(x) \text{ on } S \qquad \text{or} \qquad f(x_1) = \max_{x \in S} f(x).$$

Such a point x_1 is said to *maximize* f on S. It is clear that on S

$$\sup\left[-f(x)\right] = -\inf f(x), \qquad \inf\left[-f(x)\right] = -\sup f(x).$$

A point x_1 in S maximizes f on S if and only if x_1 minimizes $-f$ on S, and a point x_0 in S minimizes f on S if and only if x_0 minimizes $-f$ on S. A point that maximizes or minimizes f is called an *extreme point* of f.

To illustrate these ideas, consider the one-dimensional case in which S is the interval $-1 < x < 1$. The closure $\overline{S}$ of S is the interval $-1 \leqslant x \leqslant 1$. The function $f(x) = x^2$ on S has

$$f(0) = \min_{x \in S} f(x) = \inf_{x \in S} f(x) = 0, \qquad \sup_{x \in S} f(x) = 1.$$

The function $f(x) = x^2$ fails to have a maximum on S. However, it has a maximum on the closure $\overline{S}$ of S at the points $x = \pm 1$. The function $g(x) = 1/x \ (x \neq 0)$, $g(0) = 0$ has $\sup g(x) = +\infty$ and $\inf g(x) = -\infty$ on S. The function $h(x) = \sec(\pi x/2)$ has $\sup h(x) = +\infty$ on S and $\min h(x) = \inf h(x) = 1$ at $x = 0$. The function $F(x) = x$ on S and $F(x) = 0$ elsewhere has $\sup F(x) = 1$ and $\inf F(x) = -1$ on $\overline{S}$ but fails to have a maximum or minimum on $\overline{S}$.

One of the basic problems in optimization is to determine conditions which imply the existence of optima. Perhaps the simplest method is to exhibit the optimum point. This is possible when the function considered is given by a simple formula, as is illustrated by the following examples.

EXAMPLE 4.1

Let S be the real line, and let f be the function

$$f(x) = ax^2 + 2bx + c,$$

where a, b, c are real numbers $a > 0$. By completing the square, we may write f in the form

$$f(x) = a\left(x + \frac{b}{a}\right)^2 + \frac{ac - b^2}{a}.$$

Clearly f has a minimum at $x = -b/a$. Moreover, the minimum of f is $(ac - b^2)/a$.

EXAMPLE 4.2

By writing the function

$$f(x,y) = x^4 - 2x^2 + 3y^2 - 12y + 5$$

in the form

$$f(x,y) = (x^2 - 1)^2 + 3(y - 2)^2 - 8,$$

we see that on the xy-plane f has a minimum at the points $(1,2)$ and $(-1,2)$.

EXAMPLE 4.3

The function

$$f(x) = |x - 1| + |x + 1|$$

has the minimum value $f(x) = 2$ on the interval $-1 \leqslant x \leqslant 1$. At all other points $f(x) > 2$.

EXAMPLE 4.4

If S is the real line, the function $f(x) = e^{-x^2}$ attains its maximum at $x = 0$. Moreover, $f(x) > 0$ on S and $\inf f(x) = 0$. Consequently f has no minimum point on S.

In general, it is very difficult if not impossible to exhibit the extreme points of a given function. A condition that will ensure the existence of an extreme point of a function f is given in the following theorem.

THEOREM 4.1

A real-valued continuous function on a nonempty compact (bounded and closed) set S attains its maximum and minimum values on S.

To prove this result, let $m = \inf f(x)$ on S. Select a sequence $\{x_q\}$ of points in S such that

$$m = \lim_{q \to \infty} f(x_q).$$

Since S is bounded, it follows from the Bolzano-Weierstrass Theorem 3.2 that the sequence $\{x_q\}$ has a convergent subsequence $\{y_q\}$. Because of the closure of S the limit $x_0 = \lim_{q \to \infty} y_q$ is in S. By continuity we have

$$f(x_0) = \lim_{q \to \infty} f(y_q) = m = \inf f(x) \text{ on } S.$$

The point x_0 accordingly minimizes f on S. When this result is applied to the function $-f$, it is seen that there is a point x_1 in S at which $-f$ has a minimum. The point x_1 maximizes f on S. This proves the theorem.

The following example illustrates an application of Theorem 4.1.

EXAMPLE 4.5

Let S be a bounded interval $a \leqslant x \leqslant b$ of real numbers. Let f be a real-valued continuous function on S having $f(a) = f(b) = 0$. Then there exists an extreme point x_0 of f on the open interval $a < x < b$. To prove this fact, note first that it is clearly true if $f(x) \equiv 0$ on $a \leqslant x \leqslant b$, since in this case every point in S is an extreme point of f. If there is a point x in S at which $f(x) < 0$, then $m = \inf f(x) < 0$. By Theorem 4.1, there is a minimum point x_0 on S. Since $f(x_0) = m < 0$ and $f(a) = f(b) = 0$, it follows that $a < x_0 < b$. On the other hand, if $f(x) \geqslant 0$ on S but is not identically zero, the maximum x_0 of f on S is on $a < x < b$. Consequently in all cases f has an extreme point on $a < x < b$.

EXERCISES

1. Find the supremum, infimum, and extrema (when they exist) for the following functions of a real variable x on the indicated set:

    $(a) f(x) = 3x^2 + 12x - 15$ $(-\infty < x < \infty)$,
    $(b) f(x) = \cosh x = (e^x + e^{-x})/2$ $(-\infty < x < \infty)$,
    $(c) f(x) = x^2/(1 + x^2)$ $(-\infty < x < \infty)$,
    $(d) f(x) = x/(1 + |x|)$ $(-\infty < x < \infty)$,

    $(e) f(x) = x + 2\sqrt{1 - x}$ $(-\infty < x \leqslant 1)$,
    $(f) f(x) = |1 - x^2|$ $(-2 < x < 2)$,
    $(g) f(x) = |x - 1| + |x - 2|$ $(0 \leqslant x < 10)$,
    $(h) f(x) = x + 4/x$ $(0 < x \leqslant 10)$,
    $(i) f(x) = |x| - 4|x - 1|$ $(-1 \leqslant x \leqslant 2)$,
    $(j) f(x) = |x - a_1| + |x - a_2| + \cdots + |x - a_n|$ $(-\infty < x < \infty)$.
    Here $a_1 < a_2 < \cdots < a_n$. Specialize to the cases $n = 2, 3, 4, 5$.

2. By inspection find the extrema of $f(x, y) = 2x + 3y - 5$ on the following sets:

    $(a) |x| \leqslant 1, |y| \leqslant 1$; $(b) x^2 + y^2 \leqslant 1$;
    $(c) x \geqslant 0, y \geqslant 0$; $(d) |x| + |y| \leqslant 1$.

3. Given a linear function $f(x, y) = ax + by + c$, where a, b, c are constants with

$(a,b)\neq(0,0)$, show that the extreme points of f on a bounded closed set S lie on the boundary of S.

4.   With the help of Example 4.1 show that, if $a>0$ and $ac>b^2$, the function

$$f(x,y)=ax^2+2bxy+cy^2$$

has a unique minimum point at $(x,y)=(0,0)$. *Hint*: Show that

$$f(x,y)=a\left(x+\frac{by}{a}\right)^2+\frac{(ac-b^2)y^2}{a}.$$

5.   Applying the result given in Exercise 4 to the cases (a) $a=5,b=-2,c=1$; (b) $a=1,b=0,c=1$; (c) $a=-4,b=3,c=-1$; (d) $a=2,b=3,c=1$, determine the ones in which f or $-f$ has a minimum at the origin.

6.   Given the quadratic function

$$f(x,y)=ax^2+2bxy+cy^2+2\alpha x+2\beta y+\gamma,$$

show that, if $ac\neq b^2$ and (x_0,y_0) is a solution of the equations

$$ax+by=-\alpha,\qquad bx+cy=-\beta,$$

then f is expressible in the form

$$f(x,y)=f(x_0,y_0)+a(x-x_0)^2+2b(x-x_0)(y-y_0)+c(y-y_0)^2.$$

With the help of Exercise 4 show that (x_0,y_0) minimizes f whenever $a>0$ and $ac>b^2$. Apply this result to obtain the minimum point of

$$f(x,y)=5x^2-4xy+y^2+2x-2y+7.$$

7.   In each of the following cases sketch the set of points (x,y) having $f(x,y)\leqslant b$. Where are the minimum points of f?
(a) $f(x,y)=x+y,b=1,b=0,b=-1$;
(b) $f(xy)=xy,b=1,b=0,b=-1$;
(c) $f(x,y)=x^2/16+y^2/4,b=1,b=0,b=-1$;
(d) $f(x,y)=(x^2-2)^2+y^2,b=5,b=2,b=0$;
(e) $f(x,y)=|x|-y,b=0,b=5$;
(f) $f(x,y)=(x-1)^2+(y-x^2)^2,b=0,b=1,b=2$;
(g) $f(x,y)=(x-1)^2+10(y-x^2)^2,b=0,b=10,b=40$.

8.   Let f be a continuous function on a set S in $\mathcal{E}^n$, and let $m=\inf f(x)$ on S. Suppose that there is a constant $b>m$ such that the set S_b of points x in S at which $f(x)\leqslant b$ is compact. Show that there is a minimum point x_0 of f in S.

9.   Show that, if $f(x)$ is continuous on a sphere $|x|\leqslant r$ in $\mathcal{E}^n$ and $f(x)=0$ whenever $|x|=r$, then f has an extreme point in the open sphere $|x|<r$.

5.   LOCAL MINIMA AND MAXIMA—THE ONE-VARIABLE CASE

In Section 4 we were concerned with global maxima and minima, that is, maxima and minima of a function f on a set S. A common procedure for finding a global minimum is to locate all the local minima and to determine which, if any, affords a global minimum to f on S. Global and local maxima for f can be found by obtaining global and local minima for $-f$. Accordingly we shall concentrate on finding global and local minima for a function f on S.

A point $x = c$ on S is said to afford a *local* or *relative minimum* to f on S if there is a neighborhood N of c such that the inequality

$$f(x) \geqslant f(c) \tag{5.1}$$

holds for all $x \neq c$ in N belonging to S. If N can be chosen so that the strict inequality

$$f(x) > f(c) \tag{5.2}$$

holds for all $x \neq c$ in N and S, then $x = c$ affords a *strict local minimum* or *strict relative minimum* to f on S. The adjective "proper" is often used instead of "strict." The terminology "f has a local minimum at c" or "f has a strict local minimum at c" is also used. It is clear that a global minimum is a local minimum. The converse, however, is not true. For example, if S is the real line and $f(x) = 2x^3 - 3x^2$, then f has a local minimum at $x = 1$ but has no global minimum point.

The corresponding definitions for a local maximum and for a strict (proper) local maximum are obtained from the definitions just given by reversing the inequalities and replacing "minimum" by "maximum."

Before studying the theory of local maxima and minima for a function of n-variables, it is instructive to review the theory for a function of a single variable x. Throughout this section we shall assume that S is a closed interval $a \leqslant x \leqslant b$. Such an interval is also denoted by $[a, b]$. The corresponding open interval is written as $a < x < b$ or by (a, b). We use the notations $f'(x), f''(x), \ldots, f^{(k)}(x)$ for the successive derivatives of f. The derivative $f'(c)$ of f at $x = c$, when it exists, is given by the formula

$$f'(c) = \lim_{x \to c} \frac{f(x) - f(c)}{x - c} = \lim_{h \to 0} \frac{f(c + h) - f(c)}{h}. \tag{5.3}$$

If c is an end point of $[a, b]$, this limit is a one-sided limit and $f'(c)$ is a one-sided derivative. A similar remark holds for higher derivatives.

Assuming the existence of derivatives, we have the following theorem on the behavior of f at an end point of $[a, b]$.

THEOREM 5.1

If f'(a)>0, *then* x=a *affords a strict local minimum to* f *on* [a,b]. *If* f'(b)<0, *then* f *has a strict local minimum at* b *on* [a,b]. *Similarly, if* f'(a)<0, *then* x=a *affords a strict local maximum to* f *on* [a,b]. *If* f'(b)>0, *then* f *has a strict local maximum at* x=b *on* [a,b].

Suppose that $f'(a)>0$. Then, upon selecting $\epsilon = f'(a)/2$, we can choose $\delta >0$ such that if $a<x<a+\delta$ we have

$$\left| \frac{f(x)-f(a)}{x-a} - f'(a) \right| < \epsilon = \frac{f'(a)}{2} .$$

Then

$$\frac{f(x)-f(a)}{x-a} > f'(a) - \epsilon = \frac{f'(a)}{2} > 0 \qquad (a<x<a+\delta).$$

Hence $f(x)>f(a)$ on $a<x<a+\delta$, that is, $x=a$ affords a strict local minimum to f on $[a,b]$. This proves the first statement in the theorem. The remaining statements are established in a similar manner.

The conditions on the derivatives of f at a and b are sufficient for a strict local extremum (maximum or minimum) of f at an end point of $[a,b]$. However, they are not necessary conditions. For example, on the interval $0 \leqslant x \leqslant 1$ the function $f(x)=x^3$ has a strict local minimum at $x=0$, while $f'(0)=0$. Necessary conditions for local extrema at a and b are given in

THEOREM 5.2

If f'(a) *exists and* x=a *affords a local minimum to* f *on* [a,b], *then* f'(a)⩾0. *If* f'(b) *exists and* x=b *affords a local minimum to* f *on* [a,b], *then* f'(b)⩽0. *Similarly* f'(a)⩽0 *if* f(a) *is a local maximum on* [a,b] *and* f'(b)⩾0 *if* f(b) *is a local maximum, assuming that* f'(a) *and* f'(b) *exist.*

By Theorem 5.1 $f(a)$ is a strict local maximum of f on $[a,b]$ if $f'(a)<0$. It follows that, if $f(a)$ is a local minimum on $[a,b]$, we must have $f'(a)\geqslant 0$. Similarly $f'(b)\leqslant 0$ if $f(b)$ is a local minimum on $[a,b]$. The last statement can be obtained by replacing f by $-f$.

THEOREM 5.3

If f *has a local extremum* (maximum *or* minimum) *at a point* x=c *on* a<x<b *and* f'(c) *exists, then* f'(c)=0.

Suppose that f has a local minimum at $x=c$. By Theorem 5.2 applied to the interval $[c,b]$, we have $f'(c)\geqslant 0$. Applying the same theorem to the interval $[a,c]$, we see that $f'(c) \leqslant 0$. Hence $f'(c) = 0$. Similarly $f'(c) = 0$ if f has a maximum at $x = c$.

If f is differentiable at $x = c$ and $f'(c) = 0$, the point c is called a *critical point of* f and $f(c)$ is termed a *critical value of* f. Theorem 5.3 states that, for a differentiable function, extreme values can occur on an open interval only at critical points. Because of this fact many numerical techniques for the determination of extreme values of functions are designed so as to systematically search out the critical points. However, as the preceding example with $f(x) = x^3$ demonstrated, a critical value need not be an extreme value; therefore a subsequent test must be applied to critical values.

The function $f(x) = |x|$ has a minimum at $x = 0$, but $f'(0)$ fails to exist. The function $f(x) = |x|$, however, has the left-hand derivative $D^- f(0) = -1$ and the right-hand derivative $D^+ f(0) = 1$ at $x = 0$.

The following mean value theorem is basic.

THEOREM 5.4   LAW OF THE MEAN

If f *is continuous on* a $\leqslant$ x $\leqslant$ b *and has a derivative at each point on* a $<$ x $<$ b, *there is a point* c *on* a $<$ x $<$ b *such that*

$$f(b) = f(a) + (b-a)f'(c). \tag{5.4}$$

The function

$$g(x) = [f(b) - f(a)](x - a) - (b - a)[f(x) - f(a)]$$

is continuous on $[a,b]$ is differentiable on (a,b) and has $g(a) = g(b) = 0$. Hence g has an extreme point at a point c on $a < x < b$. At this extreme point we have

$$g'(c) = f(b) - f(a) - (b - a)f'(c) = 0,$$

and the theorem is proved.

In applications the point c in (5.4) is often expressed in the form $a + \theta(b - a)$, where θ is some point on $0 < \theta < 1$.

Further theorems on local maxima and minima are based on the second-order Taylor expansion of f and a point $x = c$. The second-order Taylor expansion of f about $x = c$ expresses f in the form

$$f(x) = f(c) + f'(c)(x - c) + f''(c)\frac{(x - c)^2}{2!} + r_2(c, x - c) \tag{5.5}$$

or in the alternative form

$$f(c+h)=f(c)+f'(c)h+f''(c)\frac{h^2}{2}+r_2(c,h), \qquad (5.6)$$

where

$$\lim_{h\to 0}\frac{r_2(c,h)}{h^2}=0. \qquad (5.7)$$

This expansion is valid if f is differentiable on $[a,b]$ and $f''(c)$ exists. For, by L'Hospital's rule,

$$\lim_{h\to 0}\frac{r_2(c,h)}{h^2}=\lim_{h\to 0}\frac{f(c+h)-f(c)-f'(c)h-f''(c)h^2/2}{h^2}$$

$$=\lim_{h\to 0}\frac{f'(c+h)-f'(c)-f''(c)h}{2h}=\tfrac{1}{2}\lim_{h\to 0}\left[\frac{f'(c+h)-f'(c)}{h}-f''(c)\right]=0.$$

If $f'''(x)$ exists on $[a,b]$, the remainder term $r_2(c,h)$ is given by a formula of the form

$$r_2(c,h)=\frac{h^3}{3!}f'''(c+\theta_3 h) \qquad (0<\theta_3<1). \qquad (5.8)$$

If $f'''(x)$ is continuous, we have the integral formula

$$r_2(c,h)=\frac{h^3}{2}\int_0^1(1-\theta)^2 f'''(c+\theta h)\,d\theta. \qquad (5.9)$$

To establish these formulas, we introduce the function

$$R(t)=-r_2(c+t,h-t)$$

$$=-f(c+h)+f(c+t)+f'(c+t)(h-t)+f''(c+t)\frac{(h-t)^2}{2!}.$$

Observe that its derivative is

$$R'(t)=\frac{(h-t)^2}{2!}f'''(c+t).$$

Since $R(h) = 0$ and $R(0) = -r_2(c, h)$, we have

$$r_2(c, h) = R(h) - R(0) = \int_0^h R'(t)\,dt = \int_0^h \frac{(h-t)^2}{2}\, f'''(c+t)\,dt.$$

Introducing θ as the variable of integration by the formula $t = \theta h$, we obtain formula (5.9). To obtain (5.8), we choose m so that

$$r_2(c, h) = m \frac{h^3}{3!}. \tag{5.10}$$

Then the function

$$G(t) = R(t) + m \frac{(h-t)^3}{3!}$$

has $G(h) = G(0) = 0$. By the law of the mean there is a point $t_3 = \theta_3 h$, where $0 < \theta_3 < 1$, such that

$$0 = G'(t_3) = R'(t_3) - m \frac{(h-t_3)^2}{2} = \frac{(h-t_3)^2}{2} \left[f'''(c + \theta_3 h) - m \right].$$

Consequently

$$m = f'''(c + \theta_3 h).$$

Combining this result with (5.10), we obtain the desired formula (5.8). Additional formulas for $r_2(c, h)$ can be established. For example,

$$r_2(c, h) = h^2 \int_0^1 (1 - \theta)[f''(c + \theta h) - f''(c)]\,d\theta, \tag{5.11}$$

$$r_2(c, h) = \frac{h^2}{2}[f''(c + \theta_2 h) - f''(c)], \tag{5.12}$$

for a suitable point θ_2 on $0 < \theta < 1$. Equation (5.11) is valid whenever $f''(x)$ is continuous; (5.12), whenever $f''(x)$ exists. One important aspect of the integral formulas for the remainder is that they are valid when f is a vector function, whereas the other forms need modification in this event.

In the general case in which f has derivatives of the first $k - 1$ orders on $[a, b]$ and the kth derivative exists at $x = c$, the kth-order Taylor expansion of f about $x = c$ is given by the formula

$$f(x) = f(c) + f'(c) \frac{x - c}{1!} + \cdots + f^{(k)}(c) \frac{(x - c)^k}{k!} + r_k(c, x - c) \tag{5.13}$$

or, alternatively, by

$$f(c+h)=f(c)+f'(c)\frac{h}{1!}+\cdots+f^{(k)}(c)\frac{h^k}{k!}+r_k(c,h), \qquad (5.14)$$

where

$$\lim_{h\to 0}\frac{r_k(c,h)}{h^k}=0. \qquad (5.15)$$

If $f^{(k)}(x)$ exists on (a,b), we have

$$r_k(c,h)=\frac{h^k}{k!}\left[f^{(k)}(c+\theta_k h)-f^{(k)}(c)\right] \qquad (5.16)$$

for a suitably chosen constant θ_k on $0<\theta<1$. If $f^{(k)}(x)$ is continuous, then

$$r_k(c,h)=\frac{h^k}{(k-1)!}\int_0^1 (1-\theta)^{k-1}\left[f^{(k)}(c+\theta h)-f^{(k)}(c)\right]d\theta. \qquad (5.17)$$

In addition, if $f^{(k+1)}(x)$ exists, then

$$r_k(c,h)=\frac{h^{k+1}}{(k+1)!}f^{(k+1)}(c+\theta_{k+1}h) \qquad (0<\theta_{k+1}<1) \qquad (5.18)$$

and

$$r_k(c,h)=\frac{h^{k+1}}{k!}\int_0^1 (1-\theta)^k f^{(k+1)}(c+\theta h)\,d\theta \qquad (5.19)$$

whenever $f^{(k+1)}(x)$ is continuous. The proof of these statements is like that for $k=2$ and will be left to the reader.

We are now in a position to establish the following sufficiency theorem for a local extremum. It is often referred to as the "second derivative test."

THEOREM 5.5

Suppose that f *is differentiable near* x = c *and that* f''(c) *exists. Suppose that* f'(c) = 0 *and that* f''(c) ≠ 0. *Choose* m *such that* 0 < 2m < |f''(c)|. *Then there is a constant* δ > 0 *such that*

$$f(x) \geqslant f(c) + m(x-c)^2 \qquad \textit{if } f''(c) > 0 \textit{ and } c-\delta < x < c+\delta, \qquad (5.20)$$

and such that

$$f(x) \leqslant f(c) - m(x-c)^2 \qquad if\ f''(c) < 0\ and\ c - \delta < x < c + \delta. \quad (5.21)$$

Hence, if $f'(c) = 0$, *the point* c *affords a strict local minimum to* f *if* $f''(c) > 0$ *and a strict local maximum to* f *if* $f''(c) < 0$.

To prove this result, we observe that by virtue of (5.7) and our choice of m there is a constant $\delta > 0$ such that

$$\left| \frac{r_2(c,h)}{h^2} \right| \leqslant \tfrac{1}{2} |f''(c)| - m \qquad \text{whenever } 0 < |h| < \delta.$$

If $f''(c) > 0$, this inequality yields the relation

$$r_2(c,h) \geqslant h^2 [m - \tfrac{1}{2} f''(c)] \qquad (0 \leqslant |h| < \delta).$$

Applying the Taylor formula (5.6) with $f'(c) = 0$, we find that

$$f(c+h) - f(c) = \frac{h^2}{2} f''(c) + r_2(c,h) \geqslant mh^2.$$

Setting $x = c + h$, we obtain (5.20). Relation (5.21) is obtained similarly from the inequality

$$r_2(c,h) \leqslant h^2 [-m - f''(c)],$$

which holds when $f''(c) < 0$.

Necessary conditions for local extrema are given in

THEOREM 5.6

Suppose that f *is differentiable on a neighborhood of* x = c *and that* f''(c) *exists. Suppose that* c *affords a local minimum to* f. *If* a < c < b, *then* f'(c) = 0 *and* f''(c) ⩾ 0. *If* c = a, *the either* f'(c) > 0 *or else* f'(c) = 0 *and* f''(c) ⩾ 0. *If* c = b, *then either* f'(c) < 0 *or else* f'(c) = 0 *and* f''(c) ⩾ 0. *If* c *affords a local maximum to* f, *the inequality signs in these statements are reversed.*

This result is a simple consequence of Theorems 5.5 and 5.1.

EXERCISES

In the following exercises it will be assumed that f is a differentiable function on $[a,b]$ unless otherwise stated or implied. In some exercises it will be assumed further that f is of class $C^{(k)}$ for some integer k. A function f is of *class* $C^{(k)}$ on $[a,b]$ if it is continuous and possesses continuous derivatives of orders $\leqslant k$ on $[a,b]$. It is of *class* $C^{(\infty)}$ in $[a,b]$ if it is of class $C^{(k)}$ on $[a,b]$ for every integer k. We normally write C' for $C^{(1)}$, C'' for $C^{(2)}$, and C''' for $C^{(3)}$.

1. The function $f(x)=|x|$ has a minimum at the origin but has no derivative at this point. It does have a left-hand derivative $D^-f(0)=-1$ and a right-hand derivative $D^+f(0)=1$ at this point. Show that, in general, if f has a minimum at $x=c$ in (a,b) and the left- and right-hand derivatives $D^-f(c),D^+f(c)$ exist, then $D^-f(c)\leqslant 0$ and $D^+f(c)\geqslant 0$. Moreover show that

$$\lim_{h \to 0} \frac{f(c+h)-f(c-h)}{2h} = \tfrac{1}{2}[D^+f(c)+D^-f(c)].$$

2. Suppose that $f'(a)<0$ and $f'(b)>0$. Show that there is a point c on $a<x<b$ at which f has a minimum. Why is $f'(c)=0$?

3. Show that if $f'(a)<m<f'(b)$ there is a point c on $a<x<b$ such that $f'(c)=m$. Obtain a similar result for the case in which $f'(a)>m>f'(b)$. *Hint*: Apply the result given in Exercise 2 to the function $F(x)=f(x)-mx$.

4. Show that if $f'(x)\neq0$ on (a,b) then either $f'(x)>0$ on (a,b) or else $f'(x)<0$ on (a,b).

5. A function f is said to be *increasing* on $[a,b]$ if $f(\alpha)<f(\beta)$ whenever $a\leqslant\alpha<\beta\leqslant b$. It is *nondecreasing* on $[a,b]$ if $f(\alpha)\leqslant f(\beta)$ whenever $a\leqslant\alpha<\beta\leqslant b$. Show that if $f'(x)>0$ on (a,b) then $f(x)$ is increasing on (a,b). Show that f is nondecreasing if $f'(x)\geqslant0$ on (a,b). Show that f is increasing on $[a,b]$ if $f'(x)>0$ on (a,b), except possibly at a finite number of points. Apply this result to $f(x)=x^3$ on $-1\leqslant x\leqslant1$.

6. A function f is said to be *decreasing* on $[a,b]$ if $f(\alpha)>f(\beta)$ whenever $a\leqslant\alpha<\beta\leqslant b$. It is *nonincreasing* on $[a,b]$ if $f(\alpha)\geqslant f(\beta)$ whenever $a\leqslant\alpha<\beta\leqslant b$. Show that f is nonincreasing if $f'(x)\leqslant0$ on $[a,b]$ and is decreasing if the equality holds, at most, at a finite number of points.

7. Suppose that $f'(c)=0$ at a point c on (a,b). Show that, if $f'(x)<0$ on (a,c) and $f'(x)>0$ on (c,b), then f has a minimum at $x=c$. State a corresponding sufficiency theorem for a maximum. This result is often referred to as the "first derivative test" for an extremum.

8. Show that the result given in Exercise 7 holds even if $f'(c)$ fails to exist.

9. Establish Theorem 5.6.

10. Suppose that $f''(x)>0$ on $a\leqslant x\leqslant b$. Show that f can have only one minimum point c on $a\leqslant x\leqslant b$. Show that, if $f'(x)\neq0$ on $a<x<b$, then either $c=a$ or else $c=b$. In this event, is $f'(c)=0$?

11. Recall that a point $x=c$ at which $f'(c)=0$ is called a *critical point* of f and $f(c)$ is termed a *critical value*. A critical point c is said to be *nondegenerate* if $f''(c)\neq0$. Show that a nondegenerate critical point affords either a proper local minimum or a proper local maximum to f.

12. Find the critical points and the critical values of the following functions:
     (a) $f(x)=ax^2+2bx+c$ $(a\neq0)$,
     (b) $f(x)=x^3-24\ln x$,
     (c) $f(x)=x^n-nb\ln x$ $(b>0)$,
     (d) $f(x)=(n-3)x^{(n+3)/2}-(n+3)c^3x^{(n-3)/2}$ $(x>0)$, $(c>0)$.

13. Discuss the critical points of f if

$$f(x)=x^m\sin\frac{1}{x}\quad(x\neq0),\qquad f(0)=0$$

     for $m=1$ and for $m=2$.

14. Show that, if $f''(x)\neq0$ on $[a,b]$, then f has at most one critical point on $[a,b]$. Show that $x=-b/a$ $(a\neq0)$ is a nonsingular critical point of $f(x)=ax^2+2bx+c$. What is the corresponding critical value?

15. Show that, if a continuous function f on $[a,b]$ has a local minimum at $x=\alpha$ and $x=\beta$ $(a\leqslant\alpha<\beta\leqslant b)$, then f has a local maximum at some point c on $\alpha<x<\beta$.

16. Show that, if $f'(c)=0$ and $f''(c)>0$ at some point c on $a<x<b$, there is a constant $\delta>0$ such that $f'(x)\neq0$ if $0<|x-c|<\delta$. *Hint*: Use Theorem 5.1. Note that $f'(x)$ need not be continuous except at $x=c$, since we assume that $f''(x)$ exists only at $x=c$.

17. Suppose that f is of class C''. Show that, if $f'(x)$ and $f''(x)$ do not vanish simultaneously on $[a,b]$, then f has a finite number of extreme points (local maxima and minima) on $[a,b]$.

18. Show that, if $f(x)$ is constant on $\alpha\leqslant x\leqslant\beta$, every point on $\alpha<x<\beta$ affords a local maximum and a local minimum to f. Show conversely that, if every point x in a neighborhood of $x=c$ affords a local maximum and a local minimum to f, then f is a constant on this neighborhood.

19. Establish relations (5.13) to (5.19).

20. Suppose that f is of class $C^{(k)}$ on $[a,b]$ and that the first $k-1$ derivatives of f vanish at $x=c$. If $a<c<b$ and f has a local minimum at c, show that $f^{(k)}(c)=0$, if k is odd and $f^{(k)}(c)\geqslant0$ if k is even. Show that, if k is even and $f^{(k)}(c)>0$, then f has a local minimum at $x=c$. What are corresponding results for the cases $c=a$ and $c=b$?

21. Show that, if $u\geqslant0,v\geqslant0,0<\epsilon<1$, then

$$u^\epsilon v^{1-\epsilon}\leqslant\epsilon u+(1-\epsilon)v,$$

     the equality holding only if $u=v$. *Hint*: Maximize the function $f(t)=t^\epsilon-\epsilon t+\epsilon-1$ on $0\leqslant t<\infty$, and set $t=u/v$.

22. If $p>1$ and $1/p+1/q=1$, the inequality

$$xy\leqslant\frac{x^p}{p}+\frac{y^q}{q}$$

is valid for all $x \geqslant 0$ and $y \geqslant 0$. *Hint*: Use Exercise 21 with $\epsilon = 1/p, u = x^p, v = x^q$, or else establish this inequality for $y > 0$ by holding y fast and maximizing

$$f(x) = \frac{xy}{qx^p + py^q}$$

on the set $0 < x < \infty$.

23. Suppose that the kth derivatives of f exist on $[a, b]$ and that $f^{(k+1)}(c)$ exists at $x = c$. Using the relationship

$$r_k(c, h) = \frac{h^{k+1}}{(k+1)!} f^{(k+1)}(c) + r_{k+1}(c, h)$$

between the remainders in Taylor's formula (5.15), show that

$$\lim_{h \to 0} \frac{r_k(c, h)}{h^{k+1}} = \frac{1}{(k+1)!} f^{(k+1)}(c).$$

With the help of the alternative formula (5.16) for the remainder, show that if $f^{(k+1)}(c) \neq 0$ we have

$$\lim_{h \to 0} \theta_k = \frac{1}{k+1}.$$

24. Show that, if n is any number (positive or negative),

$$\lim_{t \to \infty} t^n e^{-t} = 0.$$

Use this fact to show that if $g(x)$ is a rational function then

$$\lim_{x \to 0} g(x) e^{-(1/x^2)} = 0.$$

A rational function is one that is expressible as the quotient of two polynomials. *Hint*: Write $g(x) = x^n G(x)$, where $G(0) \neq 0$, and set $t = 1/x^2$. Use this result to show that the function

$$f(x) = e^{-(1/x^2)} \quad (x \neq 0), \qquad f(0) = 0$$

is of class C^∞ and has $f^{(k)}(0) = 0$ for all k. The point $x = 0$ minimizes $f(x)$. Show that the remainder $r_k(0, h)$ in the Taylor formula (3.24) for f is $r_k(0, h) = f(h)$.

25. Newton's algorithm for finding a point c at which $g(c) = 0$ is given by the formula

$$x_{n+1} = x_n + h_n, \qquad h_n = -\frac{g(x_n)}{g'(x_n)}. \tag{5.22}$$

Consequently (with $g = f'$) Newton's algorithm for finding a minimum point c of f is given by

$$x_{n+1} = x_n + h_n, \qquad h_n = -\frac{f'(x_n)}{f''(x_n)}, \qquad (5.23)$$

where it is assumed that $f''(x) \neq 0$ on $[a, b]$. Show that, if we approximate $f(x_n + h)$ by the quadratic

$$P_n(h) = f(x_n) + f'(x_n)h + f''(x_n)\frac{h^2}{2}$$

appearing in Taylor's formula (5.6) with $c = x_n$, then h_n minimizes $P_n(h)$. Interpret these results geometrically. Use this algorithm to find the minimum point c of the function

$$f(x) = x^3 - 3b \ln x, \qquad b = 2$$

on the interval $0 < x < \infty$ with the initial estimate $x_0 = 1$. Here $c = \sqrt[3]{2}$. Find a similar algorithm for minimizing

$$f(x) = (k-3)x^{(k+3)/2} + (k+3)bx^{-(k-3)/2} \qquad (b > 0, k \neq 3)$$

on $0 < x < \infty$ whose solution is $c = b^{1/k}$.

26. A sequence $\{x_n\}$ is said to *converge linearly* to $x = c$ if there is a constant K such that

$$|x_{n+1} - c| \leq K|x_n - c| \qquad (K < 1)$$

and to *converge quadratically* to $x = c$ if K can be chosen so that

$$|x_{n+1} - c| \leq K|x_n - c|^2.$$

What is meant by *cubic convergence*? Show that, if

$$g(x) = x^{-m}(x^k - b) \qquad (0 \leq m \leq k, b > 0)$$

on $0 < x < \infty$ and $x_0 > 0$, then algorithm (5.22) given in Exercise 24 can be expressed in the form

$$x_{n+1} = \frac{(m+1)bx_n + (k-m-1)x_n^{k+1}}{mb + (k-m)x_n^k}.$$

Show that this sequence converges quadratically to $c = b^{1/n}$ if $0 \leq m \leq k$ and converges cubically if $m = (k-1)/2$.

27. Show that the function defined by the relations

$$f(x)=\exp\left(\frac{1}{x^2-1}\right) \quad \text{on} \ -1<x<1, \qquad f(x)=0 \quad \text{elsewhere}$$

is of class C^∞ that is positive on the interval $-1<x<1$.

28. Let

$$f(x)=0 \quad (x\leqslant 1), \qquad f(x)=1 \quad (x\geqslant 2), \qquad \text{and} \qquad f(x)=\exp\left[\frac{g(x)}{1-x}\right]$$

$$\text{with} \ g(x)=\exp\left(\frac{1}{x-2}\right) \ (1<x<2).$$

Show that $f(x)$ is of class C^∞ on $-\infty<x<\infty$. Sketch the graph of $h(x)$ $=f(x)+f(-x)$ and of $1-h(x)$.

6. FUNCTIONS OF CLASS $C^{(k)}$

A real-valued function f will be said to be of *class* $\mathrm{C}^{(k)}$ *on an open set* S in $\mathcal{E}^n$ if it is continuous and possesses continuous partial derivatives of all orders $\leqslant k$. It is of *class* $\mathrm{C}^{(\infty)}$ *on* S if it is of class $C^{(k)}$ for every k. It will be said to be of *calss* $\mathrm{C}^{(k)}$ on an *arbitrary set* S if it is of class $C^{(k)}$ on a neighborhood of S. We use the alternative notation C' for $C^{(1)}$, C'' for $C^{(2)}$, and C''' for $C^{(3)}$. It is clear that, if f is of class $C^{(k+1)}$ on S, it is of class $C^{(k)}$ on S. We shall use the notations

$$f_{x^i}=\frac{\partial f}{\partial x^i}, \qquad f_{x^ix^j}=\frac{\partial^2 f}{\partial x^i \partial x^j}, \qquad f_{x^ix^jx^k}=\frac{\partial^3 f}{\partial x^i \partial x^j \partial x^k}, \qquad \cdots$$

for the partial derivatives of f. It will be convenient to introduce the notations

$$f'(x,h)=f^{(1)}(x,h)= \sum_{i=1}^{n} f_{x^i}(x)h^i, \tag{6.1}$$

$$f''(x,h)=f^{(2)}(x,h)= \sum_{i,j=1}^{n} f_{x^ix^j}(x)h^ih^j, \tag{6.2}$$

for the first and second differentials of f at x. The kth differential of f at x will be denoted by $f^{(k)}(x,h)$.

In the two-dimensional case when x and y coordinates are used, the derivatives of $f(x,y)$ are denoted by the usual symbols

$$f_x, f_y, f_{xx}, f_{xy}, f_{yy}, f_{xxx}, f_{xxy}, f_{xyy}, f_{yyy}, \dots .$$

The first and second differentials (6.1) and (6.2) take the forms

$$f'(x,y; h,k) = f_x(x,y)h + f_y(x,y)k,$$

$$f''(x,y; h,k) = f_{xx}(x,y)h^2 + 2f_{xy}(x,y)hk + f_{yy}(x,y)k^2.$$

For example, if $f(x,y) = x^3y^2$, then

$$f'(x,y; h,k) = 3x^2y^2h + 2x^3yk,$$

$$f''(x,y; h,k) = 6xy^2h^2 + 12x^2yhk + 2x^3k^2.$$

Observe that $f'(x,y; h,k)$ is the inner product of (h,k) and the vectors $\nabla f = (3x^2y^2, 2x^3y)$ defined by the partial derivatives f_x and f_y.

The vector defined by the partial derivatives of f at x is called the *gradient of* f *at* x and is denoted by various symbols, such as

$$\operatorname{grad} f = \nabla f = f'(x) = f_x = (f_{x^i}) = \left(\frac{\partial f}{\partial x^i} \right).$$

In terms of the inner product we have

$$f'(x,h) = \langle f'(x), h \rangle = \langle \nabla f, h \rangle.$$

Similarly the matrix of the second derivatives of f is denoted by

$$f''(x) = f_{xx} = (f_{x^i x^j}) = \left(\frac{\partial^2 f}{\partial x^i \partial x^j} \right).$$

This matrix is called the *Hessian of* f *at* x.

It is desirable at times to use the symbols δx or dx in place of h and $\delta f, \delta^2 f, \dots$ or $df, d^2 f, \dots$ in place of $f'(x,h), f''(x,h), \dots$. We then have

$$\delta f = f'(x, \delta x) = \sum_i f_{x^i}(x)\delta x^i, \qquad \delta^2 f = f''(x, \delta x) = \sum_i \sum_j f_{x^i x^j}(x)\delta x^i \delta x^j.$$

Similarly

$$df = \sum_i f_{x^i} dx^i, \qquad d^2 f = \sum_i \sum_j f_{x^i x^j} dx^i dx^j.$$

In the three-dimensional case we have

$$df = f_x \, dx + f_y \, dy + f_z \, dz$$

$$d^2f = f_{xx} \, dx^2 + f_{yy} \, dy^2 + f_{zz} \, dz^2 + 2f_{xy} \, dx \, dy + 2f_{yz} \, dy \, dz + 2f_{xz} \, dx \, dz.$$

The vector (f_x, f_y, f_z) is the gradient ∇f of f, and the Hessian f'' is the matrix

$$\begin{bmatrix} f_{xx} & f_{xy} & f_{xz} \\ f_{yx} & f_{yy} & f_{yz} \\ f_{zx} & f_{zy} & f_{zz} \end{bmatrix}$$

The set of points satisfying the equation

$$f(x) = c = \text{constant}$$

forms a *level surface* of f. If f is of the form

$$f(x) = \sum_i b_i x^i + \text{constant}, \qquad (b \neq 0)$$

then the level surfaces of f are $(n-1)$-dimensional hyperplanes of $(n-1)$-planes. Moreover the vector $b = \text{grad} f$ is the normal to the hyperplane. Similarly, if f is of class C' and the gradient ∇f of f is not zero at a point x_0 in S, then $\nabla f(x_0)$ is the normal to the level surface

$$f(x) = f(x_0).$$

The tangent hyperplane to this surface at x_0 is given by the formula

$$f'(x_0, x - x_0) = \langle \nabla f(x_0), x - x_0 \rangle = 0.$$

The level surface $f(x) = c$ with $c = f(x_0)$ divides a sufficiently small r-neighborhood into three sets according as $f(x) < c$, $f(x) = c$, or $f(x) > c$, as indicated schematically in Figure 6.1.

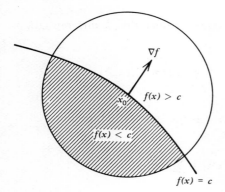

$f(x) = c$ **Figure 6.1**

The differentials $f'(x,h), f''(x,h), \ldots$ of f can also be interpreted as directional derivatives at a point x in S. This interpretation is basic in the theory of optimization. With x held fast and a fixed vector h, the set of points $y = x + th$ ($-\infty < t < \infty$) defines a line through x in the direction h. If δ is a small positive number, the points $y = x + th$ ($-\delta < t < \delta$) will be in S, and the function

$$g(t) = f(x + th) = f(x^1 + th^1, \ldots, x^n + th^n) \qquad (-\delta < t < \delta)$$

is of class $C^{(k)}$ in t whenever f is of class $C^{(k)}$ on S. If f is of class C', then, by the chain rule for differentiation, we have

$$g'(t) = \frac{\partial f}{\partial x^1}(x + th)h^1 + \cdots + \frac{\partial f}{\partial x^n}(x + th)h^n.$$

Hence

$$g'(t) = f'(x + th, h), \qquad g'(0) = f'(x, h).$$

This result is frequently expressed in the form

$$\frac{d}{dt} f(x + th)\Big|^{t=0} = f'(x, h).$$

In view of this formula we interpret $f'(x, h)$ to be the *derivative of* f *in the direction* h. If $h = (1, 0, \ldots, 0)$, then $f'(x, h) = (\partial f / \partial x^1)(x)$ is the derivative of f in the direction of the positive x^1-axis. Similarly $\partial f / \partial x^i$ is the derivative of f in the x^i-direction. If f is of class C'', a second differentiation yields

$$g''(t) = f''(x + th, h), \qquad g''(0) = f''(x, h).$$

If f is of class $C^{(k)}$, it is seen in the same manner that k-differentiations yield

$$g^{(k)}(t) = f^{(k)}(x + th, h), \qquad g^{(k)}(0) = f^{(k)}(x, h).$$

To illustrate these ideas, suppose that f is the quadratic function

$$f(x) = \frac{1}{2} \sum_i \sum_j a_{ij} x^i x^j + \sum_i b_i x^i + c,$$

where $a_{ij}=a_{ji}, b_i, c$ are constants and i,j are summed from 1 to n. Then

$$f_{x^i}=\sum_j a_{ij}x^j+b_i, \qquad f_{x^i x^j}=a_{ij},$$

$$f'(x,h)=\sum_i\left(\sum_j a_{ij}x^j+b_i\right)h^i=\sum_{i,j}a_{ij}h^i x^j+\sum_i b_i h^i,$$

$$f''(x,h)=\sum_{i,j}a_{ij}h^i h^j, \qquad f^{(k)}(x,h)\equiv 0 \qquad (k\geqslant 3).$$

Moreover

$$f'(x+th,h)=\sum_{i,j}a_{ij}h^i(x^j+th^j)+\sum_i b_i h^i=f'(x,h)+tf''(x,h),$$

$$f''(x+th,h)=\sum_{i,j}a_{ij}h^i h^j=f''(x,h).$$

The gradient $f'(x)$ and the Hessian $f''(x)$ are accordingly the vector and the matrix

$$f'(x)=\sum_j a_{ij}x^j+b_i, \qquad f''(x)=(a_{ij}).$$

In matrix notation with $A=(a_{ij})$ and $b=(b_i)$, we have

$$f(x)=\tfrac{1}{2}x^* Ax+b^* x+c$$

and

$$\nabla f(x)=f'(x)=Ax+b, \qquad f''(x)=A.$$

Here

$$b^* x=(b_1 b_2 \cdots b_n)\begin{bmatrix}x^1\\x^2\\\vdots\\x^n\end{bmatrix}=b_1 x^1+b_2 x^2+\cdots+b_n x^n,$$

$$x^* Ax=(x^1 x^2\cdots x^n)\begin{bmatrix}a_{11}&a_{12}&\cdots&a_{1n}\\a_{21}&a_{22}&\cdots&a_{2n}\\\vdots&\vdots&&\vdots\\a_{n1}&a_{n2}&\cdots&a_{nn}\end{bmatrix}\begin{bmatrix}x^1\\x^2\\\vdots\\x^n\end{bmatrix}.$$

Taylor's formula for a real-valued function $f(x)$ can be derived from the Taylor formula for

$$g(t) = f(x + th)$$

under the assumption that h is chosen so that the line segment $y = x + th$ $(0 \leqslant t \leqslant 1)$ is in S. Then $g(t)$ is defined on the interval $0 \leqslant t \leqslant 1$. If f is of calss C', we have

$$g(1) = f(x + h), \qquad g(0) = f(x), \qquad g'(\theta) = f'(x + \theta h, h). \qquad (6.3)$$

Hence by the law of the mean for g on $0 \leqslant t \leqslant 1$ there is a number θ_1 on $0 < \theta < 1$ such that the first of the relations

$$g(1) = g(0) + g'(\theta_1) = g(0) + \int_0^1 g'(\theta) \, d\theta \qquad (0 < \theta_1 < 1)$$

holds. The second follows by integration. Using (6.3), we obtain the corresponding formulas.

$$f(x + h) = f(x) + f'(x + \theta_1 h, h) = f(x) + \int_0^1 f'(x + \theta h, h) \, d\theta \qquad (0 < \theta_1 < 1)$$

$$(6.4)$$

for f. If f is of class C'', so also is g. By virtue of the second-order Taylor formula for g, we have

$$g(1) - g(0) - g'(0) = \tfrac{1}{2} g''(\theta_2) = \int_0^1 (1 - \theta) g''(\theta) \, d\theta \qquad (0 < \theta_2 < 1)$$

for some point θ_2 on $0 < \theta < 1$. When this result is expressed in terms of f, we obtain the Taylor formula

$$f(x + h) = f(x) + f'(x, h) + \tfrac{1}{2} f''(x + \theta_2 h, h)$$

$$= f(x) + f'(x, h) + \int_0^1 f''(x + \theta h, h) \, d\theta.$$

This formula can be written in the alternative form

$$f(x + h) = f(x) + f'(x, h) + \tfrac{1}{2} f''(x, h) + r_2(x, h), \qquad (6.5)$$

where the remainder $r_2(x,h)$ is given by either of the formulas

$$r_2(x,h) = \tfrac{1}{2}[f''(x+\theta_2 h,h) - f''(x,h)] \quad (0<\theta_2<1), \quad (6.6)$$

$$r_2(x,h) = \int_0^1 (1-\theta)[f''(x+\theta h,h) - f''(x,h)]\,d\theta, \quad (6.7)$$

where θ_2 is a point on $0<\theta<1$ dependent on x and h. If f is of class C''', so also is g and the third-order remainder term in the Taylor expansion for g yields the alternative formulas

$$r_2(x,h) = \frac{1}{3!} f'''(x+\theta_3 h,h) \quad (0<\theta_3<1), \quad (6.8)$$

$$r_2(x,h) = \frac{1}{2}\int_0^1 (1-\theta)^2 f'''(x+\theta h,h)\,d\theta, \quad (6.9)$$

where θ_3 is suitably chosen. In the same manner, if f is of class $C^{(k)}$ on S, we obtain the Taylor formula

$$f(x+h) = f(x) + f'(x,h) + \tfrac{1}{2}f''(x,h) + \cdots + \frac{1}{k!}f^{(k)}(x,h) + r_k(x,h),$$
$$(6.10)$$

where

$$r_k(x,h) = \frac{1}{k!}\left[f^{(k)}(x+\theta_k h,h) - f^{(k)}(x,h)\right] \quad (0<\theta_k<1), \quad (6.11)$$

$$r_k(x,h) = \frac{1}{(k-1)!}\int_0^1 (1-\theta)^{k-1}\left[f^{(k)}(x+\theta h,h) - f(x,h)\right]d\theta, \quad (6.12)$$

for some θ_k on $0<\theta<1$. If f is of class $C^{(k+1)}$ on S, we also have

$$r_k(x,h) = \frac{1}{(k+1)!}f^{(k+1)}(x+\theta_{k+1}h,h) \quad (0<\theta_{k+1}<1), \quad (6.13)$$

$$r_k(x,h) = \frac{1}{k!}\int_0^1 (1-\theta)^k f^{(k+1)}(x+\theta h,h)\,d\theta, \quad (6.14)$$

with a suitable choice of θ_{k+1}. In these formulas it is understood that x and h are restricted so that the points $x+th$ $(0\leqslant t\leqslant 1)$ are in S.

The basic property of the remainder $r_k(x,h)$ is given in

THEOREM 6.1

If f *is of class* $C^{(k)}$ *on* S, *then the remainder* $r_k(x, h)$ *in the Taylor formula* (6.10) *for* f *satisfies the relation*

$$\lim_{h \to 0} \frac{r_k(x, h)}{|h|^k} = 0. \tag{6.15}$$

We shall establish this result for the case $k = 2$. The proof in the general case is similar. If $k = 2$, we have, by (6.7),

$$\frac{r_2(x, h)}{|h|^2} = \sum_i \sum_j A_{ij}(x, h) z^i z^j,$$

where z is the unit vector $z = h/|h|$, and

$$A_{ij}(x, h) = \int_0^1 (1 - \theta) [f_{x^i x^j}(x + \theta h) - f_{x^i x^j}(x)] d\theta. \tag{6.16}$$

The function $A_{ij}(x, h)$ is a continuous function of h having $A_{ij}(x, 0) = 0$. Hence $\lim_{h \to 0} A_{ij}(x, h) = 0$. Since $|z| = 1$, it follows that

$$\lim_{h \to 0} \frac{r_2(x, h)}{|h|^2} = \lim_{h \to 0} \sum_i \sum_j A_{ij}(x, h) z^i z^j = 0, \tag{6.17}$$

as was to be proved.

It should be noted that Taylor's formula is valid when $f(x)$ is a point in an m-dimensional Euclidean space. Formulas (6.12) and (6.14) for the remainder are valid for this case. However, formulas (6.11) and (6.13) are invalid because the value of θ_k is normally different for each component of $f(x)$.

The kth differential $f^{(k)}(x_0, h)$ of f at a point x_0 is a homogeneous function of h of degree k in the sense that we shall now describe. Let S be a set of points x with the property that, if x is in S, so also is tx for all real numbers $t \neq 0$. A function F on S will be said to be *homogeneous of degree* k *on* S if

$$F(tx) = t^k F(x) \qquad (t \neq 0) \tag{6.18}$$

for all x in S and all numbers $t \neq 0$. Here k is any real number for which t^k is real when t is negative. For example, $k = \frac{3}{2}$ is excluded but $k = \frac{2}{3}$ is not. A linear form $L(x)=\sum_{i=1}^{n} b_i x^i$ is homogeneous of degree 1. A quadratic form $Q(x)=\sum_{i,j=1}^{n} a_{ij} x^i x^j$ is homogeneous of degree 2. The second differential $f''(x,h)$ of f at x is a quadratic form in h and is accordingly homogeneous in h of degree 2. In the xy-plane the functions $xy/(x^2+y^2), x^4+xy^3, (x^2+y^2)^{1/3}, x/(x^2-y^2)$ are homogeneous in x and y of degrees $0, 4, \frac{2}{3}, -1$, respectively. If $x=0$ is in S and $k>0$, we admit the value $t=0$ in (6.18).

A function F will be said to be *positively homogeneous of degree* k *on* S if relation (6.18) holds for all x in S and all $t>0$. In this event S is a set such that tx is in S whenever x is in S and $t>0$. An homogeneous function is positively homogeneous, but the converse is not true. For example, $F(x)=|x|$ is positively homogeneous but is not homogeneous.

EXERCISES

1. Let $h(t)$ $(-\infty<t<\infty)$ be the function of class C^{∞} described in Exercise 27 of Section 5. Given a point x_0 and a positive number r, show that the function

$$f(x)=h\left(\frac{|x-x_0|}{r}\right)$$

is of class $C^{(\infty)}$ such that $f(x)=0$ if $|x-x_0|\leqslant r$ and $f(x)=1$ if $|x-x_0|\geqslant 2r$.

2. Sketch typical portions of the level surfaces of f in xyz-space in each of the following cases:
    (a) $x+y+z$,   (b) $x^2/a^2+y^2/b^2+z^2/c^2$,
    (c) $x^2+y^2-z^2$,   (d) $z-x^2-y^2$,
    (e) $z-x^2+y^2$.

3. Suppose that $f'(x)\neq 0$, and set $h_0=f'(x)/|f'(x)|$. Show that h_0 maximizes the directional derivative $f'(x,h)$ on the class of unit vectors h.

4. Establish Theorem 6.1 for the case $k=1$.

5. Suppose that

$$f(x)=\frac{1}{2}\sum_i\sum_j a_{ij} x^i x^j - \sum_i b_i x^i + c,$$

where $a_{ij}=a_{ji}$. Show that

$$f_{x^i}=\sum_j a_{ij} x^j - b, \qquad f_{x^i x^j}=a_{ij}.$$

Set $r_i=b_i-\sum_j a_{ij} x^j$. Show that

$$f(x+h)=f(x)-\sum_i r_i h^i + \frac{1}{2}\sum_i\sum_j a_{ij} h^i h^j.$$

6. Express the result given in Exercise 5 in matrix notation with $A = (a_{ij})$, $b = (b_i), r = (r_i)$, and $h = (h^i)$. Observe that $r = -f'(x)$.

7. Show that the gradient of $f(x) = \frac{1}{2}|x - x_0|^2$ is $\nabla f(x) = f'(x) = x - x_0$.

8. Show that

$$\left| \sum_i \sum_j a_{ij} h^i h^j \right| \leqslant |h|^2 \left(\sum_i \sum_j a_{ij} a_{ij} \right)^{1/2}.$$

Use this result to obtain relation (6.17). *Hint:* Consider (a_{ij}) and $(h^i h^j)$ to be vectors with n^2-elements, and apply the Cauchy-Schwartz inequality (2.5).

9. Show that

$$\left| \sum a_{ijk} h^i h^j h^k \right| \leqslant |h|^3 \left(\sum a_{ijk} a_{ijk} \right)^{1/2}.$$

Use this result to prove Theorem 6.1 for the case $k = 3$.

10. Write the first- and second-order Taylor expansions for a function $f(x, y)$ in two variables x and y.

BIBLIOGRAPHY

To assist the reader who wishes to make a more thorough study of optimization theory, we have included in the bibliography titles of books on infinite dimensional as well as finite dimensional optimization theory. Further references can be found in these books and in an article by F. Gerber entitled "Mathematical Programming Book Reviews: 1965–1972," *Management Science*, Vol 20 (1974), 875–895. No attempt has been made to include research papers published in journals. A few journal articles are cited in the text, with full information given in accompanying footnotes.

J. Abadie (ed.), *Nonlinear Programming*, North-Holland Publishing Co., Amsterdam, 1967.

P. Adby and M. Dempster, *Introduction to Optimization Methods*, Halsted Press, John Wiley and Sons, New York, 1974.

N. Akhiezer, *The Calculus of Variations*, Ginn (Blaisdell), Boston, 1962.

N. Akhiezer and I. Glazman, *Theory of Linear Operators in Hilbert Space*, Vols. 1 and 2, Frederick Ungar, New York, 1961.

B. Anderson and J. Moore, *Linear Optimal Control*, Prentice-Hall, Englewood Cliffs, N. J., 1971.

M. Aoki, *Optimization of Stochastic Systems*, Academic Press, New York, 1967.

M. Aoki, *Introduction to Optimization Techniques*, Macmillan Co., New York, 1971.

R. Aris, *The Optimal Design of Chemical Reactors*, Academic Press, New York, 1961.

K. Arrow, L. Hurwics, and H. Uzawa, *Studies in Linear and Non-Linear Programming*, Stanford University Press, Stanford, Calif., 1958.

A. Arthurs, *Complementary Variational Principles*, Oxford University Press, London, 1970.

K. Astrom, *Introduction to Stochastic Control Theory*, Academic Press, New York, 1970.

M. Athans and P. Falb, *Optimal Control*, McGraw-Hill Book Co., New York, 1966.

M. Avriel, M. Rijckaert, and D. Wilde (eds)., *Optimization and Design*, Prentice-Hall, Englewood Cliffs, N. J., 1973.

A. Balakrishnan (ed.), *Control Theory and the Calculus of Variations*, Acadmeic Press, New York, 1969.

A. Balakrishnan (ed.), *Techniques of Optimization*, Academic Press, New York, 1972.

A. Balakrishnan, M. Contensou, B. de Veubeke, P. Kree, and J. Lions (eds.), *Symposium on Optimization, Held in Nice, June–July*, 1969, Springer-Verlag, New York, 1970.

A. Balakrishnan and L. Neustadt, *Computing Methods in Optimization Problems*, Academic Press, New York, 1964.

E. Beale, *Mathematical Programming in Practice*, John Wiley and Sons, New York, 1968.

D. Bell and A. W. Griffin, *Modern Control Theory and Computing*, McGraw-Hill Book Co., New York, 1969.

R. Bellman, *Dynamic Programming*, Princeton University Press, Princeton, N. J., 1957.

R. Bellman (ed.), *Mathematical Optimization Techniques*, University of California Press, Berkeley, Calif., 1963.

R. Bellman, *Introduction to the Mathematical Theory of Control Processes*, Vol. 1: *Linear Equations and Quadratic Criteria*, Academic Press, New York, 1967.

R. Bellman, *Introduction to the Mathematical Theory of Control Processes*, Vol. 2: *Nonlinear Processes and Quadratic Criteria*, Academic Press, New York, 1971.

R. Bellman and S. Dreyfus, *Applied Dynamic Programming*, Princeton University Press, Princeton, N. J., 1962.

R. Bellman, R. Glicksberg, and O. Gross, *Some Aspects of the Mathematical Theory of Control Processes*, Rand Corporation, Santa Monica, Calif., 1958.

R. Bellman and R. Kalaba, *Quasilinearization and Nonlinear Boundary-Value Problems*, American Elsevier Publishing Co., New York, 1965.

E. Beltrami, *An Algorithmic Approach to Nonlinear Analysis and Optimization*, Academic Press, New York, 1970.

N. Bertele and F. Brioschi, *Nonserial Dynamic Programming*, Academic Press, New York, 1972.

G. Beveridge and R. Schechter, *Optimization: Theory and Practice*, McGraw-Hill Book Co., New York, 1970.

G. Bliss, *Calculus of Variations*, Open Court Publishing Co., Chicago, 1925.

G. Bliss, *Lectures on the Calculus of Variations*, University of Chicago Press, Chicago, 1946.

V. Boltyanski, *Mathematical Methods of Optimal Control*, Holt, Rinehart and Winston, New York, 1971.

O. Bolza, *Vorlesugen uber Variationsrechnung*, Chelsea Publishing Co., New York (reprint of 1909 edition).

O. Bolza, *Lectures on the Calculus of Variations* (Eng. transl.), Dover Publications, New York, 1961.

J. Boot, Quadratic Programming, *Algorithms—Anomalies—Applications*, North-Holland Publishing Co., Amsterdam, Rand McNally and Co.,, Chicago, 1964.

R. Boundarel, J. Delmas, and P. Guichet, *Dynamic Programming and Its Application to Optimal Control*, Academic Press, New York, 1971.

M. Box, D. Davies, and M. Swann, *Nonlinear Optimization Techniques*, Oliver and Boyd, London.

J. Bracken and G. McCormick, *Selected Applications of Nonlinear Programming*, John Wiley and Sons, New York, 1968.

R. Brent, *Algorithms for Minimization without Derivatives*, Prentice-Hall, Englewood Cliffs, N. J., 1973.

A. Bryson and Y. Ho, *Applied Optimal Control*, Blaisdell Publishing Co., Waltham, Mass., 1969.

D. Burley, *Studies in Optimization*, Halsted Press, John Wiley and Sons, New York, 1974.

M. Canon, C. Culum, Jr., and E. Polak, *Theory of Optimal Control and Mathematical Programming*, McGraw-Hill Book Co., New York, 1970.

C. Caratheodory, *Calculus of Variations and Partial Differential Equations of the First Order*, Vols. 1 and 2, Holden-Day, San Francisco, 1965, 1967.

S. Chang, *Synthesis of Optimal Control Systems*, McGraw-Hill Book Co., New York, 1961.

S. Citron, *Elements of Optimal Control*, Holt, Rinehart and Winston, New York, 1969.

J. Clegg, *Calculus of Variations*, Oliver and Boyd, Edinburgh, 1968.

L. Collatz, *Functional Analysis and Numerical Mathematics*, Academic Press, New York, 1966.

A. Converse, *Optimization*, Holt, Rinehart and Winston, New York, 1970.

L. Cooper and D. Steinberg, *Introduction to Methods of Optimization*, W. B. Saunders Co., Philadelphia, 1970.

R. Courant, *Calculus of Variations and Supplementary Notes and Exercises* (revised and amended by J. Moser), New York University, 1962.

R. Courant and D. Hilbert, *Methods of Mathematical Physics*, Vol. 1, Interscience Publishing Co., New York, 1953.

J. Daniel, *The Approximate Minimization of Functionals*, Prentice-Hall, Englewood Cliffs, N. J., 1971.

G. Dantzig and B. Eaves (eds.), *Studies in Optimization*, Studies in Mathematics, vol. 10, Mathematical Association of America, 1974.

G. Dantzig and A. Veinott (eds.), *Mathematics of the Decision Sciences*, Vol. 2: *Lectures in Applied Sciences*, American Mathematical Society, Providence, R. I., 1969.

R. De La Barriere, *Optimal Control Theory*, W. B. Saunders Co., Philadelphia, 1967.

V. Demyanov and V. Malozemov, *Introduction to Minimax*, John Wiley and Sons, 1974.

V. Demyanov and A. Rubinov, *Approximate Methods in Optimization Problems*, American Elsevier Publishing Co., New York, 1970.

M. Denn, *Optimization by Variational Methods*, McGraw-Hill Book Co., New York, 1969.

J. Dennis, *Mathematical Programming and Electrical Networks*, John Wiley and Sons, New York, 1959. Department of Mathematics, University of Chicago, *Contributions to the Calculus of Variations*, 1930, 1931–1932, 1933–1937, 1938–1941, University of Chicago Press, Chicago (reprinted by R. E. Johnson Reprint Co.).

L. Dixon, *Nonlinear Optimisation*, Crane-Russak and Co., New York, 1972.

A. Dold and B. Eckmann (eds.), *Symposium on Optimization*, Lecture Notes in Mathematics, No. 132, Springer-Verlag, New York, 1970.

S. Dreyfus, *Dynamic Programming and the Calculus of Variations*, Academic Press, New York, 1965.

R. Duffin, E. Peterson, and C. Zener, *Geometric Programming*, John Wiley and Sons, New York, 1967.

P. Dyer and S. McReynolds, *The Computation and Theory of Optimal Control*, Academic Press, New York, 1970.

M. El-Hodiri, *Constrained Extrema: Introduction to the Differentiable Case with Economic Applications*, Springer-Verlag, New York, 1971.

L. Elsgolc, *Calculus of Variations*, Pergamon Press, London, 1961.

L. Elsgolc, *Qualitative Methods in Mathematical Analysis*, American Mathematical Society, Providence, R. I., 1964.

V. Eveleigh, *Adaptive Control and Optimization Techniques*, McGraw-Hill Book Co., New York, 1967.

G. Ewing, *Calculus of Variations with Applications*, W. Norton Co., 1969.

440 BIBLIOGRAPHY

P. Falb and J. de Jong, *Some Successive Approximation Methods in Control and Oscillation Theory*, Academic Press, New York, 1969.

A. Feldbaum, *Optimal Control Systems*, Academic Press, New York, 1965.

A. Fiacco and G. McCormick, *Nonlinear Programming: Sequential Unconstrained Minimization Techniques*, John Wiley and Sons, New York, 1968.

R. Fletcher (ed.), *Optimization*, Academic Press, New York, 1969.

I. Flugge-Lotz, *Discontinuous and Optimal Control*, McGraw-Hill Book Co., New York, 1968.

M. Forray, *Variational Calculus in Science and Engineering*, McGraw-Hill Book Co., New York, 1968.

A. Forsyth, *Calculus of Variations*, reprinted by Dover Publications, New York, 1960.

C. Fox, *Introduction to the Calculus of Variations*, Oxford University Press, New York, 1950.

R. Fox, *Optimization Methods for Engineering Design*, Addison-Wesley Publishing Co., Reading, Mass., 1971.

P. Funk, *Variationsrechnung und ihre Anwendung in Physik und Technik*, Springer, Berlin, 1962.

I. Gelfand and S. Fomin, *Calculus of Variations*, Prentice-Hall, Englewood Cliffs, N. J., 1963.

B. Gluss, *An Elementary Introduction to Dynamic Programming*, Allyn and Bacon, Boston, 1972.

A. Goldstein, *Constructive Real Analysis*, Harper and Row, New York, 1967.

G. Goos and J. Hartmanis (eds.), *5th Conference on Optimization Techniques*, Part I, Lecture Notes in Computer Science, No. 3, Springer-Verlag, New York, 1973.

B. Gottfried and J. Weisman, *Introduction to Optimization Theory*, Prentice-Hall, Englewood Cliffs, New Jersey, 1973.

S. Gould, *Variational Methods for Eigenvalue Problems*, University of Toronto Press, Toronto, Canada, 1957.

E. Goursat, *A Course in Mathematical Analysis*, Vol. III, Part 2, reprinted by Dover Publications, New York, 1964.

L. Graves (ed.), *Calculus of Variations and Its Applications, Proceedings of Symposia in Applied Mathematics*, Vol. 8, McGraw-Hill Book Co., New York, 1958.

R. Graves and P. Wolfe (eds.), *Recent Advances in Mathematical Programming*, McGraw-Hill Book Co., New York, 1963.

G. Grüss, *Variationsrechnung*, Quelle and Meyer, Heidelberg, 1955.

I. Gumowski and C. Mina, *Optimization in Control Theory and Practice*, Cambridge University Press, Cambridge, 1968.

J. Hadamard, *Leçons sur le Calcul des Variations*, Vol. 1, A. Hermann et Fils, Paris, 1910.

G. Hadley, *Nonlinear and Dynamic Programming*, Addison-Wesley Publishing Co., Reading, Mass., 1964.

N. Hastings, *Dynamic Programming*, Crane, Russak and Co., New York, 1973.

W. Hemp, *Optimum Structures*, Clarendon Press, Oxford, 1973.

H. Hermes and J. LaSalle, *Functional Analysis and Time Optimal Control*, Academic Press, New York, 1969.

M. Hestenes, *Calculus of Variations and Optimal Control Theory*, John Wiley and Sons, New York, 1966.

F. Hillier and G. Lieberman, *Introduction to Operations Research*, 2nd ed., Holden-Day, San Francisco, 1974.

R. Holmes, *A Course on Optimization and Best Approximation*, Springer-Verlag, New York, 1972.

T. Hu, *Integer Programming and Network Flows*, Addison-Wesley Publishing Co., Reading, Mass., 1969.

T. Hu and S. Robinson (eds.), *Mathematical Programming*, Academic Press, New York, 1973.

M. Intriligator, *Mathematical Optimization and Economic Theory*, Prentice-Hall, Englewood Cliffs, N. J., 1971.

D. Jacobson, *Differential Dynamic Programming*, American Elsevier Publishing Co., New York, 1970.

S. Jacoby, J. Kowalik, and J. Pizzo, *Iterative Methods for Nonlinear Optimization Problems*, Prentice-Hall, Englewood Cliffs, N. J., 1972.

L. Kantorovich and G. Akilov, *Functional Analysis in Normed Spaces*, Pergamon Press (Macmillan Co.), New York, 1964.

L. Kantorovich and V. Krylov, *Approximate Methods of Higher Analysis*, P. Noordhoff, Groningen, 1958.

S. Karlin, *Mathematical Methods and Theory in Games, Programming and Economics*, Vols. 1 and 2, Addison-Wesley Publishing Co., Reading, Mass., 1959.

A. Kaufmann and R. Cruon, *Dynamic Programming: Sequential Scientific Management*, Academic Press, New York, 1967.

W. Kipiniak, *Dynamic Optimization and Control: A Variational Approach*, M.I.T. Press and John Wiley and Sons, New York, 1961.

D. Kirk, *Optimal Control: An Introduction*, Prentice-Hall, Englewood Cliffs, N. J., 1971.

R. Klotzler, *Mehrdimensionale Variationsrechnung*, VEB Deutscher Verlag, Berlin, 1970.

A. Kneser, *Lehrbuch der Variationsrechnung*, Fried. Vieweg und Sohn, Braunschweig, Germany, 1900, 1925.

V. Komkov, *Optimal Control Theory for the Damping of Vibrations of Simple Elastic Systems*, Springer-Verlag, New York, 1972.

J. Kowalik and M. Osborne, *Methods for Unconstrained Optimization Problems*, American Elsevier Publishing Co., New York, 1968.

H. Kuhn and A. Tucker, *Linear Inequalities and Related Systems, Annals of Mathematics Studies* No. 38, Princeton University Press, Princeton, N. J., 1956.

H. Kunzi, W. Krelle, and W. Oettli, *Nonlinear Programming*, Blaisdell Publishing Co., Waltham, Mass., 1966.

H. Kunzi, H. Tzschach, and C. Zehnder, *Numerical Methods of Mathematical Optimization*, Academic Press, New York, 1968.

B. Kuo and D. Tabak, *Optimal Control by Mathematical Programming*, Prentice-Hall, Englewood Cliffs, N. J., 1971.

H. Kushner, *Introduction to Stochastic Control*, Holt, Rinehart and Winston, New York, 1971.

C. Lanczos, *The Variational Principles of Mechanics*, University of Toronto Press, Toronto, Canada, 1949.

L. Lapidus and R. Luus, *Optimal Control of Engineering Processes*, Blaisdell Publishing Co., Waltham, Mass., 1967.

L. Lasdon, *Optimization Theory for Large Systems*, Macmillan Company, New York, 1970.

A. Lavi and T. Vogl (eds.), *Proceedings of Symposium on Recent Advances in Optimization Techniques*, John Wiley and Sons, New York, 1966.

D. Lawden, *Optimal Trajectories for Space Navigation*, Butterworths, London, 1963.

E. Lee and L. Markus, *Foundations of Optimal Control Theory*, John Wiley and Sons, New York, 1967.

G. Leitmann (ed.), *Optimization Techniques, with Applications to Aerospace Systems*, Academic Press, New York, 1962.

G. Leitmann, *An Introduction to Optimal Control*, McGraw-Hill Book Co., New York, 1966.

G. Leitmann (ed.), *Topics in Optimization*, Academic Press, New York, 1967.

C. Leondes (ed.), *Advances in Control Systems: Theory and Applications*, Academic Press, New York, 1964.

J. Lions, *Optimal Control of Systems Governed by Partial Differential Equations*, Springer-Verlag, New York, 1970.

F. Lootsma (ed.), *Numerical Methods for Non-linear Optimization*, Academic Press, New York, 1973.

D. Luenberger, *Optimization by Vector Space Methods*, John Wiley and Sons, New York, 1969.

O. Mangasarian, *Nonlinear Programming*, McGraw-Hill Book Co., New York, 1969.

O. Mangasarian, S. Robinson, and R. Meyer, *Nonlinear Programming 2*, Academic Press, New York, 1975.

B. Martos, *Nonlinear Programming, Theory and Applications*, American Elsevier Publishing Company, New York, 1975.

J. Matyas, *Optimal Control Systems*, Illiffe Books, London.

I. McCausland, *Introduction to Optimal Control*, John Wiley and Sons, New York, 1969.

C. McMillan, Jr., *Mathematical Programming: An Introduction to the Design and Application of Optimal Decision Machines*, John Wiley and Sons, New York, 1970.

J. Meditch, *Stochastic Optimal Linear Estimation and Control*, McGraw-Hill Book Co., New York, 1969.

A. Mercier, *Analytical and Canonical Formalism in Physics*, Dover Publications, New York, 1963.

C. Merriam, *Optimization Theory and the Design of Feedback Control Systems*, McGraw-Hill Book Co., New York, 1964.

S. Milhlin, *Variational Methods in Mathematical Physics*, Pergamon Press (Macmillan Co.), New York, 1964.

B. Moiseiwitsch, *Variational Principles*, Interscience Publishing Co., New York, 1966.

C. Morrey, *Multiple Integral Problems in the Calculus of Variations and Related Topics*, University of California Press, Berkeley, Calif., 1943.

M. Morse, *The Calculus of Variations in the Large*, American Mathematical Society, Providence, R. I., 1934.

M. Morse, *Variational Analysis*, John Wiley and Sons, New York, 1973.

F. Murnaghan, *The Calculus of Variations*, Spartan Books, Washington, D. C., 1962.

W. Murray (ed.), *Numerical Methods for Unconstrained Optimization*, Academic Press, New York, 1972.

P. Naslin, *Essentials of Optimal Controls*, Blaisdell Publishing Co., New York, 1969.

G. Nemhauser, *Introduction to Dynamic Programming*, John Wiley and Sons, New York, 1966.

T. Nicholson, *Optimization in Industry*, Vol. 1: *Optimization Techniques*, Longman Group, London, 1971.

T. Nicholson, *Optimization in Industry*, Vol. 2: *Industrial Applications*, Longman Group, London, 1971.

A. Noton, *Introduction to Variational Methods in Control Engineering*, Pergamon Press, Oxford, 1965.

R. Oldenburger, *Optimal Control*, Holt, Rinehart and Winston, New York, 1966.

A. Ostrowski, *Solutions of Equations and Systems of Equations*, 2nd ed., Academic Press, New York, 1966.

L. Pars, *An Introduction to the Calculus of Variations*, John Wiley and Sons, New York, 1963.

I. Petrov, *Variational Methods in Optimum Control Theory*, Academic Press, New York, 1968.

D. Pierre, *Optimization Theory with Applications*, John Wiley and Sons, New York, 1969.

D. Plane and C. McMillan, *Discrete Optimization*, Prentice-Hall, Englewood Cliffs, New Jersey, 1971.

E. Polak, *Computational Methods in Optimization: A Unified Approach*, Academic Press, New York, 1971.

L. Pontryagin, V. Boltyanskii, R. Gamkrelidze, and E. Mishchenko, *The Mathematical Theory of Optimal Process*, John Wiley and Sons, New York, 1962.

W. Porter, *Modern Foundations of Systems Engineering*, Macmillan Co., New York, 1966.

B. Pshenichnyi, *Necessary Conditions for an Extremum*, Marcel Dekker Publishing Co., New York, 1971.

L. Pun, *Introduction to Optimization Practice*, John Wiley and Sons, New York, 1969.

A. Roberts and D. Varberg, *Convex Functions*, Academic Press, New York, 1973.

S. Roberts, *Dynamic Programming in Chemical Engineering and Process Control*, Academic Press, New York, 1964.

S. Roberts, *Dynamic Programming in Chemical Engineering and Process Control*, Academic Press, New York, 1964.

R. Rockafellar, *Convex Analysis*, Princeton University Press, Princeton, N. J., 1969.

J. Rosen, O. Mangasarian, and K. Ritter (eds.), *Nonlinear Programming*, Academic Press, New York, 1971.

H. Rund, *The Hamilton-Jacobi Theory in the Calculus of Variations*, D. Van Nostrand Co., Princeton, N. J., 1966.

D. Russel, *Optimization Theory*, W. A. Benjamin, New York, 1970.

H. Sagan, *Introduction to the Calculus of Variations*, McGraw-Hill Book Co., New York, 1969.

D. Smith, *Variational Methods in Optimization*, Prentice-Hall, Englewood Cliffs, N. J., 1974.

W. Spivey and R. Thrall, *Linear Optimization*, Holt, Rinehart and Winston, New York, 1970.

J. Stoer and C. Witzgall, *Convexity and Optimization in Finite Dimensions*, Vol. I, Springer-Verlag, New York, 1970.

A. Strauss, *An Introduction to Optimal Control Theory*, Springer-Verlag, New York, 1968.

G. Szegö (ed.), *Minimization Algorithms, Mathematical Theories and Computer Results*, Academic Press, New York, 1972.

H. Taha, *Operations Research: An Introduction*, Macmillan Co., New York, 1971.

G. Temple and W. Bickley, *Rayleigh's Principle and Its Applications to Engineering*, Dover Publications, New York, 1956.

J. Todd (ed.), *Survey of Numerical Analysis*, McGraw-Hill, New York, 1962.

H. Tolle, *Optimierungsverfahren*, Springer-Verlag, New York.

L. Tonelli, *Fondamenti di Calcolo delle Variazoni*, Vols 1 and 2, Nicola Zanichelli, Bolgona, 1921–1923.

J. Tou, *Modern Control Theory*, McGraw-Hill Book Co., New York, 1964.

M. Vainberg, *Variational Methods for the Study of Nonlinear Operators*, Holden-Day, San Francisco, 1964.

P. Varaiya, *Notes on Optimization*, Van Nostrand Reinhold Co., New York, 1972.

Y. Vorobyev, *Method of Moments in Applied Mathematics*, Gordon and Breach Publishers, New York, 1965.

R. Weinstock, *Calculus of Variations, with Applications to Physics and Engineering*, McGraw-Hill Book Co., New York, 1952.

P. Whittle, *Optimization under Constraints*, John Wiley and Sons, New York, 1971.

D. Wilde, *Optimum Seeking Methods*, Prentice-Hall, Englewood Cliffs, N. J., 1964.

D. Wilde and C. Beightler, *Foundations of Optimization*, Prentice-Hall, Englewood Cliffs, N. J., 1967.

D. Wismer (ed.), *Optimization Methods for Large-Scale Systems, with Applications*, McGraw-Hill Book Co., New York, 1971.

L. Young, *Lectures on the Calculus of Variations and Optimal Control Theory*, W. B. Saunders Co., Philadelphia, 1969.

W. Yourgrau and S. Mandelstam, *Variational Principles in Dynamics and Quantum Theory*, Pitman and Sons, London, 1955.

L. Zadeh, L. Neustadt, and A. Balakrishnan (eds.), *Computing Methods in Optimization Problems*, Vol. 2, Academic Press, New York, 1969.

R. Zahradnik, *Theory and Techniques of Optimization for Practicing Engineers*, Barnes and Noble, New York, 1971.

W. Zangwill, *Nonlinear Programming—A Unified Approach*, Prentice-Hall, Englewood Cliffs, N. J., 1969.

C. Zener, *Engineering Design by Geometric Programming*, John Wiley and Sons, New York, 1971.

G. Zoutendijk, *Methods of Feasible Directions*, Elsevier Publishing Co., Amsterdam, 1960.

S. Zukhovitskiy and L. Avdeyeva, *Linear and Convex Programming*, W. B. Saunders Co., Philadelphia, 1966.

INDEX

Optimum solution, 235
Orthogonality, 60, 398
Orthogonal complement, 398
  projection, 399
Orthonormal, 60, 77, 398

Parallel displacement, 56
Penalty function, 255, 307
Pennissi, L. L., 178
Plane, k-plane, 37
  conjugate, 47
Polak, E., 340, 371
Polytope, polyhedron, 411
Positively homogeneous function, 10, 435
Powell, M. D. J., 254
Power method, 84
Principal values and vectors, 119
Principle of reciprocity, 156
Programming, convex, 324
  linear, 234
  quadratic, 234
Pseudoinverse, 124, 130, 131

Quadratic form, 5, 112, 354
  of arcs, 101
  eigenvalues and vectors of, 92, 94, 101, 102
  positive, nonnegative, negative, nonpositive, 6
Quadratic function, 9, 22, 46
  programming, 234
Quadric surface, 24
Quasinormality, 244, 296
Quasiregularity, 223
Quotient, Rayleigh, 73, 86, 92, 102, 106

*-reciprocal, 130
Reciprocity, principle of, 156
Reeves, Fletcher and, 171
Regularity, 165, 221, 237
  quasi, 223
  complete, 243
Regular point, 165, 221, 237, 243, 245
Reid, W. T., ix
Rockafellar, R., 312
Rupp, R., x, 312

Saddle point, 18, 157
Sequences, bounded, convergent, Cauchy, limit of, 3, 407
  directionally convergent, 204
  liminf, limsup, 408
Sequential tangent, 204
Set, bounded, open, closed, compact, complement of, 3, 406
  convex, 27, 409
  neighborhood of, 7, 407
Set, interior, exterior, limit, accumulation, isolated points of, 406
Simplex, 404
Space, linear, 394
  Euclidean, 393
  half, 411
Steepest ascent, descent, 12, 45, 169
Stein, J., x
Stiefel, E., 46, 57, 171
Supremum, sup f(x), 2, 411

Tangent vector, 37, 161, 204
  linear, curvilinear, sequential, 203, 204
Tangent space, cone, 37, 161, 205
Tangential constraints, 163, 221, 245
Taylor's theorem, 418, 420, 432, 433
Tucker, A. W., viii, 178

Upper bound, least, 2, 411
Upper limit, limsup, 408

Valentine, F., 178
Vectors, collinear, 397
  conjugate, 49, 56, 65
    mutually conjugate, 65
  inner product of, 57, 396
  linearly independent, 394
  norm of, 57, 396
  orthogonal, mutually orthogonal, orthonormal, 60, 77, 398
  tangent, 37, 161, 204
  normal, 162, 207

Wolfe, P., viii, ix, 230, 234

Young, L. C., ix